5

INTRODUCTION TO
Fluid Mechanics

JERZY A. OWCZAREK

Professor of Mechanical Engineering
Lehigh University

INTERNATIONAL TEXTBOOK COMPANY

Scranton, Pennsylvania

To Elisa

Preface

The main purpose of this book is to provide an introduction to the study of fluid mechanics for students of engineering and science. While the fundamental physical and analytical aspects of fluid motion are emphasized throughout, the practical applications also receive attention both in the text and in the problem assignments.

This text is based on my lecture notes prepared for an elective course offered in the Department of Mechanical Engineering at Lehigh University in 1966 and 1967. It is at present offered for all second-semester Junior students of mechanical engineering at Lehigh. It is available, as an elective course, to students from other departments. A fluid mechanics Laboratory course is offered concurrently to the students. The course in thermodynamics is not a prerequisite for this course.

At the universities in this country, in the departments of mechanical engineering, such an introductory course is usually followed by a senior-year elective course on gas dynamics and by the graduate courses on boundary-layer theory, advanced gas dynamics, hydrodynamics, and turbomachinery. The students on civil engineering normally follow the introductory course on fluid mechanics with a course on hydraulics.

Many writers have exerted their influence on the manner in which various topics are presented in this book. Among the most prominent are L. Prandtl, C. Truesdell, M. J. Lighthill, H. Schlichting, and A. D. Young.

I am grateful to Professors B. Johnson of the U.S. Naval Academy, Annapolis, Md., T. Sarpkaya of the University of Nebraska, and P. Wegener of the Yale University for their critical review of the manuscript. I also appreciate the assistance of my publishers in getting the manuscript typed and their friendly cooperation.

JERZY A. OWCZAREK

Bethlehem, Pennsylvania
March, 1968

Contents

Symbols

Letter Symbols

a speed of sound, component of acceleration

$\mathbf{a}$ acceleration

A cross-sectional area, area

C wetted perimeter

C_c contraction coefficient

C_d discharge coefficient

C_D drag coefficient

C_F mean skin-friction coefficient

C_L lift coefficient

C_p pressure coefficient

C_v velocity coefficient

c_f resistance coefficient

c_P specific heat capacity at constant pressure

c_V specific heat capacity at constant volume

D diameter, drag

D_h hydraulic diameter

d diameter

e specific internal energy

E bulk modulus

f a function, magnitude of body force, resistance coefficient

$\mathbf{f}$ body force

F Froude number

$\mathbf{F}$ force, a vector-field function

g magnitude of acceleration due to gravity, a function

h specific enthalpy, ratio of the differential arc length to the differential of the coordinate parameter, distance variable

h_L head loss

$\mathbf{i}$ unit vector in the direction of the x-axis

i $= \sqrt{-1}$

j   unit vector in the direction of the y-axis

J Jacobian determinant

k thermal conductivity, a coefficient, height of a roughness element

k   unit vector in the direction of the z-axis

K Knudsen number

l distance, length

L length, lift

m mass, hydraulic mean depth

$\dot{m}$ rate of mass flow

M Mach number, mass

M_{∞} free-stream Mach number

n line normal to a surface, a direction cosine

n   unit vector along a normal to a surface

P pressure

P_v vapor pressure

P_t total pressure

$\bar{P}$ negative of the arithmetic mean of the three normal stress components

q heat transfer per unit mass

Q volumetric rate of flow, heat transfer

r radius

r   position vector

$\sim$ radius

R gas constant, radius

R   position vector

Re   Reynolds number

S   Strouhal number

s specific gravity

t time

t   stress, unit vector tangent to the shock wave surface

T absolute temperature, time, torque, turbulence intensity

u component of velocity, a curvilinear coordinate

u_τ friction velocity

u   unit vector

U   a vector-field function

v specific volume, component of velocity

V magnitude of velocity, a volume

V   velocity, a vector-field function

$\mathcal{V}$ volume

w component of velocity, work, complex potential

W work, Weber number

W   a vector-field function

x distance coordinate
X distance coordinate
y distance coordinate
Y distance coordinate
z distance coordinate, complex variable
Z distance coordinate

Greek Letters

α angle, kinetic energy correction factor
β compressibility, momentum correction factor
γ ratio of specific heats $(= c_p/c_V)$, rate of shear deformation, specific weight, intermittency factor
Γ circulation
δ boundary-layer thickness
δ^* boundary-layer displacement thickness
δ_{ij} Kronecker delta
ϵ_{ij} component of a tensor, rate of strain
$\mathbf{E}$ rate-of-strain tensor
ζ vertical distance coordinate
θ angle, boundary-layer momentum thickness
$\mathbf{I}$ unit dyadic
κ coefficient of bulk viscosity, curvature
λ mean free path of a molecule, resistance coefficient, wavelength
μ Mach angle, shear coefficient of viscosity
μ' dilatational, or second, coefficient of viscosity
ν kinematic viscosity $(= \mu/\rho)$
π_{ij} component of a tensor
$\sqcap$ similarity parameter
Π viscous stress tensor
ρ density
σ component of normal stress, surface tension
τ component of tangential stress
$\mathbf{T}$ stress tensor
ϕ angle, velocity potential
Φ a dyadic
ψ stream function
ω vorticity
ω_P angular velocity
$\tilde{\omega}$ local angular velocity of the fluid
Ω potential energy per unit mass
Ω a dyadic, vorticity tensor

The meaning of other symbols not given above is explained on first use in the text.

INTRODUCTION TO
Fluid Mechanics

CHAPTER 1

Fundamental Concepts

1-1. INTRODUCTION

In a study of fluid flow we are concerned with the observed behavior of flowing fluids and with the mathematical analyses which aim at formulation of rules of behavior of fluids in various circumstances.

Whenever we want to make an analysis of the behavior of a physical system (such as a fluid in motion relative to an object), so as to be able to predict it in conditions in which the system has not been tested, we consider an imaginary simplified physical model which represents, as closely as possible, the real system. Subsequently, we apply the pertinent physical laws in form of equations, together with appropriate initial and boundary conditions. If the mathematical equations which we thus obtain are too complicated for a successful analysis, then we are forced to consider a simpler model.

With the aid of the mathematical analysis we check the usefulness of the model by comparing the predicted behavior of the system with the one observed experimentally. Once we are satisfied that, in certain conditions, the predicted behavior resembles the observed one closely enough for the purpose at hand, we are satisfied that, in not too much different conditions, the theoretical predictions will be of value. We must remember, however, that such predictions, being based on a model that only approximately resembles the physical system, may provide erroneous information in circumstances to which the assumptions made in building the model do not apply. In the end, the success of our analysis can only be judged on its agreement with observations.

At the same time we must keep in mind the fact that the experimental results are subject to errors, and that our interpretations of experimental observations may not always be correct.

An important part of this chapter will be a brief discussion of various physical phenomena occurring in flowing fluids. This discussion should give us an appreciation of the fact that the behavior of flowing fluids is very complicated and that, as a consequence, only certain types of flows can be analyzed successfully.

1-2. THE CONCEPT OF A CONTINUUM; FRAMES OF REFERENCE

In this text we will study the behavior, in various force fields, of a certain class of substances known as fluids, considered to be physically continuous. By saying that a substance is physically continuous, or is a *continuum*, we mean that it possesses properties that (if not constant) vary in a continuous manner in space. By a *property of a substance* we mean any observable quantity that describes its state.

The concept of a continuum is an abstract one because all matter is composed of molecules—the fundamental, tiny conglomerations of matter possessing identifiable characteristic chemical and physical properties. A flowing homogeneous fluid can, on the macroscopic scale, be considered as a continuum if the changes in its state brought about by the motion—changes that are very small yet significant when compared to the total change in state of the fluid due to the motion—take much longer time than that necessary for the attainment of equilibrium conditions in the translatory motion of the molecules of the fluid caused by molecular collisions. (The equilibrium conditions in the translatory state of motion of the molecules usually require only a few collisions.) As a result of these equilibrium conditions, a fluid considered to be a continuum flowing along a surface possesses no relative velocity at the surface; that is, its relative flow speed decreases to zero at the surface. This fact is usually expressed by saying that there is no slip at a surface of a fluid treated as a continuum.

Although we may be justified in considering a fluid to be a continuum (on the macroscopic scale) when it flows past a wing of an aircraft, such assumption may not be valid when studying the flow of the same fluid past a minute object. In the former case, the time necessary to change slightly yet significantly the state of the fluid flowing past the wing when compared with the total change in state of the fluid caused by the motion of the wing should be much longer than the time necessary for the attainment of translational equilibrium between the molecules.

We can devise a criterion to define a continuum flow which is based on some significant physical quantity of the flow field having linear dimension rather than on the time necessary for a significant change of state of the flowing fluid to take place. Such criterion is the ratio of the mean free path of a molecule to a significant physical quantity of the flow field having linear dimension. This ratio is known as the *Knudsen number*. (The mean free path of a molecule is the average distance traversed by molecules between collisions which take place as a result of their random motion. In a flowing fluid, the motion of molecules consists of a regular mean motion resulting from the flow and the random motion relative to it.) The flow of a fluid in which the Knudsen number is very small is called a *continuum flow*, and the fluid is then referred to as a continuum.

The flows of all liquids, and, in general, of gases that are not in a very rarefied state (in which the density of the gas is very low), can for all practical purposes be considered as continuum flows.

The air in the upper atmosphere, which is rarefied and therefore has a large molecular mean free path, cannot be treated as a continuum when flowing at high speed past even such large objects as a rocket.

The concept of a continuum cannot, obviously, be extended to a non-homogeneous fluid. A pure or nonpure substance in which two or more phases are present cannot be considered as a continuum, although each of the phases separately may be so considered.

In our study we will not concern ourselves with the flow of rarefied gases, with the multiphase flow (although we will briefly discuss the phenomenon of cavitation), or with the flows within such special phenomena as shock waves that occur in high-speed flows of gases where, in general, the time interval during which the gradient of velocity and temperature affects the molecules is of the same order of magnitude as the time required for the attainment of translational equilibrium conditions by molecular collisions. Thus we will concern ourselves only with fluid flows for which the continuum approach is valid.

We must always realize that special conditions exist under which fluid cannot be represented by the model of a continuum. We must also appreciate the great usefulness of this approach which enables us to formulate mathematically and subsequently to analyze various fluid flow problems.

Let us now discuss the consequences of the continuum approach to the study of fluid motion. Since the fluid cannot be created or destroyed, we can consider it to be made up of very small fluid masses occupying volume elements which are large when compared with the dimensions of the molecules and their mean free paths, yet small enough so that these fluid masses can be considered as points of uniform state in space. These very small fluid masses, which retain their individuality, whose volumes may change, and whose (imaginary) bounding surfaces may distort while in motion, we call *fluid elements*, or *fluid particles*. Since the homogeneous matter composed of such fluid elements possesses continuous properties, the concept of a fluid element follows directly from the continuum approach.

Figure 1-1 illustrates the motion of a fluid element whose volume at some initial time $t = 0$ is denoted by $d\mathcal{V}_0$, and at time t by $d\mathcal{V}$.[1]

---

[1] To be precise, we should say that symbol t represents the measure of time rather than time itself; similarly, symbol $\mathcal{V}$ denotes the measure of the volume rather than the volume. We should keep in mind that it is only for convenience that we refer to the symbols representing the measures of various physical quantities as the physical quantities themselves.

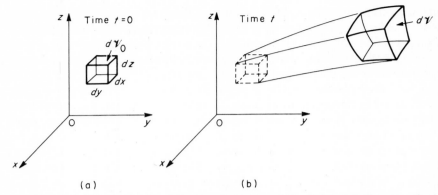

FIG. 1-1. Volume element following the motion of the fluid.   (a) Time $t = 0$.
(b) Time t.

Once we have created the concept of fluid elements, or infinitesimal elements of volume occupied by the fluid, we can introduce the concept of the *fluid density at a point*. We denote this density by the Greek letter ρ (rho) and define it by the equation

$$\rho = \frac{dm}{d\mathcal{V}}$$

where *dm* denotes the mass, and *d𝒱* the volume of a fluid element.   The above equation can also be written as

$$\rho = \lim_{\mathcal{V} \to \mathcal{V}'} \frac{m}{\mathcal{V}}$$

where *m* denotes the mass of the fluid within volume $\mathcal{V}$, and $\mathcal{V}'$ denotes a very small volume element occupied by the fluid which can still be considered macroscopically, that is, the volume of a fluid element.

In the macroscopic description of motion of a continuum the common velocity of all the molecules within each fluid element represents the velocity of a fluid element.   That is, we exclude from the concept of velocity of a fluid element the velocities of the random translational motion of molecules.   We define the *fluid velocity at a point*, or the *flow velocity* (at a point) as the velocity (a vector) of a fluid element relative to a certain reference frame.   If the reference frame is not specifically defined, then it corresponds to the reference frame in which the flow is studied.   By the *flow speed*, or the speed of the fluid at a point, we mean the magnitude of the flow velocity (or, in other words, the magnitude of the fluid velocity at a point).   If the flow is uniform everywhere in the region of space considered, we speak of the *stream velocity*, or of the *stream speed*.

Note that when defining the fluid velocity at a point we used the concept of a *reference frame*.   Since it is impossible to detect the absolute motion of a system by studying its response to the action of forces, only relative and not absolute motion through space can be detected. (This statement describes what is known as the *Newtonian relativity*.) As a result, when we say that a fluid flows we are considering its motion *relative* to a certain frame of reference.

Note further that, although in the continuum approach we concentrate on the motion of the (artificially created) fluid elements, we nevertheless take into account the molecular activity of the fluid by endowing each fluid element of mass $\rho d\mathcal{V}$ with a temperature T. (The kinetic theory of gases states that the temperature T is proportional to the average kinetic energy of the random translatory motion of the molecules.) Further, we take into account the kinetic energy of the random translatory motion, the kinetic and potential energies of the internal motion of the atoms in polyatomic molecules, and the potential energies due to the intermolecular forces, by endowing each fluid element with *internal energy*, $e\rho d\mathcal{V}$, where symbol e denotes the internal energy per unit mass of the substance, or the specific internal energy. Thus, in order for our physical model of the fluid to conform as closely as possible to reality, we allow for effects due to the random translatory and internal motions of the molecules.

The above-mentioned effects, in general, are not the only ones taken into account. Consider two very small volume elements $d\mathcal{V}_1$, and $d\mathcal{V}_2$ occupied by a fluid, which touch each other—that is, two neighboring fluid elements. If initially the average speed of the random translatory motion of the molecules in the volume element $d\mathcal{V}_1$ is larger than in the volume element $d\mathcal{V}_2$, as time goes on, due to the random motion of the molecules across the imaginary surface separating the volume elements, a decrease in the difference of the average speed of the motion of the molecules in the two volume elements takes place. That is, due to the penetration by the molecules of the (imaginary) surface between the two volume elements caused by the random motion of the molecules, the average speed of the molecules inside the fluid element occupying volume $d\mathcal{V}_1$ decreases, while the average speed of the molecules inside the fluid element occupying volume $d\mathcal{V}_2$ increases. As a result, the temperature (and the internal energy) of the fluid in the volume element $d\mathcal{V}_1$ decreases, while the temperature (and the internal energy) of the fluid in the volume element $d\mathcal{V}_2$ increases. This is the phenomenon of *heat conduction* in the fluid which, as described above, allows us to introduce the concept of the *coefficient of heat conductivity* of a substance treated as a continuum. This is accomplished by writing

$$\mathbf{q} = -k \, \nabla T$$

where $\mathbf{q}$ denotes the vector of heat flux by convection, and the letter k denotes the coefficient of heat conductivity, known also as the coefficient of thermal conductivity.

Consider further two neighboring fluid elements moving in direction perpendicular to the line joining their centers. If there exists a difference in the speed of the common regular, translatory, motion of the molecules of these neighboring fluid elements then, as a result of the random motion of the molecules across the (imaginary) surface that separates the fluid elements, transfer of momentum associated with the regular motion takes place. In addition, since the fluid element possessing larger regular velocity tends to leave the slower fluid element behind, the intermolecular attraction forces oppose this relative motion. We can consider therefore that, on the macroscopic scale, the fluid elements exert frictional, or shearing, force on each other. This is the phenomenon of *viscous friction*. The above description of this phenomenon allows us to introduce the concept of the *shear coefficient of viscosity* in a fluid treated as a continuum (Sec. 1-4). It is sufficient at this point to say that the shear coefficient of viscosity enters into the relation between the shearing stress and the rate of angular (or shear) deformation in the fluid.

The simplest example of angular (or shear) deformation of a fluid, which is caused by a velocity gradient in a plane two-dimensional motion, is illustrated in Fig. 1-2.

In addition to the phenomenon of heat conductivity and viscous friction, the random motion of the molecules of a fluid (that is, the molecular diffusion) is responsible for the phenomenon of diffusion of different fluids.

The above discussion should make it clear that we *can* allow for the transfer of energy and momentum in the fluid due to the random motion of the molecules within the concept of a continuum. (The only stipulation

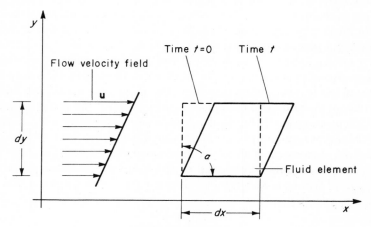

FIG. 1-2. Simple angular (or shear) deformation of a fluid element in the x,y plane.

we have to make is that there can be no *net* increase or decrease of the number of molecules in a fluid element; that is, the mass of the fluid elements must remain constant.) This discussion should bring out the realism of the physical model of a fluid composed of (imaginary) fluid elements, or very small volume elements filled with fluid, which remain distinct in their motion.

As we shall see later, our physical model of a real fluid often has to be further simplified by restrictive assumptions. All such simplifications, although they take us further away from physical reality, nevertheless allow us to obtain an insight into the behavior of real fluids by providing us with physical models whose behavior we can analyze. As was stated in Sec 1-1, however, care must be exercised when predicting the behavior of real fluids from the calculated behavior of a simple physical model of a fluid.

Since in a continuum the physical properties vary in a continuous manner in space, in the study of fluid flow where fluids are treated as continua we deal with physically continuous *scalar, vector,* and *tensor distributions* or *fields*.

The concept of fluid elements makes it possible for us to study the motion of a fluid by studying the motion of individual fluid elements. Thus, we can study a fluid motion by "following" the fluid elements and determining how their positions, velocities, accelerations, and states vary with time. Such description of fluid motion, which is concerned with the motion of individual fluid elements, is known as the *material description* of motion. It is due to L. Euler (1759), but in the literature it is often referred to as the *Lagrangean description.*

The material description of fluid motion is not the only description that can be devised for a fluid treated as a continuum. Such description also provides us with much more information than is usually required, while the method of solution of a flow problem, which yields such description, is usually quite complicated. For that reason, another description of fluid motion, known as *spatial description*, is almost exclusively used (although there are special types of flow in which the material description is preferred.) The spatial description of motion, first formulated by J. L. d'Alembert in 1749 and subsequently generalized by Euler (1752–1755), is concerned with the state of motion at each position in a region of space. In this method the flow is considered as fully described if we are able to determine, in the reference frame in which the flow is studied, the magnitude and direction of the flow velocity and the relevant properties of the fluid (and their variation with time, if any) at every point of the region of space under consideration.

Frames of Reference. As was mentioned earlier, since it is impossible to detect the absolute motion of a system by studying its reponse to the action of forces, it follows that only relative and not absolute motion through space can be detected. Thus when we are talking about a flow of fluid we are considering its motion *relative* to a certain frame of reference. In our study we will consider flows which can be studied using the laws of nonrelativistic classical (Newtonian) mechanics. A frame of reference in which Newton's laws of motion hold is called an *inertial (reference) frame*, or an *inertial system*.

A frame of reference which is in uniform linear motion relative to an inertial frame is also an inertial frame. This is so because the acceleration is the same in both such reference frames, and hence the form of the Newton's laws is the same in them. The transformation from one reference frame to another which is in uniform linear relative motion is known as the *Galilean transformation*. We will make use of this transformation in our study.

It is the postulate of classical mechanics that the frame of reference attached to fixed stars is an inertial frame. The motions on earth are usually studied in reference frames stationary with respect to the earth which is in rotation with respect to the sun. In a reference frame which is rotating uniformly with respect to an inertial frame, the equations of motion have to account for such inertia forces as the centrifugal and Coriolis forces.

In certain such "accelerated" reference frames (like the reference frame of a turbine rotor) these forces may be quite large. The term "accelerated reference frame" applies not only to the frames which rotate uniformly with respect to an inertial frame, but also to those which possess angular and linear accelerations with respect to it.

In most fluid motions on earth, the effects of the centrifugal and Coriolis forces arising because of the rotation of the earth with respect to the sun are small and can be neglected. However, there are some fluid motions in which this is not the case. For example, in the motion of the atmospheric air, the Coriolis forces affect the circulation of the wind. As a result, the winds in the cyclones which form in the Northern Hemisphere circulate in the counterclockwise direction, and in the Southern Hemisphere in the clockwise direction.

Figures 1-3 and 1-4 show photographs of cyclones in the atmosphere of the earth taken by the TIROS weather satellites. Note the directions in which the air masses circulate in the Northern and Southern Hemispheres.

For all flows that we will analyze we will be justified in neglecting the fact that the earth is rotating with respect to the sun, and in considering the reference frame of the earth to be an inertial frame. In addition, except for a brief treatment in Sec. 5-6, we will limit ourselves to a study of flows in inertial reference frames.

Steady and Unsteady Flows. One of the main classifications divides the fluid flows into steady and unsteady flows. A flow in a region of space

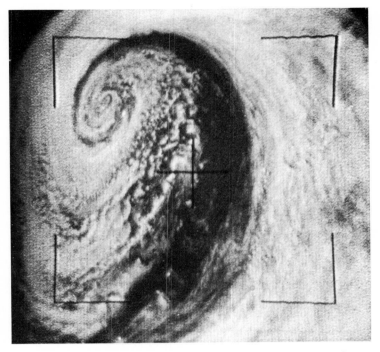

FIG. 1-3. Vortex west of British Isles. (Courtesy of NASA Goddard Space Flight Center, Virginia.)

is said to be *steady* in a certain frame of reference if at every location within the region the fluid velocity and its properties do not change with time. Otherwise the fluid flow is said to be *unsteady*. Often by unsteady flow we mean only the flow that cannot be made steady by a proper choice of the reference frame.

As an example of an unsteady flow which can be made steady by a proper choice of the reference frame, consider the flow of air around an airplane in uniform level flight. In the reference frame of the air, the flow is unsteady; in the reference frame of the airplane, it is steady. In both cases the flow pattern produced in the air is the same, but in the first case it moves with the velocity of the airplane whereas in the second case it appears stationary. If the velocity of the airplane were to vary with time, the flow around the airplane would be truly unsteady, and it could not be made steady by a proper choice of the reference frame.

So far in our discussion we have refrained from stating a definition of a fluid. The concept of a continuum allows us to make such definition. Before we can do that, however, we must discuss the concept of stress in a continuum.

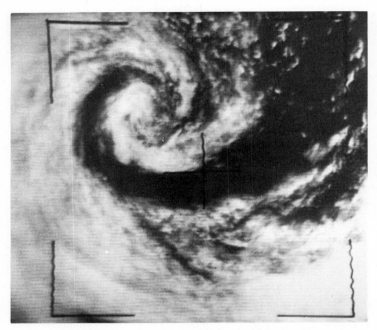

FIG. 1-4. Vortex near 50 S, 135 E. (Courtesy of NASA Goddard
Space Flight Center, Virginia.)

1-3. STRESS IN A CONTINUUM; DEFINITION OF A FLUID

In a flowing fluid, treated as a continuum, consider a surface S
oriented by a normal unit vector **n** along the normal n to the surface
passing through a point P, as shown in Fig. 1-5. After A. L. Cauchy, we
assume that the action of the fluid on one side of the surface S on the
fluid on the other side of S can be represented in form of stress vectors
acting on this oriented fluid surface. This interpretation of the action of
molecular forces is known as the *Cauchy's stress principle.*

The stress **t** (a vector) across a surface at a point in a fluid is defined
by

$$\mathbf{t} = \lim_{A \to 0} \frac{\mathbf{F}}{A}$$

where **F** denotes the force exerted by the fluid toward which points the
normal unit vector **n** orienting the surface. (If the surface is closed, we
will assume that it is oriented by the outward normal unit vector or
vectors.) The normal resolute of **t**, σ, is taken as positive when it points
in the direction of **n**. The positive normal stress, σ (it is the stress which
pulls the fluid under surface S toward the fluid above it in Fig. 1-5), is

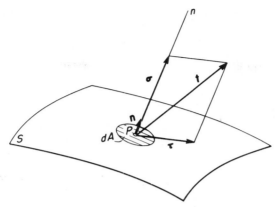

Fig. 1-5. The concept of stress in a continuum.

called *tensile stress*. The negative normal stress is known as *compressive stress*. Since fluids in stable thermodynamic equilibrium do not support tension, it is the compressive, negative, normal stresses which will concern us. The resolute of **t** which is tangent to the surface S at the point considered, τ, is known as the *tangential*, or *shearing*, *stress*.

As will become clear from our discussion in Chapter 7, if we were to consider another surface S' passing through point P in a flowing fluid (say a surface obtained by rotating surface S shown in Fig. 1-5 by some amount), we would find that the new stress **t'** acting across the surface S' at P has a different magnitude than stress **t** and that its direction, relative to the normal to the surface, is also different. Thus, in order to specify the stress (across a surface) at a point in a continuum, we need to know its magnitude and two directions—that of the normal unit vector which orients the element of surface on which the stress acts and which contains the point, and the direction of the stress itself. For that reason, the concept of a vector is not sufficient to describe a stress field in a continuum; we must introduce the concept of a *tensor*.

Definition of a Fluid. Now that we have considered the concept of stress in a continuum, we can give a definition of a fluid: *A fluid is a substance that does not support the existence of tangential, or shearing, stress when in equilibrium* (that is, when at rest). This definition should be qualified by saying that the tangential stress, under whose action a substance "flows" if it is a (real) fluid in the ordinary sense of the word, should be infinitesimal. This is so because there exists a large number of substances, not classified as (ordinary) fluids, that flow only under action of finite tangential stresses. Such substances are often referred to as "plastic fluids," and the study of the behavior of such substances and of other substances whose behavior falls somewhere between that of an ordinary fluid and a solid, is known as *rheology*. We will not concern ourselves with the flow of such substances.

We have already indicated that the phenomenon of frictional, or shearing, force in a fluid can be related to the rate of angular deformation in the fluid which can exist only if there is a difference in the speed of the regular motion of the molecules in the neighboring fluid elements. Thus in a fluid, the difference in the speed of the regular motion of the molecules is necessary for the existence of such a force; *a real fluid can support the existence of tangential stresses only when in motion.* (By a "real fluid" we mean a fluid which we encounter in practice—that is, a viscous and heat-conducting fluid.)

We can also say that when a tangential force, however small, is applied to a fluid surface the fluid is unable to resist it—that is, to remain in equilibrium; as a result, the fluid adjacent to the surface accelerates. (In the case of a solid, if the tangential force is not too large, deformation of the material under the surface on which the force acts takes place; forces resisting this deformation arise in the material, and equilibrium is reestablished.)

A good example of the behavior of fluids is provided by the following experiment. Consider a stationary fluid in a vertical circular cylinder. If the cylinder containing the fluid is made to rotate, the fluid in contact with the cylindrical surface rotates with it. At first only the layer adjacent to the surface of the cylinder is in motion, while the main body of the fluid is stationary. As time goes on, due to the action of viscosity (that is, the action of the tangential forces between the neighboring fluid elements, which are related to the rate of angular deformation of the fluid elements), more and more fluid begins to move. After sufficient time has elapsed, all fluid in the cylinder rotates as though it were a solid. When that state of motion is reached, the tangential stresses in the fluid vanish.

Hydrostatic State of Stress. When a fluid is at rest, i.e., when there is no relative motion and accompanying deformation of the fluid elements, the state of stress in the fluid is said to be *hydrostatic*. From the definition of a fluid it follows that then there are no shearing stresses in the fluid.

Perfect Fluids. The fluids assumed to be nonviscous and nonconducting, which represent a simplified physical model generally used in the first analysis of flows of fluids having very small (coefficients of) viscosity and heat conductivity, are called *perfect fluids.* We may try to look upon this model as representing not a fluid having zero viscosity and heat conductivity, but rather as the limit of a real fluid of small viscosity and heat conductivity as the viscosity and conductivity tend to zero. (See Ref. 23, p. 22.) Such viewpoint provides justification for introduction of singularities in form of concentrated vortices in such field; there would be no physical reason for their existence in a fluid having zero viscosity.

From our definition of a perfect fluid it follows that it does not support shearing stresses. Thus in a perfect fluid, whether its elements become deformed (as a result of the flow) or not (when the fluid is at rest), the state of stress is always hydrostatic (i.e., the state of stress is the same as in a real fluid at rest). In an analysis of flow of such a fictitious fluid we relax the no-slip condition at the wall; such a fluid is imagined to slide on the surfaces along which it flows.

It is important to realize the limitations and also the advantages of the perfect-fluid model. In its defense we can say that a study of a perfect fluid flow is the necessary task before a study of a real fluid having small viscosity (and heat conductivity) is attempted. Such a study results in a number of solutions of flow problems which may approximate quite well the behavior of such real fluids in many respects.

In what follows we shall show that when the state of stress in a fluid is hydrostatic the magnitude of the normal stress (across a surface) at a point (normal stress is the only stress which can then exist) has the same value in all directions. This magnitude of the negative normal stress (compressive stress) is called the *static pressure*, or just *pressure*, and is denoted by the letter P.

Consider a very small mass of fluid in the form of a prism, as shown in Fig. 1-6, and the forces acting on it. As a consequence of the Newton's

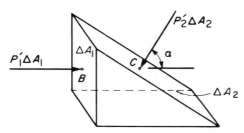

FIG. 1-6. Small volume element in form
of a prism.

second law of motion we can write the following equation relating the horizontal components of forces and accelerations:

$$P_1'\Delta A_1 - P_2'\Delta A_2 \cos \alpha + f\rho'\Delta V = a\rho'\Delta V$$

where the primes refer to the average pressures and densities, f denotes the horizontal component of the body forces (if any), and a denotes the horizontal component of the acceleration.[2] ΔV denotes the volume of the

[2] By the *body*, or *extraneous*, *forces* we mean those forces that arise from action at a distance. These forces are proportional to the mass or volume of the system on which they act. Typical examples of body forces are the force of gravitational attraction and, in the case of electrically conducting fluids in magnetic fields, the electromagnetic force. In our study of flow of electrically nonconducting fluids, the only body force we will consider is the gravitational force. For a fluid at rest $a = 0$ in the above equation.

fluid mass considered. Since $\Delta A_2 \cos \alpha = \Delta A_1 = \Delta A$, we have

$$P'_1 - P'_2 = (a - f)\rho' \frac{\Delta \mathscr{V}}{\Delta A}$$

If we let the volume of the prism tend to zero and the bounding surface shrink to a point, the ratio $\Delta \mathscr{V}/\Delta A$ tends to zero while the average fluid density ρ' tends to the density at a point ρ and the average pressures P'_1 and P'_2 tend to pressures P_1 and P_2, while P_2 tends to P_1. This argument is valid for any angle α.

Thus, when the state of stress is *hydrostatic*—that is, when a (real) fluid is at rest, or the (fictitious) perfect fluid at rest or in motion—we can represent the stress (across a surface) at a point in the fluid by relation

$$\mathbf{t} = -P\mathbf{n} \tag{1-1}$$

where $\mathbf{n}$ denotes the (local) normal unit vector orienting the element of surface considered (see Fig. 1-7), and P the (static) pressure. Thus the (static) pressure at a point, or the magnitude of the (negative) hydrostatic stress across a surface at a point, *has the same value in all directions and can, therefore, be considered as a scalar-field function (function of position).*

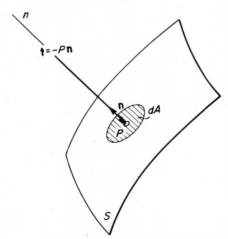

FIG. 1-7. Hydrostatic   state   of
stress at a point P.

1-4. PHYSICAL PHENOMENA OCCURRING IN FLOWING FLUIDS

Viscous Friction and Heat Conduction. The phenomenon of viscous friction in a flowing fluid was described in Sec. 1-2. Most fluids resist a gradient in the regular (flow) velocity in such a way that the shearing stress produced by it in the fluid is proportional to the rate of angular, or shear, deformation (or strain). Consider the flow of such a fluid between two parallel planes, one stationary and one in a uniform translatory motion with speed U, as shown in Fig. 1-8. The motion of the upper plane is, in this example, responsible for the fluid flow. When steady-flow condition is reached, we find that the magnitude of the shearing stress can be related to the magnitude of the velocity gradient by

$$\tau = \mu \frac{U}{Y} \tag{1-2}$$

where μ denotes the shear coefficient of viscosity which, in general, is a function of temperature and pressure. [The shear coefficient of viscosity is sometimes referred to as the (*coefficient of*) *absolute*, or *dynamic*, *viscosity*.]

The rate of shear deformation corresponds in this case to the rate of change of the magnitude of the flow velocity, u, in the direction y perpendicular to **u**. We have

$$\text{Rate of shear deformation} = \frac{du}{dy} = \frac{U}{Y}$$

and Eq. 1-2 becomes[3]

$$\tau = \mu \frac{du}{dy} = \mu \, (\text{rate of shear deformation}) \tag{1-3}$$

[3]Note that, in the more general case of flow in which the velocity component in the y-direction does not vanish, the rate of shear deformation of the fluid in the (x, y) plane is equal to

$$\frac{\partial u}{\partial y} + \frac{\partial v}{\partial x}$$

This follows from the inspection of the following sketch:

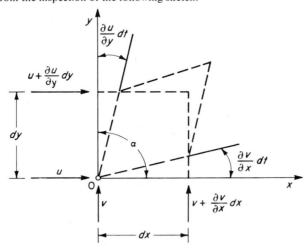

For a plane flow, the rate of shear deformation represents the rate of decrease of the angle between the orthogonal line elements parallel to the x-axis and y-axis respectively. In this case the magnitude of the shearing stress is given by

$$\tau_{xy} = \mu \left(\frac{\partial u}{\partial y} + \frac{\partial v}{\partial x} \right)$$

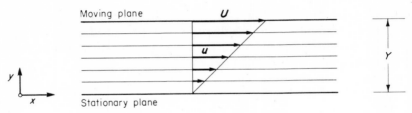

FIG. 1-8. The simple motion of shearing.

Fluids which, in the flow under consideration, obey the last equation are known as *Newtonian fluids*. Generally, by Newtonian fluids we mean fluids in which the components of stress (both, normal and tangential components) are linearly dependent on the rates of deformation of the fluid. Most gases (except when sufficiently rarefied, so that the concept of continuum is not applicable to them), water, and other liquids and homogeneous solutions of substances of small or moderate molecular weights can be classified as Newtonian fluids.

The non-Newtonian fluids do not exhibit the simple linear relationship between the shearing stress and the rate of shear deformation. This fact is illustrated in Fig. 1-9 where the shearing stress/rate-of-shear deformation relations are shown for various types of fluids and for the "plastic fluid." In non-Newtonian fluids, at a given temperature and pressure, the apparent coefficient of viscosity is not constant, but may depend on the rate of shear deformation and sometimes even on the previous history of the fluid. The typical examples of non-Newtonian fluids are plastics, slurries, oil paints, high polymers, and pitch.

The fluids in which, at a given temperature and pressure, the shearing stress is not proportional to the rate of shear deformation (that is, the non-Newtonian fluids) may, in general, be classified as follows:

(a) fluids for which the shearing stress is only a function of the rate of shear deformation,

(b) fluids for which the relation between the shearing stress and the rate of shear deformation involves the previous history of the fluid (for example, it may involve the time during which the fluid has been subjected to shearing stress), and

(c) fluids which, after deformation, can partially recover their shape (such fluids are known as the viscoelastic fluids).

When discussing flows of real fluids, we will concern ourselves only with the Newtonian fluids.

Newtonian fluids whose behavior when in motion is of most practical interest to us (such as water or air) possess very small (shear co-

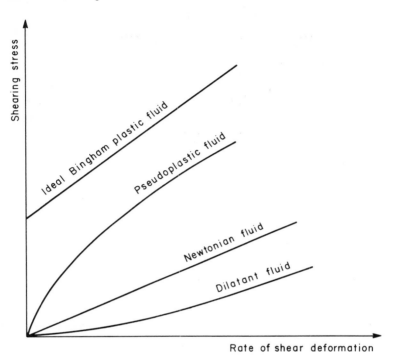

FIG. 1-9. Shearing stress in Newtonian and non-Newtonian fluids.

efficient of) viscosity. (The values of the shear coefficient of viscosity of various substances will be given in Sec. 1-5.) When the flow speeds of such fluids are not too small, the effect of viscosity manifests itself only in relatively thin regions adjacent to the surface of the object over which the fluid flows. In these regions the velocity gradients are large; across them the magnitude of the flow velocity relative to the surface decreases to zero, since there can be no slip at a surface of a fluid which may be treated as a continuum. These flow regions, in which the effect of viscosity of the fluid comes into play, are known as the (velocity) *boundary layers*.

Figure 1-10a shows a photograph of a flow of water over a flat plate. It illustrates the formation of the boundary layer. (The direction of flow is indicated by an arrow.) The long exposure time helps to indicate the velocity of the fluid at various locations by means of the visible white line segments that can be considered to represent the paths of various fluid particles. These paths were made visible by spraying the water surface with aluminium powder. Figure 1-10b shows a sketch of the velocity variation across a boundary layer. Downstream of the plate we can see a region where the flow velocity is low. Such region, formed by merging of

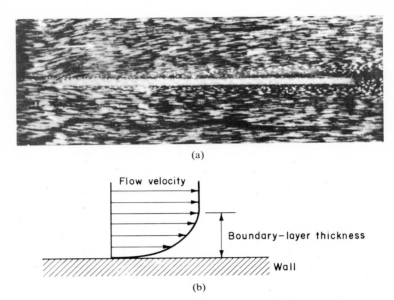

FIG. 1-10. Velocity boundary layer in a flowing fluid. (a) Photograph of a flow over a flat plate (By permission from Ref. 10, Chap. 1.) (b) A sketch of the velocity variation in a boundary layer.

the boundary layer flow from the upper and lower sides of the object over which fluid flows is known as the *wake*.

In general, with possible exception of flows along heated or cooled walls (and of certain high-speed flows of gases), the effect of heat conduction on a fluid flow can be neglected. In the flows along walls in which the effect of heat conduction exists—in fluids whose coefficient of heat conductivity is very small—this effect manifests itself in thin regions adjacent to the walls. These regions, in which large temperature gradients exist, are known as *thermal boundary layers*. In our study we will not consider the effects of heat transfer on fluid flow.

The effects of the boundary layers on a fluid flow are important in the consideration of the resistance to motion (or drag) of bodies in contact with the fluid, of the energy losses brought about by the effects of viscosity and heat conductivity, of the rate of heat transfer between the fluid and the surface along which it flows, and of possible separation of the fluid from such surface.

Figure 1-11 illustrates the change in the flow pattern brought about by the separation of fluid flowing about an airfoil immersed in water. As before, the white lines on the photographs were obtained by spraying aluminium powder on the water surface. In a steady flow such lines represent the paths of the fluid elements. Figure 1-12 shows the separation of flow in a duct possessing a sharp corner.

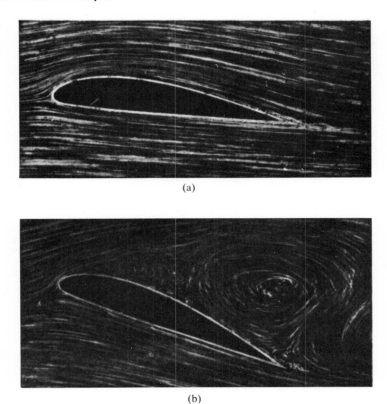

(a)

(b)

FIG. 1-11. Flow about an airfoil immersed in water. (a) Flow
without separation. (b) Flow separated from the upper surface
of the airfoil. (By permission from Ref. 13, Chap. 1.)

Often the velocity boundary layers have only a modifying effect on the
analytical solutions of flows determined under the assumption that the
fluid is nonviscous. For that reason many flows are analyzed, neglecting
at first the effects of viscosity of the fluid (that is, using the perfect fluid
model in the analysis). Once the flow pattern is determined, an analysis
can be made of the boundary-layer flow (using simplified equations of
flow of viscous fluids) and of the effect of the boundary layer on the flow
considered. The type and behavior of the boundary-layer flow depends on
the flow outside it. That is why the knowledge of the main flow, outside
the boundary layer, which usually can be considered as that of a nonviscous fluid, is necessary before the formation and behavior of the
boundary-layer flow can be investigated. However, if a separation of flow
occurs from the surface along which the fluid flows, the nonviscous-fluid
solution to the main flow no longer applies.

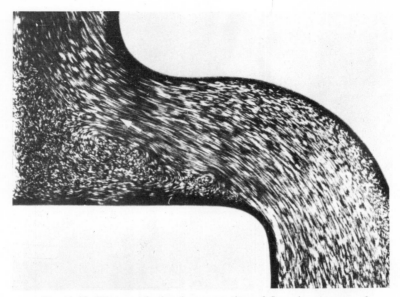

FIG. 1-12. Photograph showing separation of flow downstream of the inner bend in a duct possessing a sharp corner. The arrow indicates the direction of flow. The flow was made visible by spraying aluminium powder on the water surface. (By permission from Ref. 10, Chap. 1.)

Hydrodynamics and Hydraulics. If we look back in history, the first important developments in fluid mechanics were made in the eighteenth century. At that time, J. L. d'Alembert, L. Euler, and J. L. Lagrange laid the foundations of mechanics of a nonviscous and nonconducting incompressible fluid, (such fluid model is often referred to in the literature as the *ideal fluid*), which is called *hydrodynamics*. Since hydrodynamics could not explain such phenomena as the drag of objects moving in a fluid (this was known as the d'Alembert paradox), or any other effect of viscosity, the practicing engineers developed a purely empirical approach to the study of fluid flow, known as *hydraulics*. The equations of motion of viscous Newtonian fluids were not written until the nineteenth century [C. L. M. H. Navier (1822), A. L. Cauchy (1828), S. D. Poisson (1829), G. G. Stokes (1845)]. The first attempt to establish the mechanics of fluids possessing small viscosity on a firm basis by reconciling the analytical treatment of fluid flow with the experimental observations was made by L. Prandtl in 1904, who then introduced the concept of the boundary layer.

Wave Motions in Fluids. The wave motions in fluids can be classified into two groups: those whose existence is contingent on the compressibility of the fluid and those whose existence is contingent on a free surface and which, therefore, can only occur in liquids. The first group of waves includes the compression and expansion waves.   These are discussed briefly in Sec. 9-1. The second group includes the surface waves resulting from the action of gravity or surface tension, or both. Surface waves are discussed briefly in Sec. 9-3.

Discontinuities in the Flow Field.   Consider two streams of a fluid, flowing at different speeds, getting into contact as shown in Fig. 1-13.

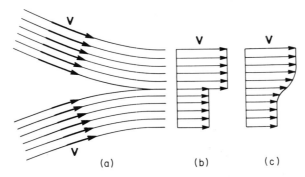

FIG. 1-13. (a) Two streams of a fluid, flowing at different speeds, getting in contact.   (b) Velocity distribution at the location where the streams get in contact.   (c) Velocity distribution downstream of the location where the streams get in contact.

The surface separating the two streams at the location where the streams get in contact may be considered as a surface of discontinuity. Across it the flow speed changes abruptly. As a result of viscous friction, which exists even in the fluids possessing very small shear coefficient of viscosity, the change in the flow speed between the streams quickly becomes gradual, and the discontinuity surface becomes a thin layer. (The term *pseudodiscontinuity surface* may be more appropriate to describe such layer than the term *discontinuity surface*, which we are using here. This is so because the term "discontinuity surface" represents an idealized mathematical description of what in a real fluid is a very thin layer. The discontinuity surface is often referred to as *separation surface* or *free layer*.) In an experiment, we observe that the discontuity surface is unstable and quickly breaks up into a large number of eddies (vortices). At a certain distance downstream of the location where the streams meet the velocity distribution in the fluid is approximately that shown in Fig. 1-13c.

A discontinuity surface, which breaks up into vortices, can also be formed in a flow over a sharp edge of a wall. Figure 1-14 shows the formation and destruction of such a surface, and the resulting separation of flow from the wall. The flow, which at the start of the motion follows the wall contour shown, soon develops a vortex and a surface of dis-

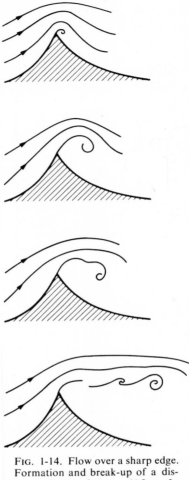

FIG. 1-14. Flow over a sharp edge.
Formation and break-up of a dis-
continuity surface.   (After   L.
Prandtl.)

continuity. Both of them grow in size and soon the vortex starts moving
downstream. Subsequently, the surface of discontinuity, which originates
at the edge, rolls up into concentrated vortices. Figure 1-15 shows the
formation of the surface of discontinuity and of the vortex soon after a
plate has been brought into motion relative to the surrounding fluid.

   The development of the discontinuity surface and of the vortices in a
flow from rest about a circular cylinder is shown in Fig. 1-16. The first
photograph shows the flow at the moment when the cylinder begins to
move relative to the fluid. The last photograph shows extensive separa-

FIG. 1-15. Formation of a discontinuity surface and of a vortex
behind a sharp edge of a plate brought into motion relative to
the fluid. (By permission from Ref. 11, Chap. 1.)

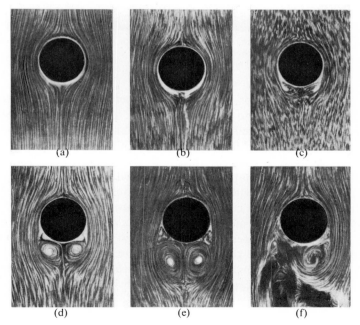

(a)   (b)   (c)

(d)   (e)   (f)

FIG. 1-16. Development of vortices in a flow past a circular
cylinder. First photograph shows the start of the fluid motion.
(By permission from Ref. 11, Chap. 1.)

tion of flow from the cylinder. As we shall discuss in Chapter 8, when the conditions are right, a periodic vortex formation may take place in a flow over a blunt object. Figure 1-17 shows a photograph of such vortex phenomenon formed in a flow over a cylinder. It is known as the *Kármán vortex street.* We shall return to it in Sec. 8-4.

FIG. 1-17. Kármán vortex street. Camera at rest with respect to the undisturbed fluid. (From Ref. 14 by permission of United Engineering Trustees, Inc.)

In compressible fluids, at very high, supersonic, speeds there occur pseudodiscontinuities, known as *shock waves.* By a *supersonic speed* of a fluid we mean a flow speed which is larger than the local speed of sound. The *local speed of sound* is the speed of propagation of very small disturbances at a given location, measured in the reference frame of the fluid; that is, in a coordinate system moving with the (local) fluid velocity.

Before proceeding with a brief discussion of shock waves we now introduce a few pertinent concepts and definitions.

One of the main classifications of flow of a compressible fluid is based on the ratio of the flow speed to the local speed of sound in the fluid (that is, to the speed of sound corresponding to the same location as the flow speed). This ratio is known as the *(flow) Mach number.* If we denote the flow speed by V, the local speed of sound by a, and the Mach number by M, then by definition

$$M = \frac{V}{a} \qquad (1\text{-}4)$$

In a subsonic flow, $0 < M < 1$ in the region considered, while in a supersonic flow, $1 < M < \infty$.

The flows of liquids which we encounter in practice are all subsonic, with the Mach number close to zero. (Whereas the speed of sound is quite high in liquids, the attainable flow speeds, for reasonable pressure drops, are quite low.) In such flows the change in the fluid density, brought about by the motion, is very small when compared with the fluid density at rest. In the flows of gases or vapors in which the flow speed is everywhere much smaller than the local speed of sound, the effect on the flow of the relatively small change in the density of the fluid brought about by the motion can usually be neglected. (This limit, below which the effects of compressibility are neglected, is usually taken as corresponding to the flow Mach number of 0.3.) For the high-Mach-number flows the compressibility effects must be considered.

Thus the flows of gases in which the flow speed is everywhere sufficiently small when compared to the local speed of sound and the flows of liquids under normal conditions can be considered as *incompressible flows*, or flows of *incompressible fluids*. Therefore the term incompressible fluid (or flow) when applied to a real fluid (or flow) which satisfies the conditions mentioned above should not be taken literally. In the analysis of such flows we use physical model of a fluid whose density is constant—that is, truly incompressible.

The *free-stream Mach number*, M_∞, is defined as the ratio of the speed of an object relative to free stream to the speed of sound in the free stream. By *free stream* we mean here the stream of fluid ahead of an object in motion relative to the fluid, which is free of the disturbances produced by the object.

The shock waves are very thin regions across which the flow, which

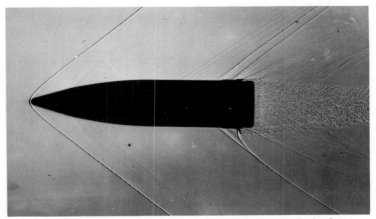

Fig. 1-18. A shadowgraph picture of a 20-mm projectile in free flight at supersonic velocity in a ballistic range. (Crown Copyright; Courtesy of the National Physical Laboratory, Teddington, Middlesex, England.)

is supersonic relative to it, changes to another flow, either supersonic or subsonic, depending on the inclination of the upstream (relative) flow velocity to the line normal to the shock wave at the point considered. Figure 1-18 shows a photograph of shock waves formed in air by a projectile traveling at supersonic velocity ($M_\infty > 1$). The boundary layer on the projectile and the wake are also clearly visible.

In high-speed flows of gases which contain moisture, the phenomenon known as *condensation shock waves* can occur. Across these regions the condensation of the moisture takes place. In our consideration of flow of compressible fluids in Chapter 9 we will assume that the flowing gases are free of moisture.

In flows of mixtures of reacting gases we may come across another pseudodiscontinuity known as the *combustion wave*. A combustion wave represents a burning zone in a reacting fluid across which the changes in the fluid temperature may be large. In our study we will not concern ourselves with the combustion waves.

Cavitation. When the pressure in a flowing liquid falls below the vapor pressure (corresponding to the temperature of the liquid), vapor bubbles form in it. (The vapor pressure of a given liquid depends on whether it is a pure substance or a solution.) The process of formation of the vapor phase in a flowing liquid is known as *cavitation*. When a gas is dissolved in the liquid, it is the gas pressure rather than the vapor pres-

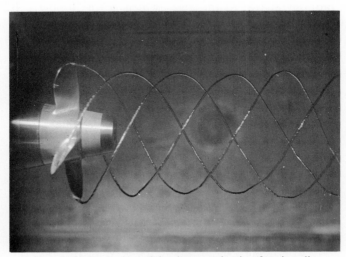

FIG. 1-19. Cavitation originating near the tip of an impeller in water. Water speed, 16.2 ft/sec; pressure, 20.9 psig; rpm = 2072. (Courtesy of the Garfield Thomas Water Tunnel, Ordnance Research Laboratory, Pennsylvania State University.)

sure on which the occurence of cavitation depends. (The gas pressure represents the sum of the partial pressures of the vapor and of the dissolved gas.) The commercially available liquids usually contain dissolved gases. The tap water contains a large quantity of dissolved gases and of solid particles.

The experiments show that the drag, or resistance to flow, of an object immersed in a liquid may increase with an increase in the amount of cavitation. This is not the only harmful effect of cavitation. In hydraulic machinery, when cavitation occurs, a damage to the solid surfaces exposed to the cavitating liquid occurs. The rise in pressure associated with the collapse of the vapor bubbles (in the regions in which the liquid pressure is too high for cavitation) is believed to be responsible for this damage.

Figure 1-19 shows the beginning of appearance of cavitation in a flow of a liquid past a rotating propeller. Here, the cavitation takes place near the tip of the propeller, where the pressure is low as a result of formation of tip vortices. Figure 1-20 shows cavitation in a flow past a disk.

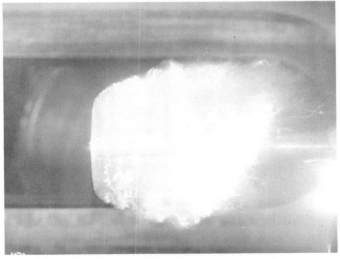

FIG. 1-20. Cavitation behind a disk in water. (Flow from left to right.) Water speed well upstream of the disk, 51.3 ft/sec; pressure, 20 psig. (Courtesy of the Garfield Thomas Water Tunnel, Ordnance Research Laboratory, Pennsylvania State University.)

The cavities filled with the vapor of the flowing liquid are not the only cavities that can be observed. Figure 1-21 shows an air-filled cavity formed by the entry of a sphere into the water.

The term *cavitating flow* is reserved for the two-phase flow composed of a liquid and its vapor in which the change of phase is produced by local pressure drop in the flowing liquid. The flow illustrated in Fig. 1-21 does not fall into that category.

(a)   (b)

FIG 1-21. (a) Formation of an air-filled cavity behind a sphere during entry into water. (b) Air-filled cavity behind the sphere. The diameter of the sphere d = 2 in.; the entry speed V = 19.6 ft/sec. (Courtesy of Admiralty Research Laboratory, Teddington, Middlesex, England.)

Surface Tension. Experiments show that liquids, at their free surface, behave as though the free surface were an elastic membrane of constant tension per unit width. This behavior of liquids is the result of the fluid property known as *cohesion*, which can be explained by the forces of attraction between the molecules. The tension per unit width in the free surface, which is a *force per unit length*, is known as the *surface tension*. Its magnitude is usually denoted by symbol σ.

As a result of surface tension, pressure differences exist across the free surface of a liquid. Referring to Fig. 1-22, we find that since $d\theta = ds_1/R_1$ and $d\phi = ds_2/R_2$,

$$(P_i - P_o)ds_1 ds_2 = 2\sigma ds_1 \frac{d\phi}{2} + 2\sigma ds_2 \frac{d\theta}{2}$$

$$= \sigma \left(\frac{1}{R_1} + \frac{1}{R_2} \right) ds_1\, ds_2$$

and that

$$P_i - P_o = \sigma \left(\frac{1}{R_1} + \frac{1}{R_2} \right) \tag{1-5}$$

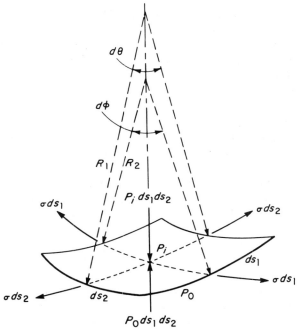

FIG. 1-22. Forces acting on an element of a free
surface.

In the above equation, R_1 and R_2 denote the radii of curvature, in mutually perpendicular planes, which are also perpendicular to the tangent plane, of the element of the free surface considered, while P_i and P_o denote the pressures on the concave and convex sides of the free surface respectively.

Equation 1-5 shows that the pressure difference acting across a free surface is large when the radii of curvature of the surface are very small. For that reason, in certain flows, such as the flows of liquid jets, sheets, and droplets, the forces acting due to the surface tension may be large when compared with other forces acting on the liquid, such as the force of gravitational attraction or the drag force.

If a free surface becomes disturbed, as a result of the tendency of the surface to return to the undisturbed (smallest area) configuration, surface waves, known as the *surface-tension waves*, form. In a liquid jet, these waves may result in a breakup of the jet and formation of droplets.

The magnitude of the surface tension of a given liquid depends on the temperature and pressure, and on the substance with which it is in contact.

Turbulence. The experiments on the pressure loss in flows of fluids through pipes, performed in the eighteenth and early nineteenth centuries, seemed to indicate that no general law for such loss, which results from the internal (viscous) friction in the fluid, can be established. Around the middle of the nineteenth century the results of careful experiments and analyses of G. Hagen (1839) and J. Poiseuille (1840, 1841, 1846) produced an understanding of the low-speed fluid flows in pipes. Their experimentally verified formula for the pressure drop in pipes represents one of the few existing solutions of the equations of flow of viscous fluids. It states that the pressure drop in a flow through a pipe, excluding the region near the entrance to the pipe, is proportional to the first power of the mean flow speed and length of pipe, and is inversely proportional to the square of the pipe radius. (The volumetric rate of flow was found by Poiseuille to be proportional to the pressure drop and to the fourth power of the radius, and inversely proportional to the length of the pipe.)

In the vast majority of fluid flows, however, the observed pressure drop was found to be proportional to the second, rather than first, power of the mean speed. Thus from the practical point of view the results of Hagen and Poiseuille were of limited use. The reason for this is that they are valid only for a certain type of flow, the so-called *laminar flow*, in which, on the macroscopic scale, the fluid travels in regular paths. In most flows of practical interest, the (macroscopic) motion of the fluid is irregular, with the paths of the fluid elements winding tortuously through the flow field. We may consider that their motion is made up of two: the primary motion (in the direction of the axis in the case of a flow through a duct), and an irregular secondary flow. Such fluid flow is called the *turbulent flow*.

The classification of fluid flows into the laminar and turbulent flows is one of the main classifications of fluid flow.

Hagen, in his tests, observed that the jet of water leaving a pipe changed appearance from a regular and glasslike to an oscillating and irregular one when the flow speed was increased beyond a certain value. In 1854 he was able to show that the transition from a laminar to turbulent flow depended not only on the mean flow speed but also on the viscosity of the fluid. At that time he thought that the irregular motion of the fluid was caused either by the irregularities of the pipe wall or by the disturbances coming from the entrance to the pipe. By 1869 he had demonstrated that the transition of flow from laminar to turbulent, or vice versa, depended on the mean flow speed, the radius of the pipe, and on the temperature of the water. When any one of these quantities was decreased below a certain limit, the flow would change from turbulent to laminar.

It remained for Osborne Reynolds, in 1883, to show that the transition from laminar to turbulent flow in a pipe depends only on the value of the dimensionless expression

$$\frac{\rho \overline{V} r}{\mu}$$

Where $\overline{V}$ denotes the magnitude of the mean flow velocity, ρ the density of the fluid, μ the shear coefficient of viscosity, and r the radius of the pipe. While his own experimental data indicated that the pressure drop varied as the 1.722 power of the mean flow speed, the experimental data of Darcy, plotted by Reynolds, showed this power to lie anywhere between 1.746 and 2. This discrepancy was attributed by Reynolds to the roughness of the pipe walls.

Reynolds' experiments on the appearance of eddies characterizing turbulent flow consisted of visual observations of flow of water in glass tubes into which a dye was introduced. His apparatus is sketched in Fig. 1-23. When investigating the law of resistance to flow, Reynolds measured the pressure drop in pipes 16 ft long and having inside diameters of $\frac{1}{4}$ and $\frac{1}{2}$ in. The static pressure taps were 5 ft apart, with the first tap being about 10 ft downstream of the inlet to the pipe. The ratio

$$\frac{\rho V l}{\mu}$$

where l denotes a significant physical quantity of the flow field having dimension of length (in the case of a flow through a pipe, it may be the

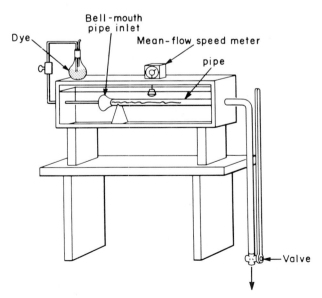

FIG. 1-23. The apparatus of O. Reynolds.

radius or diameter of the pipe) is known as the *Reynolds number*, and is denoted by the symbol Re. The physical quantity on which it is based is usually indicated by a subscript. (For example, the Reynolds number based on a pipe diameter is denoted by symbol Re_d.)

While Reynolds was able only to draw pictures of the patterns formed by the dye which he observed, we have available photographs taken in an apparatus similar to his by W. Dubs in 1939 [16]*. These are shown in Fig. 1-24. The photographs were taken about 35 to 40 tube diameters downstream of the inlet. These tests indicated that the laminar flow persisted at the values of the Reynolds number based on the pipe diameter below about 1050, that the transition between laminar and turbulent flow was taking place in the range $1050 < Re_d < 3500$, and that at $Re_d > 3500$ the flow was turbulent.

The tests show that we cannot expect to find a specific value of the Reynolds number at which a laminar flow changes to turbulent, but rather a range of values. We also know that the flow conditions at the inlet to the pipe affect the transition. The smoother and more disturbance-free is the flow at the inlet, the higher is the value of the Reynolds number at which eddy motion can be first observed. In Chapter 7 we will return to the discussion of the problem of stability of laminar flow.

In practice we often speak about the values of the Reynolds number below which the flow is supposed to be laminar and above which it is supposed to be turbulent (although by doing this we disregard the existence of the range of values of the Reynolds number at which flow is neither laminar nor fully turbulent, which flow is referred to as the *transition flow*). We refer to such values of the Reynolds number as the *critical values*.

Just as the flow in a duct may be laminar or turbulent, so a boundary-layer flow can be laminar or turbulent. A boundary-layer flow, unless tripped by a disturbing obstacle, starts as a laminar flow and, after a certain distance, changes into a turbulent flow. Hence we speak about the laminar and turbulent boundary layers. The distance from the leading edge of the surface along which fluid flows, measured in the direction of flow, to the location at which a laminar boundary layer changes into a turbulent boundary layer depends on many factors. The most important one is the Reynolds number based on the distance from the leading edge. Some of the other factors that affect the transition are the pressure gradient in the flow outside of the boundary layer, the roughness of the surface, the rate of heat transfer to the surface, and the intensity of the turbulence of the outside flow.

Turbulence, *whose very existence is connected with the shear flow*, can be present in flows unbounded by solid walls. Such flows, which can be

---

*Numbers in brackets indicate references at end of chapter.

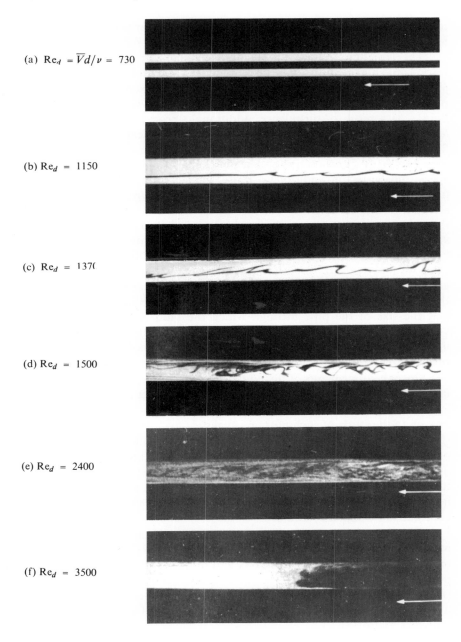

(a) $\mathrm{Re}_d = \overline{V}d/\nu = 730$

(b) $\mathrm{Re}_d = 1150$

(c) $\mathrm{Re}_d = 137($

(d) $\mathrm{Re}_d = 1500$

(e) $\mathrm{Re}_d = 2400$

(f) $\mathrm{Re}_d = 3500$

FIG. 1-24. Effect of the Reynolds number on a flow in a tube (the flowing fluid is water.) Experiments of W. Dubs [16]. (Reproduced by permission of Birkhäuser Verlag, Basel, Switzerland.)

found in jets, wakes, and zones in which two fluid streams moving at different velocities mix, are known as the *free turbulent flows*.

The irregular motion of the fluid elements in a turbulent flow is responsible for the diffusion process which, *except in the region adjacent to the wall*, predominates over the process of molecular diffusion [which process is responsible for the property of (shear) viscosity of a flowing fluid]. As a result of turbulence, additional stresses, known as the *turbulent stresses*, are produced in a flowing fluid. In dealing with turbulent flowes, we build a fictitious model of a fluid whose flow is laminar and may be steady and laminar and which behaves as though it possessed special properties in addition to those which fluids exhibit in a laminar flow: the "*eddy viscosity*" and the "*eddy heat conductivity*." [From our description of the turbulent flow it should be clear that it is never steady in the strict definition of a steady flow. However, if in a turbulent flow the values of the flow variables averaged over a period of time (which is sufficiently long to include a large number of fluctuations) do not vary with time, we may consider such flow as quasi-steady. We refer to such flows as steady (turbulent) flows. The eddy viscosity is usually very much larger than the ordinary viscosity, and it increases with the size of the flow field (say the size of the pipe through which the fluid flows) and the overall velocity (rate of flow in the case of the flow through a pipe) [17]. Thus, unlike the ordinary viscosity, the eddy viscosity is not a thermodynamic property of the fluid.

Since the dimensions of the eddies characterizing a turbulent flow are large compared to the mean free path of a molecule, the turbulent motion is macroscopic (and not molecular) and, as a result, the continuum approach to the study of such motion is valid.

This brief discussion of turbulence should give us some feel for this phenomenon which is of fundamental importance in the study of fluid flow. Despite large effort directed toward a better understanding of turbulence over the last decades, we have to admit that our knowledge of it is still very limited. The discussion of turbulence and turbulent flow is continued in Chapters 7 and 8.

The phenomenon of turbulence necessitates reexamination of the meaning of our definition of a perfect fluid. When we consider a physical model of a fluid which is nonviscous and nonconducting, we mean that it possesses neither the ordinary nor eddy viscosities and heat conductivities. (As was stated earlier, a perfect fluid does not support shearing stresses—it supports only normal stresses; therefore the state of stress in such a fluid is always hydrostatic.)

1-5. PHYSICAL PROPERTIES OF FLUIDS

The fluid properties which we have already discussed are the (static) pressure, density, viscosity, and surface tension.

Both gases and liquids are classified as fluids. The property which distinguishes a gaseous phase of a substance from a liquid phase is that a gas, when introduced into an empty container, fills the container completely even though the quantity of the gas may be very small. A liquid in similar circumstances, if its quantity is small enough so that it does not fill the container, but not so small that it all evaporates, collects (under the action of the gravitational field) at the bottom of the container so that a distinct boundary is formed between it and its vapor.

The liquids can be broadly classified as viscous liquids and thin liquids, depending on whether they offer a large or small resistance to motion relative to a solid surface. Typical viscous liquids are thick oils and glycerine, while typical thin liquids are water and gasoline. The shear coefficients of viscosity of the typical viscous liquids are high, about 100 times higher than the shear coefficients of viscosity of the typical thin liquids (which, in turn, are about 10 times as high as those of gases). The thin liquids and gases are considered as fluids having very small (shear coefficient of) viscosity.

Figure 1-25 gives the values of the shear coefficient of viscosity (also referred to as the absolute viscosity, or simply as the viscosity) and of the (coefficient of) kinematic viscosity $\nu = \mu/\rho$ for a number of liquids and gases at various temperatures and pressures. The most common unit of the shear coefficient of viscosity is the centipoise ($= 10^{-2}$ gm cm^{-1} sec^{-1}, where symbol gm refers to a gram mass). In Fig. 1-25a a scale in lbf sec/ft^2 is also provided. The units of the coefficient of kinematic viscosity are ft^2/sec or cm^2/sec. (The conversion factors between various units are given in Appendix C.) In general, the shear coefficient of viscosity depends on temperature and pressure. For pressures lower than a few atmospheres the shear coefficient of viscosity of liquids decreases with temperatures, and its dependence on pressure is very small. For gases, except when the pressure is high so that their behavior deviates substantially from that of an ideal gas, the shear coefficient of viscosity is independent of pressure and depends on temperature only. It increases with increasing temperature. Figure 1-25b indicates large influence of pressure on the kinematic viscosity of gases and vapors (through the dependence of density on pressure).

Table 1-1 gives the values of the shear coefficient of viscosity of air as a function of temperature.

Table 1-2 gives the values of the shear coefficient of viscosity and of the (coefficient of) kinematic viscosity of water at various temperatures at nearly atmospheric pressure.

Figure 1-26 shows the variation of the specific weight of pure water with temperature at a location where the magnitude of the acceleration due to gravity is standard (that is, $g = 32.174$ ft/sec^2). Note that the *specific weight of a substance*, γ, represents its weight per unit volume. At

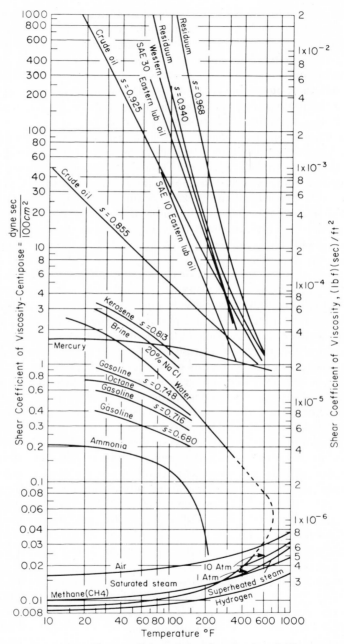

Fig. 1-25a. Shear coefficient of viscosity of various fluids.

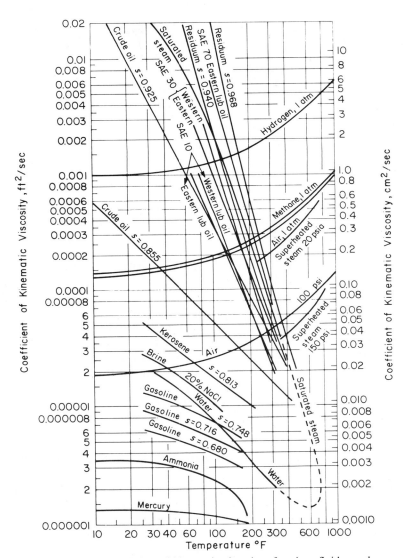

FIG. 1-25b. Coefficient of kinematic viscosity of various fluids. *s* denotes the density of the substance relative to that of water at 60°F (that is, specific gravity.) (From V. L. Streeter (ed.), *Handbook of Fluid Dynamics*, copyright 1961 by McGraw-Hill, Inc. Used by permission of McGraw-Hill Book Co.)

TABLE 1-1

THE VISCOSITY OF AIR

Temp., (°C)	$10^4 \mu$ in gm/(cm sec)	$10^5 \mu$ in lbm/(ft sec)	Temp., (°C)	$10^4 \mu$ in gm/(cm sec)	$10^5 \mu$ in lbm/(ft sec)
0°	1.709	1.148	260	2.806	1.886
20	1.808	1.215	280	2.877	1.933
40	1.904	1.279	300	2.946	1.980
60	1.997	1.342	320	3.014	2.025
80	2.088	1.403	340	3.080	2.070
100	2.175	1.462	360	3.146	2.114
120	2.260	1.519	380	3.212	2.158
140	2.344	1.575	400	3.277	2.202
160	2.425	1.630	420	3.340	2.244
180	2.505	1.683	440	3.402	2.286
200	2.582	1.735	460	3.463	2.327
220	2.658	1.787	480	3.523	2.367
240	2.733	1.837	500	3.583	2.408

(By permission, from S. Goldstein, *Modern Developments in Fluid Dynamics*, Dover Publications, Inc., New York.)

a given temperature and pressure the mass of a unit volume of a substance is constant, while its weight depends on the prevailing acceleration due to gravity. At a location where the magnitude of the gravitational acceleration is standard, the numerical value of specific weight may or may not be the same as that of density because the units are different. The unit of the specific weight is lbf/ft³ (pounds of force per cubic foot), while the unit of density is slug/ft³ or lbm/ft³ (pounds of mass per cubic foot). [The numerical value of specific weight expressed in lbf/ft³ is the same as the numerical value of density expressed in lbm/ft³ when the magnitude of the gravitational acceleration is standard (since at such conditions 1 lbm weighs 1 lbf).] We have by definition,

$$\gamma = \rho g$$

where g denotes the prevailing magnitude of the acceleration due to gravity.

By *specific gravity*, *s*, of a substance we mean the ratio of the mass of the substance to the mass of an equal volume of water. This ratio is therefore also equivalent to the ratio of the density of the substance to the density of the water. The density of a substance is, in general, a function of temperature and pressure. Since the density of liquids and solids depends very little on pressure, and since the concept of specific gravity is used almost exclusively for substances in such states, only the temperature is usually specified with the value of specific gravity. In physical and chemical tables, the values of specific gravity of substances are given at 4°C. Often 60°F is used as the reference temperature. At that temperature, and at atmospheric pressure, the density of water is 62.37 lbm/ft³. Note that the specific gravity is a nondimensional quantity.

TABLE 1-2
THE VISCOSITY AND KINEMATIC VISCOSITY OF WATER

Temp., °C	100μ in gm/(cm sec)	100ν in cm²/sec	Temp., °F	Temp., °C	100μ in gm/(cm sec)	100ν in cm²/sec	Temp., °F
0°	1.792	1.792	32	38	0.681	0.686	
1	1.731	1.731		39	0.668	0.673	
2	1.673	1.673		40	0.656	0.661	104
3	1.619	1.619		41	0.644	0.649	
4	1.567	1.567		42	0.632	0.637	
5	1.519	1.519		43	0.621	0.627	
6	1.473	₁1.473		44	0.610	0.616	
7	1.428	1.428		45	0.599	0.605	
8	1.386	1.386		46	0.588	0.594	
9	1.346	1.346		47	0.578	0.584	
10	1.308	1.308	50	48	0.568	0.574	
11	1.271	1.271		49	0.559	0.565	
12	1.236	1.237		50	0.549	0.556	122
13	1.203	1.204		52	0.532	0.539	
14	1.171	1.172		54	0.515	0.522	
15	1.140	1.141		56	0.499	0.506	
16	1.111	1.112		58	0.483	0.491	
17	1.083	1.084		60	0.469	0.477	140
18	1.056	1.057		62	0.455	0.463	
19	1.030	1.032		64	0.442	0.451	
20	1.005	1.007	68	66	0.429	0.438	
21	0.981	0.983		68	0.417	0.426	
22	0.958	0.960		70	0.406	0.415	158
23	0.936	0.938		72	0.395	0.404	
24	0.914	0.917		74	0.385	0.395	
25	0.894	0.897		76	0.375	0.385	
26	0.874	0.877		78	0.366	0.376	
27	0.855	0.858		80	0.357	0.367	176
28	0.836	0.839		82	0.348	0.358	
29	0.818	0.821		84	0.339	0.350	
30	0.801	0.804	86	86	0.331	0.342	
31	0.784	0.788		88	0.324	0.335	
32	0.768	0.772		90	0.317	0.328	194
33	0.752	0.756		92	0.310	0.322	
34	0.737	0.741		94	0.303	0.315	
35	0.723	0.727		96	0.296	0.308	
36	0.709	0.713		98	0.290	0.302	
37	0.695	0.700		100	0.284	0.296	212

(By permission, from S. Goldstein, *Modern Developments in Fluid Dynamics*, Dover Publications, Inc., New York.)

While the effect of temperature and pressure on the density of liquids is small, this effect is, in general, large for gases.[4] In our study we will concern ourselves with gases at small densities and low pressures. In such conditions the equation of state of the gases can be written in the

[4]Only when the relative pressure and temperature changes in a flowing gas are small, can, in many instances, the variations in the density be neglected and the gas considered approximately incompressible, just like a liquid.

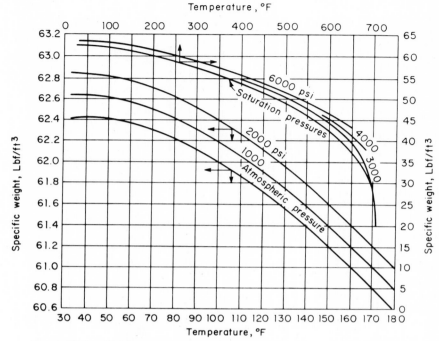

FIG. 1-26. Specific weight of pure water at a location where g = 32.174 ft/sec². (From V. L. Streeter (ed.), *Handbook of Fluid Dynamics*, copyright 1961 by McGraw-Hill, Inc. Used by permission of McGraw-Hill Book Co.)

form

$$P = \rho RT \qquad (1\text{-}6)$$

where T denotes the absolute temperature, and R the gas constant per unit mass which is independent of the temperature and pressure but whose value depends on the gas. The gases which obey exactly the above equation of the state are called *ideal gases*.

The reciprocal of the density is known as the *specific volume*. It is denoted by symbol v. Thus by definition

$$v = \frac{1}{\rho}$$

The measure of dependence of the volume of a fluid on pressure is provided by the *volume modulus of elasticity*, or *bulk modulus*, of the fluid. It is defined by the relation

$$E = -v \frac{dP}{dv}$$

or by its equivalent

$$E = \rho \frac{dP}{d\rho}$$

For finite changes in pressure we may estimate the corresponding change in volume by using the relation

$$\Delta v = -v \frac{\Delta P}{E_{av}}$$

where E_{av} denotes the average value of the bulk modulus.

The *compressibility* of a fluid, usually denoted by the symbol β, is defined as the reciprocal the bulk modulus. Thus

$$\beta = -\frac{1}{v} \frac{dv}{dP}$$

For many practical applications the water can be considered as incompressible. This conclusion follows from an inspection of Table 1-3 giving the bulk modulus of water at various temperatures and pressures, and of Fig. 1-26. That a large pressure rise results in a decrease in its volume, however, illustrates the fact that if water were truly incompressible the sea level would rise through about 500 feet [19].

TABLE 1-3

BULK MODULUS OF WATER, IN LBF/IN.^{2}

Pressure, lbf/in.^{2}	Temp., °F				
	32	68	120	200	300
15	292,000	320,000	332,000	308,000	. . . . .
1,500	300,000	330,000	342,000	319,000	248,000
4,500	317,000	348,000	362,000	338,000	271,000
15,000	380,000	410,000.	426,000	405,000	350,000

(From V. L. Streeter (ed.), *Handbook of Fluid Dynamics*, copyright 1961 by McGraw-Hill, Inc. Used by permission of McGraw-Hill Book Co.)

The value of the compressibility depends on the condition at which change in volume is taking place as a result of a change in pressure. This is especially true for gases. We may consider the compressibility evaluated at a constant temperature, β_T, or at the adiabatic (that is, no heat flow) conditions, β_s. Similarly, we differentiate between E_T and E_s.

By the *specific heat capacity*, or *specific heat* for short, of a substance we mean the amount of heat necessary to raise the temperature of a unit mass of the substance by a unit of temperature. The value of the specific heat of a substance depends on the conditions at which the heating takes place, and we differentiate between the specific heat at constant pressure c_P, and the specific heat at constant volume, c_V. While for a gas the value of c_P is appreciably larger than the value of c_V, for liquids the difference between these two values is very small. Thermodynamic considerations show that

$$\frac{E_s}{E_T} = \frac{c_P}{c_V} = \gamma$$

where the symbol γ is used for the ratio c_P/c_V.

The (local) speed of propagation of sound a is given by

$$a = \sqrt{\frac{E_s}{\rho}}$$

$$= \sqrt{\left(\frac{\partial P}{\partial \rho}\right)_s} \tag{1-7}$$

where the subscript s refers to the reversible adiabatic conditions. This will be shown in Chapter 9.

Table 1-4 gives the values of the surface tension of water and mercury in contact with air, at various temperatures.

The properties of fluids discussed in this section represent the most important properties that we will have to consider in our study of fluid flow.

TABLE 1-4
VALUES OF SURFACE TENSION OF WATER AND MERCURY
IN CONTACT WITH AIR

Liquid	Temp., °F	lbf/ft	Liquid	Temp., °F	lbf/ft
Water......	32	0.00518	Water..........	120	0.00467
	40	0.00514		140	0.00454
	50	0.00509		160	0.00440
	60	0.00504		180	0.00427
	70	0.00498		200	0.00413
	80	0.00492		212	0.00404
	90	0.00486	Mercury......	59	0.0333
	100	0.00480		68	0.0324

(From V. L. Streeter (ed.), *Handbook of Fluid Dynamics*, copyright 1961 by McGraw-Hill, Inc. Used by permission of McGraw-Hill Book Co.)

1-6. FLUID STATICS

In this section we will consider the forces acting on fluids at rest. The only forces we will consider will be the (body) forces due to the gravitational attraction. We will assume that the intensity of the gravitational field g (that is, the magnitude of the acceleration due to gravity) is constant, and that the gravitational acceleration acts downward—that is, toward the earth. From the considerations in Sec. 1-3 it follows that the state of stress which we will consider is hydrostatic, i.e., the state in which the normal stresses at a point in a fluid are the same in all directions and there are no tangential stresses.

Note that the assumption of a constant value of the gravitational acceleration on earth g is valid only when the differences in height between the fluid masses considered are small compared with the distances of these masses from the center of the earth. This is the case in most engineering considerations, except perhaps in meteorology.

As a direct consequence of our assumption that the magnitude of the gravitational acceleration is constant, and that the forces due to gravity are the only body forces we will consider in our analysis (we exclude from our discussion electrically conducting fluids in magnetic and electrostatic fields), *the (static) pressure in a fluid at rest is the same at any location on a horizontal plane.* That this must be so (as long as our assumptions are valid) can be easily verified by writing equation of balance of vertical forces acting on an element of fluid of height dz shown in Fig. 1-27.

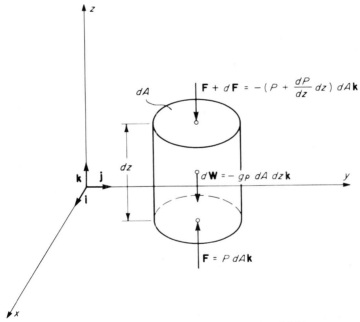

FIG. 1-27. Element of fluid in the gravitational field.

(We assume the z-axis to be the vertical axis in whose negative direction acts the gravitational acceleration whose magnitude we assume to be constant.) We have

$$d\mathbf{F} + d\mathbf{W} = 0$$

where $\mathbf{F}$ denotes the force due to the pressure acting on the fluid element, and $\mathbf{W}$ denotes the gravity force, or weight, of the fluid within the element. Since

$$d\mathbf{W} = -g\rho \, dA \, dz \, \mathbf{k}$$

where **k** denotes the unit vector in the direction of the positive z-axis, the equation of balance of vertical forces can be written as

$$\frac{dP}{dz} = -g\rho \tag{1-8}$$

which indicates that P = constant if z = const., that is, in horizontal planes.

The pressure in a fluid is usually measured, by a pressure gage, relative to the local prevailing atmospheric pressure P_a. This value is known as *gage pressure*. To differentiate between the actual (static) pressure (P) in a fluid and the gage pressure, we often refer to the (static) pressure as the *absolute (static) pressure*. The value of the absolute pressure is

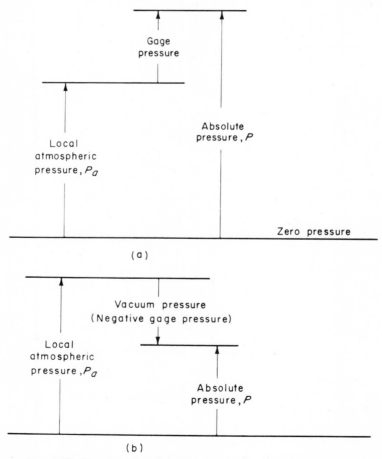

FIG. 1-28. Meaning of terms having to do with pressure. (a) Absolute pressure larger than the local atmospheric pressure. (b) Absolute pressure smaller than the local atmospheric pressure.

obtained from the value of the gage pressure by adding to it the prevailing atmospheric pressure. If the absolute pressure is lower than the atmospheric pressure, we refer to the difference between the absolute and atmospheric pressures [that is, to the (negative) gage pressure] as the *vacuum pressure*. Figure 1-28 illustrates the meaning of these various terms.

When English engineering units are employed, we often use the symbol "psi" to represent the unit of pressure 1 lbf/in^2. To distinguish between the absolute and gage pressures we then use the symbols "psia" and "psig" respectively, while the vacuum pressure is indicated by writing "psi vac."

Note that the local atmospheric pressure on earth is not constant but, even at a given elevation above the sea level, varies constantly with time in a certain narrow range. The so-called *standard atmospheric pressure* corresponds to 14.696 lbf/in^2, which is equivalent to the level difference of 29.92 in. of mercury in a mercury manometer.

For *incompressible fluids*, Eq. 1-8 can easily be integrated, giving

$$P - P_0 = -g\rho z \tag{1-9}$$

where P_0 denotes the (static) pressure at $z = 0$.

When dealing with a body of a liquid [which we consider to behave like an incompressible fluid when the differences between the pressures acting on it are not too large (see Sec. 1-5)] possessing a free surface, we usually consider the $z = 0$ plane to coincide with the free surface and, with P_a denoting the atmospheric pressure acting on the free surface, write

$$P = P_a + g\rho h \tag{1-10}$$

where $h = -z$ denotes the vertical distance below the free surface, as indicated in Fig. 1-29. The term $g\rho h$ represents (the value of) the pressure in the (incompressible) fluid in excess of the atmospheric pressure— that is, the gage pressure.

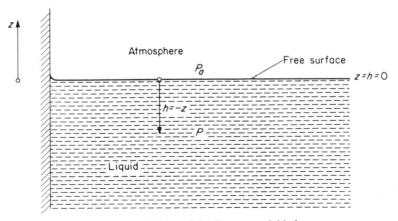

FIG. 1-29. Definition of the distance variable h.

Equation 1-10 can be written in the form

$$P = P_a + \gamma h \qquad (1\text{-}11)$$

if we introduce the (constant) specific weight γ into it.

From Eq. 1-11 it follows that, for an incompressible fluid (having constant specific weight), we can determine the gage pressure $(P - P_a)$ if the distance h, referred to as the *head*, is known.

In the case of connected vessels in which different pressures act on the free surfaces of a liquid, as shown in Fig. 1-30, since the pressure in a fluid at rest is the same at any location in a horizontal plane, we have

$$P = P_{a1} + \gamma h_1$$
$$= P_{a2} + \gamma h_2$$

where P denotes the pressure acting in the horizontal plane $A - A$ which is distance h_1 below the free surface in vessel 1 and distance h_2 below the

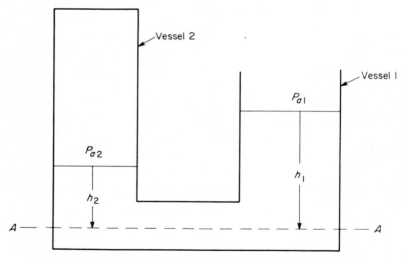

Fig. 1-30. Connected vessels in which different pressures act on the free surfaces of the liquid.

free surface in vessel 2. As a result,

$$P_{a2} - P_{a1} = \gamma(h_1 - h_2)$$

For *compressible fluids*, Eq. 1-8 can be integrated only if we assume a certain relationship between the pressure and the density.

In the atmosphere of the earth, within the limits of the so-called troposphere, the average variation of the air temperature with the distance from the earth may be approximated by equation

$$T = T_0 - az$$

where the lapse rate

$$a = -\frac{dT}{dz} = 0.00356616°F/ft$$

and $T_0 = 518.688°R$ ($=288.16°K$) denotes the standard absolute temperature at sea level [21]. The atmosphere for which the above relations are valid is known as the "standard atmosphere."

Making use of the equation of state, we obtain the following relationship between the pressure and the density of air in the troposphere and the height in the "standard atmosphere":

$$P = \rho RT$$
$$= \rho R(T_0 - az)$$

Introducing this relation into Eq. 1-8 gives, upon integration,

$$\frac{P}{P_0} = \left(\frac{T_0 - az}{T_0}\right)^n$$

where P_0 denotes the standard air pressure at sea level ($z = 0$), and the dimensionless exponent $n = g/aR = 5.2561$.

Forces Acting on Surfaces Immersed in a Liquid. Let us consider the forces due to gravity acting on a plane surface S immersed in a liquid at rest and possessing constant density.[5] We assume, as usual, that the gravitational acceleration is constant. The plane of the surface makes an angle α with the free surface of the liquid, as shown in Fig. 1-31. The gravity forces which act on the surface S represent the gravity forces acting on the liquid and the gravity forces acting on the atmosphere above the free surface. The latter forces can be assumed to result in a uniform (atmospheric) pressure P_a acting on the free surface of the liquid. In our considerations we will concern ourselves only with the gravitational forces acting on the liquid; that is, we will consider only the forces produced by the gage pressures. (The magnitudes of the forces produced by the absolute static pressures can be obtained by adding the constant atmospheric pressure to the gage pressures.)

The magnitude of the force acting on surface S as a result of the weight of the liquid is

$$F = \int g\rho hc \, dy$$
$$= g\rho \sin \alpha \int cy \, dy \qquad (1\text{-}12)$$

where c denotes the width of the surface in the x-direction (see Fig. 1-31), because the magnitude of this force acting on an element of surface area $c \, dy$ is $g\rho hc \, dy$ (the state of stress being hydrostatic). Introducing the distance of the centroid of the area of surface S from the x-axis

[5] We will concern ourselves with the forces acting on the upper side of surface S which may be a real or imaginary surface in the liquid.

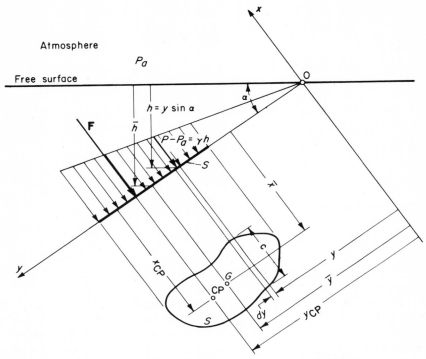

FIG. 1-31. An inclined plane surface immersed in a liquid.

$$\bar{y} = \frac{\int cy\, dy}{A} \tag{1-13}$$

where A denotes the surface area, we can write

$$F = g\rho \sin \alpha\, \bar{y}A$$
$$= g\rho \bar{h}A$$
$$= P_G A \tag{1-14}$$

where $\bar{h}$ denotes the distance of the centroid of area G from the free surface, and P_G represents the (gage) pressure acting at the centroid G.

The last equation says that the magnitude of the force acting on an inclined plane surface fully immersed in a uniform liquid at rest, as a result of the gravity, can be determined by taking the product of the surface area and the pressure acting at its centroid $(= g\rho \bar{h})$.

The point at which the line of action of the force $\mathbf{F}$ intersects the surface S is called the *center of pressure*. It is left as a problem assignment to find the general expressions for the coordinates x_{CP}, y_{CP} of the center of pressure CP of a plane surface immersed in a liquid.

In the case when the surface S is not a plane surface, the force acting in a uniform gravitational field on such a surface S immersed in a liquid whose density is constant can be determined from the general formula

$$\mathbf{F} = \int_S (-g\rho h)\mathbf{n}\, dA$$

$$= -g\rho \int_S h\mathbf{n}\, dA \qquad (1\text{-}15)$$

where $\mathbf{n}$ denotes the normal unit vector orienting the surface area element dA (see Fig. 1-32). (Since the state of stress is hydrostatic, the stress acting across a fluid surface at a point is normal to the surface.) The vertical component of this force is given by

$$F_z = \mathbf{F} \cdot \mathbf{k}$$

$$= -g\rho \int_S h(\mathbf{n} \cdot \mathbf{k})\, dA$$

$$= -g\rho \int_S h \cos \alpha_z\, dA$$

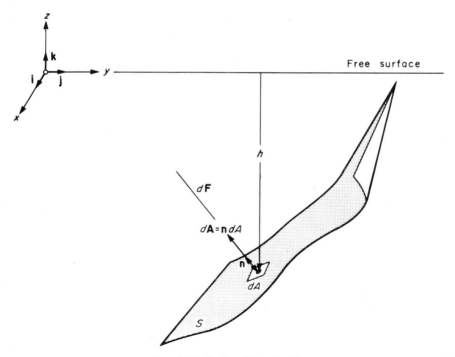

FIG. 1-32. Surface S in a liquid.

where α_z denotes the angle between the unit vectors **k** and **n**. (Note that this angle lies in the plane of these two unit vectors.) The term

$$\int_S h \cos \alpha_z \, dA$$

represents the volume of the liquid above surface S. The line of action of the vertical resolute of the force due to gravity **F** acting on this mass of liquid passes through the centroid of this volume. The expressions for the horizontal components F_x and F_y of the force **F** can be obtained from Eq. 1-15 by forming scalar products of **F** with the unit vectors **i** and **j** respectively.

Note that if we are interested in accounting for the absolute pressures on an immersed surface, rather than only for the gage pressures (which arise as a result of the weight of the liquid), we can modify the values of the depth of the liquid h in the Eqs. 1-12 and 1-15 (and in equations derived from them) by adding to it a vertical distance Δh such that

$$\Delta h = \frac{P_a}{g\rho}$$

where P_a denotes the atmospheric pressure acting on the free surface of the liquid whose density is ρ.

Capillarity. Consider a liquid in contact with the solid walls of a container and with a gas (or a lighter liquid) above it. Let us assume the

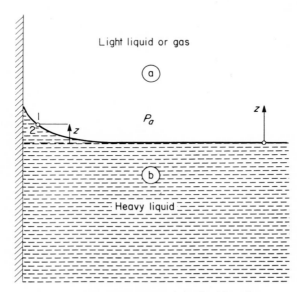

Fig. 1-33. Assumed shape of the liquid surface
near a solid wall.

shape of the liquid surface near the solid wall as shown in Fig. 1-33. The pressure difference at a point across the curved part of the surface is given by

$$P_1 - P_2 = (P_a - g\rho_a z) - (P_a - g\rho_b z)$$
$$= g(\rho_b - \rho_a)z \tag{1-16}$$

in view of Eq. 1-9. In the above equation P_a denotes the atmospheric pressure acting on the free surface (having an infinite radius of curvature), and ρ_b and ρ_a denote the densities of the heavy liquid and of the gas (or, the light liquid), respectively.

In Sec. 1-4 we showed that the pressure difference which exists as a result of the surface tension across a free surface of a liquid is given by

$$P_i - P_0 = \sigma\left(\frac{1}{R_1} + \frac{1}{R_2}\right) \tag{1-5}$$

where σ denotes the magnitude of the surface tension, and R_1 and R_2 denote the radii of curvature (in mutually perpendicular planes which are also perpendicular to the tangent plane) of the element of free surface. For the shape of the liquid surface which is concave upward as shown in Fig. 1-33 we have $P_i = P_1$ and $P_0 = P_2$, and we can write

$$P_1 - P_2 = \sigma\left(\frac{1}{R_1} + \frac{1}{R_2}\right)$$

Combining the last equation with Eq. 1-16 we obtain

$$\frac{1}{R_1} + \frac{1}{R_2} = \frac{g(\rho_b - \rho_a)}{\sigma} z$$
$$= \frac{\gamma_b - \gamma_a}{\sigma} z \tag{1-17}$$

where $\gamma = g\rho$ denotes the specific weight. The above equation is known as the "law of curvature of the boundary surface" [13].

Consider the boundary on which three fluids a, b, and c meet (at least two of them must be in liquid state), as shown in Fig. 1-34. In equilibrium, the values of the surface tensions $\sigma_{ab}, \sigma_{ac}, \sigma_{bc}$, fix the values of the angles at which the fluids meet. No equilibrium is possible when

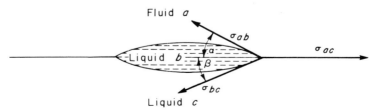

FIG. 1-34. Surface tensions acting on the boundary on which three fluids meet.

$\sigma_{ac} > \sigma_{ab} + \sigma_{bc}$. In such case, liquid b will spread over the surface of liquid c. (This situation exists when fluid b is a mineral oil, fluid c is water, and fluid a is air.) When analyzing the angle at which fluid surfaces meet in the case when a liquid and some other fluid (either another liquid or a gas) are in contact with a solid surface, as shown in Fig. 1-35a, we are concerned only with the equilibrium of forces parallel to the solid surface since the fluids are free to move under the influence of such forces. At equilibrium we have

$$\sigma_{ab} \cos \alpha + \sigma_{bc} = \sigma_{ac}$$

or

$$\cos \alpha = \frac{\sigma_{ac} - \sigma_{bc}}{\sigma_{ab}}$$

where angle α denotes the angle of contact measured from the solid surface covered by the liquid, as shown in Fig. 1-35.

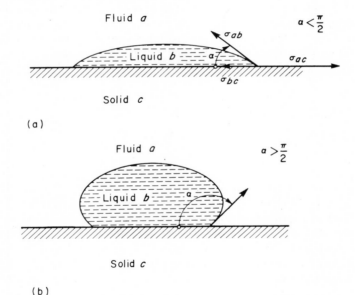

FIG. 1-35. (a) Liquid wetting a solid surface. (b) Liquid not wetting a solid surface.

The values of $(\sigma_{ac} - \sigma_{bc})$ can be positive or negative. In the latter case, illustrated in Fig. 1-35b, the angle $\alpha > 90$ deg. Such is the case when the fluid a is air, fluid b mercury, and solid c is glass. When the angle $\alpha < 90$ deg we say that the liquid is "wetting" the surface.

When one end of a narrow tube is immersed in a liquid which wets its surface, the liquid level in the tube rises above the level of the liquid out-

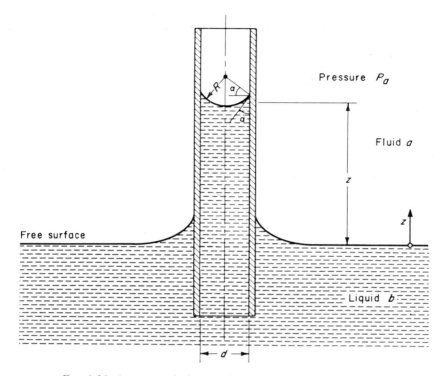

FIG. 1-36. A narrow tube immersed in a liquid which wets its surface.

side, as shown in Fig. 1-36. In the case when the liquid does not wet the tube surface (that is, when $\alpha > 90$ deg), we observe depression of the liquid surface in the tube below the level of the liquid outside, as shown in Fig. 1-37.

When $d \ll |z|$ where $|z|$ denotes the absolute value of the elevation or depression of the liquid in the tube with respect to the liquid outside and d the inner diameter of the tube, then we may consider the surface of the liquid in the tube to be spherical. In such case, if we denote the radius of the spherical liquid surface by R, we have

$$R = \frac{d}{2 \cos \alpha}$$

and from Eq. 1-17 it follows that

$$z = \frac{4\sigma_{ab} \cos \alpha}{g(\rho_b - \rho_a)d}$$

$$= \frac{4\sigma_{ab} \cos \alpha}{(\gamma_b - \gamma_a)d} \tag{1-18}$$

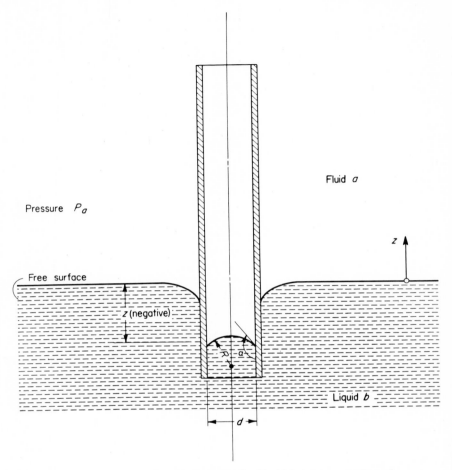

Fig. 1-37. A narrow tube immersed in a liquid which does not wet its surface.

since $R_1 = R_2 = R$. Note that the elevation (or depression) of a liquid in a tube can be very large when d is very small.

Buoyancy.   By the buoyancy we mean the force which acts on a body immersed in a fluid at rest as a result of displacement of the fluid by the body. This force represents the resultant thrust of the fluid on the body. The buoyancy can exist only when the fluid and the body are situated in a field of a body force.

The magnitude of the buoyancy acting on a body completely immersed in a fluid in the field of gravitational force is equal to the weight of the fluid displaced by the body, the line of action of buoyancy (in this case lift acting on the body which results in an apparent decrease in its weight) being the same as that of the resultant force (weight) which would act on

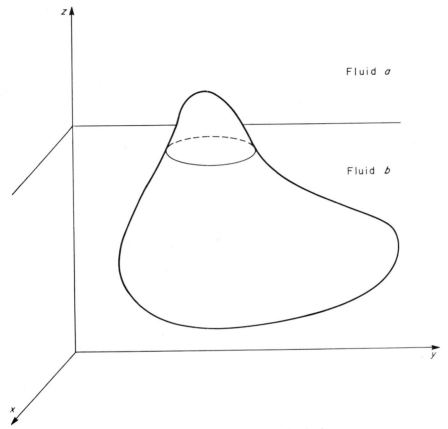

FIG. 1-38. A partially immersed floating body.

the displaced fluid. The above statement describes what is known as the *principle of Archimedes*.

The proof of this principle follows directly from our discussion of forces acting on curved surfaces immersed in a fluid.

When the principle of Archimedes is applied to a floating body such as that shown in Fig. 1-38, we have in general, to consider separately the buoyancy forces resulting from the displacement of the two fluids. In the case where the fluid *a* is a gas (such as air) and the fluid *b* is a liquid (such as water), the buoyancy force due to the displacement of the gas is negligible. Then, we consider the weight of the floating body to be equal to the weight of the liquid displaced.

By the *center of buoyancy* we mean the point at which the buoyancy force may be considered to act. When the fluid, in which the body is immersed has uniform composition and properties and the force field is constant, the center of buoyancy corresponds to the centroid of the displaced fluid volume.

REFERENCES

1. B. Thwaites (ed.), *Incompressible Aerodynamics.* Oxford: Clarendon, 1960.
2. C. Truesdell, *Principles of Continuum Mechanics.* Dallas, Texas: Socony Mobil Oil Company, Inc. Field Research Laboratory, 1961.
3. C. Truesdell, *The Kinematics of Vorticity.* Bloomington, Ind.: Indiana U. P., 1954.
4. L. Prandtl and O. G. Tietjens, *Fundamentals of Hydro- and Aeromechanics.* (First published in 1934), New York: Dover, 1957.
5. R. R. Long, *Mechanics of Solids and Fluids.* Englewood Cliffs, N. J.: Prentice-Hall, 1961.
6. W. J. Duncan, A. S. Thom, and A. D. Young, *Mechanics of Fluids.* London: E. B. Arnold, Ltd., 1960.
7. E. B. McLeod, *Introduction to Fluid Dynamics.* New York: Macmillan, 1963.
8. J. A. Owczarek, *Fundamentals of Gas Dynamics.* Scranton, Pa.: International Textbook, 1964.
9. W. L. Wilkinson, *Non-Newtonian Fluids.* New York: Pergamon, 1960.
10. B. Eck, *Technische Strömungslehre*, 6th ed. Berlin: Springer, 1961.
11. *Ludwig Prandtl Gesammelte Abhandlungen.* Third Part. Berlin: Springer, 1961.
12. *Ludwig Prandtl Gesammelte Abhandlungen.* First Part. Berlin: Springer, 1961.
13. L. Prandtl, *Essentials of Fluid Dynamics*, London: Blackie and Son, Ltd., 1952.
14. L. Prandtl and O. G. Tietjens, *Applied Hydro- and Aeromechanics.* (First published in 1934), New York: Dover, 1957.
15. O. Reynolds, "An Experimental Investigation of the Circumstances which determine whether the Motion of Water shall be Direct or Sinuous, and of the Law of Resistance in Parallel Channels," *Philosophical Transactions of the Royal Society*, (London), Vol. 174, Part III, (1883), pp. 935–982; also, somewhat enlarged version in *Papers on Mechanical and Physical Subject*, Cambridge, Cambridge U. P., Vol. II, 1901, pp. 51–105.
16. W. Dubs, "Über den Einfluss laminarer und turbulenter Strömung auf das Röntgenstreubild von Wasser und Nitrobenzol. Ein röntgenofraphischer Beitrag zum Turbulenzproblem," *Helvetica Physica Acta* (Switz.), vol. 12 (1939), pp. 169–228.
17. G. B. Schubauer and C. M. Tchen, *Turbulent Flow*, No. 9, Princeton Aeronautical Paperbacks, Princeton, N. J.: Princeton University Press, 1961.
18. R. L. Daugherty, "Fluid Properties," in V. L. Streeter, ed., Handbook of Fluid Dynamics. New York: McGraw-Hill, 1961, pp. 1-1-1-22.
19. G. Temple, *An Introduction to Fluid Dynamics.* Oxford: Clarendon, 1958.
20. S. Goldstein, *Modern Developments in Fluid Dynamics.* New York: Dover, 1965 (first published by Clarendon Press, Oxford, in 1938).
21. "Standard Atmosphere—Tables and Data for Altitudes to 65,800 Feet," *NACA Report* 1235 (1955).

22. Theodor von Kármán, *Aerodynamics*. Ithaca: Cornell U. P., 1954.
23. S. Goldstein, *Lectures on Fluid Mechanics*. New York: Interscience, 1960.

PROBLEMS

1-1. The specific gravity of olive oil at 60°F is 0.917. Calculate (a) density (in lbm/ft^3 and in $slug/ft^3$), (b) specific volume, and (c) specific weight at a location where the magnitude of gravitational acceleration is $g = 32.10$ ft/sec². (Sec. 1-5.)

1-2. Calculate the pressure in lbf/in^2 in excess of the atmospheric pressure in a spherical water droplet whose diameter is (a) 0.25 in., (b) 0.025 in., (c) 0.0025 in. at a temperature of 60°F. (Sec. 1-5.)

1-3. Consider a liquid having density $\rho = 62.4$ lbm/ft^3 in a container shown in the accompanying sketch, which is open to the atmosphere. If the height h of the liquid in the container is 2 ft, and the atmospheric pressure is 14.7 $lbf/in.^2$, determine (a) the mass of the liquid in the container, (b) the gage pressure acting on the base of the container in $lbf/in.^2$, and (c) the force acting from above on the base on the container in lbf. (Sec. 1-6.)

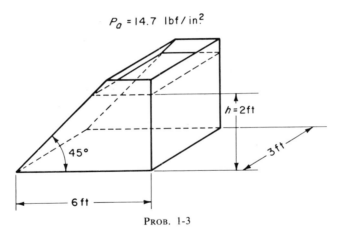

$P_a = 14.7$ lbf / in²

$h = 2$ ft

3 ft

45°

6 ft

PROB. 1-3

1-4. Taking moments of the hydrostatic forces about the x-and y-axes shown in Fig. 1-31 and making use of Eq. 1-14, show that the coordinates of the center of pressure of surface S are given by

$$y_{CP} = \frac{I_x}{\bar{y}A} \quad \text{and} \quad x_{CP} = \frac{I_{xy}}{\bar{y}A}$$

where $I_x = \int cy^2\,dy$, $I_{xy} = \int\int xy\,dx\,dy$, and $\bar{y}$ denotes the distance of the centroid of the area of the surface from the x-axis. (Sec. 1-6.)

1-5. If the diameter of the small piston in a hydraulic press shown in the accompanying sketch is $D_1 = 1$ in., and the diameter of the large piston is $D_2 = 3$ ft, find the magnitude of the force $\mathbf{F}_2$ acting on the large piston if the magnitude of the force $\mathbf{F}_1$ acting on the small piston is 100 lbf. What is the effect of the difference in elevation of the pistons on the magnitude of F_2 if the fluid is water? Assume $\rho_{water} = 62.4$ lbm/ft^3. (Sec. 1-6.)

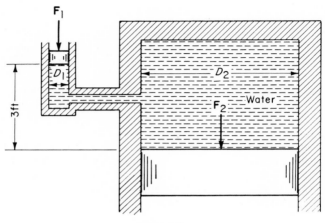

PROB. 1-5

1-6. Making use of the values of the surface tension given in Table 1-4, determine the depression of mercury in contact with air in a glass manometer. The inside diameter of the manometer tube is 0.1 in., and the temperature is 68°F. Assume that the contact angle between the mercury and glass in air is 140 deg, that the specific weight of mercury $\gamma_m = 845.7$ lbf/ft^3, and that $\gamma_{air} = 0.075$ lbf/ft^3. (Sec. 1-6.)

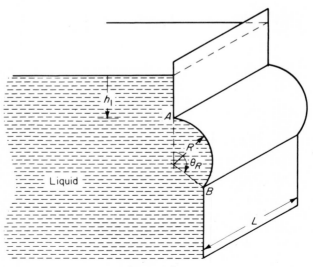

PROB. 1-7

1-7. Find the expression for the vertical and horizontal forces acting on cylindrical section AB of a reservoir wall, shown in the accompanying sketch, in terms of pertinent parameters. Assume that the liquid has uniform density and that the gravitational field is uniform. (Sec. 1-6.)

1-8. Determine the depth of submersion of a wooden log floating in water. Assume that the log has a circular cylindrical shape and that the specific gravity of the wood is 0.509. Express the depth of submersion as a function of radius of the log. What would be the depth of submersion of the log if the specific gravity of the wood were 0.50? (Sec. 1-6.)

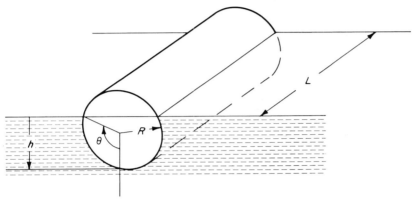

PROB. 1-8

1-9. (a) Consider a liquid partially filling a tank of a car moving horizontally with a constant acceleration **a**. At equilibrium, that is, when the liquid is at rest with respect to the tank, what is the angle of inclination of the free surface of the liquid to the horizontal plane? (b) Consider a liquid in a cylindrical vessel rotating with a constant angular velocity ω with respect to its axis, as shown in the accompanying sketch. The centripetal acceleration acting on the fluid elements acts radially inward, and its magnitude is $\omega^2 r$. The variation of the pressure in the fluid, sufficiently long time after initiation of rotation, when all fluid elements rotate with respect to the axis of the cylinder with its angular velocity ω, (the fluid experiences then the "rigid-body rotation"), can be determined by considering the fluid at rest on which act the hydrostatic force and the radially outward-acting centrifugal force of magnitude $\omega^2 r$. Write the equations for the radial and vertical pressure gradients ($\partial P/\partial r$ and $\partial P/\partial z$). Subsequently, using the coordinate system shown in the sketch, integrate them [integrate the equation for $\partial P/\partial r$ in the $z = 0$ plane adding an unknown function of elevation, $f_1(z)$, to account for the variation of pressure with the elevation z, and integrate the equation for $\partial P/\partial z$ at $r = 0$, adding an unknown function of radius, $f_2(r)$, to account for the variation of pressure with radius r], and show that the surfaces of constant pressure P are parabolas of revolution given by equation

$$z = \frac{\omega^2 r^2}{2g} + \frac{P_0 - P}{g\rho}$$

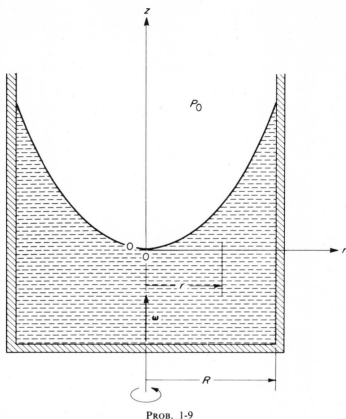

PROB. 1-9

where P_0 denotes the outside (atmospheric) pressure. Assume the density of the liquid to be constant. (Sec. 1-6.)

1-10. A circular cylindrical vessel of length L and diameter $D = 4$ ft is fully filled with water and lies horizontally on its curved surface as shown in the accompanying sketch. The vessel has an atmospheric vent as shown. Calculate the magnitude and the point of action of the resultant force **F** acting on a side of the vessel. (Sec. 1-6.)

1-11. To measure a small pressure difference we often use an inclined manometer. If the reading on a manometer inclined at an angle of 10 deg to the horizontal is 16 in., and the manometer fluid has specific gravity of 0.8 (at a temperature of 60°F), find the gage pressure in lbf/in.^{2} of the fluid in vessel A shown in the accompanying sketch. What is the absolute pressure of the fluid in the vessel A, in inches of mercury, if the atmospheric pressure is 14.50 lbf/in.^{2}. Assume that the gravitational acceleration is standard. (Sec. 1-6.)

1-12. Consider two vessels, filled with fluids a and b and connected with a

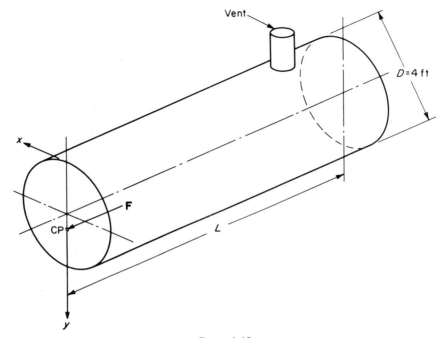

Vent

$D = 4$ ft

F

CP

L

x

y

PROB. 1-10

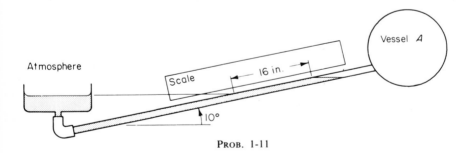

Vessel A

Atmosphere

Scale

16 in.

10°

PROB. 1-11

manometer, as shown in the accompanying sketch. If the difference between the levels of the (immiscible) manometer fluid c is $\Delta z = z_1 - z_2$, show that the pressure difference between the level A in the vessel containing fluid a and the level B in the vessel containing fluid b is given by

$$P_A - P_B = -g[\rho_a(z_A - z_1) + \rho_c\Delta z + \rho_b(z_2 - z_B)]$$

where ρ_a, ρ_b, and ρ_c denote the densities of the fluids a, b, and c, respectively, while z_A and z_B denote the elevations of the levels A and B measured from a common datum line. (Sec. 1-6.)

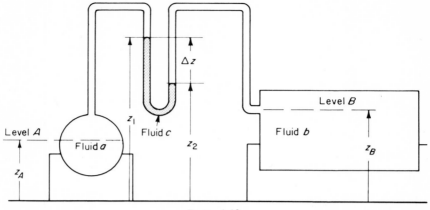

PROB. 1-12

1-13. A tank, open to the atmosphere, is filled with a heavy liquid to a depth h_1 from the bottom, and with water to a depth H from the bottom, as shown in the sketch. Find the expression for the magnitude of the force acting on the side of the tank of length L_1, and the position of the center of pressure as functions of the pertinent variables. If the heavy liquid is mercury (the specific gravity of mercury at 60°F is 13.6), $H = 5$ ft, $L_1 = 3$ ft, and $h_1 = 2$ ft, calculate the magnitude of the total force acting on the side of the tank of length L_1, and the position of the center of pressure, if the magnitude of the gravitational acceleration $g = 32.10$ ft/sec² and the temperature is 60°F. (Sec. 1-6.)

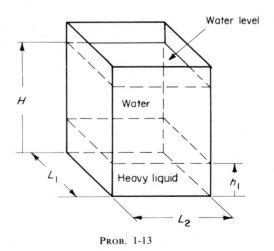

PROB. 1-13

1-14. A mercury manometer is used to measure the pressure difference between locations A and B of a pipe filled with flowing water. For the conditions

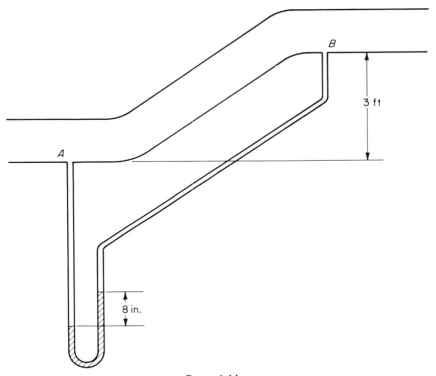

PROB. 1-14

shown in the accompanying sketch, what is the pressure difference $P_A - P_B$ in lbf/in.²? Take the specific gravity of mercury to be 13.6 and g = 32.174 ft/sec². (Sec. 1-6.)

CHAPTER 2

Physical Similarity;
Dimensional Analysis

2-1. INTRODUCTION

It was pointed out in Sec. 1-1 that a study of a physical phenomenon involves experiments and analysis of the equations derived for an imaginary physical model which represents, as closely as possible, the real system. The experimental part of the study is often complicated by the fact that the real system may be very large or may involve a fluid that is difficult to handle in a laboratory. To be able to build a representative model of the real system which could be used in the laboratory experiments we must ensure that both are physically similar. To be able to correlate the experimental results intelligently we must know the parameters that should be used. The knowledge of such parameters can be obtained from the study of *dimensional analysis*. These two topics, that of physical similarity and of dimensional analysis, are dealt with in this chapter.

When studying fluid motions we consider two systems to be physically similar when they are geometrically similar, have (macroscopic) physical properties similar at geometrically similar locations, and are kinematically and dynamically similar.

For steady-flow systems, the similarity between physical quantities implies a constant ratio between their measures at all times. (This constant ratio, or proportionality constant, is in general different for different physical quantities.) When these quantities are vectors, which possess direction in addition to magnitude, the similarity implies also the same directions of these quantities at geometrically similar locations in the systems considered.

The *geometric similarity* of two systems implies that the position vectors from a chosen fixed point in space to corresponding points of the

64

systems can be related by

$$\mathbf{r}_1 = k\mathbf{r}_2 \qquad (2\text{-}1)$$

when the systems are properly placed and oriented with respect to the chosen fixed point in space. In the above relation, subscripts 1 and 2 refer to the two systems, and k represents a proportionality constant known as the linear scale factor.

By the physical properties of a system, we will mean those macroscopic observable characteristics of the system that are relevant to the study of fluid flow. [Note that the physical properties of system identify its (macroscopic) condition, or (macroscopic) state.]

By the *kinematic similarity* we mean the similarity of the velocities of the fluid elements at geometrically similar locations.

By the *dynamic similarity* we mean the similarity of the forces acting at geometrically similar locations. For systems whose physical properties at geometrically similar locations are similar, the dynamic similarity also means that the accelerations acting on corresponding masses at geometrically similar locations are similar, because these masses are then also similar.

Note that when two systems are physically similar at one instant, they will behave similarly; that is, they will always be physically similar. This fact allows us to study a physical phenomenon, such as fluid flow past an object, by studying it in a physically similar system which may involve a different fluid and a different-size (though geometrically similar) object and boundaries.

In our considerations we will concern ourselves with the study of parameters relating the (measures of) various flow variables (physical properties of the fluid and the flow speed), whose values at corresponding (that is, geometrically similar) locations in systems possessing physical similarity are identical at all times when the flow is steady. The knowledge of these similarity parameters is necessary in the construction of physically similar models. (Observe that in systems involving unsteady flow physical similarity implies geometric, kinematic and dynamic similarity and similarity of physical properties at corresponding times only.)

2-2. SIMILARITY PARAMETERS

General Similarity Parameter Involving Force. Consider two physically similar systems involving steady fluid flow. As a result of geometrical similarity we can write

$$l_1 = k_l l_{2(1)}$$

where l_1 and $l_{2(1)}$ denote geometrically corresponding distances in systems 1 and 2, and k_l denotes the linear scale factor (a proportionality constant). Subscript (1) is used to indicate that the distance in system 2 corresponds to that in system 1 (the distance between geometrically similar points). We will use this notation consistently in our subsequent discussion. Similar relation is valid also for the magnitudes of the position vectors, from some fixed point in space, of corresponding points of systems 1 and 2. Thus we can write

$$r_1 = k_l r_{2(1)}$$

(We assume that the physical systems are so oriented with respect to the fixed point that Eq. 2-1 is valid.)

Since the two systems are physically similar, they are kinematically similar, and therefore

$$V_1 = \lim_{\Delta t_1 \to 0} \frac{\Delta r_1}{\Delta t_1} = \frac{dr_1}{dt_1} = k_V V_{2(1)}$$

where V_1 and V_2 denote the magnitudes of the flow velocities at geometrically similar locations in systems 1 and 2, Δt_1 represents the time necessary for a fluid element in system 1 to move through distance Δr_1, and k_V denotes the proportionality constant (scale factor) between corresponding speeds. Since

$$V_{2(1)} = \lim_{\Delta t_2 \to 0} \frac{\Delta r_{2(1)}}{\Delta t_{2(1)}} = \frac{dr_{2(1)}}{dt_{2(1)}}$$

where $\Delta r_{2(1)} = (1/k_l)\Delta r_1$, and $\Delta t_{2(1)}$ represents the time necessary for the fluid element in system 2 (corresponding to the fluid element in system 1 which traveled distance Δr_1) to travel distance $\Delta r_{2(1)}$, we have

$$\frac{dt_1}{dt_{2(1)}} = \frac{dr_1}{dr_{2(1)}} \left(\frac{1}{k_V} \right) = \frac{k_l}{k_V} \qquad (2\text{-}2)$$

The dynamic similarity between the two systems requires that

$$F_1 = m_1 a_1 = \rho_1 l_1^3 \frac{dV_1}{dt_1} = k_F F_{2(1)} = k_F m_{2(1)} a_{2(1)} = k_F \left(\rho_2 l_2^3 \frac{dV_2}{dt_2} \right)_{(1)}$$

where symbols F_1 and $F_{2(1)}$ denote the magnitudes of the forces acting at geometrically similar locations in systems 1 and 2, k_F denotes the proportionality constant between the magnitudes of the corresponding forces, while m and a denote the mass and the magnitude of the acceleration of fluid elements respectively and l denotes the linear dimension of a fluid element.

Since the systems have similar properties at geometrically similar locations,

$$\rho_1 = k_\rho \rho_{2(1)}$$

where k_ρ denotes the proportionality constant between the corresponding densities, and we can write

$$k_\rho k_l^3 k_V \frac{k_V}{k_l} \rho_{2(1)} l_{2(1)}^3 \frac{dV_{2(1)}}{dt_{2(1)}} = k_F F_{2(1)}$$

$$= k_F \rho_{2(1)} l_{2(1)}^3 \frac{dV_{2(1)}}{dt_{2(1)}}$$

because $dV_1 = k_V dV_{2(1)}$ in order that relation $V_1 = k_V V_{2(1)}$ be satisfied. From the last relation it follows that

$$\frac{k_F}{k_\rho k_V^2 k_l^2} = 1 \tag{2-3}$$

with $k_l = l_1/l_{2(1)}$, $k_\rho = \rho_1/\rho_{2(1)}$, $k_V = V_1/V_{2(1)}$, $k_F = F_1/F_{2(1)}$. As a result,

$$\frac{F_1}{\rho_1 V_1^2 l_1^2} = \frac{k_F}{k_\rho k_V^2 k_l^2} \left(\frac{F_2}{\rho_2 V_2^2 l_2^2}\right)_{(1)} = \left(\frac{F_2}{\rho_2 V_2^2 l_2^2}\right)_{(1)} \tag{2-4}$$

Note that the quantity $F/\rho V^2 l^2$ is nondimensional.

From the above discussion we can conclude that *in physically similar systems involving steady fluid flow acted upon by force field* **F**, *the values of the nondimensional parameter* $F/\rho V^2 l^2$ *are always the same at geometrically similar locations.*

In general, the force field **F** can be made up of force fields whose origin or character is different. Say the force field **F** is made up of two such force fields $\mathbf{F}_j$ and $\mathbf{F}_k$. Then, in physically similar systems 1 and 2

$$\frac{F_{j,1}}{\rho_1 V_1^2 l_1^2} + \frac{F_{k,1}}{\rho_1 V_1^2 l_1^2} = \left(\frac{F_{j,2}}{\rho_2 V_2^2 l_2^2}\right)_{(1)} + \left(\frac{F_{k,2}}{\rho_2 V_2^2 l_2^2}\right)_{(1)} \tag{2-5}$$

This fact allows us to consider separately the nondimensional parameters $F/\rho V^2 l^2$ for each of the force fields acting in the systems, because, when the relations

$$\left.\begin{array}{c} \dfrac{F_{j,1}}{\rho_1 V_1^2 l_1^2} = \left(\dfrac{F_{j,2}}{\rho_2 V_2^2 l_2^2}\right)_{(1)} \\[3mm] \dfrac{F_{k,1}}{\rho_1 V_1^2 l_1^2} = \left(\dfrac{F_{k,2}}{\rho_2 V_2^2 l_2^2}\right)_{(1)} \end{array}\right\} \tag{2-6}$$

are satisfied separately, the relation given by Eq. 2-5 is also satisfied. Note that the relations given by Eq. 2-6 are sufficient but not always necessary for the relations given by Eq. 2-5 to be satisfied. They are, in general, more restrictive. However, since the forces in Eq. 2-5 which make up force **F** are different in origin or character, in most practical consider-ations the physical similarity of two systems requires that the nondimensional parameter $F/\rho V^2 l^2$, evaluated at geometrically similar locations in the two systems, be equal for each of these forces separately.

From our discussion it should be clear that since we wrote

$$k_F = \frac{F_1}{F_{2(1)}} = \frac{(ma)_1}{(ma)_{2(1)}} = \left(k_\rho k_V^2 k_l^2 = \frac{\rho_1 V_1^2 l_1^2}{(\rho_2 V_2^2 l_2^2)_{(1)}} \right)$$

while

$$\frac{(ma)_1}{(ma)_{2(1)}} = \frac{F_{i,1}}{F_{i,2(1)}}$$

where symbol F_i denotes the inertia force, it follows that

$$\frac{F_{i,1}}{F_{i,2(1)}} = \frac{\rho_1 V_1^2 l_1^2}{(\rho_2 V_2^2 l_2^2)_{(1)}} \qquad (2\text{-}7)$$

that is, the term $\rho V^2 l^2$ is proportional to the inertia force.

From the requirement of dynamic similarity in two physically similar systems, (as well as from Eq. 2-6), it follows that there exists a constant ratio between the magnitudes of the different forces acting at corresponding locations in two physically similar systems, namely:

$$\frac{F_{j,1}}{F_{k,1}} = \frac{F_{j,2(1)}}{F_{k,2(1)}} \qquad (2\text{-}8)$$

Some Important Similarity Parameters and Their Physical Meaning. In the discussion that follows we shall derive a number of nondimensional physical similarity parameters for systems involving fluid flow. We will keep our discussion completely general although, for pedagogical reasons, we will keep on referring to one type of a fluid-flow system chosen as an example.

Let us consider two physically similar systems, system 1 and system 2, in form of a solid object, such as a ship, in a steady motion with speed V_b relative to a liquid. To have the fluid flow steady, we will consider it in the reference frame of the object; that is, we will consider the object to be stationary and that the fluid flows at a constant rate past it, as shown in Fig. 2-1. (Such situation may in fact exist in a laboratory, where a study of flow past a stationary model of a ship is made.) The (nondimensional) physical similarity parameter

$$\frac{F}{\rho V^2 l^2} = \frac{F_1}{\rho_1 V_1^2 l_1^2} = \left(\frac{F_2}{\rho_2 V_2^2 l_2^2} \right)_{(1)} \qquad (2\text{-}9)$$

in which all quantities correspond to geometrically similar locations in the systems, involves all forces which act in the systems. These forces are the surface forces and the body forces. The surface forces can be subdivided into the forces due to the normal stresses, the forces due to the tangential stresses, and the surface tension force (which acts on the free surface of the liquid, if any). The net effect of the force due to the normal

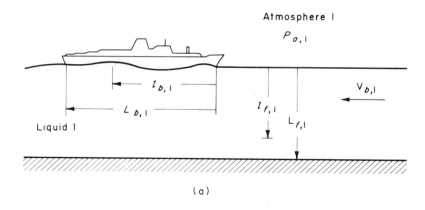

(a)

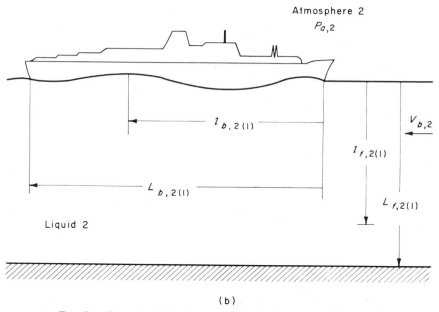

(b)

FIG. 2-1. Two physically similar systems. (a) System 1. (b) System 2.

stresses in the fluid can, for the purpose of this discussion, be considered as that of the force due to the static pressure. The force due to the tangential stresses in the fluid resists the shear deformation. [It vanishes in fluids at rest (in which case there is no deformation of the fluid).] In this discussion we shall concern ourselves only with the shearing (tangential) forces related directly to the (ordinary) viscosity of the fluid. The dimensionless physical similarity parameter based on the viscous forces, known as the Reynolds number, is used in the classification of flow into laminar and turbulent. (See our discussion of turbulence in Sec. 1-4.) The effects of turbulence on similarity of physical systems are considered separately. As was discussed in Sec. 1-4, the surface tension force, which acts on the free surface of the liquid, is the result of the fluid properly known as cohesion. The body force which must be considered in the physical system under consideration is the force due to the gravitational attraction of the earth.

The magnitude of the force due to the static pressure acting on an area element dA of a fluid surface is given by

$$dF_p = PdA$$

The ratio of the magnitudes of the static pressure forces acting on corresponding fluid surface area elements is

$$\frac{F_{p,1}}{F_{p,2(1)}} = \frac{P_1 l_1^2}{P_{2(1)} l_{2(1)}^2} \tag{2-10}$$

The magnitude of the force due to the viscous (shearing, or tangential) stresses acting on an area element of a fluid surface is proportional to a local rate of shear deformation of the fluid and to the surface area, the proportionality constant being the shear coefficient of viscosity μ. That is,

$$dF_t = \mu(\text{rate of shear deformation})\,dA$$

A rate of shear deformation involves, in general, a sum of velocity gradients which are proportional to V/l. Therefore, the ratio of the magnitudes of the forces due to the viscous stresses acting on corresponding fluid surface area elements in both systems is

$$\frac{F_{t,1}}{F_{t,2(1)}} = \frac{\mu_1 V_1 l_1^2 l_{2(1)}}{l_1 \mu_{2(1)} V_{2(1)} l_{2(1)}^2} = \frac{\mu_1 V_1 l_1}{\mu_{2(1)} V_{2(1)} l_{2(1)}} \tag{2-11}$$

The magnitude of the surface tension force is given by expression

$$dF_s = \sigma\left(\frac{1}{R_1} + \frac{1}{R_2}\right)dA$$

where R_1 and R_2 denote the radii of curvature of the area element dA of the free surface (this follows from Eq. 1-5). The ratio of the magnitudes of the surface tension forces acting at geometrically similar locations on the free surface of the liquid in the two systems is

$$\frac{F_{s,1}}{F_{s,2}} = \frac{\sigma_1 l_1^2 l_{2(1)}}{l_1 \sigma_{2(1)} l_{2(1)}^2} = \frac{\sigma_1 l_1}{\sigma_{2(1)} l_{2(1)}} \tag{2-12}$$

The magnitude of the gravity force acting on an element of area dA of a fluid surface is given by

$$dF_g = g\rho h dA$$

(if we do not consider here the effect of the atmospheric pressure P_a). The ratio of the magnitudes of the gravity force acting at geometrically similar locations in our two physically similar systems is

$$\frac{F_{g,1}}{F_{g,2(1)}} = \frac{g_1 \rho_1 l_1^3}{g_2 \rho_{2(1)} l_{2(1)}^3} \tag{2-13}$$

The expressions for the ratios of the magnitudes of the various forces which we have discussed are collected in Table 2-1. In addition to the

TABLE 2-1
RATIOS OF MAGNITUDES OF FORCES

Expression	Expression
Forces due to static pressure (Eq. 2-10):	Surface-tension forces (Eq. 2-12):
$\dfrac{F_{p,1}}{F_{p,2(1)}} = \dfrac{P_1 l_1^2}{P_{2(1)} l_{2(1)}^2}$	$\dfrac{F_{s,1}}{F_{s,2(1)}} = \dfrac{\sigma_1 l_1}{\sigma_{2(1)} l_{2(1)}}$
Viscous forces (Eq. 2-11):	Gravity forces (Eq. 2-13):
$\dfrac{F_{t,1}}{F_{t,2(1)}} = \dfrac{\mu_1 V_1 l_1}{\mu_{2(1)} V_{2(1)} l_{2(1)}}$	$\dfrac{F_{g,1}}{F_{g,2(1)}} = \dfrac{g_1 \rho_1 l_1^3}{g_{2(1)} \rho_{2(1)} l_{2(1)}^3}$

relations tabulated in Table 2-1, we have at our disposal the relation

$$\frac{F}{\rho V^2 l^2} = \frac{F_1}{\rho_1 V_1^2 l_1^2} = \left(\frac{F_2}{\rho_2 V_2^2 l_2^2}\right)_{(1)} \tag{2-9}$$

and the relations

$$\rho_1 = k_\rho \rho_{2(1)}$$
$$V_1 = k_V V_{2(1)}$$
$$\mu_1 = k_\mu \mu_{2(1)}$$
$$\sigma_1 = k_\sigma \sigma_{2(1)}$$
$$l_1 = k_l l_{2(1)}$$
$$F_1 = k_F F_{2(1)}$$
$$P_1 = k_p P_{2(1)}$$
$$g_1 = k_g g_2$$

All these relations are valid in physically similar systems.

The forces in the relations given by Eqs. 2-10 to 2-13 are of different origin or character. As a result, we can consider them separately, and form nondimensional parameters $F/\rho V^2 l^2$ in the manner indicated by Eq. 2-6. From Eq. 2-10 we obtain

$$\frac{P_1}{\rho_1 V_1^2} = \left(\frac{P_2}{\rho_2 V_2^2}\right)_{(1)} \tag{2-14}$$

Equation 2-11 results in the relation

$$\frac{\mu_1}{\rho_1 V_1 l_1} = \left(\frac{\mu_2}{\rho_2 V_2 l_2}\right)_{(1)} \tag{2-15}$$

while Eqs. 2-12 and 2-13 result in

$$\frac{\sigma_1}{\rho_1 V_1^2 l_1} = \left(\frac{\sigma_2}{\rho_2 V_2^2 l_2}\right)_{(1)} \tag{2-16}$$

and

$$\frac{g_1 l_1}{V_1^2} = \left(\frac{g_2 l_2}{V_2^2}\right)_{(1)} \tag{2-17}$$

The last four relations (Eqs. 2-14 to 2-17) tell that in physically similar systems, as a result of dynamic similarity, there exist certain relations between the proportionality constants k. As a result, if a system is built so as to be physically similar to another system, the values of the proportionality constants k cannot be chosen arbitrarily. They must be chosen so that the relations given by Eqs. 2-14 to 2-17 are all satisfied. Only if the effects of some of the forces acting are negligible compared to those of other forces can we, as an approximation, disregard the corresponding requirements put on the values of the constants k by these relations.

The relations between various proportionality constants (scale factors) which follow from Eqs. 2-14 to 2-17 are

$$\frac{k_p}{k_\rho k_V^2} = 1 \tag{2-18}$$

$$\frac{k_\mu}{k_\rho k_V k_l} = 1 \tag{2-19}$$

$$\frac{k_\sigma}{k_\rho k_V^2 k_l} = 1 \tag{2-20}$$

and

$$\frac{k_g k_l}{k_V^2} = 1 \tag{2-21}$$

These relations represent special cases of the relation given by Eq. 2-3.

The relations given by Eqs. 2-14 and 2-17 represent dimensionless similarity parameters (derived from consideration of dynamic similarity) whose values in physically similar steady-flow systems, determined at geometrically similar locations, are always the same.

The Similarity Parameter Π. The relation given by Eq. 2-14 tells us that there exists a dimensionless parameter

$$\Pi = \frac{P}{\rho V^2} \tag{2-22}$$

The equality of the values of the corresponding parameters Π in two physically similar systems means that the ratio of the magnitudes of the pressure and inertia forces is the same at corresponding points (that is, at geometrically similar locations) in the systems.

For *liquids*—that is, for fluids whose behavior (as far as the flow is concerned) can usually be approximated by that of the fictitious *incompressible* fluids, since in general the pressure level has no effect on their flow (except when the pressure somewhere in the fluid drops so low that the cavitation conditions are reached)—we need not consider the parameter Π when studying physical similarity of flow systems. When there is a possibility of cavitation, the physical similarity of systems requires that the ratio of the static pressures which would exist at corresponding points in the systems when the vapor bubbles started forming (such low static pressure can be produced in an initially cavitation-free flow by an appropriate increase in the flow speed) be related by

$$\frac{P_{v,1}}{P_{v,2(1)}} = k_p = \frac{P_1}{P_{2(1)}} \tag{2-23}$$

where P_v denotes the vapor pressure (we consider the liquid to be pure and free of dissolved gases), and we can use the similarity parameter

$$\Pi_v = \frac{P_v}{\rho V^2} \tag{2-24}$$

or the similarity parameter

$$\Pi_c = \frac{P_\infty - P_v}{\frac{1}{2}\rho V^2} \tag{2-25}$$

where P_∞ denotes any suitable constant reference pressure in the flow field.

Note that the occurrence of cavitation in a flow of a liquid can be suppressed by increasing the pressure level of the system.

For *gases and vapors* (i.e., fluids which, in general, must be treated as *compressible*) whose behavior approximates that of ideal gases, since (as will be shown in Chapter 9) the square of the (local) speed of sound is then given by

$$a^2 = \frac{E_s}{\rho} = \left(\frac{\partial P}{\partial \rho}\right)_s = \gamma \frac{P}{\rho}$$

where γ denotes the ratio of specific heats c_p/c_v, we have

$$\Pi = \frac{1}{\gamma M^2}$$

where

$$M = \frac{V}{a} \tag{1-4}$$

denotes the (flow) Mach number. Hence, for such fluids we can use the

similarity parameter γM^2 or $\sqrt{\gamma} M$ in place of the similarity parameter $\sqcap$. As will be clear from our discussion in Chapter 9, however, to
account for the similarity of the compression and expansion waves, we
have to use the Mach number alone as the similarity parameter. As a
result, for compressible fluids, we use, separately, the similarity parameters M and

$$\gamma = \frac{c_P}{c_V} \qquad (2\text{-}26)$$

Note that the similarity of the Mach numbers at geometrically similar
locations in two physically similar systems can be deduced from the
requirement of kinematic similarity and from the similarity of physical
properties. (The local speed of sound is a physical property of a system.)
Hence the Mach number is a valid similarity parameter also for fluids
whose behavior does not approximate that of ideal gases.

The use of the similarity parameters M and γ, for compressible fluids,
is much more preferable to the use of the similarity parameter $\sqcap$. This is
so because the flow patterns differ greatly depending on whether the flow
is subsonic ($M < 1$) or supersonic ($M > 1$), and the Mach number serves
as a simple indicator which distinguishes between these two types of flow.

The effect of the Mach number on a flow pattern is important only for
high-speed flows of gases. This effect on the flow of the atmospheric gas
past the slow-moving ship in the physical system under consideration is
negligible, because the ratio of the speed of the ship to the speed of sound
in the atmosphere is very small (that is, $M_\infty \approx 0$ and the flow of the
atmospheric gas can be considered as an incompressible flow). Since the
value of the speed of sound in a liquid is much higher than in a gas, this
conclusion is even more valid as far as the liquid is concerned. (This is in
agreement with the conclusion reached earlier that we need not consider
the similarity parameter $\sqcap$ for liquids, except when there is a possibility
of cavitation.) The propagation of sound waves through a liquid is of importance mainly from the point of view of underwater detection of objects.

The Similarity Parameter Re. From the relation given by Eq. 2-15 it
follows that there exists a (dimensionless) similarity parameter $\mu/\rho Vl$.
The reciprocal of this parameter is known as the *Reynolds number*. It is
denoted by the symbol Re. Thus

$$\text{Re} = \frac{\rho Vl}{\mu} \qquad (2\text{-}27)$$

The equality of the values of the corresponding Reynolds numbers
in two physically similar systems indicates that the ratio of the magnitudes
of the inertia and viscous forces is the same at corresponding points in
the systems.

We encountered the Reynolds number in our discussion in Sec. 1-4. There we learned about the importance of the Reynolds number on the character of the fluid flow, which was laminar at small Reynolds numbers (based on the diameter or radius of the pipe), and turbulent at high Reynolds numbers.

Note that the Reynolds number has no significance in a study of flows of (fictitious) perfect fluids—fluids that behave as though they possessed no viscosity.

The Similarity Parameter We. The relation given by Eq. 2-16 points to the existence of the (dimensionless) physical similarity parameter $\sigma/\rho V^2 l$. The reciprocal of this parameter is known as the *Weber number*. It is denoted by the letters We. Thus

$$\text{We} = \frac{\rho V^2 l}{\sigma} \qquad (2\text{-}28)$$

The equality of the values of the corresponding Weber numbers in two physically similar systems means that the ratio of the magnitudes of the inertia and surface tension forces is the same at corresponding points in the systems.

The Weber number enters into consideration when the physical system under consideration includes a liquid with a free surface. It is of importance in the study of the surface tension (or capillary) waves, and of the stability of drops and liquid films.

The Similarity Parameter Fr. The relation given by Eq. 2-17 indicates that there exists a (dimensionless) similarity parameter gl/V^2. Usually the square root of the reciprocal of this parameter is used. It is known as the *Froude number*, and is denoted by the letters Fr. We have

$$\text{Fr} = \frac{V}{\sqrt{gl}} \qquad (2\text{-}29)$$

The equality of the values of the corresponding Froude numbers in the physically similar systems means that the ratio of the magnitudes of the inertia and gravity forces is the same at corresponding points in the systems.

In flow systems involving liquids possessing a free surface, the Froude number is, in general, an important similarity parameter. This is so, because the gravity surface waves involve an interaction between the inertia and gravity forces. If a flowing liquid possesses no free surface, however, then we need not consider the Froude number when studying physical similarity of flow systems. We shall elaborate on this last statement in Sec. 7-3.

Further Remarks on the Similarity Parameters. The similarity parameters we have just discussed represent the most important parameters for systems involving fluid flows. With the dynamic similarity accounted for, we can expect similarity in the resistance of the objects (ships in the systems under consideration, moving through the free surface separating two fluids) to the flow. The *resistance*, or *drag force*, acting on an object such as a ship moving through a fluid is considered to be made up of the *skin friction drag* (resulting from shear stresses due to viscosity and acting on the surface of the object), the *wave-making drag* (which represents a part of the so-called *pressure drag*; it exists because the waves, produced by the displacement of the liquid by the moving object (ship), carry away from the object a certain amount of kinetic energy), and the *boundary-layer pressure drag*. The boundary-layer pressure drag is the force, resisting the motion of an object, which results from the fact that the pressures acting on the rear (i.e., facing downstream) parts of the object are lower than the pressures acting on the front (upstream or facing forward) parts as a result of the formation of the boundary layer. In the case when a body is bluff a separation of flow from a part of the body may occur. In such case, instead of the boundary-layer pressure drag we speak about the *wake drag*. The boundary-layer pressure drag and the wake drag which exists when separation of flow occurs are often referred to as the *form drag*. (In the case of a flow past a lifting object, such as a wing, we have in addition the so-called *induced drag*.) We shall return to the discussion of the drag force in Sec. 8-5.

In our discussion so far we did not concern ourselves with the possibility of an oscillatory, periodic, fluid motion in the physical systems under consideration (shown in Fig. 2-1). From our discussion in Sec. 1-4 it follows that if the stern of the ship (immersed in the water) were blunt, periodic vortex shedding from the ships could take place. What is the similarity parameter which relates the vortex-shedding frequencies in the two systems? Since the acceleration in a simple harmonic motion (which may be associated with the vortex shedding) is proportional to the square of the frequency f and to the amplitude X, we obtain, from Eq. 2-9, the physical similarity parameter

$$\frac{(\rho l^3)(f^2 l)}{\rho V^2 l^2} = \frac{f^2 l^2}{V^2} \tag{2-30}$$

The square root of this parameter is normally used, and it is known as the *Strouhal number*, S. Thus we use the similarity parameter

$$S = \frac{fl}{V} \tag{2-31}$$

In physically similar systems we have

$$\frac{f_1 l_1}{V_1} = \left(\frac{f_2 l_2}{V_2}\right)_{(1)} \tag{2-32}$$

from which the frequency f_2 can be determined if the vortex-shedding frequency in system 1 and the scale factors $k_l = l_1/l_{2(1)}$ and $k_V = V_1/V_{2(1)}$ are known.

2-3. BUILDING OF PHYSICALLY SIMILAR SYSTEMS

From the way in which the similarity parameters just discussed were derived, it would appear that the values of all the quantities involved in them must correspond to the same locations in a system. However, as a result of physical similarity, we have not only

$$\rho_1 = k_\rho \rho_{2(1)}$$

but also

$$\rho_{b,1} = k_\rho \rho_{b,2(1)}$$

where symbol ρ denotes the density of the fluid, and ρ_b the (average) density of the object (a ship in our example). Hence

$$\frac{\rho_1}{\rho_{2(1)}} = \frac{\rho_{b,1}}{\rho_{b,2(1)}} \qquad (2\text{-}33)$$

Similarly,

$$\frac{V_1}{V_{2(1)}} = \frac{V_{b,1}}{V_{b,2(1)}} = \frac{V_{\infty,1}}{V_{\infty,2(1)}} \qquad (2\text{-}34)$$

where V_1 and $V_{2(1)}$ denote the flow speeds at any geometrically similar locations in the systems, V_b denotes the speed of the object relative to the fluid well upstream of it (or, in the reference frame of the object, the uniform flow speed of the incoming fluid), while V_∞ denotes any suitable reference speed in the flow field. Also,

$$\frac{l_1}{l_2(1)} = \frac{l_{f,1}}{l_{f,2(1)}} = \frac{l_{b,1}}{l_{b,2(1)}} = \frac{\lambda_1}{\lambda_{2(1)}} = \frac{L_{f,1}}{L_{f,2(1)}} = \frac{L_{b,1}}{L_{b,2(1)}} = \frac{L_{\infty,1}}{L_{\infty,2(1)}} \qquad (2\text{-}35)$$

where l_f denotes the depth of a particular fluid element below the free surface, l_b denotes the distance measured along the object from its leading edge (stem of the ship) [at the free surface of the liquid (that is, at the so-called "water line"), or in some other horizontal plane], λ denotes the wave length of the surface (gravity or capillary) waves at a particular location on the free surface of the liquid, L_f denotes the total depth of the liquid (at a given location in the horizontal plane), L_b denotes the length of the object in a particular horizontal plane, and L_∞ denotes any suitable constant reference length in the flow field.

As a result, it follows that we are permitted to use in the similarity parameters various (corresponding) quantities which do not all correspond to one location in each system. For example, we can rewrite the relation

$$\frac{\rho_1 V_1 l_1}{\mu_1} = \left(\frac{\rho_2 V_2 l_2}{\mu_2}\right)_{(1)}$$

in the form

$$\frac{\rho_1 V_{b,1} L_{b,1}}{\mu_1} = \left(\frac{\rho_2 V_{b,2} L_{b,2}}{\mu_2}\right)_{(1)}$$

That is, we can use the Reynolds number written in the form

$$\mathrm{Re}_{L_b} = \frac{\rho V_b L_b}{\mu}$$

as a criterion required for the physical similarity of systems. Similarly, we can use the Froude number written in the form

$$\mathrm{Fr} = \frac{V}{\sqrt{gL_f}}$$

and so on. We can also write the similarity parameter Π_c (given by Eq. 2-25) as

$$\Pi_c = \frac{P_\infty - P_v}{\frac{1}{2}\rho V_\infty^2} \tag{2-36}$$

Written in this form, the parameter Π_c is known as the "cavitation number" and is often denoted by the Greek letter σ.

Let us now consider that the physical system shown in Fig. 2-1b represents a full-scale physical system involving fluid flow (a prototype) which we want to study by studying the flow in another more convenient, smaller, system (a model), that shown in Fig. 2-1a. Say we want to study the resistance of the object (ship). (Such technique, in which a physical phenomenon is reproduced on a different scale, is known as *modeling*.) To accomplish this, we should design the model so that is is physically similar to the full-scale system. As we shall see, such an undertaking is difficult, and often not possible to accomplish in practice.

The equality of the (corresponding) Froude numbers results in the following expressions relating the speeds and distances:

$$\frac{V_{b,1}}{V_{b,2}} = \sqrt{\frac{L_{b,1}}{L_{b,2}}} \tag{a}$$

$$\frac{V_{b,1}}{V_{b,2}} = \sqrt{\frac{L_{f,1}}{L_{f,2}}} \tag{a'}$$

with $L_{b,2} = L_{b,2(1)}$ [that is, the distance L_b in the prototype is measured in the horizontal plane corresponding to that in the model; for brevity we will omit now the subscript (1)], etc., when the magnitude of the gravitational attraction is the same in both systems. (The term $V/\sqrt{L}$ is known as the "reduced speed" or the "speed-length ratio.")

The equality of the (corresponding) Reynolds number results in the relation

$$\frac{V_{b,1}}{V_{b,2}} = \frac{\rho_2 \mu_1 L_{b,2}}{\rho_1 \mu_2 L_{b,1}} = \frac{\nu_1 L_{b,2}}{\nu_2 L_{b,1}} \tag{b}$$

where $\rho_2 = \rho_{2(1)}$, $\mu_2 = \mu_{2(1)}$, and $\nu_2 = \mu_2/\rho_2 = \nu_{2(1)}$, which stipulation is not necessary if we assume uniform values of ρ and μ in both systems.

The equality of the (corresponding) Weber numbers results in the relation

$$\frac{V_{b,1}}{V_{b,2}} = \sqrt{\frac{\sigma_1 \rho_2 L_{b,2}}{\sigma_2 \rho_1 L_{b,1}}} \tag{c}$$

where $\sigma_2 = \sigma_{2(1)}$.

Since the compressibility effects in the flow under consideration are negligible, Fr, Re, and We are all the dynamic similarity parameters which should be taken into account when building the model.

The surface tension waves are waves of small wavelengths (that is, only for such waves the surface tension effects are of importance). (The surface tension tends to flatten out the wavy surface of the liquid, and to increase the speed of propagation of the surface waves.) Except for a model of a very small size, we can safely disregard the effect of the surface tension on the wave-making drag of the ship, since the large wavelength (gravity) surface waves will predominate, and not insist on the equality of the Weber number in both systems. For that reason, we shall consider only requirements (a) and (b).

Note that the requirements (a) and (b) cannot be met by testing the model of the ship in the same liquid as that involved in the prototype. By comparing relations (a) and (b) we find that the ratio of the coefficients of kinematic viscosity of the two liquids is related by

$$\frac{\nu_1}{\nu_2} = \left(\frac{L_{b,1}}{L_{b,2}}\right)^{3/2} \quad \text{and} \quad \frac{\nu_1}{\nu_2} = \left(\frac{V_{b,1}}{V_{b,2}}\right)^3$$

to the lengths of the ships and to their speeds.

In practice, in the tests of ship models, the same fluid (water) is used as that involved in the prototype. What we do is separate the resistance of the ship into the skin friction drag, the wave-making drag, and the boundary-layer pressure drag (as was mentioned earlier). We assume that the wave-making drag, with the small boundary-layer pressure drag added to it, is independent of the Reynolds number. The model of a ship is built and tested according to relation (a), and the total resistance found from experiments. Subsequently, the skin-friction drag, which depends on the Reynolds number and which is estimated from separate tests (made usually with a fluid flowing over a flat plate), is subtracted from the measured resistance of the model. The rest of the resistance (almost all of which represents the wave-making drag, R_w) is then calculated for the prototype from the relation

$$\frac{R_{w,1}}{R_{w,2}} = \left(\frac{L_{b,1}}{L_{b,2}}\right)^3$$

[This relation follows from

$$\frac{R_{w,1}}{\rho_1 V_1^2 l_1^2} = \left(\frac{R_{w,2}}{\rho_2 V_2^2 l_2^2}\right)_{(1)}$$

which can be considered as a special form of Eq. 2-6, and from the equality of Froude numbers—relation (a).] Finally, the skin-friction drag is added to it to obtain the total resistance of the prototype. This method of determining the resistance of a ship is not very accurate, mainly because the boundary-layer pressure drag, which is rather difficult to determine, does depend on the Reynolds number. The error can be appreciable if the model is very much smaller than the prototype.

If the model of the ship is made small, then, as was indicated earlier, the effect of the surface-tension forces on the surface waves, which is certainly negligible for the prototype, may become important when equality of the Froude numbers between the model and the prototype is maintained. In such case we may not be able to find a liquid which would allow the relations (a), (b), and (c) to be satisfied simultaneously. What can be done in such case is to reduce the surface tension of the liquid in which the model is to be tested (by adding a surface tension agent) sufficiently so that the relation (c) can be disregarded.

Quite often, especially when making flow models representing the tidal flows in harbors or estuaries, we have to resort to scaling of horizontal and vertical distances differently in order to avoid effects of various physical phenomena (such as those of viscosity when the model is too shallow) which are unimportant in the actual system. It should be clear then that often, in the model studies, we have to be satisfied with an incomplete similarity.

In the case of model testing in wind tunnels, while we can without much difficulty achieve the desired Mach number of the flow, it may be difficult to achieve proper Reynolds number if the model is much smaller than the prototype. One way to increase the Reynolds number in wind-tunnel testing is to raise the pressure of the flowing air (resulting in a decrease of the coefficient of the kinematic viscosity of the air; see Fig. 1-25b), or to decrease the temperature of the air. In the case of wind-tunnel testing, in addition to the equality of the dimensionless parameters such as the Reynolds and Mach numbers (and the ratio of specific heats, γ), the dynamic similarity between the model and the prototype requires that such physical quantities as the free-stream turbulence (whose effect can be expressed in terms of a dimensionless parameter relating the fluctuating velocity components to the average flow speed) and the surface roughness (whose effect can be expressed with the aid of a dimensionless parameter related to the ratio of the average height of the surface-roughness elements to a pertinent quantity having dimension of length, which depends on the type of the roughness elements) be the same for the prototype and for the model. [The free-stream turbulence and the surface roughness affect the transition of the boundary-layer flow from laminar to turbulent (see Sec. 1-4). With transition of the boundary layer the shearing stress increases. The equality of the surface roughness and of the free-stream turbulence in the model and the prototype has been tacitly assumed in our discussion of resistance of a ship.] When the tests are made at conditions at which there is an incomplete dynamic similitude with the prototype, then the effect of this departure from the similitude on the measured quantity is known as the *scale effect*.

EXAMPLE 2-1. What must be the speed of water having temperature of 70°F and flowing in a 2 in. diameter pipe to produce a flow which is physically similar to that of crude oil having temperature of 80°F and specific gravity $s = 0.855$ whose speed in a 3-in. diameter pipe is 3 ft per sec? The physical similarity is sought far downstream of the inlet to the pipes where the flow is fully developed, that is, where the effect of the inlet conditions is negligible. (This effect is discussed in Secs. 7-4 and 8-3).

For physical similarity between flows in a pipe to exist, we must have geometrically similar pipes—that is, geometrically similar inlets, surface finish, etc. Assuming fully filled pipes and the pressure levels in the fluids high enough so that a single-phase (liquid) flow takes place, we have only the Reynolds number based on diameter to consider.

From Fig. 1-25b, for water at 70°F the coefficient of kinematic viscosity $\nu = \mu/\rho = 0.000011$ ft^2/sec, while for the crude oil having $s = 0.855$ at 80°F, $\nu = \mu/\rho = 0.000068$ ft^2/sec. Since

$$\left(\frac{Vd}{\nu}\right)_{\text{water}} = \left(\frac{Vd}{\nu}\right)_{\text{oil}}$$

we have

$$V_{\text{water}} = V_{\text{oil}} \frac{d_{\text{oil}} \nu_{\text{water}}}{d_{\text{water}} \nu_{\text{oil}}} = \frac{3 \times 0.000011}{2 \times 0.000068} = 0.728 \text{ ft/sec}$$

2-4. DIMENSIONAL ANALYSIS

The dimensionless parameters which we have discussed are the most important parameters on which the behavior of flowing fluids depends. Occasionally, especially when studying flows of fluids in which heat transfer takes place, we have to consider additional dimensionless parameters which influence the behavior of the flow system under consideration.

These additional dimensionless parameters, which involve heat-transfer rates, can be obtained using the method already explained. They can also be obtained by an analysis of the equations of flow applicable to the particular flow problem (if such equations are available). Such an analysis will be made in Sec. 7-3. Still another approach leading to the expressions for the dimensionless parameters is the technique of *dimensional analysis*.

The dimensional analysis can give us more than only the (dimensionless) parameters on which the behavior of a particular system depends. It can also provide us with information on the relation between some unknown of interest in the particular phenomenon under consideration—an unknown on which the behavior of the system may not depend but which is one of the variables that can be used in the description of the observable effects of the system (such as the rate of flow over a weir, or the moment exerted by the flowing fluid on an object, or the frequency of oscillation of a liquid jet or a drop)—and the other pertinent physical quantities on which the phenomenon under consideration depends. The dimensional analysis accomplishes this by supplying us with additional dimensionless parameters involving these unknowns. (The number of these dimensionless parameters is smaller than the number of the flow variables.) In this way it can provide us with the information about the relationship between a particular physical quantity and all the other physical quantities on which the given phenomenon depends, although it does not give us the exact form of this relationship, which must be sought either experimentally or analytically. The discussion of this technique will now be given.

In order to be able to formulate physical relationships mathematically, we express the physical quantities in form of a product of their measure (which is a number) and their unit. The physical quantities are analyzed in terms of certain fundamental quantities whose number is kept to a necessary minimum. The units of measurement of these fundamental quantities are referred to as the *fundamental*, or *basic*, *units* (*of measurement*). As is discussed in Appendix B, there are three systems of fundamental units (corresponding to three systems of fundamental quantities) in use in mechanics. In this discussion we will consider the mass, lengths, and time to be the fundamental quantities, and therefore the units of mass, lengths, and time to be the fundamental units of measurement. [This is the generally accepted choice of fundamental quantities in dimensional analysis in mechanics. Of course, the results would be the same if force were used instead of mass as one of the fundamental quantities. If the problem involves heat transfer, then the temperature should be considered as an additional fundamental quantity (unless we defined the temperature in terms of the mean kinetic energy of translation of the molecules of a gas).]

Any physical quantity that can be analyzed in terms of the (chosen) fundamental quantities has its unit of measurement, known as the *derived unit*, expressed in terms of the fundamental units, and has a corresponding *dimension*. By a dimension of a physical quantity we mean, after J. Clerk Maxwell, the expression formed by the fundamental quantities corresponding to the fundamental units which form the derived unit of measurement. For example, the dimension of area is (length)^2, while the dimension of density is mass/(length)^3 (if the mass, length, and time are used as the fundamental quantities). [Note that we distinguish between dimensional and dimensionless (or nondimensional) physical quantities. The quantities are dimensional if their measures (numerical values) depend on the system of units of measurement. Examples of dimensionless quantities are: an angle (measured in radians), the ratio of two speeds, or two lengths, etc., the Reynolds number.]

Assigning the capital letters M, L, and T to the fundamental quantities of mass, length, and time, respectively, and making use of brackets to mean "the dimension of" (the quantity, whose symbol is enclosed), we can write

$$[\text{area}] = L^2$$

$$[\text{density}] = \frac{M}{L^3} \quad (\text{or } ML^{-3})$$

$$[\text{force}] = \frac{ML}{T^2} \quad (\text{or } MLT^{-2})$$

$$[\text{pressure}] = \frac{[\text{force}]}{[\text{area}]} = \frac{M}{LT^2}$$

$$[\text{Froude number}] = \left[\frac{V}{\sqrt{gl}}\right] = \frac{L}{T\left(\dfrac{L}{T^2}\,L\right)^{1/2}} = 1 \quad (\text{no dimension})$$

The expressions involving the fundamental quantities (such as M/L^3, etc.), are usually referred to as *dimensional formulas*.

Table 2-2 gives the dimensional formulas of a number of physical quantities encountered in the study of fluid mechanics.

The fundamental principle that allows us to find the relationship between a particular variable and the other variables of a given physical phenomenon is the *principle of dimensional homogeneity*. This principle states that the dimension of every term in an equation which represents the mathematical formulation of a single physical law is the same. [The restriction which states that the equation must represent a single physical law is very important. For example, the equation obtained from the addition of the equation of state of a fluid and of the continuity equation is

TABLE 2-2
DIMENSIONAL FORMULAS OF VARIOUS PHYSICAL QUANTITIES

Quantity	Dimensional Formula	Quantity	Dimensional Formula
Acceleration (linear)	$\dfrac{L}{T^2}$	Mass	M
Angular acceleration	$\dfrac{1}{T^2}$	Rate of mass flow	$\dfrac{M}{T}$
Angular velocity	$\dfrac{1}{T}$	Rate of volume flow	$\dfrac{L^3}{T}$
Area	L^2	Shear coefficient of viscosity	$\dfrac{M}{LT}$
Density	$\dfrac{M}{L^3}$	Specific weight	$\dfrac{M}{L^2 T^2}$
Energy and work	$\dfrac{ML^2}{T^2}$	Speed	$\dfrac{L}{T}$
Force	$\dfrac{ML}{T^2}$	Stress or pressure	$\dfrac{M}{LT^2}$
Kinematic viscosity (coefficient of)	$\dfrac{L^2}{T}$	Time	T
Length	L	Vorticity	$\dfrac{1}{T}$

not dimensionally homogeneous (although the equation of state is dimensionally homogeneous, and so is the continuity equation which expresses the principle of conservation of mass).]

The technique of dimensional analysis follows directly from the principle of dimensional homogeneity. The most straightforward approach to the dimensional analysis is the *step-by-step approach* [6]. As in any other approach, we start our analysis by assuming that the physical quantity of interest depends on certain other physical quantities. (All these physical quantities represent the variables pertinent in the description of the physical phenomenon under consideration.) The dimensionless parameters are formed by dividing or multiplying the various quantities by themselves so that, each time, one fundamental quantity is eliminated from one or more derived units, and the number of variables is reduced by one.

As an example, let us consider the problem of small oscillation of a small drop of a liquid. (This is a problem considered by Lord Rayleigh in 1915.) We are interested in finding out how the time of oscillations (periodic, slight changes of figure) of the small drop depends on the variables which determine the behavior. The important restrictions on the phenomenon under consideration are that the drop and the magnitude of oscillation are assumed to be small. To a person with some experience in analysis of physical phenomena these restrictions immediately imply that the effect of the gravitational attraction on the oscillations should be negligible (due to the smallness of the droplet), and that the flow speeds within the drop (or of the fluid outside) will be very small (or their effect on the oscillations will be negligible). Removing the flow speed from our considerations as a pertinent physical variable removes the Reynolds and Weber numbers and the parameter Π from the list of the dimensionless parameters which would have been derived otherwise. (The Froude number has already been removed as a possible parameter with the assumption that the effect of the gravitational attraction is negligible.) As a result, we have eliminated from our consideration all the parameters involving ratios of various forces to the inertia force on which behavior of flow systems depends. (Note that the Strouhal number has also been eliminated as a possible parameter.) This may cause us some concern at this stage of our analysis. However, the dimensional analysis must be applicable also to the no-flow systems which our small drop undergoing small oscillations approximates. We can reasonably expect that the time of small oscillations depends on the radius of the drop r, on the density of the liquid ρ, and on the surface tension σ. Writing

$$t = \mathscr{F}(r, \rho, \sigma)$$

where symbol $\mathscr{F}$ stands for any functional relationship such that it holds numerically whatever the size of the fundamental units in terms of which the variables r, ρ, and σ are measured, with

$$[t] = T$$
$$[r] = L$$
$$[\rho] = \frac{M}{L^3}$$
$$[\sigma] = \frac{M}{T^2}$$

we can eliminate the length from the dimension of ρ by multiplying it by r^3. We obtain

$$t = \mathscr{F}(r, \rho r^3, \sigma)$$

with

$$[\rho r^3] = M$$

Since the radius r is the only quantity left whose dimension involves the length, it obviously does not belong in the functional relationship (this follows from the principle of dimensional homogeneity) and we can write

$$t = \mathscr{F}(\rho r^3, \sigma)$$

Eliminating the mass from the dimension of σ by dividing it by ρr^3 gives

$$t = \mathscr{F}\left(\frac{\sigma}{\rho r^3}\right)$$

with

$$[t] = T$$

$$\left[\frac{\sigma}{\rho r^3}\right] = \frac{1}{T^2}$$

Eliminating the time from the dimension of t with the aid of $\sigma/\rho r^3$ gives

$$\frac{t\sigma^{1/2}}{\rho^{1/2}r^{3/2}} = \text{const.} \tag{2-37}$$

or

$$t = \text{const.} \sqrt{\frac{\rho r^3}{\sigma}} \tag{2-37a}$$

This result has been confirmed by experiment. Note that the dimensional analysis does not tell us what the value of the constant is.

As another example, let us consider the flow of a liquid over a weir, as in Fig. 2-2 [5]. We consider that the weir has a triangular shape which is symmetrical with respect to the vertical [case (a) in Fig. 2-2], and that

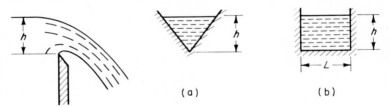

FIG. 2-2. Flow of a liquid over a weir.

the vessel containing the fluid is large enough so that the flow may be considered as steady and that the flow speed approaching the weir is negligible. We are interested in finding out how a physical quantity such as the rate of weight flow of the liquid W depends on the physical quantities which determine the behavior of the liquid. Disregarding the formation and effect of the surface waves (the gravity waves can be neglected if the vessel is deep, and the surface tension waves if the weir is not very small) on the flow, we eliminate the Froude and the Weber numbers from the list of the parameters which we will obtain. We will not consider the surface tension as a pertinent variable, although we will retain the magnitude of the acceleration due to gravity, since there would be no flow if the gravity were absent. In addition, we expect that the effects of viscosity on the flow are negligible and, as a result, do not consider the shear coefficient of viscosity as a significant variable. (This eliminates the

Reynolds number from the parameters on which the rate of weight flow depends.) The physical quantities which are pertinent to the full description of this flow problem are therefore only the fluid density ρ, the magnitude of the acceleration due to gravity g, and the head h (which is the height of the water level far from the weir above the vertex of its triangular outlet). Therefore we can write

$$W = \mathscr{F}(\rho, g, h) \tag{2-38}$$

with

$$[W] = \frac{ML}{T^3}$$

$$[\rho] = \frac{M}{L^3}$$

$$[g] = \frac{L}{T^2}$$

$$[h] = L$$

Eliminating the mass from the dimension of W with the aid of ρ we obtain

$$\frac{W}{\rho} = \mathscr{F}(g, h)$$

with

$$\left[\frac{W}{\rho}\right] = \frac{L^4}{T^3}$$

Dividing the term W/ρ by h^4, and g by h, we eliminate the length from the dimensions and obtain

$$\frac{W}{\rho h^4} = \mathscr{F}\left(\frac{g}{h}\right) \tag{2-39}$$

with

$$\left[\frac{W}{\rho h^4}\right] = \frac{1}{T^3}$$

and

$$\left[\frac{g}{h}\right] = \frac{1}{T^2}$$

Dividing the term $W/\rho h^4$ by $(g/h)^{3/2}$ we finally eliminate the time and obtain

$$\frac{W}{\rho g^{3/2} h^{5/2}} = C \tag{2-40}$$

where C is a constant whose value, for a particular weir can be obtained by experiment. The term $W/\rho g^{3/2} h^{5/2}$ is a nondimensional parameter, and we have

$$W = C\rho g^{3/2} h^{5/2} \tag{2-40a}$$

If we include the angle α of the weir as a variable, then

$$W = C(\alpha)\rho g^{3/2} h^{5/2} \qquad (2\text{-}41)$$

If the weir has a rectangular cross section of width L such as shown in Fig. 2-2b, then, using the method outlined, we find that

$$\frac{W}{\rho g^{3/2} h^{5/2}} = \mathscr{F}\left(\frac{h}{L}\right) \qquad (2\text{-}42)$$

or that

$$W = \rho g^{3/2} h^{5/2} \mathscr{F}\left(\frac{h}{L}\right) \qquad (2\text{-}42a)$$

Thus, the dimensional analysis has supplied us with the form of the relationship between the rate of weight flow of a liquid over a weir and the other pertinent variables. The experimental results thus represented for the rate of weight flow of one liquid can be used to calculate the rate of weight flow of another.

As another example, let us consider the flow of a fluid past an object such as a cylinder, which involves heat transfer. We shall assume that the flowing fluid is a liquid (which does not possess free surface in the region of flow under consideration—i.e., there are no surface waves to be considered); or, if a gas, that the speed of the fluid everywhere in the flow field is very small compared with the local speed of sound in the fluid, and therefore neglect the effects of compressibility (i.e., of the Mach number and of γ) on the flow. In addition, we shall assume that the effect of the pressure level (in case when the flowing fluid is a liquid), is of no significance (we expect no cavitation). We are interested in finding out how the heat-transfer coefficient by convection, h, depends on other physical quantities. We expect that h depends on the diameter of the cylinder D, the flow speed V (say at a location well upstream of the cylinder), on the fluid density ρ, shear coefficient of viscosity μ, the specific heat at constant pressure c_P, and the coefficient of thermal (or heat) conductivity k. If we assume that the cylinder is very long, then we do not have to consider its length as an additional variable. Thus we expect

$$h = \mathscr{F}(D, V, \rho, \mu, c_P, k) \qquad (2\text{-}43)$$

where again the symbol $\mathscr{F}$ is used for any functional relationship (it is a different relationship in different equations). The dimensions of the physical quantities involved are

$$[h] = \frac{M}{T^3 \theta}$$

Where θ denotes the fundamental quantity temperature, which is now considered in addition to the mass, length, and time since the problem involves heat transfer,

$$[D] = L$$

$$[V] = \frac{L}{T}$$

$$[\rho] = \frac{M}{L^3}$$

$$[\mu] = \frac{M}{LT}$$

$$[c_P] = \frac{L^2}{T^2\theta}$$

$$[k] = \frac{ML}{T^3\theta}$$

The mass can be eliminated from the relationship given by Eq. 2-43 by dividing h, μ, and k by ρ. We obtain relation

$$\frac{h}{\rho} = \mathscr{F}\left(D, V, \frac{\mu}{\rho}, c_P, \frac{k}{\rho}\right) \tag{2-44}$$

(with ρ omitted in the parentheses since now it is the only quantity involving the mass.) We now have

$$\left[\frac{h}{\rho}\right] = \frac{L^3}{T^3\theta}$$

$$[D] = L$$

$$[V] = \frac{L}{T}$$

$$\left[\frac{\mu}{\rho}\right] = \frac{L^2}{T}$$

$$[c_P] = \frac{L^2}{T^2\theta}$$

$$\left[\frac{k}{\rho}\right] = \frac{L^4}{T^3\theta}$$

The temperature can now be eliminated by dividing the terms h/ρ and c_P by k/ρ. We obtain

$$\frac{h}{k} = \mathscr{F}\left(D, V, \frac{\mu}{\rho}, \frac{c_P\rho}{k}\right) \tag{2-45}$$

with

$$\left[\frac{h}{k}\right] = \frac{1}{L}$$

$$[D] = L$$

$$[V] = \frac{L}{T}$$

$$\left[\frac{\mu}{\rho}\right] = \frac{L^2}{T}$$

$$\left[\frac{c_P\rho}{k}\right] = \frac{T}{L^2}$$

The length can now be eliminated by multiplying the term h/k by D, $c_P\rho/k$ by D^2, and by dividing the term V by D and the term μ/ρ by D^2. The result is

$$\frac{hD}{k} = \mathscr{F}\left(\frac{V}{D}, \frac{\mu}{\rho D^2}, \frac{c_P\rho D^2}{k}\right) \tag{2-46}$$

with

$$\left[\frac{hD}{k}\right] = 1$$

$$\left[\frac{V}{D}\right] = \frac{1}{T}$$

$$\left[\frac{\mu}{\rho D^2}\right] = \frac{1}{T}$$

$$\left[\frac{c_P\rho D^2}{k}\right] = T$$

The time can finally be eliminated by dividing the term V/D, and multiplying the term $c_P D^2/k$, by the term $\mu/\rho D^2$. As a result, we end up with the following expression involving dimensionless quantities:

$$\frac{hD}{k} = \mathscr{F}\left(\frac{\rho VD}{\mu}, \frac{c_P\mu}{k}\right) \tag{2-47}$$

or the sought relation

$$h = \frac{k}{D}\mathscr{F}\left(\frac{\rho VD}{\mu}, \frac{c_P\mu}{k}\right) \tag{2-47a}$$

The dimensionless quantity

$$\mathrm{Nu} = \frac{hD}{k} \tag{2-48}$$

is known as the Nusselt number, while the dimensionless quantity

$$\mathrm{Pr} = \frac{c_P\mu}{k} \tag{2-49}$$

is known as the Prandtl number, and

$$\mathrm{Re} = \frac{\rho VD}{\mu} \tag{2-50}$$

is the Reynolds number. In this case, the dimensional analysis has shown that, although there are seven variables in the flow problem considered, there exist only three dimensionless quantities which are uniquely related (this relation the analysis does not provide, however). It is these three dimensionless parameters which should be used in the correlation of the experimental data in this flow problem. In addition, we can say that two systems involving heat transfer to a fluid (without the free surface) flowing at a relatively low speed past a long cylinder can be physically similar only if these dimensionless quantities have the same values in the two systems.

Note that Nu, Pr, and Re are not the only dimensionless groups that can be formed for the problem just discussed. For example, if the length were eliminated from the dimensions of the terms of Eq. 2-45 with the aid of the flow speed V, we would have obtained

$$\frac{hV}{k} = \mathscr{F}\left(\frac{D}{V}, \frac{\mu}{\rho V^2}, \frac{c_P \rho V^2}{k}\right)$$

with

$$\left[\frac{hV}{k}\right] = \frac{1}{T}$$

$$\left[\frac{D}{V}\right] = T$$

$$\left[\frac{\mu}{\rho V^2}\right] = T$$

$$\left[\frac{c_P \rho V^2}{k}\right] = \frac{1}{T}$$

Eliminating the time with the aid of the term $c_P \rho V^2/k$ would result in

$$\frac{h}{c_P \rho V} = \mathscr{F}\left(\frac{c_P D \rho V}{k}, \frac{c_P \mu}{k}\right) \tag{2-51}$$

where the term

$$\frac{h}{c_P \rho V} = \text{St} \left(= \frac{\text{Nu}}{\text{PrRe}}\right) \tag{2-52}$$

is the dimensionless parameter known as the Stanton number (it is usually denoted by symbol St), and

$$\frac{c_P D \rho V}{k} = \text{RePr}$$

On the other hand, if the time were eliminated from Eq. 2-46 with the aid of the term $c_P \rho D^2/k$ (and not the term $\mu/\rho D^2$), we would have obtained expression

$$\frac{hD}{k} = \mathscr{F}\left(\frac{c_P D \rho V}{k}, \frac{c_P \mu}{k}\right) \tag{2-53}$$

or

$$\text{Nu} = \mathscr{F}\,(\text{RePr, Pr}) \qquad\qquad (2\text{-}53a)$$

This indicates that, for a given problem, there exists a large number of dimensionless parameters with the aid of which the relation between the relevant physical quantities can be correctly represented. Observe that whichever way we proceed in this case, we always end up with three dimensionless parameters. Although these parameters may vary depending on the way in which the fundamental quantities are eliminated, they can always be obtained from some chosen three by the process of multiplication or division. Thus the dimensional analysis does not guarantee that we will always come up with certain, commonly used, dimensionless parameters which may have easily interpretable physical meanings and which have been given names after their discoverers. Unless we obtain an entirely new group which has special usefulness, it is customary to represent the expression of a functional relationship (such as that given by Eq. 2-53) in terms of such groups. That is, we would normally rewrite Eq. 2-53 in the form of Eq. 2-47.

Another approach to the dimensional analysis (other than the step-by-step approach just discussed) is one that follows most directly from the principle of dimensional homogeneity. This approach will now be discussed with the aid of the last example. As in the previous method, we start our analysis by deciding on which physical quantities the physical quantity of interest depends, and then writing an expression of a general functional relationship such as the Eq. 2-43. Subsequently, we assume that (in this case) Eq. 2-43 can be represented in terms of a power series

$$h = C_1(D^{a_1}V^{b_1}\rho^{c_1}\mu^{d_1}c_p^{e_1}k^{f_1}) + C_2(D^{a_2}V^{b_2}\rho^{c_2}\mu^{d_2}c_p^{e_2}k^{f_2}) + \cdots \qquad (2\text{-}54)$$

where $C_1, C_2, \ldots$ are dimensionless coefficients. From the principle of dimensional homogeneity it follows that the dimension of a group $D^a V^b \rho^c \mu^d c_p^e k^f$ must be the same as that of h. As a result, we can write

$$\frac{M}{T^3\theta} = (L)^a\left(\frac{L}{T}\right)^b\left(\frac{M}{L^3}\right)^c\left(\frac{M}{LT}\right)^d\left(\frac{L^2}{T^2\theta}\right)^e\left(\frac{ML}{T^3\theta}\right)^f \qquad (2\text{-}55)$$

Another equivalent way in which we often proceed is to include the quantity h in the terms of the power series. In such case, denoting the physical quantities by symbol α with a subscript, instead of writing Eq. 2-43 in the form

$$\alpha_1 = \mathscr{F}(\alpha_2, \alpha_3, \ldots, \alpha_n)$$

we write

$$\mathscr{F}(\alpha_1, \alpha_2, \alpha_3, \ldots, \alpha_n) = 0$$

where $\mathscr{F}$ stands for any functional relationship. The expression for the power series then becomes

$$C_3(D^{a_1}V^{b_1}\rho^{c_1}\mu^{d_1}c_P^{e_1}k^{f_1}h^{g_1}) + C_4(D^{a_2}V^{b_2}\rho^{c_2}\mu^{d_2}c_P^{e_2}k^{f_2}h^{g_2}) + \cdots + \cdots = 0$$

(2-56)

and, as a result of the principle of dimensional homogeneity, we obtain relation

$$(L)^a\left(\frac{L}{T}\right)^b\left(\frac{M}{L^3}\right)^c\left(\frac{M}{LT}\right)^d\left(\frac{L^2}{T^2\theta}\right)^e\left(\frac{ML}{T^3\theta}\right)^f\left(\frac{M}{T^3\theta}\right)^g = M^0L^0T^0\theta^0 \quad (2\text{-}57)$$

Equating the exponents of the fundamental quantities mass (M), length (L), time (T), and temperature (θ) we obtain the following equations:

For the exponents of M: $c + d + f + g = 0$

For the exponents of L: $a + b - 3c - d + 2e + f = 0$

For the exponents of T: $-b - d - 2e - 3f - 3g = 0$

For the exponents of θ: $-e - f - g = 0$

We end up in this case with four equations for seven unknowns. Hence, we can express four exponents as functions of the remaining three. Solving for the exponents a, b, c, and e, we obtain

$$a = -d - f$$
$$b = -d - f - g$$
$$c = -d - f - g$$
$$e = -f - g$$

(Observe that we cannot solve for the exponents a, b, c, and d. Why?)

As a result, we have

$$[D^{(-d-f)}V^{(-d-f-g)}\rho^{(-d-f-g)}\mu^d c_P^{(-f-g)}k^f h^g] = 1$$

When we group together the terms with like exponents, we obtain

$$\left(\frac{\mu}{\rho VD}\right)^d\left(\frac{k}{c_P D\rho V}\right)^f\left(\frac{h}{c_P\rho V}\right)^g = 1$$

and we can conclude that we have three dimensionless parameters to consider: the Reynolds number $\text{Re} = \rho VD/\mu$, $c_P D\rho V/k = \text{RePr}$, and $h/c_P\rho V = \text{Nu}/\text{PrRe} = \text{St}$. Hence, again we end up with three dimensional parameters Re, Nu, and Pr. The same result could have been obtained from Eq. 2-55.

An important theorem of the dimensional analysis, when the last approach is used, is Buckingham's "Pi Theorem," which states that if a physical relationship can be formulated mathematically in the form of equation

$$\alpha_1 = \mathscr{F}(\alpha_2, \alpha_3, \ldots, \alpha_n)$$

where α's denote the variable physical quantities and $\mathcal{F}$ represents any functional relationship, which can also be written as

$$\mathcal{F}(\alpha_1, \alpha_2, \alpha_3, \ldots, \alpha_n) = 0$$

then it can also be represented as a relationship involving a set of independent dimensionless terms π formed from the variables α involved, such that

$$\pi_1 = \mathcal{F}(\pi_2, \pi_3, \ldots, \pi_m)$$

or

$$(\pi_1, \pi_2, \pi_3, \ldots, \pi_m) = 0$$

The number m of the dimensionless term π is, in general, equal to the number of the related physical variables α less the number of the fundamental quantities used in the analysis. Denoting the number of the related physical variables α by n, and the number of the fundamental quantities used by r, we have, in general,

$$m = n - r \qquad (2\text{-}58)$$

In the example involving the flow with heat transfer, we had $n = 7$, and $r = 4$, (M, L, T, θ), giving

$$m = 7 - 4 = 3$$

This result is in agreement with the fact that we found three independent dimensionless parameters.

In special cases the number m can be larger than $n - r$. This happens when in the dimensional analysis of a particular problem it could have been possible to combine some of the fundamental quantities and use a smaller number of such combinations in place of the fundamental quantities. For example, we may find that we could have used combinations M/T, $T^2\theta$, and L in place of the fundamental quantities M, L, T, and θ.

To be able to account for such special cases, the meaning of r in Eq. 2-58 should be changed from the number of the fundamental quantities to the *rank* of the so-called *dimensional matrix* involved. The meaning of these terms will be explained with the aid of the last example. We encountered the following variables and dimensions:

	D	V	ρ	μ	c_P	k	h
M	0	0	1	1	0	1	1
L	1	1	-3	-1	2	1	0
T	0	-1	0	-1	-2	-3	-3
θ	0	0	0	0	-1	-1	-1

The above array of the numbers representing the exponents of the fundamental quantities forms the dimensional matrix

$$\begin{bmatrix} 0 & 0 & 1 & 1 & 0 & 1 & 1 \\ 1 & 1 & -3 & -1 & 2 & 1 & 0 \\ 0 & -1 & 0 & -1 & -2 & -3 & -3 \\ 0 & 0 & 0 & 0 & -1 & -1 & -1 \end{bmatrix}$$

By the *rank of a matrix* we mean the order of the largest square array in that matrix (formed by deleting certain rows and columns) whose determinant does not vanish [8]. In the case under consideration, the rank of the dimensional matrix is 4, which is the same as the number of the fundamental quantities (M, L, T, θ).

Buckingham's "Pi Theorem" is of no value when the step-by-step approach to the dimensional analysis is used.

Before we end our discussion of the dimensional analysis, a few words of caution are in order. As the examples have perhaps indicated, for this analysis to be successful we must understand the problem at hand well enough to be able to choose all the pertinent physical quantities involved. We must also be able to decide which physical quantities should be omitted from the analysis.

For a revealing discussion of the basis for our assumption made in writing Eq. 2-54, and of such finer points as the dimensional constants which in certain cases should enter the final relation (these constants have to be used in writing down the equations of motion), the reader is referred to the references at the end of the chapter, in particular to Ref. 1.

2-5. FURTHER REMARKS ON CORRELATION OF EXPERIMENTAL DATA

From our previous analysis it follows that the behavior of a particular fluid-flow system should, in general, depend only on the values of the (dimensionless) parameters (which we can now look upon as variables $\Pi = P/\rho V^2$, $\text{Re} = \rho Vl/\mu$, $\text{Fr} = V/\sqrt{gl}$, and $\text{We} = \rho V^2 l/\sigma$. [For flows of liquids (unless there is a possibility of cavitation in which case the "cavitation number" $\Pi_c = 2(P_\infty - P_v)/\rho V_\infty^2$ is used in place of Π) and for low-speed flows of gases and vapors (in which the effects of compressibility is negligible) in general the parameter Π can be disregarded, and for high-speed flows of gases and vapors the parameters M and γ are used in its place.] This is so, because the behavior of a system depends on the forces acting on it, and the parameters quoted are directly related to the various pertinent forces. (As was mentioned earlier, for unsteady flows the dependence of physical similarity on time should be taken into account.)

As a result, not only the flow pattern but also such quantities as the resistance of an object to the flow and the lift (acting on an object such as a wing) or the rate of mass flow through a duct are, in general, dependent on the variables $\sqcap$, Re, Fr, and We. Hence, for example, if we were to measure the resistance or lift of an object immersed in a fluid, we would express it, say graphically, as a function of these variables only, and not of all the flow variables such as ρ, V, μ, etc. Obviously, the resistance [which is a force obtained by summation of all forces opposing the flow (its direction is parallel to the direction of flow of the undisturbed stream)] or the lift [or lifting force (its direction being perpendicular to the direction of flow of the undisturbed stream)] or any such variable would then have to be expressed in terms of a dimensionless parameter. This follows from the principle of dimensional homogeneity (the nature of the physical relationships being such that only dimensionless variables can be expressed as functions of other dimensionless variables). Such a functional representation could subsequently be used in analyses of other, physically similar systems.

Thus, we can express the resistance and the lift (which is a force) in the form of dimensionless variables:

$$\frac{\text{(resistance to flow)}}{\rho V^2 l^2} \quad \text{and} \quad \frac{\text{(lift)}}{\rho V^2 l^2}$$

where ρ, V, and l denote suitable reference quantities, since such variables have the same values in physically similar systems. (This follows directly from Eq. 2-4 and the fact that the forces acting in physically similar systems are related by $F_{j,1} = k_F F_{j,2(1)}$.) These variables could also have been obtained from the dimensional analysis. Thus, denoting the resistance of an object to flow by the letter D, and the lift acting on the object by the letter L, we determine experimentally the functional relationship

$$\frac{D}{\rho V^2 l^2} = \mathscr{F}(\sqcap, \text{Re, Fr, We})$$

and

$$\frac{L}{\rho V^2 l^2} = \mathscr{F}(\sqcap, \text{Re, Fr, We})$$

where the symbol $\mathscr{F}$ stands for a functional relationship (which is different for the above two equations). (Unless complete analytical solutions of the flow past the given object exist, these functional relations are unknown and can be obtained only from experiments. Since only a few flow problems involving a fluid model resembling closely the real fluids have been successfully analyzed thereoretically, constant recourse to experiment is necessary.)

Much of the significance of the (dimensionless) physical similarity parameters lies in the fact that they reduce, quite significantly, the number of independent variables of a given flow problem. In the tests, to cover a broad range of flow conditions, we have to change only a few (dimensionless) variables and not all the physical quantities that are involved.

The dimensionless resistance and lift variables are usually written in the form

$$C_D = \frac{D}{\frac{1}{2}\rho V^2 A} \tag{2-59}$$

and

$$C_L = \frac{L}{\frac{1}{2}\rho V^2 A} \tag{2-60}$$

where A denotes a surface area [such as the surface area of a wing, or the projected area of the wing (or some other object) on the plane perpendicular to the direction of incoming flow]. The variables C_D and C_L are usually referred to as the *drag coefficient* and the *lift coefficient* respectively.

In the case of a flow of a liquid over a lifting surface which is deeply immersed (so that no surface waves are produced), we can expect $C_D = \mathscr{F}(\text{Re})$ and $C_L = \mathscr{F}(\text{Re})$ only, while for compressible fluids we can in general expect $C_D = \mathscr{F}(\gamma, M, \text{Re})$, and $C_L = \mathscr{F}(\gamma, M, \text{Re})$ because, in such flows, the gravity and the surface tension forces are not involved and, therefore, the Froude and Weber numbers cease to be independent variables.

Figure 2-3 illustrates two physically similar systems representing a flow of a fluid (e.g., a compressible fluid, such as air, over a wing). If the system shown in Fig. 2-3b is considered to be a model of the prototype shown in Fig. 2-3a, then the experimentally determined variation of the lift and drag coefficients with the Mach number and the Reynolds number (based on a typical physical quantity having dimension of length) from the model will correspond to that of the prototype (if the gases involved in the model and the prototype have the same values of the ratio of specific heats γ). Note that only when the angle of inclination of the wings to the incoming stream (the so-called "angle of incidence" or "angle of attack") α is the same for both the prototype and the model, are the two systems physically similar. As a result, the relations $C_D = \mathscr{F}(M, \text{Re})$ and $C_L = \mathscr{F}(M, \text{Re})$ are valid only at a particular value of angle α and in tests aiming at the determination of performance of a wing (that is, in tests in which we vary the geometry of the system) we add angle α to the other variables. (Similar situations were encountered in discussing the flow over a weir when we considered the angle α of the weir as a variable.) If we are interested in finding out the effect of the length of a wing on its performance, we also add as a variable the ratio: (chord length c)/(wing length l). Therefore, a more complete form of the relationships involving the drag and lift coefficients of a wing having a certain profile is

$$C_D = \mathscr{F}(\gamma, M, \text{Re}, \alpha, c/l)$$

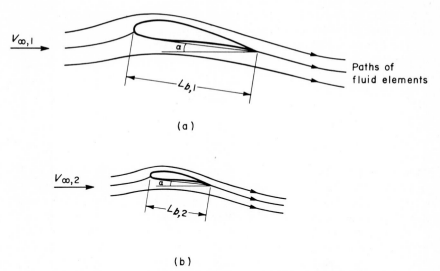

(a)

(b)

FIG. 2-3. Subsonic flow over a wing. (a) Prototype. (b) Model.

and

$$C_L = \mathscr{F}(\gamma, \text{M}, \text{Re}, \alpha, c/l)$$

[At relatively small angles of incidence α, when there is no separation of the flow from the wing, the experiments show that the lift coefficient (but not the drag coefficient) is independent of the Reynolds number.]

Only in the special case of a flow about a sphere, since the prototype and the model are always geometrically similar (and we disregard the possibility of rotation of the sphere) can the general functional relationship involving the drag coefficient be written as $C_D = \mathscr{F}(\text{Re}_d)$ for incompressible flows, and as $C_D = \mathscr{F}(\gamma, \text{M}, \text{Re}_d)$ for compressible flows, where Re_d denotes the Reynolds number based on the diameter of the sphere d.

In case of an incompressible flow past a very long cylinder (oriented in a certain way with respect to the incoming flow) the drag coefficient also is a function of the Reynolds number based on the diameter of the cylinder only. Figure 2-4 shows the experimentally determined variation of C_D (based on the projected area of the cylinder) with Re_d for circular cylinders whose axis is perpendicular to the direction of flow.

In our discussion we did not consider the effects of the free stream turbulence and of the surface roughness. Both the free stream turbulence and the surface roughness affect the boundary-layer development, transition (from laminar to turbulent), and separation, and exert influence on the flow pattern and on such quantities as the drag coefficient. These and other flow variables which effect the transition of the boundary layer are discussed in Sec. 8-2. The separation of flow is discussed in Sec. 8-4.

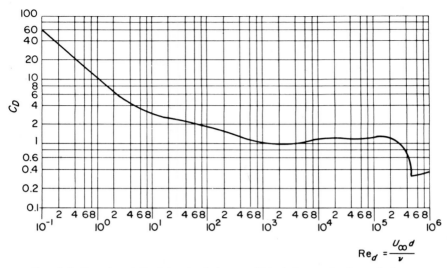

FIG. 2-4. Experimentally determined drag coefficient for a circular cylinder as a function of the Reynolds number.

We will be returning to the topic of correlation of experimental data in later chapters.

REFERENCES

1. P. W. Bridgman, *Dimensional Analysis*. New Haven: Yale U. P., 1922.

2. H. Langhaar, *Dimensional Analysis and Theory of Models*. New York: Wiley, 1951.

3. W. J. Duncan, *Physical Similarity and Dimensional Analysis*. London: Arnold, 1953.

4. C. M. Focken, *Dimensional Methods and Their Applications*. London: Arnold, 1953.

5. L. I. Sedov, *Similarity and Dimensional Methods in Mechanics* (trans. by M. Friedman). New York: Academic, 1959.

6. D. C. Ipsen, *Units, Dimensions, and Dimensionless Numbers*. New York: McGraw-Hill, 1960.

7. S. J. Kline, *Similitude and Approximation Theory*. New York: McGraw-Hill, 1965.

8. F. B. Hildebrand, *Methods of Applied Mathematics*. Englewood Cliffs, N.J.: Prentice-Hall, 1952.

PROBLEMS

2-1. Consider the flow of a liquid through a triangular weir which is discussed in the example in Sec. 2-4. With the aid of dimensional analysis find how the rate of weight flow of the liquid depends on the pertinent variables if the speed of the liquid approaching the weir is considerable. (Sec. 2-4).

2-2. An experiment is run in which a (viscous) liquid is brought to a slow rotation about a fixed axis by rotating, about its axis, a cylindrical container holding the fluid. The angular velocity ω of the cylinder, whose outer radius is R, is constant. As a result of viscous friction, the fluid acquires (circumferential) velocity V_θ which is a function only of the radial distance r from the axis of rotation and, until the fluid begins to rotate as though it were a solid, of time t. The measurements of V_θ at various radial positions are made as time goes on. What dimensionless parameters would you use to represent the variation of V_θ with r and t to ensure that your graph represents a relationship which is applicable when some other liquid is used in the experiment? Assume a laminar flow. (Sec. 2-4.)

2-3. Consider the flow of a fluid in the vicinity of a disk rotating with a constant angular velocity between two infinite flat plates. The disk is parallel to the flat plates and equidistant from them. Using the method of dimensional analysis, investigate the moment resisting the motion of the disk. Since there may be a net outward or inward flow of the fluid (like in the case of a gas- or steam-turbine wheel), take the flow speed far from the disk as one of the physical variables, and assume that the flow Mach number is everywhere small (neglect compressibility effects), and that the effect of the gravitational attraction on the flow is negligible. (Sec. 2-4.)

2-4. Using the method of dimensional analysis find how the time of swing of a simple pendulum depends on the pertinent physical variables. (Sec. 2-4.)

2-5. Consider the surface waves in a very deep liquid. Determine the pertinent variables on which the speed of propagation of the waves depends assuming: (a) negligible surface-tension effects, (b) negligible gravity effects, and (c) assuming both surface-tension and gravity effects to be important. Assume that the amplitude of the surface waves is very small compared to the wavelength, and that the effects of viscosity are negligible. (Sec. 2-4.)

2-6. Wind-tunnel tests are to be run on a model of an airplane which is being designed for a cruising speed of 250 mph at an altitude of 20,000 ft at which the kinematic viscosity of air is (according to the Standard Atmosphere Tables, NACA Report 1235) 3.0157×10^{-4} ft^2/sec, the speed of sound is 1037.26 ft/sec, and the density is 0.00107 slug/ft^3. The linear scale factor of the model $k_l = L_{model}/L_{prototype} = 1/20$ and the flow speed of air in the wind tunnel is 175 mph. If the temperature of the air in the test section is estimated to be 130°F, determine the pressure of the air which should exist in the test section to ensure test results that could be used when building the prototype. Find also the ratio of the corresponding prototype drag to the model drag at these test conditions. Treat air as an ideal gas having gas constant $R = 53.35$ lbf ft/lbm °R. Since the free-stream Mach number is small, neglect the compressibility effects. (Sec. 2-5.)

CHAPTER 3

Kinematics of Fluid Flow

3-1. INTRODUCTION

The study of kinematics is a study of motion. Any fluid motion is subject to the law of conservation of mass. An important result of the study of kinematics of fluid flow is the condition, which we formulate in a mathematical form and call the *continuity equation*, which must be satisfied by all fluid motions so that this law is not violated. The continuity equation allows us to formulate the concept of a stream function, which is very useful in the analysis of a large number of flow problems.

An additional important result of the study of kinematics of fluid flow is the decomposition of the state of fluid motion in the neighborhood of a given point into the three fundamental parts: translation, rotation, and the motion of deformation of the fluid relative to the given point (known as *pure strain*). This decomposition allows us to define an irrotational fluid motion (a motion in which there is no rotation of the fluid elements) which is of great usefulness in the analysis of flow of perfect fluids.[1] It also allows us to derive the momentum equation of viscous fluids by providing us with an expression for the pure strain which is the only state of motion resisted by the (real) fluid.

Thus in the study of kinematics of fluid flow we do not concern ourselves with the question of the physical properties a fluid must have in order to undergo this or that type of motion, or with the question of what flow will result if a given fluid is subjected to certain forces in the presence of certain solid boundaries. We concern ourselves only with the problem of motion as such, subject to the law of conservation of mass.

---

[1]From our discussion in Sec. 1-4 it should be clear that the perfect fluid represents a model of a fluid whose behavior may deviate a great deal from that of a real fluid. Nevertheless, we should not dismiss the important results that can be derived from the study of motion of such a (fictitious) fluid.

3-2. MATERIAL AND SPATIAL DESCRIPTIONS OF FLUID MOTION

As was already mentioned in Sec. 1-2, we can study motions of fluids treated as continua in two different ways. We can study the motion of the individual fluid elements by inquiring how their positions in space, velocities, accelerations, and state vary with time. Or we can inquire about the distribution of the flow velocity, acceleration, and state of the fluid in a given region of space and its variation with time, if any. The description of fluid motion concerned with the motion of every fluid element is known as the *material description*, while that concerned with the state of motion at each spatial position as the *spatial description*.

As was stated in Sec. 1-2, in our analyses of fluid flow we shall use the spatial (field) description of motion, in which we shall inquire about the distributions of various scalar and vector quantities in space (i.e., about various scalar and vector fields) and their variations with time, if any, in form of equations

$$\rho = \rho(x, y, z, t)$$
$$P = P(x, y, z, t)$$
$$\mathbf{V} = \mathbf{V}(x, y, z, t)$$

Let us consider a position in space filled with a fluid which we consider to be a continuum and whose motion we are to study. This position, or point in space, can be uniquely specified by a position vector which originates at some fixed point in space, say point O. If we choose a coordinate system in which the motion of the fluid occupying the region of space under consideration is to be studied, and locate its origin at the fixed point O, then this position vector can be specified by a certain unique coordinate triple.

Let us now consider that the point in space represents a fluid element (or, in other words, a fluid particle) which, since we consider the fluid to be a continuum, retains its individuality. Let the instant at which our fluid element is at a position (corresponding to) $\mathbf{r}$ (which originates from the fixed point O) correspond to time t, and let us assume that the instant at which we began to study the fluid motion corresponds to time $t = 0$. As a consequence of our assumption that the fluid elements remain distinct in their motion, it follows that at time $t = 0$ the fluid element under consideration was at some position specified by a position vector $\mathbf{R}$ (from the fixed point O). [A different fluid element, whose positions at time t corresponds to $\mathbf{r}_1$, was initially (that is, at time $t = 0$) at some different position corresponding to $\mathbf{R}_1$.]

Thus, for a given fluid motion the instantaneous position of a fluid element corresponding to $\mathbf{r}$ can be considered as a function of the initial position corresponding to $\mathbf{R}$ and time t. In mathematical language we can write this statement in form of the equation

$$\mathbf{r} = \mathbf{r}(\mathbf{R}, t) \tag{3-1}$$

For a given $\mathbf{R}$ (that is, if we keep $\mathbf{R}$ constant) the last equation describes the path of the fluid element which was initially at position (corresponding to) $\mathbf{R}$. If, on the other hand, we keep the time t fixed, then this equation describes a transformation of a region in space which was occupied by a fluid initially into a region which is occupied by the same fluid at time t.

It should be clear that, for a given fluid motion, the inverse of the transformation equation (Eq. 3-1) must exist. That is, we can write

$$\mathbf{R} = \mathbf{R}(\mathbf{r}, t) \tag{3-2}$$

The above discussion indicates that the mathematical description of a motion of a continuum is represented by a continuous transformation, or one-parameter mapping, of a region in space onto another region in a three-dimensional Euclidean space. The real parameter of this transformation is time. Figure 3-1, which shows a volume element following the motion of the fluid, illustrates the meaning of the vectors $\mathbf{r}$ and $\mathbf{R}$.

The coordinates (coordinate triple) which specify the position vector $\mathbf{R}$ of a fluid element are known as the *material coordinates*. Together with time, they are called the *material variables*. We can consider that every fluid element has, corresponding to it, an initial set of coordinates (coordinate triple), and hence also an initial position vector $\mathbf{R}$ which identifies it.

The coordinates (coordinate triple) which specify position vector $\mathbf{r}$ are known as *spatial coordinates*. Together with time, they are the *spatial vari-*

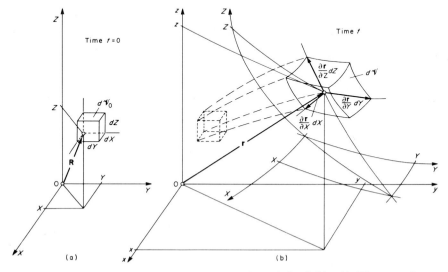

FIG. 3-1. Volume element following the motion of the fluid. (a) Time $t = 0$, (b) Time t.

ables. We can consider that every fixed position in space has, corresponding to it, a set of coordinates (coordinate triple), and hence also a position
vector **r**, which identifies it.

In the rectangular cartesian coordinate system, the initial position
vector of the fluid elements is given by the equation

$$\mathbf{R} = X\mathbf{i} + Y\mathbf{j} + Z\mathbf{k}$$

and the instantaneous position vector of the fluid elements is given by

$$\mathbf{r} = x\mathbf{i} + y\mathbf{j} + z\mathbf{k}$$

We must distinguish between the time derivatives of scalar- or vector-
field functions as we follow the fluid element **R**, such derivatives are called
the *material time derivatives*, and the time derivatives of scalar- or vector-
field function at a fixed position in space corresponding to **r**, such derivatives are called the *spatial time derivatives*.[2] We must also be able to relate
the two time derivatives. The reason for it is that many important flow
variables (such as the acceleration of a fluid element) involve, in their basic
definition, the material time derivatives, while we will need spatial time
derivatives for the spatial description of fluid motion.

If we denote a scalar- or vector-field function by letter F, then the
material time derivative of F is denoted by the symbol DF/Dt, while the
spatial line derivative is denoted by the symbol $\partial F/\partial t$.

The material and spatial time derivatives of a scalar- or vector-field
function F are related by the equation

$$\frac{DF}{Dt} = \frac{\partial F}{\partial t} + \mathbf{V} \cdot \mathbf{\nabla} F \tag{3-3}$$

That this is so results from the following reasoning: At a given point in
space the function F can change with time, while at a given time the
function F changes, in general, from point to point in space. Since the
material time derivative of F represents the rate of change of F as we
follow a moving fluid element, it must represent the sum of rates of both
of these changes. Therefore

$$\frac{DF}{Dt} dt = \frac{\partial F}{\partial t} dt + \frac{\partial F}{\partial s} ds$$

where ds represents the differential of arc length along the path of the
fluid element at a given instant, and we obtain

$$\frac{DF}{Dt} = \frac{\partial F}{\partial t} + \frac{ds}{dt} \frac{\partial F}{\partial s}$$

$$= \frac{\partial F}{\partial t} + V \frac{\partial F}{\partial s} \tag{3-4}$$

---

[2] The material time derivative is sometimes called the *substantial derivative*, or the
particle derivative.

where $V = ds/dt$ is the magnitude of the velocity of the fluid element (which is constant at the given instant) at the point at which the material time derivative is being determined. In the vectorial notation, in view of Eqs. A-48, A-51, and A-52, Eq. 3-4 can be written as Eq. 3-3.

The *velocity of a fluid element* $\mathbf{V}$ [or *velocity of a fluid particle*, or the *flow velocity* (at a point)] is defined by the relation

$$\mathbf{V} = \frac{D\mathbf{r}}{Dt} \tag{3-5}$$

(Note that, if we consider in Eq. 3-4 the function $F = \mathbf{r}$, then we obtain $D\mathbf{r}/Dt = D\mathbf{r}/Dt$ because $\mathbf{r}$ is an independent variable, just like t, and $V\partial \mathbf{r}/\partial s = \mathbf{V}$.)

The *acceleration of a fluid element* $\mathbf{a}$ is defined by the relation

$$\mathbf{a} = \frac{D\mathbf{V}}{Dt} \tag{3-6}$$

It represents the rate of change of velocity experienced by a fluid element in its motion. In view of Eq. 3-3 we have

$$\mathbf{a} = \frac{D\mathbf{V}}{Dt} = \frac{\partial \mathbf{V}}{\partial t} + \mathbf{V} \cdot \boldsymbol{\nabla} \mathbf{V} \tag{3-7}$$

This equation is known as the *d'Alembert-Euler acceleration formula* (1749, 1752) [1]. The term $\partial \mathbf{V}/\partial t$ is called the *local acceleration*, since it represents the acceleration felt by an observer fixed at a given location in space. The local acceleration exists only in an unsteady flow. The term $\mathbf{V} \cdot \boldsymbol{\nabla} \mathbf{V}$, which represents the acceleration experienced at a given instant by an observer as a result of change in position in space, is known as the *convective acceleration*.

3-3. REYNOLDS TRANSPORT THEOREM

Just as we must be able to relate the material and spatial time derivatives of a scalar- or vector-field function, we must also be able to relate the material and spatial time derivatives of volume integrals involving scalar- or vector-field functions. This is so because the fundamental laws of physics can be applied directly only to *material volumes*—that is, to volumes moving with the fluid and therefore containing always the same fluid —while we will need the spatial time derivatives for our spatial description of the fluid motion.

The relation between the material and spatial time derivatives of volume integrals involving scalar- and vector-field functions is provided by the Reynolds transport theorem which we will derive in this section. Since in this derivation we make use of the *Euler's expansion formula*, the latter will be derived first.

It follows from our discussion in Sec. A-1 of the Appendix A that we can obtain expression for a volume element $d\mathcal{V}$ in some curvilinear co-ordinate system ξ, η, ζ by forming the scalar triple product of vectors tangent at some point to the coordinate curves ξ, η, ζ and having as their lengths the arc-length differentials of these curves. If we consider the curvilinear coordinate system ξ, η, ζ in a rectangular cartesian coordinate system x, y, z, then these vectors are given by

$$\frac{\partial \mathbf{r}}{\partial \xi} d\xi = \left(\frac{\partial x}{\partial \xi} \mathbf{i} + \frac{\partial y}{\partial \xi} \mathbf{j} + \frac{\partial z}{\partial \xi} \mathbf{k} \right) d\xi$$

$$\frac{\partial \mathbf{r}}{\partial \eta} d\eta = \left(\frac{\partial x}{\partial \eta} \mathbf{i} + \frac{\partial y}{\partial \eta} \mathbf{j} + \frac{\partial z}{\partial \eta} \mathbf{k} \right) d\eta$$

$$\frac{\partial \mathbf{r}}{\partial \zeta} d\zeta = \left(\frac{\partial x}{\partial \zeta} \mathbf{i} + \frac{\partial y}{\partial \zeta} \mathbf{j} + \frac{\partial z}{\partial \zeta} \mathbf{k} \right) d\zeta$$

where $\mathbf{r} = x\mathbf{i} + y\mathbf{j} + z\mathbf{k}$ is the position vector from the origin of the x, y, z coordinate system.

From Fig. 3-1 note that since every coordinate triple (X, Y, Z) identi-fies a fluid element, the coordinate system X, Y, Z, which we consider to be a rectangular cartesian coordinate system time $t = 0$, is a system em-bedded in the fluid and therefore subject to distortion. Therefore at time t it is, in general, a curvilinear coordinate system.

Let us consider the curvilinear coordinates ξ, η, ζ to be the material coordinates X, Y, Z which specify the initial position of a fluid element. Then we can write

$$d\mathcal{V} = \left(\frac{\partial \mathbf{r}}{\partial X} dX \right) \cdot \left[\left(\frac{\partial \mathbf{r}}{\partial Y} dY \right) \times \left(\frac{\partial \mathbf{r}}{\partial Z} dZ \right) \right] \tag{3-8}$$

In view of the relation given by Eq. A-76 we can transform Eq. 3-8 into

$$d\mathcal{V} = \begin{vmatrix} \dfrac{\partial x}{\partial X} & \dfrac{\partial y}{\partial X} & \dfrac{\partial z}{\partial X} \\[2mm] \dfrac{\partial x}{\partial Y} & \dfrac{\partial y}{\partial Y} & \dfrac{\partial z}{\partial Y} \\[2mm] \dfrac{\partial x}{\partial Z} & \dfrac{\partial y}{\partial Z} & \dfrac{\partial z}{\partial Z} \end{vmatrix} dX \, dY \, dZ = J d\mathcal{V}_0 \tag{3-9}$$

where $d\mathcal{V}_0 = dX \, dY \, dZ$ represents the volume of the fluid element in the coordinate system X, Y, Z at time $t = 0$ which is then a rectangular cartesian coordinate system, and J denotes the Jacobian determinant

$$J = \begin{vmatrix} \dfrac{\partial x}{\partial X} & \dfrac{\partial y}{\partial X} & \dfrac{\partial z}{\partial X} \\[2mm] \dfrac{\partial x}{\partial Y} & \dfrac{\partial y}{\partial Y} & \dfrac{\partial z}{\partial Y} \\[2mm] \dfrac{\partial x}{\partial Z} & \dfrac{\partial y}{\partial Z} & \dfrac{\partial z}{\partial Z} \end{vmatrix} = \frac{\partial(x, y, z)}{\partial(X, Y, Z)} = \frac{d\mathcal{V}}{d\mathcal{V}_0} \tag{3-10}$$

which, as Eq. 3-10 indicates, represents the dilatation, or expansion, of an infinitesimal element of volume as it follows the motion of the fluid (that is, of a fluid element). Note that the Jacobian J must be finite, that is, it must be different from 0 or ∞ for the transformation given by Eqs. 3-1 and 3-2 to be valid.

In view of Eq. 3-10, the material time derivative of the Jacobian J can be written as

$$\frac{DJ}{Dt} = \frac{1}{d\mathcal{V}_0} \frac{D(d\mathcal{V})}{Dt}$$

and

$$\frac{1}{J}\frac{DJ}{Dt} = \frac{1}{d\mathcal{V}} \frac{D(d\mathcal{V})}{Dt} \tag{3-11}$$

Hence the term $(1/J)(DJ/Dt)$ represents the relative rate of dilatation or expansion of the fluid at a point. An alternative expression for this term can be obtained by taking material time derivatives of the terms in the Jacobian J and expanding it. Since

$$\frac{D}{Dt}\left(\frac{\partial x}{\partial X}\right) = \frac{\partial}{\partial X}\frac{Dx}{Dt} = \frac{\partial u}{\partial X}$$

$$\frac{D}{Dt}\left(\frac{\partial y}{\partial X}\right) = \frac{\partial}{\partial X}\frac{Dy}{Dt} = \frac{\partial v}{\partial X}$$

$$\frac{D}{Dt}\left(\frac{\partial z}{\partial X}\right) = \frac{\partial}{\partial X}\frac{Dz}{Dt} = \frac{\partial w}{\partial X}$$

where u, v, and w denote the velocity components in the directions of the x-, y-, and z-axes respectively, because the material time derivatives correspond to $X = $ const., $Y = $ const., $Z = $ const., and since

$$\frac{\partial}{\partial X} = \frac{\partial}{\partial x}\frac{\partial x}{\partial X} + \frac{\partial}{\partial y}\frac{\partial y}{\partial X} + \frac{\partial}{\partial z}\frac{\partial z}{\partial X}, \text{etc.}$$

taking material time derivative DJ/Dt we obtain

$$\frac{DJ}{Dt} = \left(\frac{\partial u}{\partial x} + \frac{\partial v}{\partial y} + \frac{\partial w}{\partial z}\right)J$$

and therefore

$$\frac{1}{J}\frac{DJ}{Dt} = \frac{\partial u}{\partial x} + \frac{\partial v}{\partial y} + \frac{\partial w}{\partial z} = \text{div } \mathbf{V} \tag{3-12}$$

Since, as follows from Eqs. 3-11 and 3-12,

$$\text{div } \mathbf{V} = \mathbf{\nabla} \cdot \mathbf{V} = \frac{\partial u}{\partial x} + \frac{\partial v}{\partial y} + \frac{\partial w}{\partial z} = \frac{1}{d\mathcal{V}} \frac{D(d\mathcal{V})}{Dt} \tag{3-13}$$

that is, *the divergence of the flow velocity field represents the relative rate of expansion of the fluid at a point*, Eq. 3-12 is known as *Euler's expansion formula*. It dates back to 1755 [1].

With the aid of Euler's expansion formula, the derivation of the Reynolds transport theorem is straightforward.

Let us consider the volume integral

$$\int_{\mathcal{V}} F d\mathcal{V} = \int_{\mathcal{V}} F(\mathbf{r}, t) d\mathcal{V}$$

where $\mathcal{V}$ denotes a material volume (that is, a volume moving with the fluid), and F denotes an arbitrary single-valued scalar- or vector-field function possessing continuous derivatives. This integral is some definite function of time. For the material time derivative of this volume integral we obtain

$$\frac{D}{Dt} \int_{\mathcal{V}} F d\mathcal{V} = \frac{D}{Dt} \int_{\mathcal{V}_0} F[\mathbf{r}(\mathbf{R}, t), t] J d\mathcal{V}_0$$

$$= \int_{\mathcal{V}_0} \left(J \frac{DF}{Dt} + F \frac{DJ}{Dt} \right) d\mathcal{V}_0$$

$$= \int_{\mathcal{V}_0} \left[\frac{DF}{Dt} + F(\boldsymbol{\nabla} \cdot \mathbf{V}) \right] J d\mathcal{V}_0$$

$$= \int_{\mathcal{V}} \left[\frac{DF}{Dt} + F(\boldsymbol{\nabla} \cdot \mathbf{V}) \right] d\mathcal{V}$$

$$= \int_{\mathcal{V}} \left[\frac{\partial F}{\partial t} + \mathbf{V} \cdot \boldsymbol{\nabla} F + F(\boldsymbol{\nabla} \cdot \mathbf{V}) \right] d\mathcal{V} \qquad (3\text{-}14)$$

In the case when F denotes a scalar-field function, then, since $\mathbf{V} \cdot \boldsymbol{\nabla} F + F(\boldsymbol{\nabla} \cdot \mathbf{V}) = \boldsymbol{\nabla} \cdot (F\mathbf{V})$ in view of Eq. A-43, using the divergence theorem of Gauss (Eq. A-59) we have

$$\int_{\mathcal{V}} [\mathbf{V} \cdot \boldsymbol{\nabla} F + F(\boldsymbol{\nabla} \cdot \mathbf{V})] d\mathcal{V} = \oint_{S} F(\mathbf{V} \cdot d\mathbf{A})$$

When F denotes a vector-field function, the last equation is also valid in view of Eq. A-55.

Therefore, whether F denotes a scalar- or vector-field function we can transform Eq. 3-14 into equation

$$\frac{D}{Dt} \int_{\mathcal{V}} F d\mathcal{V} = \int_{\mathcal{V}} \frac{\partial F}{\partial t} d\mathcal{V} + \oint_{S} F(\mathbf{V} \cdot d\mathbf{A}) \qquad (3\text{-}15)$$

which can also be written as

$$\frac{D}{Dt} \int_{\mathcal{V}} F d\mathcal{V} = \frac{\partial}{\partial t} \int_{\mathcal{V}} F d\mathcal{V} + \oint_{S} F(\mathbf{V} \cdot d\mathbf{A}) \qquad (3\text{-}15a)$$

where $\mathcal{V}$ denotes the volume fixed in space (relative to the coordinate system in which the flow is studied) which instantaneously coincides with the material volume $\overline{\mathcal{V}}$, S denotes the surface bounding the volume $\mathcal{V}$, and $d\mathbf{A} = \mathbf{n}\,dA$ represents the vectorial element of area of the bounding surface having direction of the outward normal unit vector $\mathbf{n}$ at the location in question.

Equation 3-15 is known as the *Reynolds transport theorem* (1903) [1]. It states that the rate of change of the integral of a scalar- or vector-field function F, taken over a material volume $\overline{\mathcal{V}}$ (that is, a moving volume containing always the same fluid), is equal to the rate of change of this integral taken over the volume fixed in space (relative to a coordinate system) which instantaneously coincides with $\overline{\mathcal{V}}$, and to the flux of F out through the bounding surface.

The *material volume* $\overline{\mathcal{V}}$ is often referred to in literature as a (closed) *system*.

The *volume fixed in space* (relative to a coordinate system) $\mathcal{V}$, is often referred to as a *control volume* or an *open system*. [More generally, the term "control volume" refers to any volume. That is, it may correspond also to a material volume. We accept here the narrower interpretation of the term control volume.] In general, the coordinate system under consideration, which represents a reference frame, may or may not be an inertial system. As was pointed out in Sec. 1-2, we will treat the non-inertial systems only in Sec. 5-6. Observe that the surface of a volume fixed in space (relative to a coordinate system) is imaginary, and therefore flow can pass through it freely. (When the term "control volume" is used, the surface which bounds it is referred to as the "control surface.")

In certain problems it is convenient to introduce the concept of a deformable control volume. The boundary of such volume is a function of time. An example of such a deformable control volume is a balloon during the process of filling up with a gas. We will not concern ourselves with such deformable control volumes.

In order to avoid confusion, since we will concern ourselves only with nondeformable control volumes, we will use almost invariably the term *volume fixed in space*, or *fixed volume* (relative to some coordinate system) rather than the term *control volume*. The name "volume fixed in space" indicates that the boundary of the volume is independent of time in the coordinate system in which the flow is studied.

3-4. CIRCULATION AND VORTICITY

By *circulation* in fluid mechanics we mean the value of the instantaneous line integral of the flow velocity $\mathbf{V}$, taken in the positive direction along a closed curve in the space filled with the fluid. Denoting this value by symbol Γ we have, by definition,

$$\Gamma = \oint_C \mathbf{V} \cdot d\mathbf{r} \qquad (3\text{-}16)$$

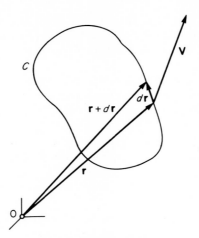

Fig. 3-2. Illustration of the concept of circulation.

where letter C refers to the closed curve.   Figure 3-2 illustrates this concept.

Let us investigate how the circulation changes with time for a closed *material line.* By a material line we mean a line made up always of the same fluid elements. We have

$$\frac{D\Gamma}{Dt} = \frac{D}{Dt} \oint_C \mathbf{V} \cdot d\mathbf{r}$$

$$= \oint_C \frac{D\mathbf{V}}{Dt} \cdot d\mathbf{r} + \oint_C \mathbf{V} \cdot \frac{D}{Dt}(d\mathbf{r})$$

If we denote by $d\mathbf{r}$ and $d\mathbf{r}'$ the differentials of the position vector along the closed material line C at time t and time $t + dt$, respectively, as indicated in Fig. 3-3, then

$$\mathbf{V}\,dt + d\mathbf{r}' = d\mathbf{r} + (\mathbf{V} + d\mathbf{V})\,dt$$

or

$$\frac{d\mathbf{r}' - d\mathbf{r}}{dt} = \frac{D}{Dt}(d\mathbf{r}) = d\mathbf{V} \tag{3-17}$$

As a result, we have

$$\frac{D\Gamma}{Dt} = \oint_C \frac{D\mathbf{V}}{Dt} \cdot d\mathbf{r} + \oint_C \mathbf{V} \cdot d\mathbf{V}$$

$$= \oint_C \frac{D\mathbf{V}}{Dt} \cdot d\mathbf{r} + \oint_C d\left(\frac{V^2}{2}\right)$$

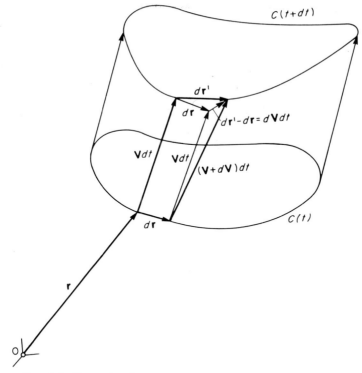

FIG. 3-3. Illustration for the derivation of the time derivative of circulation for a closed material line.

Since the flow speed V is a single-valued function of position in space, the second right-hand side term vanishes, and we obtain the relation

$$\frac{D\Gamma}{Dt} = \oint_C \frac{D\mathbf{V}}{Dt} \cdot d\mathbf{r} \tag{3-18}$$

known as *Kelvin's equation*. This equation tells us that, in general, the value of the circulation for a material line in a fluid changes with time. Only for the flows in which

$$\oint_C \frac{D\mathbf{V}}{Dt} \cdot d\mathbf{r} = 0$$

we have $D\Gamma/Dt = 0$. Such fluid motions are called *circulation preserving*. We shall return to the discussion of the circulation-preserving motion in Chapter 5 when we shall discuss the equations of flow of perfect fluids.

By the (instantaneous) *vorticity $\boldsymbol{\omega}$ at some point in a fluid* we mean the curl of the velocity field at that point. Thus, by definition,

$$\boldsymbol{\omega} = \nabla \times \mathbf{V} \tag{3-19}$$

Before we discuss the physical meaning of vorticity for a deformable substance such as fluid, let us first consider its meaning for a rigid body rotating with angular velocity $\boldsymbol{\omega}_P$, as illustrated in Fig. 3-4. [Note that we represent the angular velocity of the motion of rotation by a vector lying

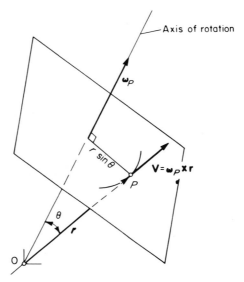

Fig. 3-4. Particle P of a rotating rigid body.

along the axis of rotation (it is perpendicular to the plane of rotation) having magnitude ω_P and pointing in the direction given by the right-hand rule (that is, by the direction of advancement of a right-handed screw subject to the rotation considered).] The velocity of a particle P of the rigid body is given by

$$\mathbf{V} = \boldsymbol{\omega}_P \times \mathbf{r}$$

where $\mathbf{r}$ denotes the position vector of particle P from the fixed point O. [Note that $V = \omega_P r \sin\theta$.] Making use of Eq. A-56 we obtain

$$\nabla \times \mathbf{V} = \boldsymbol{\omega} = \nabla \times (\boldsymbol{\omega}_P \times \mathbf{r}) = \mathbf{r} \cdot \nabla \boldsymbol{\omega}_P - \boldsymbol{\omega}_P \cdot \nabla \mathbf{r} +$$
$$\boldsymbol{\omega}_P (\nabla \cdot \mathbf{r}) - \mathbf{r} (\nabla \cdot \boldsymbol{\omega}_P)$$

which, in view of Eq. A-48, reduces to

$$\nabla \times \mathbf{V} = \boldsymbol{\omega}_P (\nabla \cdot \mathbf{r}) - \boldsymbol{\omega}_P \cdot \nabla \mathbf{r}$$

We have

$$\boldsymbol{\omega}_P \cdot \nabla \mathbf{r} = \omega_P \frac{\partial \mathbf{r}}{\partial l} = \omega_P$$

where the direction of l corresponds to that of $\boldsymbol{\omega}_P$ (see the discussion of Eq. A-48), since $\partial\mathbf{r}/\partial l$ represents the unit vector in the direction of $\boldsymbol{\omega}_P$, and also

$$\nabla \cdot \mathbf{r} = 3 \qquad\qquad [\text{A-69}]$$

As a result, in this case,

$$\nabla \times \mathbf{V} = \boldsymbol{\omega} = 2\boldsymbol{\omega}_P$$

Therefore, in the rigid-body rotation, the vorticity (or the curl of the velocity field at a point) is equal to twice the angular velocity.

This result allows us to formulate the meaning of vorticity of a deformable substance treated as a continuum. We can say now that, for a deformable substance (such as a fluid), the vorticity $\boldsymbol{\omega} = \nabla \times \mathbf{V}$ is a function of position (since the fluid velocity $\mathbf{V}$ is a function of position) representing, at each location, twice the angular velocity of a fluid element $\tilde{\boldsymbol{\omega}}$. That is,

$$\boldsymbol{\omega} = \nabla \times \mathbf{V} = 2\tilde{\boldsymbol{\omega}} \qquad\qquad (3\text{-}20)$$

To get an understanding of what we mean by the angular velocity $\tilde{\boldsymbol{\omega}}$ of a fluid element, let us consider such an element in a plane motion in the (x, y) plane, as shown in Fig. 3-5. (We disregard the motion of translation of the fluid element since such motion is irrelevant in this discussion.) By the component of the angular velocity $\tilde{\boldsymbol{\omega}}$ of the fluid

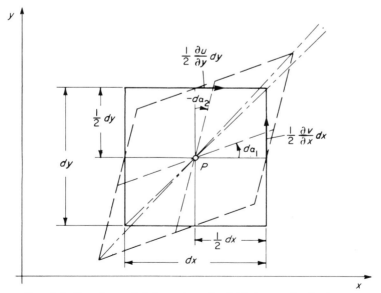

FIG. 3-5. Rotation and deformation of a fluid element in the (x, y) plane.

element at a point P corresponding to the motion in the (x, y) plane we mean the rate of right-handed rotation in that plane of the line bisecting the angle between two initially orthogonal line segments intersecting at P and lying in that plane. This rate of rotation is equal to the mean rate of rotation of these two initially orthogonal line segments.[3] That is,

$$\tilde{\omega}_{x,y} = \frac{1}{2}\left(\frac{\partial \alpha_1}{\partial t} + \frac{\partial \alpha_2}{\partial t}\right)$$

$$= \frac{1}{2}\left(\frac{\partial v}{\partial x} - \frac{\partial u}{\partial y}\right)$$

The magnitude of the vorticity (at a given instant) in this case is

$$\omega = \omega_z = 2\tilde{\omega}_{x,y} = \frac{\partial v}{\partial x} - \frac{\partial u}{\partial y}$$

The positive direction of the vorticity $\boldsymbol{\omega}$ in this case corresponds to the positive direction of the z-axis (which in this case represents the positive normal n to the (x, y) plane at point P). Thus, in this case,

$$\boldsymbol{\omega} = 2\tilde{\omega}_{x,y} = \omega_z \mathbf{k} = \left(\frac{\partial v}{\partial x} - \frac{\partial u}{\partial y}\right)\mathbf{k}$$

where $\mathbf{k}$ denotes the unit vector pointing in the direction of the positive z-axis. (In general, in the case of a three-dimensional flow studied in a rectangular cartesian coordinate system, we have $\boldsymbol{\omega} = \omega_x \mathbf{i} + \omega_y \mathbf{j} + \omega_z \mathbf{k}$. In this case the components $\omega_x = \omega_y = 0$.)

This interpretation of vorticity of a deformable substance is credited by Truesdell [1] to Cauchy who stated, "... at a given point, the length of the projection of the vorticity upon a given direction is twice the arithmetic mean of the rates of right-handed rotation about that direction of any two mutually perpendicular line segments lying in a plane through the point and perpendicular to the direction."

Note that if, in the fluid motion illustrated in Fig. 3-5, $d\alpha_1 = -d\alpha_2$ (in which case $\partial v/\partial x = \partial u/\partial y$) the fluid element becomes deformed in its motion, but it does not rotate. In this case, the bisector of the angle between the two initially orthogonal line segments passing through the fluid element remains unchanged.

From the definition of the curl of a vector field at a point (Eq. A-37) it follows that the component of vorticity at some point P in the direction of line n normal to a surface S bounded by a simple closed curve C is equal to the ratio of the circulation around C (taken in the positive direction) to the area of the surface in the limit as this area approaches

---

[3] Note that this definition of the component of the angular velocity of a material element is valid also for rigid bodies. For such bodies, for the motion under consideration, we have $\partial \alpha_1/\partial t = \partial \alpha_2/\partial t = \partial \alpha/\partial t$ and we obtain $\tilde{\omega} = \partial \alpha/\partial t = \omega_P$.

zero, shrinking to P. That is,

$$\mathbf{n} \cdot \boldsymbol{\omega} = \mathbf{n} \cdot (\boldsymbol{\nabla} \times \mathbf{V}) = \frac{d\Gamma}{dA} \qquad (3\text{-}21)$$

As a result, we can relate the vorticity and the circulation by

$$\Gamma = \oint_C \mathbf{V} \cdot d\mathbf{r} = \int_S \mathbf{n} \cdot (\boldsymbol{\nabla} \times \mathbf{V}) \, dA = \int_S \boldsymbol{\omega} \cdot d\mathbf{A} \qquad (3\text{-}22)$$

When the fluid flow is such that the fluid elements are not subject to the motion of rotation, (that is, when the vorticity $\boldsymbol{\omega} = \mathbf{0}$ throughout), then the circulation is zero for any closed circuit in the flow fluid. Otherwise the circulation is, in general, different from zero and is equal to the integral of vorticity taken over a surface whose edge is formed by the circuit (that is, closed curve) C.

Equation 3-22 further indicates that the circulation, taken in the same sense about two circuits which can be deformed into each other without cutting any vortex lines, is the same.

From our discussion in Sec. A-9 of Appendix A it also follows that in a multiply connected region free of vorticity the circulation vanishes, in general, only for reducible circuits. In a doubly connected region free of vorticity, the circulation about a circuit which is not reducible is equal to a constant Γ multiplied by the number of times the path encircled the region of nonvanishing vorticity. Only in the case in which rotation of the fluid elements in opposite direction is present in the region enclosed by the circuit (that is, when both positive and negative vorticity is present in such region), the circulation about the circuit can vanish. In such case the integral of vorticity taken over the surface whose edge is formed by the circuit must be zero.

A *vortex line* is a vector line of the vorticity field $\boldsymbol{\omega}$. Therefore, it is a continuous line whose direction at a given instant is everywhere the same as the direction of vorticity. A *vortex sheet* is a vector sheet of the vorticity field. A *vortex tube* is a vector tube of the vorticity field, and therefore represents a tube filled with the fluid and formed by vortex lines passing through a closed curve. A vortex tube is illustrated in Fig. 3-6. When the cross-sectional area of a vortex tube is very small, we speak about a *vortex filament* or, simply, a *vortex*.

An understanding of how vorticity can be produced in a flowing fluid can be obtained from the knowledge of conditions which are necessary for a fluid motion to be circulation-preserving. An analysis of these conditions will be made in Chapter 5. From our discussion in Sec. 1-4 and the discussion in this section, one source of generation of vorticity in a fluid flow (and usually the most important one) should be clear to us, however. This source is the action of viscosity of the fluid.

Consider a flat plate set into a motion in its own plane in a stationary

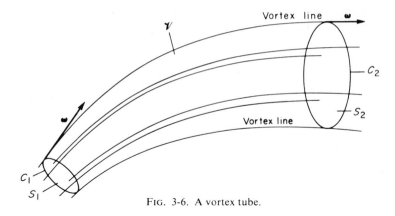

FIG. 3-6. A vortex tube.

fluid. Since we concern ourselves only with fluids which can be treated as continua, the velocity of the fluid at the surface of the plate is equal to the plate velocity. As time goes on, as a result of viscosity more and more fluid in the vicinity of the plate acquires motion in the direction of motion of the plate. The velocity distribution in the fluid at some time t after the plate was set in motion becomes approximately that shown in Fig. 3-7. If we were to calculate circulation about a rectangular circuit whose two sides are parallel to the plate and two are perpendicular, circuit $ABCD$ shown in Fig. 3-7, then, since the flow speed along path BC is smaller than the flow speed along path AD, we would find that the circulation is not equal to zero. This implies existence of vorticity in the fluid. Another way in which existence of vorticity in the flow shown in Fig. 3-7 can be demonstrated is by considering the motion of two, initially perpendicular line segments passing through a point P and lying in the plane of the flow perpendicular to the plate. Point P' in Fig. 3-7 represents a fluid element at some time t, while point P represents the same fluid element at time $t + \Delta t$. The bisector of the angle of the initially orthogonal line segments

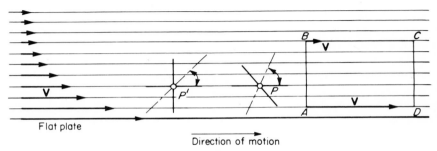

FIG. 3-7. Fluid flow formed by a flat plate set in motion in its own plane in a stationary fluid.

passing through *P* rotates in this motion, and therefore the fluid elements experience the motion of rotation.

This flow example illustrates the fact that the vorticity generated as a result of the action of viscosity at the boundary of the fluid flow (at the surface of the plate) diffuses into the surrounding fluid. Initially—that is, before the plate was brought into motion—the fluid was stationary and therefore without vorticity. In flows of fluids having small viscosity, the region into which appreciable amount of vorticity is diffused from the boundaries is called the *boundary layer* (see discussion in Sec. 1-4).

A situation similar to that described in the example of a flow just discussed exists when two streams flowing at different speeds meet. As was shown in Fig. 1-13, in such case the surface of discontinuity, which forms initially, changes into a fluid layer in which rotation of fluid elements (and therefore vorticity) is present.

The vorticity can also be found in very narrow tubes (which we call *vortices* or *vortex filaments*).

If we want to account for some effects of viscosity on the flow of (real) fluids having very small viscosity when employing the model of a (fictitious) perfect fluid, we approximate the fluid layers in which vorticity is present by vortex sheets, and vortices by line vortices.

Figure 3-8a illustrates a fluid layer in which rotation of fluid elements is present (the sense of rotation is indicated), while Fig. 3-8b illustrates how such layer can be idealized when using the perfect-fluid model in our study.

In a real fluid vorticity diffuses rapidly. In fluids assumed to be perfect there is no diffusion of vorticity and the vortex lines (or vortex sheets) once they are created, persist in the fluid. In the next section we

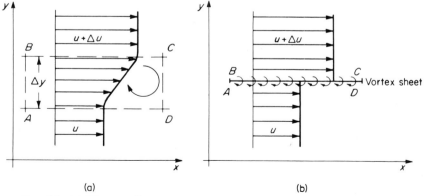

(a)   (b)

Fig. 3-8. (a) Viscous effects associated with shearing motion in a real fluid having very small viscosity (a layer with rotation). (b) Idealized representation of the viscous effects associated with shearing motion in a perfect fluid.

will show that, if certain conditions are satisfied (they can be satisfied exactly only for perfect fluids), the vortex lines are material lines (that is, they move with the fluid).

3-5. VORTICITY THEOREMS

In Appendix A we showed that the divergence of the curl of a vector field is zero. As a result, we have

$$\nabla \cdot \boldsymbol{\omega} = \nabla \cdot (\nabla \times \mathbf{V}) = 0 \qquad (3\text{-}23)$$

and therefore the vorticity field is solenoidal, and the vortex tubes are either closed in space or extend between the boundaries of the flow field (see discussion in Sec. A-5).

Consider a vector tube in a vector field $\mathbf{F}$, such as the vortex tube shown in Fig. 3-6, bounded on the ends by cross-sectional surfaces S_1 and S_2 which form circuits C_1 and C_2 on the curved surface of the tube. In view of the divergence theorem of Gauss, we can write for the region occupying volume $\mathcal{V}$ bounded by surface S representing the surfaces S_1, S_2, and the curved surface of the tube

$$\int_{\mathcal{V}} \nabla \cdot \mathbf{F} \, d\mathcal{V} = \oint_{S} d\mathbf{A} \cdot \mathbf{F}$$

Since there is no flux of $\mathbf{F}$ across the curved surface of the tube, we have

$$\oint_{S} d\mathbf{A} \cdot \mathbf{F} = \int_{S_2} d\mathbf{A} \cdot \mathbf{F} + \int_{S_1} d\mathbf{A} \cdot \mathbf{F}$$

where the unit vectors orienting surfaces S_1 and S_2 are both outward normal. If we consider now the surface S_1 to have the same orientation as surface S_2 (that is, if we assume surface S_1 to be oriented by inward normal unit vectors), then

$$\oint_{S} d\mathbf{A} \cdot \mathbf{F} = \int_{S_2} d\mathbf{A} \cdot \mathbf{F} - \int_{S_1} d\mathbf{A} \cdot \mathbf{F}$$

and we can write

$$\int_{\mathcal{V}} \nabla \cdot \mathbf{F} \, d\mathcal{V} = \int_{S_2} d\mathbf{A} \cdot \mathbf{F} - \int_{S_1} d\mathbf{A} \cdot \mathbf{F} \qquad (3\text{-}24)$$

The integral $\int_{S} d\mathbf{A} \cdot \mathbf{F}$ in which S represents a cross-sectional surface of a vector tube is called the *strength of the tube* at that cross section. Equation 3-24 states that the total divergence of a field $\mathbf{F}$ of a region occupied by a vector tube of $\mathbf{F}$ bounded by two cross-sectional surfaces is equal to the difference between the strengths of the tube at the bounding cross sections.

If we consider now the vector field $\mathbf{F}$ to be represented by the vorticity field $\boldsymbol{\omega}$, then, in view of Eq. 3-23 it follows that

$$\int_{S_2} d\mathbf{A} \cdot \boldsymbol{\omega} = \int_{S_1} d\mathbf{A} \cdot \boldsymbol{\omega} = \text{const.}$$

for any cross section of a vortex tube. That is, *the strength of a vortex tube, or the flux of vorticity across any cross section of a vortex tube, is constant.* This statement is known as the *first vorticity theorem of Helmholtz.*

From this theorem it follows that the average vorticity at a given cross section of a vortex tube is inversely proportional to the cross-sectional area of the tube.

If we apply Stokes's theorem to the curved surface S of a vortex tube bounded by two circuits C_1 and C_2, as shown in Fig. 3-9, then we can write

$$\oint_C \mathbf{V} \cdot d\mathbf{r} = \oint_{C_2} \mathbf{V} \cdot d\mathbf{r} - \oint_{C_1} \mathbf{V} \cdot d\mathbf{r} = \Gamma_2 - \Gamma_1 = \int_S d\mathbf{A} \cdot \boldsymbol{\omega} = 0$$

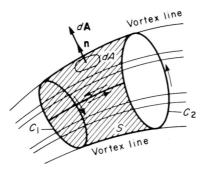

FIG. 3-9. Vortex lines bounding a
vortex tube.

because no $\boldsymbol{\omega}$ lines cross the curved surface S, while the line connecting the circuits C_1 and C_2 (which forms a partial boundary of the curved surface S of the tube) is traversed twice in opposite directions in the process of line integration (and therefore there is no contribution to the line integral from the integration along it). (Note that the line integration about the circuit C_1 is performed in a direction opposite to that about circuit C_2.) As a result,

$$\Gamma_1 = \Gamma_2 \tag{3-25}$$

and we can say that *the circulations taken in the same sense about any two reconcilable circuits lying on the surface of a vortex tube are the same.* This statement is known as the *first vortex theorem of Helmholtz in the form given by Kelvin.*

We shall consider now conditions which must be satisfied in order that the vortex lines be material lines (in which case the fluid elements which once form a vortex tube, form it also at a later time).

A curve in space

$$\mathbf{r} = \mathbf{r}(\tau)$$

where τ denotes a parameter, represents a vector line of a vector field $\mathbf{F}$ if

$$d\mathbf{r} \times \mathbf{F} = \mathbf{0} \qquad (3\text{-}26)$$

where $d\mathbf{r} = (\partial \mathbf{r}/\partial \tau)d\tau$ represents the differential of the position vector $\mathbf{r}$ having direction of the curve. From the last equation it follows that

$$d\mathbf{r} = \frac{\partial \mathbf{r}}{\partial \tau} d\tau = g\mathbf{F} \qquad (3\text{-}27)$$

where g denotes a scalar-field function.

Let us consider a material line, (that is, a line made up always of the same fluid elements), which initially coincides with a vector line of $\mathbf{F}$. This line will always coincide with this vector line if it always satisfies Eq. 3-26, that is, if

$$\frac{D}{Dt}(d\mathbf{r} \times \mathbf{F}) = \mathbf{0}$$

In view of Eq. 3-17 valid for the differential of the position vector along a material line, and Eq. A-49,

$$\frac{D}{Dt}(d\mathbf{r}) = d\mathbf{V} = d\mathbf{r} \cdot \nabla \mathbf{V}$$

where $\mathbf{V}$ denotes the flow velocity, we have

$$\frac{D}{Dt}(d\mathbf{r} \times \mathbf{F}) = (d\mathbf{r} \cdot \nabla \mathbf{V}) \times \mathbf{F} + d\mathbf{r} \times \frac{D\mathbf{F}}{Dt}$$

$$= g\mathbf{F} \times \left(\frac{D\mathbf{F}}{Dt} - \mathbf{F} \cdot \nabla \mathbf{V} \right)$$

because of Eq. 3-27.

Therefore, the vector lines of a vector field $\mathbf{F}$ are material lines if

$$\mathbf{F} \times \left(\frac{D\mathbf{F}}{Dt} - \mathbf{F} \cdot \nabla \mathbf{V} \right) = \mathbf{0} \qquad (3\text{-}28)$$

Eliminating the material time derivative with the aid of Eq. 3-3, and making use of Eq. A-56, in which we substitute $\mathbf{V}$ for $\mathbf{U}$, Eq. 3-28 can be rewritten as

$$\mathbf{F} \times \left[\frac{\partial \mathbf{F}}{\partial t} + \nabla \times (\mathbf{F} \times \mathbf{V}) + \mathbf{V}(\nabla \cdot \mathbf{F}) \right] = \mathbf{0} \qquad (3\text{-}29)$$

because $\mathbf{F} \times \mathbf{F} = \mathbf{0}$. This condition, which is valid for any vector field $\mathbf{F}$, is known as the *Helmholtz-Zorawski criterion* (1858, 1900) [1].

Making use of the vector relation

$$\mathbf{V} \cdot \nabla \mathbf{V} = (\nabla \times \mathbf{V}) \times \mathbf{V} + \nabla \left(\frac{V^2}{2} \right)$$

$$= \boldsymbol{\omega} \times \mathbf{V} + \nabla \left(\frac{V^2}{2} \right) \qquad (3\text{-}30)$$

whose proof is left as a homework assignment, and making use of Eq. 3-7 we can write for the curl of the acceleration of a fluid element

$$\nabla \times \mathbf{a} = \nabla \times \left(\frac{D\mathbf{V}}{Dt}\right) = \nabla \times \left(\frac{\partial \mathbf{V}}{\partial t} + \mathbf{V} \cdot \nabla \mathbf{V}\right)$$

$$= \nabla \times \left[\frac{\partial \mathbf{V}}{\partial t} + \boldsymbol{\omega} \times \mathbf{V} + \nabla \left(\frac{V^2}{2}\right)\right]$$

$$= \frac{\partial (\nabla \times \mathbf{V})}{\partial t} + \nabla \times (\boldsymbol{\omega} \times \mathbf{V})$$

$$= \frac{\partial \boldsymbol{\omega}}{\partial t} + \nabla \times (\boldsymbol{\omega} \times \mathbf{V})$$

If we put $\mathbf{F} = \boldsymbol{\omega}$ in Eq. 3-29 then, in view of the last equation, the Helmholtz-Zorawski criterion is satisfied—that is, the vortex lines are material lines—when

$$\boldsymbol{\omega} \times (\nabla \times \mathbf{a}) = \mathbf{0}$$

because $\nabla \cdot \boldsymbol{\omega} = 0$. This relation is satisfied when the acceleration of fluid elements is a lamellar vector field (that is, its curl vanishes):

$$\nabla \times \mathbf{a} = \nabla \times \left(\frac{D\mathbf{V}}{Dt}\right) = \mathbf{0}$$

or, in a special case, when the curl of the acceleration is parallel to the vorticity.

The vanishing curl of $\mathbf{a}$ indicates the existence of an acceleration potential ϕ^*:

$$\mathbf{a} = \frac{D\mathbf{V}}{Dt} = \nabla \phi^*$$

When this potential is single-valued then, from Eq. 3-18 it follows that

$$\frac{D\Gamma}{Dt} = \oint_C \nabla \phi^* \cdot d\mathbf{r} = \oint_C d\phi^* = 0$$

or that the motion is circulation-preserving.

The condition $D\Gamma/Dt = 0$ implies that $\nabla \times \mathbf{a} = \mathbf{0}$ which is a sufficient condition which, when satisfied, ensures that the vortex lines are material lines. We can say therefore that *the vortex lines are material lines in circulation-preserving motions.* This statement is known as the *second vorticity theorem of Helmholtz.*

In addition, we can make the following statement: *In a fluid motion in which the vortex lines are material lines, the necessary and sufficient condition for the strength of the vortex tubes to remain unchanged with time is that the motion be circulation-preserving.* This statement is known as the *third vorticity theorem of Helmholtz,* [1].

3-6. CAUCHY–STOKES DECOMPOSITION THEOREM

In our discussion so far we indicated that a fluid element can undergo
a motion of translation, rotation, and deformation.

The motion of deformation of a fluid at a point is called the *pure
strain*. It is characteristic of all deformable substances. This motion is
perpendicular to an ellipsoidal surface known as the ellipsoid of strain.
In the directions of the principal axes of the ellipsoid the deformation of
the fluid is in the direction of these axes (linear deformation). This is so
because the principal axes are perpendicular to the ellipsoid. In other
directions the deformation of the fluid is, in general, angular (shear deformation) as well as linear.

Figure 3-10 illustrates the motions of translation, rotation, and pure
strain (that is, deformation) of a fluid element.

This decomposition of the instantaneous motion of a deformable

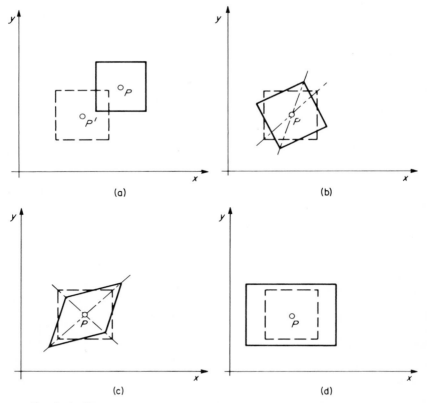

FIG. 3-10. Simple motions of a fluid element in a plane flow studied in the
(x, y) plane. (a) Motion of translation. (b) Motion of rotation. (c) Motion
of shear deformation. (d) Motion of linear deformation. Broken line indicates the initial position of the fluid element.

medium is known as the *Cauchy–Stokes decomposition theorem* (1841, 1845). Its importance in the study of fluid mechanics becomes obvious when we consider the stresses in the fluid which resist deformation of the fluid elements. [No such stresses exist in the (fictitious) nonviscous fluid model—that is, in a perfect fluid.]

Note that so far as the motion of rotation of a deforming fluid element is concerned, it does not mean that the fluid element revolves around its center, only that the bisector of two initially orthogonal line segments experiences motion of rotation. (Explained in Sec. 3-4.)

Thus far our discussion of the general state of motion of a deformable medium in the immediate neighborhood of a point was purely descriptive. Let us now derive a mathematical expression for the state of motion, and therefore also the mathematical expressions for the simple motions of fluid elements.

Consider a point P in the fluid at which the flow velocity is V_P. In its immediate neighborhood, say at the neighboring point Q shown in Fig. 3-11, the fluid velocity is

$$V = V_P + dV = V_P + d\mathbf{r} \cdot (\nabla V)_{\text{at } P} \qquad (3\text{-}31)$$

in view of Eq. A-49. When written in the component form in a rectangular Cartesian coordinate system, the last equation gives the following

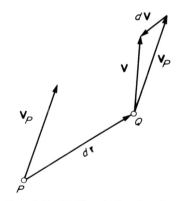

FIG. 3-11. Fluid velocity in the neighborhood of point P.

expressions for the components of the flow velocity in the x-, y-, and z-directions:

$$
\left.
\begin{aligned}
u &= u_P + \frac{\partial u}{\partial x} dx + \frac{\partial u}{\partial y} dy + \frac{\partial u}{\partial z} dz \\[2mm]
v &= v_P + \frac{\partial v}{\partial x} dx + \frac{\partial v}{\partial y} dy + \frac{\partial v}{\partial z} dz \\[2mm]
w &= w_P + \frac{\partial w}{\partial x} dx + \frac{\partial w}{\partial y} dy + \frac{\partial w}{\partial z} dz
\end{aligned}
\right\} \qquad (3\text{-}32)
$$

in view of Eq. A-84, with $\mathbf{V} = u\mathbf{i} + v\mathbf{j} + w\mathbf{k}$ and $d\mathbf{r} = dx\,\mathbf{i} + dy\mathbf{j} + dz\,\mathbf{k}$. This set of equations can be considered as representing the first (linear) terms in the Taylor expansion of the flow velocity components in the neighborhood of point P.

We can obtain the last set of equations (Eqs. 3-32) from Eq. 3-31 if we consider the term $(\nabla\,\mathbf{V})$ to represent the following operator (known as a *dyadic* or a *tensor of the second order*):

$$\nabla\,\mathbf{V} = \frac{\partial u}{\partial x}\,\mathbf{ii} + \frac{\partial v}{\partial x}\,\mathbf{ij} + \frac{\partial w}{\partial x}\,\mathbf{ik}$$

$$+ \frac{\partial u}{\partial y}\,\mathbf{ji} + \frac{\partial v}{\partial y}\,\mathbf{jj} + \frac{\partial w}{\partial y}\,\mathbf{jk}$$

$$+ \frac{\partial u}{\partial z}\,\mathbf{ki} + \frac{\partial v}{\partial z}\,\mathbf{kj} + \frac{\partial w}{\partial z}\,\mathbf{kk} \tag{3-33}$$

Forming the scalar product of the differential position vector $d\mathbf{r}$ with the above operator gives the required relations.

The expressions for the components of the fluid velocity in the neighborhood of a point, Eq. 3-32, can also be written in the form

$$u = u_P + \left[\frac{\partial u}{\partial x}dx + \frac{1}{2}\left(\frac{\partial u}{\partial y} + \frac{\partial v}{\partial x}\right)dy + \frac{1}{2}\left(\frac{\partial u}{\partial z} + \frac{\partial w}{\partial x}\right)dz\right]$$

$$+ \left[\frac{1}{2}\left(\frac{\partial u}{\partial y} - \frac{\partial v}{\partial x}\right)dy + \frac{1}{2}\left(\frac{\partial u}{\partial z} - \frac{\partial w}{\partial x}\right)dz\right]$$

$$v = v_P + \left[\frac{1}{2}\left(\frac{\partial v}{\partial x} + \frac{\partial u}{\partial y}\right)dx + \frac{\partial v}{\partial y}dy + \frac{1}{2}\left(\frac{\partial v}{\partial z} + \frac{\partial w}{\partial y}\right)dz\right]$$

$$+ \left[\frac{1}{2}\left(\frac{\partial v}{\partial x} - \frac{\partial u}{\partial y}\right)dx + \frac{1}{2}\left(\frac{\partial v}{\partial z} - \frac{\partial w}{\partial y}\right)dz\right]$$

$$w = w_P + \left[\frac{1}{2}\left(\frac{\partial w}{\partial x} + \frac{\partial u}{\partial z}\right)dx + \frac{1}{2}\left(\frac{\partial w}{\partial y} + \frac{\partial v}{\partial z}\right)dy + \frac{\partial w}{\partial z}\,dz\right]$$

$$+ \left[\frac{1}{2}\left(\frac{\partial w}{\partial x} - \frac{\partial u}{\partial z}\right)dx + \frac{1}{2}\left(\frac{\partial w}{\partial y} - \frac{\partial v}{\partial z}\right)dy\right] \tag{3-34}$$

The corresponding form of the operator $\nabla\,\mathbf{V}$ is

$$\nabla\,\mathbf{V} = \frac{\partial u}{\partial x}\,\mathbf{ii} \qquad + \frac{1}{2}\left(\frac{\partial v}{\partial x} + \frac{\partial u}{\partial y}\right)\mathbf{ij} + \frac{1}{2}\left(\frac{\partial w}{\partial x} + \frac{\partial u}{\partial z}\right)\mathbf{ik}$$

$$+ \frac{1}{2}\left(\frac{\partial u}{\partial y} + \frac{\partial v}{\partial x}\right)\mathbf{ji} + \frac{\partial v}{\partial y}\,\mathbf{jj} \qquad + \frac{1}{2}\left(\frac{\partial w}{\partial y} + \frac{\partial v}{\partial z}\right)\mathbf{jk}$$

$$+ \frac{1}{2}\left(\frac{\partial u}{\partial z} + \frac{\partial w}{\partial x}\right)\mathbf{ki} + \frac{1}{2}\left(\frac{\partial v}{\partial z} + \frac{\partial w}{\partial y}\right)\mathbf{kj} + \qquad \frac{\partial w}{\partial z}\,\mathbf{kk}$$

$$+ 0 \qquad\qquad + \frac{1}{2}\left(\frac{\partial v}{\partial x} - \frac{\partial u}{\partial y}\right)\mathbf{ij} + \frac{1}{2}\left(\frac{\partial w}{\partial x} - \frac{\partial u}{\partial z}\right)\mathbf{ik}$$

$$+ \frac{1}{2}\left(\frac{\partial u}{\partial y} - \frac{\partial v}{\partial x}\right)\mathbf{ji} + 0 + \frac{1}{2}\left(\frac{\partial w}{\partial y} - \frac{\partial v}{\partial z}\right)\mathbf{jk}$$

$$+ \frac{1}{2}\left(\frac{\partial u}{\partial z} - \frac{\partial w}{\partial x}\right)\mathbf{ki} + \frac{1}{2}\left(\frac{\partial v}{\partial z} - \frac{\partial w}{\partial y}\right)\mathbf{kj} + 0 \tag{3-35}$$

A tensor

$$\begin{aligned}
\Phi = {} & q_{11}\,\mathbf{ii} + q_{12}\,\mathbf{ij} + q_{13}\,\mathbf{ik} \\
& + q_{21}\,\mathbf{ji} + q_{22}\,\mathbf{jj} + q_{23}\,\mathbf{jk} \\
& + q_{31}\,\mathbf{ki} + q_{32}\,\mathbf{kj} + q_{33}\,\mathbf{kk}
\end{aligned} \tag{3-36}$$

in which the relation between the coefficients q is

$$\left.\begin{aligned}
q_{12} &= q_{21} \\
q_{13} &= q_{31} \\
q_{23} &= q_{32}
\end{aligned}\right\} \tag{3-37}$$

is known as a *symmetric tensor*. A tensor

$$\begin{aligned}
\Phi = {} & 0 \qquad\; + q_{12}\,\mathbf{ij} + q_{13}\,\mathbf{ik} \\
& + q_{21}\,\mathbf{ji} + 0 \qquad\; + q_{23}\,\mathbf{jk} \\
& + q_{31}\,\mathbf{ki} + q_{32}\,\mathbf{kj} + 0
\end{aligned} \tag{3-38}$$

in which the relation between the coefficients q is

$$\left.\begin{aligned}
q_{12} &= -q_{21} \\
q_{13} &= -q_{31} \\
q_{23} &= -q_{32}
\end{aligned}\right\} \tag{3-39}$$

is known as an *antisymmetric tensor*. Any tensor can be represented as a sum of a symmetric and an antisymmetric tensor.

If we exchange the coefficients of the tensor Φ (see Eq. 3-36) and form a tensor

$$\begin{aligned}
\Phi_c = {} & q_{11}\,\mathbf{ii} + q_{21}\,\mathbf{ij} + q_{31}\,\mathbf{ik} \\
& + q_{12}\,\mathbf{ji} + q_{22}\,\mathbf{jj} + q_{32}\,\mathbf{jk} \\
& + q_{13}\,\mathbf{ki} + q_{23}\,\mathbf{kj} + q_{33}\,\mathbf{kk}
\end{aligned} \tag{3-40}$$

then the tensors Φ and Φ_c are said to be conjugate. (Note that a symmetric tensor $\Phi = \Phi_c$.)

In the scalar product of a dyadic and a vector the order of the dyadic and the vector is of importance. In general, $\mathbf{u} \cdot \Phi \neq \Phi \cdot \mathbf{u}$ where $\mathbf{u}$ denotes a vector and Φ a dyadic.

We showed that the tensor ∇V can be represented as a sum of a symmetric tensor $\mathbf{E}$ and an antisymmetric tensor Ω

$$\nabla V = \mathbf{E} + \Omega \tag{3-41}$$

with

$$\mathbf{E} = \frac{\partial u}{\partial x}\mathbf{ii} \quad + \frac{1}{2}\left(\frac{\partial v}{\partial x} + \frac{\partial u}{\partial y}\right)\mathbf{ij} \quad + \frac{1}{2}\left(\frac{\partial w}{\partial x} + \frac{\partial u}{\partial z}\right)\mathbf{ik}$$

$$+ \frac{1}{2}\left(\frac{\partial u}{\partial y} + \frac{\partial v}{\partial x}\right)\mathbf{ji} \quad + \frac{\partial v}{\partial y}\mathbf{jj} \quad + \frac{1}{2}\left(\frac{\partial w}{\partial y} + \frac{\partial v}{\partial z}\right)\mathbf{jk}$$

$$+ \frac{1}{2}\left(\frac{\partial u}{\partial z} + \frac{\partial w}{\partial x}\right)\mathbf{ki} + \frac{1}{2}\left(\frac{\partial v}{\partial z} + \frac{\partial w}{\partial y}\right)\mathbf{kj} + \frac{\partial w}{\partial z}\mathbf{kk} \quad (3\text{-}42)$$

and

$$\mathbf{\Omega} = 0 \qquad\qquad + \frac{1}{2}\left(\frac{\partial v}{\partial x} - \frac{\partial u}{\partial y}\right)\mathbf{ij} \quad + \frac{1}{2}\left(\frac{\partial w}{\partial x} - \frac{\partial u}{\partial z}\right)\mathbf{ik}$$

$$+ \frac{1}{2}\left(\frac{\partial u}{\partial y} - \frac{\partial v}{\partial x}\right)\mathbf{ji} + 0 \qquad\qquad + \frac{1}{2}\left(\frac{\partial w}{\partial y} - \frac{\partial v}{\partial z}\right)\mathbf{jk}$$

$$+ \frac{1}{2}\left(\frac{\partial u}{\partial z} - \frac{\partial w}{\partial x}\right)\mathbf{ki} + \frac{1}{2}\left(\frac{\partial v}{\partial z} - \frac{\partial w}{\partial y}\right)\mathbf{kj} + 0 \qquad (3\text{-}43)$$

We therefore can rewrite Eq. 3-31 as

$$\mathbf{V} = \mathbf{V}_P + d\mathbf{V} = \mathbf{V}_P + d\mathbf{r} \cdot \mathbf{E} + d\mathbf{r} \cdot \mathbf{\Omega} \qquad (3\text{-}44)$$

The last term represents the rotation of the fluid, because,

$$d\mathbf{r} \cdot \mathbf{\Omega} = \left[\frac{1}{2}\left(\frac{\partial u}{\partial y} - \frac{\partial v}{\partial x}\right)dy + \frac{1}{2}\left(\frac{\partial u}{\partial z} - \frac{\partial w}{\partial x}\right)dz\right]\mathbf{i}$$

$$+ \left[\frac{1}{2}\left(\frac{\partial v}{\partial x} - \frac{\partial u}{\partial y}\right)dx + \frac{1}{2}\left(\frac{\partial v}{\partial z} - \frac{\partial w}{\partial y}\right)dz\right]\mathbf{j}$$

$$+ \left[\frac{1}{2}\left(\frac{\partial w}{\partial x} - \frac{\partial u}{\partial z}\right)dx + \frac{1}{2}\left(\frac{\partial w}{\partial y} - \frac{\partial v}{\partial z}\right)dy\right]\mathbf{k}$$

$$= \frac{1}{2}(\mathbf{\nabla} \times \mathbf{V}) \times d\mathbf{r} = \frac{1}{2}\boldsymbol{\omega} \times d\mathbf{r} = \tilde{\boldsymbol{\omega}} \times d\mathbf{r} \qquad (3\text{-}45)$$

The antisymmetric tensor $\mathbf{\Omega}$ is known as the *vorticity tensor*.

The second term on the right-hand side of Eq. 3-44 represents the deformation (pure strain) of the fluid. It can be rewritten in the form

$$d\mathbf{r} \cdot \mathbf{E} = \frac{1}{2} d\mathbf{r} \cdot [\mathbf{\nabla}\mathbf{V} + (\mathbf{\nabla}\mathbf{V})_c] \qquad (3\text{-}46)$$

where $(\mathbf{\nabla}\mathbf{V})_c$ represents the conjugate tensor of tensor $\mathbf{\nabla}\mathbf{V}$.

The symmetric tensor $\mathbf{E}$ is known as the *rate of strain tensor*. It can be represented in the form

$$\mathbf{E} = \epsilon_{11}\mathbf{ii} + \epsilon_{12}\mathbf{ij} + \epsilon_{13}\mathbf{ik}$$

$$+ \epsilon_{21}\mathbf{ji} + \epsilon_{22}\mathbf{jj} + \epsilon_{23}\mathbf{jk}$$

$$+ \epsilon_{31}\mathbf{ki} + \epsilon_{32}\mathbf{kj} + \epsilon_{33}\mathbf{kk} \qquad (3\text{-}47)$$

with

$$\epsilon_{11} = \frac{\partial u}{\partial x} = \epsilon_x$$

$$\epsilon_{22} = \frac{\partial v}{\partial y} = \epsilon_y$$

$$\epsilon_{33} = \frac{\partial w}{\partial z} = \epsilon_z$$

$$\epsilon_{12} = \epsilon_{21} = \frac{1}{2}\left(\frac{\partial u}{\partial y} + \frac{\partial v}{\partial x}\right) = \frac{1}{2}\gamma_{xy}$$

$$\epsilon_{13} = \epsilon_{31} = \frac{1}{2}\left(\frac{\partial w}{\partial x} + \frac{\partial u}{\partial z}\right) = \frac{1}{2}\gamma_{zx}$$

$$\epsilon_{23} = \epsilon_{32} = \frac{1}{2}\left(\frac{\partial v}{\partial z} + \frac{\partial w}{\partial y}\right) = \frac{1}{2}\gamma_{yz}$$

(3-48)

The coefficients $\epsilon_{11} = \epsilon_x$, $\epsilon_{22} = \epsilon_y$, $\epsilon_{33} = \epsilon_z$ represent the components of the rates of relative elongation (or contraction), that is, of longitudinal strain, of fluid elements in the directions of the x-, y-, and z-axes, respectively. They are called the *normal rates of strain*. The coefficients $\epsilon_{12} = \epsilon_{21} = \frac{1}{2}\gamma_{xy}$, $\epsilon_{13} = \epsilon_{31} = \frac{1}{2}\gamma_{zx}$, and $\epsilon_{23} = \epsilon_{32} = \frac{1}{2}\gamma_{yz}$ represent halves of the *rates of shear deformation* (or *strain*), that is, halves of the rates of decrease of the angle between the orthogonal line segments parallel to the x-, y-; x-, z-; and y-, z-axes in the fluid at a point.

By proper rotation of the x-, y-, z-axes, say into ξ-, η-, ζ-axes, the symmetric tensor **E** can be transformed into a form in which only the so-called leading diagonal coefficients remain while all other coefficients vanish. We then have

$$\mathbf{E} = \epsilon_1\mathbf{i}'\mathbf{i}' + \epsilon_2\mathbf{j}'\mathbf{j}' + \epsilon_3\mathbf{k}'\mathbf{k}' \qquad (3\text{-}49)$$

where $\mathbf{i}'$, $\mathbf{j}'$, and $\mathbf{k}'$ represent unit vectors along the ξ-, η-, ζ-axes, respectively. The coefficients $\epsilon_1\left(= \dfrac{\partial V_\xi}{\partial \xi}\right)$, $\epsilon_2\left(= \dfrac{\partial V_\eta}{\partial \eta}\right)$, and $\epsilon_3 = \left(= \dfrac{\partial V_\zeta}{\partial \zeta}\right)$ are known as the *principal rates of strain*, while the ξ-, η-, ζ-axes are known as the *principal axes of the rate of strain*. In the directions of the principal axes the fluid experiences a pure extension or contraction but no change in direction of a line element. V_ξ, V_η, and V_ζ denote the velocity components in the ξ-, η-, and ζ-directions respectively.

Note that

$$\frac{1}{d\mathcal{V}}\frac{D(d\mathcal{V})}{Dt} = \epsilon_1 + \epsilon_2 + \epsilon_3$$

$$= \frac{\partial V_\xi}{\partial \xi} + \frac{\partial V_\eta}{\partial \eta} + \frac{\partial V_\zeta}{\partial \zeta} = \nabla \cdot \mathbf{V} \qquad (3\text{-}50)$$

which we already concluded in Sec. 3-2 (Eq. 3-13).

From our discussion it follows that we can write the following expression for the fluid velocity in the immediate neighborhood of a point P:

$$\mathbf{V} = \mathbf{V}_P + d\mathbf{V}$$

$$= \mathbf{V}_P + \frac{1}{2} d\mathbf{r} \cdot [\boldsymbol{\nabla} \mathbf{V} + (\boldsymbol{\nabla} \mathbf{V})_c] + \tilde{\boldsymbol{\omega}} \times d\mathbf{r} \qquad (3\text{-}51)$$

This expression can be looked upon as the mathematical formulation of the Cauchy-Stokes decomposition theorem.

We shall return to this discussion when deriving the momentum equation of viscous fluids (in Chapter 7).

3-7. DEFINITION OF IRROTATIONAL MOTION; VELOCITY POTENTIAL

A fluid motion is said to be irrotational if the fluid elements do not experience rotation in their motion. Using the results of our discussion in Sec. 3-4 we can therefore say that a fluid flow is irrotational when the vorticity is zero, that is, when

$$\boldsymbol{\omega} = \boldsymbol{\nabla} \times \mathbf{V} = \mathbf{0} \qquad (3\text{-}52)$$

everywhere in the flow field.

From our discussion in Sec. A-9 (of Appendix A) it follows that in an irrotational fluid flow the flow velocity $\mathbf{V}$ can be expressed as the gradient of a scalar-field function. That is, when a fluid flow is irrotational, we can write

$$\mathbf{V} = \boldsymbol{\nabla} \phi \qquad (3\text{-}53)[4]$$

The scalar-field function ϕ is called the *velocity potential*, and an irrotational flow is often called a *potential flow* to indicate that it is a flow in which velocity potential exist.

From the definition of the gradient of a scalar-field function (Sec. A-5) it follows that the magnitude of the flow velocity at a given point in an irrotational flow field is equal to the derivative $\partial\phi/\partial n$, where n is a line perpendicular to the equipotential surface (that is, ϕ = constant surface) passing through that point. Hence, the magnitude of the flow velocity is equal to the maximum directional derivative of ϕ at the point in question. The direction of the flow velocity is that of the normal unit vector $\mathbf{n}$ along the normal n to the surface ϕ = const., pointing in the direction of increasing ϕ.

Equation 3-52 expresses the fact that *an irrotational fluid motion is characterized by the absence of vortex lines.* Equation 3-53 says that *the vector lines of the flow velocity field* $\mathbf{V}$, *which are known as streamlines, are normal to the equipotential surfaces.* From our discussion in Sec. 3-6 it follows that, in an irrotational flow, the instantaneous state of relative motion of the fluid at a point is that of pure strain.

[4] Sometimes the velocity potential ϕ is defined by writing $\mathbf{V} = -\boldsymbol{\nabla} \phi$.

From our discussion in Sec. A-9 it should be clear that the velocity potential ϕ is a single-valued scalar-field function in simply connected regions of an irrotational flow. In multiply connected regions in which vorticity vanishes, for reducible circuits

$$\oint_C \mathbf{V} \cdot d\mathbf{r} = \Gamma = \oint_C (\nabla \phi) \cdot d\mathbf{r} = \oint_C d\phi = 0$$

that is, the velocity potential ϕ is single-valued, but for circuits which are not reducible, in general,

$$\oint_C \mathbf{V} \cdot d\mathbf{r} = \Gamma = \oint_C (\nabla \phi) \cdot d\mathbf{r} = \oint_C d\phi \neq 0$$

that is, the velocity potential is multiple-valued. We can therefore define an irrotational flow as a flow in which the circulation about every reducible circuit is zero. This statement is known as *Kelvin's kinematic theorem* (1869).

The Combination of Motions. Let us consider an irrotational and incompressible fluid motion. Since we can write $\mathbf{V} = u\mathbf{i} + v\mathbf{j} + w\mathbf{k} = \nabla \phi$, we have

$$\frac{\partial \phi}{\partial x} = u; \quad \frac{\partial \phi}{\partial y} = v; \quad \frac{\partial \phi}{\partial z} = w$$

When an incompressible fluid motion is considered to be made up of two (or more) usually simpler, fluid motions such that $\mathbf{V} = \mathbf{V}_1 + \mathbf{V}_2 = (u_1 + u_2)\mathbf{i} + (v_1 + v_2)\mathbf{j} + (w_1 + w_2)\mathbf{k}$, then it follows that the velocity potential $\phi = \phi_1 + \phi_2$ with $\partial\phi_1/\partial x = u_1$, $\partial\phi_1/\partial y = v_1$, $\partial\phi_1/\partial z = w_1$, and $\partial\phi_2/\partial x = u_2$, $\partial\phi_2/\partial y = v_2$, $\partial\phi_2/\partial z = w_2$. Therefore *addition of velocity potentials results in fluid motions in which the velocities of the motions corresponding to each velocity potential are added* (*vectorially*). (Note that this conclusion is not restricted to the flows studied in a rectangular cartesian coordinate system.) Such combination of fluid motions is restricted to incompressible flows. For compressible flows, it would result in violation of the law of conservation of mass. This can easily be shown using Eq. 3-61 derived in the next section.

Velocity Potential for Incompressible Fluids. When a fluid is assumed to be incompressible, the continuity equation, which represents the mathematical formulation of the law of conservation of mass, expressed in the spatial form becomes

$$\nabla \cdot \mathbf{V} = 0 \qquad\qquad [3\text{-}64]$$

throughout the flow field. (This will be shown in the next section.) For irrotational flows of such fluids the velocity potential satisfies therefore the equation

$$\nabla \cdot \mathbf{V} = \nabla \cdot \nabla \phi = \nabla^2 \phi = 0 \qquad\qquad (3\text{-}54)$$

known as Laplace's equation, which is a linear equation of the second order. (For the expression for the Laplacian operator ∇^2 in various orthogonal coordinate systems, see Appendix A.)

Remarks on Irrotational Flows. In Sec. 3-4 we showed that vorticity is generated in a (real) fluid flowing along a plate. Since fluid flows involve either relative motions between objects and unbounded fluid, or motion of fluids in ducts, vorticity is present, in general, in all flows of real fluids. In the flows of fluids having very small viscosity, the significant effects of vorticity are usually found only in the boundary layers. (In the case of a flow in a duct, the boundary-layer flow may fill the whole cross section of the duct. We exclude from our considerations supersonic flows of gases in which curved shock waves are present, and other special types of flows to be discussed briefly in Chapter 5, in which circulation is also not preserved.)

When approximating the behavior of a fluid flowing outside of the boundary layers by that of the (fictitious) perfect fluid, we are quite often permitted to assume that there the flow is irrotational if it starts as an irrotational flow.[5] For this to be the case, the flow must be circulation-preserving (see discussion following Eq. 3-22 in Sec. 3-4).

One reason why irrotational flows are of great interest is largely because the equations of such motions are particularly amenable to analysis. (One simplification: in place of the three velocity components $u(x, y, z, t)$, $v(x, y, z, t)$, and $w(x, y, z, t)$, we have only one dependent variable $\phi(x, y, z, t)$.) This is especially the case when the fluid, in addition to being assumed to behave like a perfect fluid (this assumption must be made for otherwise a flow can not, in general, be irrotational everywhere), is considered to be incompressible, and the flow two-dimensional. (We shall devote Chapter 6 to a study of such fluid flows.) In addition, as was mentioned earlier, the potential flow solutions are usually the starting point for more realistic analyses of fluid flows.

3-8. CONTINUITY EQUATION

In Sec. 3-3 we defined the concept of a material volume. We said that a material volume is a volume moving with the fluid, and therefore contains always the same fluid (it is made up always of the same fluid elements). The (closed) material surface which bounds the material volume always passes through the same fluid elements, always is a connected surface, and always contains the same fluid.

The law of conservation of mass can be expressed by saying that the mass of a material volume $\mathscr{V}$ remains unchanged. The mathematical

---

[5] An example of a flow which starts as an irrotational flow is one in which a (homogeneous) fluid having uniform state flows out of a large reservoir in which it may be considered to be at rest.

formulation of the law of conservation of mass for a fluid which is treated as a continuum is known as the *continuity equation*. It can be written in the form

$$\frac{D}{Dt} \int_{\mathcal{V}} \rho \, d\mathcal{V} = 0 \tag{3-55}$$

where ρ denotes the density of the fluid. Note that in writing the continuity equation we place no restrictions on the type of the fluid or on its properties, except that it can be treated as a continuum. Therefore it is valid for real fluids as well as for the (fictitious) perfect fluids.

Making use of Eq. 3-14, we obtain

$$\int_{\mathcal{V}} \left(\frac{\partial \rho}{\partial t} + \mathbf{V} \cdot \nabla \rho + \rho \nabla \cdot \mathbf{V} \right) d\mathcal{V} = 0$$

because $F = \rho$. (Observe that this expression can also be obtained by performing differentiation of the terms ρ and $d\,\mathcal{V}$ inside the integral in Eq. 3-55 and by making use of Eqs. 3-3 and 3-50 or 3-13.) Since the material volume $\mathcal{V}$ is arbitrary, the integrand vanishes everywhere in the flow field and therefore

$$\frac{\partial \rho}{\partial t} + \mathbf{V} \cdot \nabla \rho + \rho \nabla \cdot \mathbf{V} = 0 \tag{3-56}$$

or

$$\frac{\partial \rho}{\partial t} + \nabla \cdot (\rho \mathbf{V}) = 0 \tag{3-56a}$$

which is the *spatial form of the continuity equation*, often referred to as the *Eulerian continuity equation*.

Equation 3-56 can also be written in the form

$$\frac{D\rho}{Dt} + \rho \nabla \cdot \mathbf{V} = 0 \tag{3-56b}$$

in view of Eq. 3-3, which includes a material time derivative and spatial distance derivatives (in the divergence of $\mathbf{V}$).

Making use of the Reynolds transport theorem, we can transform the continuity equation involving the material time derivative of a volume integral into the form involving only spatial derivatives. This way we obtain

$$\frac{\partial}{\partial t} \int_{\mathcal{V}} \rho \, d\mathcal{V} + \oint_{S} \rho \mathbf{V} \cdot d\mathbf{A} = 0 \tag{3-57}$$

or

$$-\frac{\partial}{\partial t} \int_{\mathcal{V}} \rho \, d\mathcal{V} = \oint_{S} \rho \mathbf{V} \cdot d\mathbf{A} \tag{3-57a}$$

which is the form of the continuity equation valid for a *volume fixed in space* $\mathcal{V}$ (relative to the coordinate system in which the flow is studied).

This equation states that the rate at which the mass of the fluid decreases within the bounding surface of a fixed volume $\mathscr{V}$ is equal to the net rate of outflow of the mass of the fluid across the bounding surface.

Making use of the divergence theorem of Gauss, Eq. 3-57 can be transformed into equation

$$\int_{\mathscr{V}} \left[\frac{\partial \rho}{\partial t} + \nabla \cdot (\rho \mathbf{V}) \right] d\mathscr{V} = 0$$

because for a volume fixed in space

$$\frac{\partial}{\partial t} \int_{\mathscr{V}} \rho \, d\mathscr{V} = \int_{\mathscr{V}} \frac{\partial \rho}{\partial t} \, d\mathscr{V}$$

from which equation 3-56a follows.

For a fluid element, the continuity equation (Eq. 3-55) can be written in the form

$$\frac{D}{Dt} (\rho \, d\mathscr{V}) = 0 \qquad\qquad (3\text{-}58)$$

or

$$\rho \, d\mathscr{V} = \text{const.} \qquad\qquad (3\text{-}58a)$$

From Eq. 3-58 it follows that

$$\frac{1}{\rho} \frac{D\rho}{Dt} = - \frac{1}{d\mathscr{V}} \frac{D(d\mathscr{V})}{Dt} \qquad\qquad (3\text{-}58b)$$

If we eliminate the term $1/\rho(D\rho/Dt)$ from the above equation making use of Eq. 3-56b, we obtain

$$\nabla \cdot \mathbf{V} = \frac{1}{d\mathscr{V}} \frac{D(d\mathscr{V})}{Dt} \qquad\qquad [3\text{-}13]$$

which relation was already obtained in Sec. 3-3.

Since for a fluid element

$$\rho \, d\mathscr{V} = \rho_0 d\mathscr{V}_0$$

where subscript 0 refers to the initial values of the quantities involved (that is, to the values corresponding to time $t = 0$), in view of the meaning of the Jacobian J (Eq. 3-10) we can write the continuity equation for a fluid element in the form

$$\rho J = \rho_0$$

where $J \neq 0$ and $J \neq \infty$. This equation represents the *material form of the continuity equation*, and is often referred to in literature as the *Lagragean continuity equation*.

Note that, in view of Eq. 3-58, we have the relation

$$\frac{D}{Dt} \int_{\mathscr{V}} F\rho \, d\mathscr{V} = \int_{\mathscr{V}} \frac{DF}{Dt} \rho \, d\mathscr{V} \qquad\qquad (3\text{-}59)$$

where F denotes a scalar- or vector-field function.

For a steady flow of a compressible fluid, since $\partial\rho/\partial t = 0$ in such flow, while the continuity equation written in the (integral) form valid for material volumes (Eq. 3-55) remains unchanged, the continuity equation written in the (integral) form valid for volumes fixed in space reduces to

$$\oint_S \rho\mathbf{V} \cdot d\mathbf{A} = 0 \tag{3-60}$$

and the continuity equation written in the form valid at a point in a fluid reduces to

$$\nabla \cdot (\rho\mathbf{V}) = 0 \tag{3-61}$$

For fluids assumed to be incompressible, since $D\rho/Dt = 0$ in them, the continuity equation for material volumes reduces to

$$\frac{D}{Dt}\int_{\mathscr{V}} \rho\, d\mathscr{V} = \int_{\mathscr{V}} \frac{D\rho}{Dt}\, d\mathscr{V} + \int_{\mathscr{V}} \frac{1}{d\mathscr{V}} \frac{D(d\mathscr{V})}{Dt}\, d\mathscr{V}$$

$$= \int_{\mathscr{V}} (\nabla \cdot \mathbf{V})d\mathscr{V} = 0 \tag{3-62}$$

in view of the meaning of the divergence of the flow velocity (Eq. 3-13). The continuity equation for volumes fixed in space (relative to the coordinate system in which the flow is studied) reduces to

$$\oint_S \mathbf{V} \cdot d\mathbf{A} = 0 \tag{3-63}$$

which is equivalent to writing

$$\int_{\mathscr{V}} (\nabla \cdot \mathbf{V})d\mathscr{V} = 0 \tag{3-63a}$$

in view of the divergence theorem of Gauss. The continuity equation written in the form valid at a point in a fluid reduces to

$$\nabla \cdot \mathbf{V} = 0 \tag{3-64}$$

That is, *for fluids assumed to be incompressible, the divergence of the flow velocity field is zero.*

It was stated at the beginning of this section that the continuity equation (Eq. 3-55) is valid for any fluid provided that it can be treated as a continuum. In the study of flow of compressible perfect fluids we assume that the shock waves, owing to their thinness, can be represented as surfaces of discontinuity in the mathematical sense. The continuity equation is still applicable to such flows. That is, the physical continuity of a fluid allows existence in the flow field of surfaces of discontinuity at which some of the flow variables are discontinuous. However, as can be seen from Eq. 3-60, it demands that the product of fluid density and velocity component normal to such a surface shall remain mathematically continuous.

3-9. STREAMLINES; STREAM TUBES; STREAM FUNCTION

A *streamline* is a vector line of a flow velocity field **V**. Therefore, it is a continuous line whose direction *at a given instant* is everywhere the same as the direction of flow of the fluid elements.   Along a streamline the velocities of the fluid elements are everywhere tangent to it.

As was pointed out in Sec. 3-5, the curve

$$\mathbf{r} = \mathbf{r}(\tau)$$

where τ denotes a parameter, represents a streamline at a given instant if the relation

$$d\mathbf{r} \times \mathbf{V} = \mathbf{0}$$

where $d\mathbf{r} = (\partial \mathbf{r}/\partial \tau)\, d\tau$ represents the differential of the position vector **r** having the direction of the curve, is satisfied along it. From the last relation it follows that

$$d\mathbf{r} = \frac{\partial \mathbf{r}}{\partial \tau}\, d\tau = g\,\mathbf{V} \tag{3-65}$$

where g denotes a scalar-field function.

In a rectangular cartesian coordinate system, with $d\mathbf{r} = dx\,\mathbf{i} + dy\,\mathbf{j} + dz\,\mathbf{k}$ and $\mathbf{V} = u\mathbf{i} + v\mathbf{j} + w\mathbf{k}$, the following relations hold along a streamline:

$$\frac{dx}{u} = \frac{dy}{v} = \frac{dz}{w} \tag{3-66}$$

Figure 3-12 illustrates the relation given by Eq. 3-66 for a plane flow.

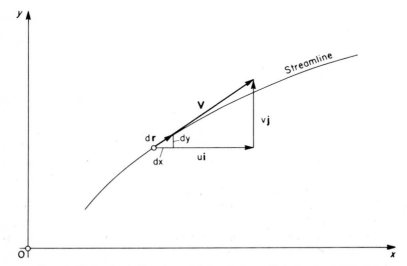

FIG. 3-12. A streamline in a plane flow studied in a rectangular cartesian coordinate system.

The fact that a function f is constant along a streamline can be expressed by

$$\mathbf{V} \cdot \nabla f = 0 \qquad (3\text{-}67)$$

A *stream tube* is a vector tube of the flow velocity field and is therefore defined as a tube filled with the flowing fluid and formed by the streamlines passing through a closed curve. A stream tube is illustrated in Fig. 3-13.

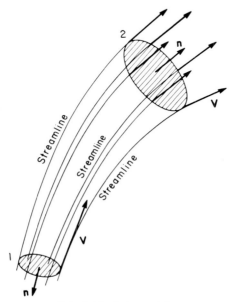

FIG. 3-13. A stream tube.

Making use of subscripts 1 and 2 to refer to two cross sections of a stream tube, we can write the continuity equation (Eq. 3-60) applied to a stream tube as

$$\int_{A_1} \rho \mathbf{V} \cdot d\mathbf{A} + \int_{A_2} \rho \mathbf{V} \cdot d\mathbf{A} = 0 \qquad (3\text{-}68)$$

with $\int_A \rho \mathbf{V} \cdot d\mathbf{A}$ representing the rate of mass flow $\dot{m} = dm/dt$ (in units of mass per unit of time, say in of lbm/sec) across the area A of an oriented fluid surface. Assuming the cross sections 1 and 2 to be normal cross sections of the stream tube, that is cross sections which are intersected by the streamlines at right angles, we can write

$$\int_{A_2} \rho V dA = \int_{A_1} \rho V dA = \dot{m} = \text{const.} \qquad (3\text{-}69)$$

This is so because, since we consider a closed surface to be oriented by a field of outward normal unit vectors, the normal unit vectors **n** orienting the area elements of the normal cross section 1 point in the direction opposite to that of the flow velocity **V**, while at cross section 2 they point in the same direction as the flow velocity, and therefore

$$\int_{A_1} \rho V dA + \int_{A_2} \rho V dA = 0$$

Also, there is no flow of the fluid through the curved surface of the stream tube.

*In the case when the flow variables ρ and **V** are constant on the normal cross-sectional area A of a stream tube*, the continuity equation applied to a stream tube becomes

$$\dot{m} = A\rho V = \text{const.} \tag{3-70}$$

at each (normal) cross section of the stream tube. For example, referring to the cross sections 1 and 2 we can write

$$A_1 \rho_1 V_1 = A_2 \rho_2 V_2 \tag{3-71}$$

When the fluid is treated as incompressible, Eq. 3-70 can be written as

$$Q = AV = \text{const.} \tag{3-72}$$

across each normal cross section of the stream tube, where Q represents the volumetric rate of flow of the fluid (in units of volume per unit of time, say in ft^3/sec).

A flow in which the variables depend on only one distance variable is known as a *one-dimensional flow*. Equations 3-70 through 3-72 are valid for such flows.

Stream Function. In the study of flows for which the continuity equation can be written as a sum of two derivatives, we can introduce the *stream function ψ* as a dependent variable.

In the case of a plane (two-dimensional) *steady flow of a compressible fluid*, studied in a rectangular cartesian coordinate system, the continuity equation (Eq. 3-61) reads

$$\frac{\partial(\rho u)}{\partial x} + \frac{\partial(\rho v)}{\partial y} = 0 \tag{3-73}$$

where u and v denote the components of the flow velocity in the x- and y-directions, respectively. This equation allows us to introduce the stream function ψ such that

$$\frac{\partial \psi}{\partial y} = \rho u$$

and

$$\frac{\partial \psi}{\partial x} = -\rho v \tag{3-74}$$

So defined stream function satisfies exactly the continuity equation. Since $\psi = \psi(x, y)$,

$$d\psi = \frac{\partial \psi}{\partial y} dy + \frac{\partial \psi}{\partial x} dx = \rho u\, dy - \rho v\, dx \qquad (3\text{-}75)$$

The continuity equation applied to the cross section a–b of the stream tube bounded partially by the streamlines whose projection on the (x, y) plane coincides with the streamlines a and b shown in Fig. 3-14, and hav-

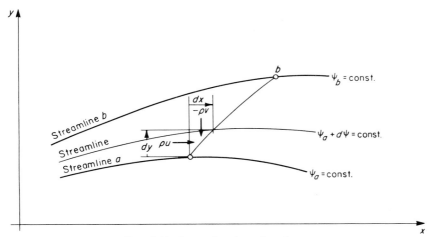

FIG. 3-14. Streamlines in a plane flow.

ing unit height in the direction perpendicular to the (x, y) plane can be written as

$$\dot{m}_{a\text{-}b} = \int_{A_{a\text{-}b}} \rho \mathbf{V} \cdot d\mathbf{A}$$

$$= \int_a^b \rho u\, dy + \int_a^b (-\rho v)\, dx \qquad (3\text{-}76)$$

where $\dot{m}_{a\text{-}b}$ represents the rate of mass flow of the fluid through the stream tube. Since Eq. 3-76 is valid for an arbitrary cross section of the stream tube considered, that is, it is valid for an arbitrary point a on streamline a and an arbitrary point b on streamline b, and since (in view of Eq. 3-75)

$$\dot{m}_{a\text{-}b} = \int_a^b d\psi = \psi_b - \psi_a$$

it follows that *we can identify the streamlines with the lines representing constant values of the stream function.* [Another way in which this statement can be verified is by using Eq. 3-67. For ψ to be constant along a streamline we must have $\mathbf{V} \cdot \nabla \psi = 0$. In this case

$$\mathbf{V} \cdot \nabla \psi = (u\mathbf{i} + v\mathbf{j}) \cdot \left(\mathbf{i}\, \frac{\partial \psi}{\partial x} + \mathbf{j}\, \frac{\partial \psi}{\partial y} \right)$$

$$= u\, \frac{\partial \psi}{\partial x} + v\, \frac{\partial \psi}{\partial y} = -\rho u v + \rho u v = 0$$

as it should.]

The difference between the values of the stream function (defined by Eq. 3-74) corresponding to any two streamlines represents the rate of mass flow through the stream tube of unit height whose projection in the (x, y) plane coincides with the two streamlines.

The differential of the stream function $d\psi$ represents the differential rate of mass flow through the stream tube of unit height whose projection in the (x, y) plane coincides with the streamlines ψ and $\psi + d\psi$.

In the case of a plane (two-dimensional) *flow of a fluid considered to be incompressible*, studied in a rectangular cartesian coordinate system, the continuity equation (Eq. 3-64) reads

$$\frac{\partial u}{\partial x} + \frac{\partial v}{\partial y} = 0 \qquad (3\text{-}77)$$

where u and v denote the velocity components in the x- and y-directions respectively (we have $\mathbf{V} = u\mathbf{i} + v\mathbf{j}$), and therefore we can introduce the stream function ψ defined by equations

$$\left. \begin{array}{c} \dfrac{\partial \psi}{\partial y} = u \\[2em] \dfrac{\partial \psi}{\partial x} = -v \end{array} \right\} \qquad (3\text{-}78)[6]$$

and

In this case, for a flow of unit depth,

$$Q_{a-b} = \int_a^b d\psi = \psi_b - \psi_a$$

and our conclusion that we can identify the streamlines with the lines representing constant values of the stream function remains unchanged. (Note that we could have retained the definition of the stream function as given by Eq. 3-74. However, since for fluids assumed to be incompressible $\rho = $ const., it is customary to define the stream function by Eq. 3-78.) The difference between the values of the stream function (defined by Eq. 3-78) corresponding to any two streamlines represents the volumetric rate of flow through the stream tube of unit height whose projection on the (x, y) plane coincides with the two streamlines.

---

[6]Sometimes the stream function is defined so that the signs are opposite to those in Eq. 3-78.

In the case of a plane flow studied in a circular cylindrical coordinate system, for an incompressible fluid flow, the continuity equation reads

$$\frac{1}{r}\frac{\partial(rV_r)}{\partial r} + \frac{1}{r}\left(\frac{\partial V_\theta}{\partial \theta}\right) = 0$$

or

$$\frac{\partial(rV_r)}{\partial r} + \frac{\partial V_\theta}{\partial \theta} = 0$$

where V_r and V_θ denote the radial and circumferential velocity components, as shown in Fig. 3-15. We can, therefore, define for such flow the

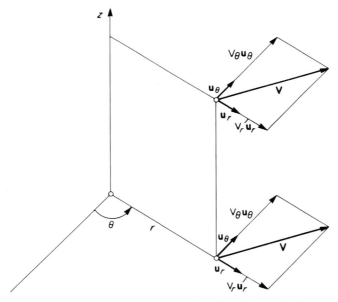

FIG. 3-15. Velocity components in a plane flow studied in a circular cylindrical coordinate system.

stream function ψ by

$$\left.\begin{aligned}\frac{\partial \psi}{\partial r} &= -V_\theta \\[2mm] \frac{\partial \psi}{\partial \theta} &= rV_r\end{aligned}\right\} \tag{3-79}$$

The stream function can also be introduced as a dependent variable when studying three-dimensional axisymmetrical flow. Our discussion of the stream function will be limited to two-dimensional flows. In addition, we will in general assume that the fluid is incompressible.

The Combination of Motions. Let us consider a plane (two-dimensional) motion of an incompressible fluid. We have

$$\frac{\partial \psi_1}{\partial y} = u_1 \quad \text{and} \quad \frac{\partial \psi_1}{\partial x} = -v_1$$

with $\mathbf{V}_1(x, y) = u_1 \mathbf{i} + v_1 \mathbf{j}$. Let us add another motion, say one given by $\mathbf{V}_2(x, y) = u_2 \mathbf{i} + v_2 \mathbf{j}$, to this motion, so that the resultant motion is given by $\mathbf{V} = \mathbf{V}_1 + \mathbf{V}_2 = u\mathbf{i} + v\mathbf{j} = (u_1 + u_2)\mathbf{i} + (v_1 + v_2)\mathbf{j}$. Since

$$\frac{\partial \psi_2}{\partial y} = u_2 \quad \text{and} \quad \frac{\partial \psi_2}{\partial x} = -v_2$$

we have

$$u = \frac{\partial \psi}{\partial y} = \frac{\partial \psi_1}{\partial y} + \frac{\partial \psi_2}{\partial y} = \frac{\partial (\psi_1 + \psi_2)}{\partial y}$$

and

$$-v = \frac{\partial \psi}{\partial x} = \frac{\partial \psi_1}{\partial x} + \frac{\partial \psi_2}{\partial x} = \frac{\partial (\psi_1 + \psi_2)}{\partial x}$$

We can conclude, therefore, that *a (vectorial) combination of two-dimensional incompressible flow fields can be accomplished by addition of their stream functions.*

Figure 3-16 illustrates the streamlines obtained from combination of two motions. The differences between the values of the stream functions have been chosen to be constant. This is the usual procedure. (These differences represent the volumetric rates of flow through stream tubes of unit height whose projection on the (x, y) plane coincides with the stream-

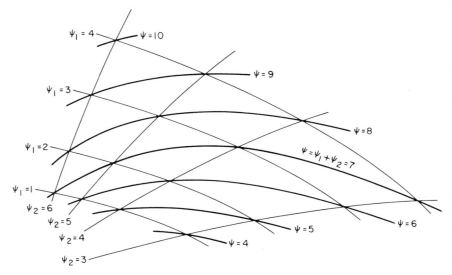

FIG. 3-16. Streamlines resulting from combination of two plane fluid motions.

lines.) The absolute values of the stream function do not have, in general, any meaning. In the case of a flow over a surface, we usually take the value of the stream function corresponding to the surface to be zero.

Stream Function for Incompressible Flows. Since the value of the stream function ψ is constant along a streamline:

$$\mathbf{V} \cdot \nabla \psi = 0$$

For a plane (two-dimensional) flow of an incompressible fluid, this equation can be written as

$$u \frac{\partial \psi}{\partial x} + v \frac{\partial \psi}{\partial y} = 0$$

where u and v denote the components of the flow velocity $\mathbf{V}$ in the directions of the x- and y- axes of a rectangular cartesian coordinate system, ($\mathbf{V} = u\mathbf{i} + v\mathbf{j}$).

Differentiating the last equation with respect to x and subsequently dividing the resulting equation by u, then differentiating it with respect to y and dividing by v, and adding these expressions, we obtain

$$\frac{\partial^2 \psi}{\partial x^2} + \frac{\partial^2 \psi}{\partial y^2} + \left(\frac{1}{u} \frac{\partial u}{\partial x} + \frac{1}{v} \frac{\partial u}{\partial y} \right) \frac{\partial \psi}{\partial x} + \left(\frac{1}{u} \frac{\partial v}{\partial x} + \frac{1}{v} \frac{\partial v}{\partial y} \right) \frac{\partial \psi}{\partial y} +$$

$$+ \left(\frac{v}{u} + \frac{u}{v} \right) \frac{\partial^2 \psi}{\partial x \partial y} = 0$$

Since

$$\frac{\partial \psi}{\partial y} = u$$

and

$$\frac{\partial \psi}{\partial x} = -v$$

the last equation transforms into

$$\frac{\partial^2 \psi}{\partial x^2} + \frac{\partial^2 \psi}{\partial y^2} = \frac{\partial u}{\partial y} - \frac{\partial v}{\partial x} - \frac{u}{v} \left(\frac{\partial v}{\partial y} - \frac{\partial u}{\partial x} \right)$$

$$= \frac{\partial u}{\partial y} - \frac{\partial v}{\partial x} - \frac{u}{v} \left(-\frac{\partial^2 \psi}{\partial x \partial y} + \frac{\partial^2 \psi}{\partial y \partial x} \right)$$

$$= \frac{\partial u}{\partial y} - \frac{\partial v}{\partial x}$$

Using vectorial notation, we can write

$$\frac{\partial^2 \psi}{\partial x^2} + \frac{\partial^2 \psi}{\partial y^2} = \nabla^2 \psi \qquad (3\text{-}80)$$

where ∇^2 represents the Laplacian operator. The term

$$\frac{\partial u}{\partial y} - \frac{\partial v}{\partial x} = -\omega_z$$

represents the negative of the magnitude of the vorticity **ω** in the plane flow under consideration.

Therefore, we have shown that for a plane flow of an incompressible fluid

$$\nabla^2 \psi = \frac{\partial^2 \psi}{\partial x^2} + \frac{\partial^2 \psi}{\partial y^2} = -\omega_z \qquad (3\text{-}81)$$

As a direct consequence it follows that *in an irrotational plane flow of an incompressible fluid, the stream function satisfies Laplace's equation;* that is,

$$\nabla^2 \psi = 0 \qquad (3\text{-}82)$$

3-10. STREAM FUNCTION AND VELOCITY POTENTIAL FOR SIMPLE FLOWS; APPARENT MASS

Uniform Flow. Consider a plane uniform stream of unit depth flowing with a constant velocity **V** inclined at an angle α to the x-axis in the (x, y) plane in which the flow is studied, as shown in Fig. 3-17. Assuming the fluid to be incompressible, we can write

$$\frac{\partial \psi}{\partial y} = u = V \cos \alpha \quad \text{and} \quad \frac{\partial \psi}{\partial x} = -v = -V \sin \alpha$$

The expression for the stream function ψ is therefore

$$\psi = Vy \cos \alpha - Vx \sin \alpha + C_1 \qquad (3\text{-}83)$$

where C_1 is an arbitrary constant.

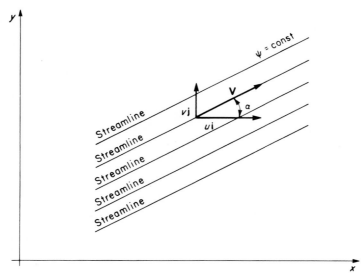

FIG. 3-17. Uniform flow.

Since the flow velocity $\mathbf{V}$ is constant in the flow, there is no vorticity (we have $\boldsymbol{\omega} = \nabla \times \mathbf{V} = \mathbf{0}$ throughout the flow region under consideration), and there exists (single-valued) velocity potential ϕ given by

$$\phi = Vx \cos \alpha + Vy \sin \alpha + C_2 \qquad (3\text{-}84)$$

where C_2 is an arbitrary constant, because $\mathbf{V} = \nabla \phi$ and therefore $u = \partial\phi/\partial x$ and $v = \partial\phi/\partial y$.

Source and Sink Flows; General Concept.   In an incompressible fluid, a *source* is defined as a point in the fluid from which the fluid flows radially outward at a uniform rate in all directions.   The concept of a sink is opposite to that of a source.   A *sink* in an incompressible fluid is defined as a point in the fluid into which the fluid flows radially at a uniform rate in all directions.   By the *strength of a source* (or a sink) in an incompressible fluid we mean the volumetric rate of flow from the source (or the sink).   (Therefore the strength of a sink is a negative quantity.)

Figure 3-18 illustrates the concept of source and sink flows in an incompressible fluid.   [When the fluid is highly compressible (such is the

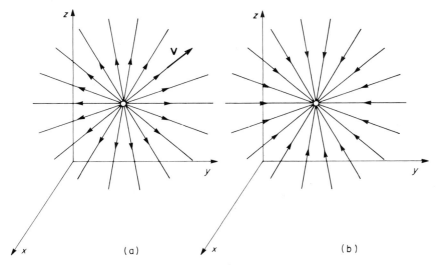

FIG. 3-18. (a) Incompressible source flow. (b) Incompressible sink flow.

case when a gas flows at large speeds), the concept of a source and a sink has to be modified.   In such case a source or sink flow can exist only outside of a sphere of a certain radius at which the flow Mach number is unity.   Our discussion will be limited to the flows of fluids which can be considered incompressible.]

The concept of a source or a sink is a mathematical abstraction, since the law of conservation of mass states that the fluid cannot be created or destroyed. [We can approximate a source (or a sink) in practice by inserting into a fluid a thin tube which ends with a small spherical rose having a multitude of uniformly distributed holes, and introducing (or removing) through it the fluid.] As a result, in a mathematical analysis, a source or a sink in a flow field represent singularities at which the continuity equation has to be modified to account for the artificial generation or withdrawal of the fluid. As will soon become clear, the concept of a source or a sink is very useful in making analyses of certain types of flows.

If we denote the strength of a source by Q then the magnitude of the (radial) velocity of the fluid resulting from a source flow is

$$V = \frac{Q}{A} = \frac{Q}{4\pi r^2} \qquad (3\text{-}85)$$

in view of Eq. 3-72, where r denotes the magnitude of the position vector from the origin of the source.

Two-Dimensional Source and Sink. By a two-dimensional source in an incompressible fluid we mean a line source, that is, a line from which the fluid flows radially outward at a uniform rate. Similarly, by a two-dimensional sink we mean a line sink. The two-dimensional source and sink are illustrated in Fig. 3-19. The source is indicated by symbol S_+ and the sink by S_-.

The definition of the strength Q of a source (or a sink) remains the same as in the case of a three-dimensional source (or sink), only the flow is considered to be of unit depth. As a result, for a fluid layer of unit depth, the magnitude of the (radial) fluid velocity resulting from a two-dimensional source flow is

$$V = \frac{Q}{A} = \frac{Q}{2\pi r} \qquad (3\text{-}86)$$

$$\left[\text{Observe that when we write } V = \frac{Q}{2\pi r}, \text{ the unit of the source strength } Q \right.$$

becomes: (unit of length)^2/(unit of time). $\Big]$ For the flow velocity $\mathbf{V}$, we

can write the expression

$$\mathbf{V} = V\mathbf{u}_r = \frac{Q}{2\pi r}\mathbf{u}_r = \frac{Q}{2\pi r^2}\mathbf{r} \qquad (3\text{-}87)$$

where $\mathbf{u}_r$ denotes a unit vector in the radial direction from the source (and therefore in the direction of the flow velocity $\mathbf{V} = V_r$), and $\mathbf{r}$ denotes a position vector from the origin S_+ of the source.

Since the curl of the position vector is zero (see Eq. A-70) and $\mathbf{u}_r \times \mathbf{r} = \mathbf{0}$, we have $\nabla \times \mathbf{V} = \mathbf{0}$, the source flow is irrotational, and there exists a velocity potential ϕ. Denoting the coordinates of the origin of the source by x_s and y_s, we have

$$\mathbf{r} = (x - x_s)\mathbf{i} + (y - y_s)\mathbf{j}$$

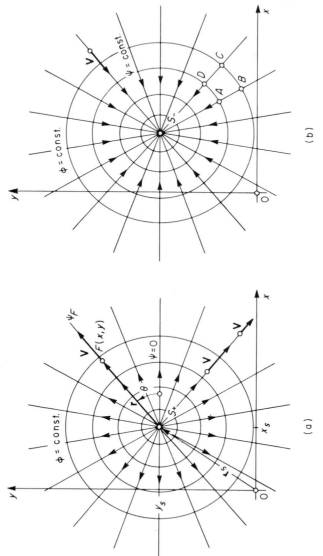

Fig. 3-19. (a) Two-dimensional incompressible source flow. (b) Two-dimensional incompressible sink flow.

and since, in the rectangular cartesian coordinate system,

$$\mathbf{V} = u\mathbf{i} + v\mathbf{j} = \nabla\phi = \frac{\partial\phi}{\partial x}\mathbf{i} + \frac{\partial\phi}{\partial y}\mathbf{j}$$

we have

$$u = \frac{\partial\phi}{\partial x} = \frac{Q(x - x_s)}{2\pi r^2} \left(= \frac{Q}{2\pi}\frac{\cos\theta}{r} \right)$$

$$v = \frac{\partial\theta}{\partial y} = \frac{Q(y - y_s)}{2\pi r^2} \left(= \frac{Q}{2\pi}\frac{\sin\theta}{r} \right)$$

with $r^2 = (x - x_s)^2 + (y - y_s)^2$, where θ denotes the angle measured from the horizontal line passing through the source as shown in Fig. 3-19. (The positive values of angle θ are measured in the counterclockwise direction.) Therefore the expression for the velocity potential for the flow resulting from a two-dimensional source in an incompressible fluid is

$$\phi = \frac{Q}{2\pi}\ln r + \text{const.} \qquad (3\text{-}88)$$

or

$$\phi = \frac{Q}{2\pi}\ln r \qquad (3\text{-}88a)$$

if we take the constant of integration to be zero, because $\partial r/\partial x = (x - x_s)/r$ and $\partial r/\partial y = (y - y_s)/r$. This equation indicates that, in the flow under consideration, the equipotential lines (that is, the $\phi = $ constant lines) are circles with the origin at the source.

Equation 3-88 can be derived more quickly by writing the expression for the gradient of ϕ in circular cylindrical coordinates. Since $\mathbf{V} = V_r\mathbf{u}_r$, because $V_\theta = 0$, we have

$$\mathbf{V} = V_r\mathbf{u}_r = \frac{\partial\phi}{\partial r}\mathbf{u}_r + \frac{\partial\phi}{r\partial\theta}\mathbf{u}_\theta$$

Therefore

$$\frac{\partial\phi}{\partial r} = V_r = \frac{Q}{2\pi r}$$

from which Eq. 3-88 follows.

The expression for the stream function for the flow resulting from a two-dimensional source in an incompressible fluid can be obtained from

$$\frac{\partial\psi}{\partial\theta} = rV_r$$

which follows from Eq. 3-79. We have

$$\psi = rV_r\theta + \text{const.} = \frac{Q}{2\pi}\theta + \text{const.} \quad (0 \leq \theta \leq 2\pi) \qquad (3\text{-}89)$$

or

$$\psi = \frac{Q}{2\pi}\theta \qquad (0 \le \theta \le 2\pi) \qquad \text{(3-89a)}$$

if we choose $\psi = 0$ to correspond to the horizontal streamline extending in the direction of the positive x-axis from the origin of the source, as shown in Fig. 3-19. The value of the stream function on the streamline passing through a point F, $\psi_F = Q\,\theta_F/2\pi$ represents the fraction $\theta_F/2\pi$ of the volumetric rate of flow Q from the source.

For a sink we should put $-Q$ in place of Q in the formulas derived here.

Two-Dimensional Vortex. In an incompressible fluid, by a *two-dimensional vortex* we mean a straight vortex filament, or a line vortex in the idealized description. (Our considerations involving vortices will be limited to incompressible fluids.) In practice, the velocity field induced by a straight vortex can be considered to correspond to that of a two-dimensional vortex only if the vortex is long enough so that the end effects can be ignored. For a two-dimensional vortex, the cross-sectional area of the vortex filament is constant, and therefore the strength of the vortex is constant along its length, and the circulation Γ about any circuit in the fluid lying in a plane perpendicular to the vortex and enclosing it is the same. At a given distance from the vortex, the velocity induced in a stationary fluid by a two-dimensional vortex is the same in all parallel planes perpendicular to the vortex, and is at right angle to the radius r from the vortex.

Consider the flow induced in a stationary fluid by a two-dimensional vortex. We have $V_r = 0$ and $V_\theta = V_\theta(r)$. From Eq. 3-79 it follows that the streamlines of such flow and circles (because $\partial\psi/\partial\theta = 0$) as we would expect.

The velocity potential ϕ exists (outside of the vortex filament) only if the fluid motion induced by the vortex is irrotational. Since the expression for $\boldsymbol{\omega} = \text{curl } \mathbf{V} = \mathbf{0}$ in a circular cylindrical coordinate system with $V_r = 0$ (and $V_z = 0$) and $\partial V_\theta/\partial z = 0$ becomes

$$\frac{1}{r}\frac{\partial(rV_\theta)}{\partial r}\,\mathbf{u}_z = 0$$

the fluid motion induced by a vortex is irrotational only when $V_\theta r = $ constant throughout the flow region.

A vortex which induces an irrotational fluid motion is known as a *free vortex*. Since in a free vortex the circulation

$$\Gamma = 2\pi r V_\theta$$

for all circuits enclosing the vortex ($\Gamma = 0$ for all reducible circuits, that is, for circuits which do not enclose the free vortex where $\nabla \times \mathbf{V} \ne \mathbf{0}$), we can write

$$V_\theta = \frac{\Gamma}{2\pi r} \qquad (3\text{-}90)$$

for the magnitude of the flow velocity induced by a free vortex.

The expression for the velocity potential of the flow induced by a two-dimensional free vortex can be obtained from the relation

$$\mathbf{V} = \mathbf{V}_\theta = \frac{\Gamma}{2\pi r}\mathbf{u}_\theta = \nabla\phi = \mathbf{u}_r\frac{\partial\phi}{\partial r} + \frac{\mathbf{u}_\theta}{r}\frac{\partial\phi}{\partial\theta}$$

which results in

$$\frac{\partial\phi}{\partial\theta} = \frac{\Gamma}{2\pi}$$

and

$$\phi = \frac{\Gamma}{2\pi}\theta + \text{const.} \qquad (0 \le \theta \le 2\pi) \qquad (3\text{-}91)$$

or

$$\phi = \frac{\Gamma}{2\pi}\theta \qquad (0 \le \theta \le 2\pi) \qquad (3\text{-}91\text{a})$$

if we take $\phi = 0$ for $\theta = 0$.

The expression for the stream function of the flow induced by a two-dimensional free vortex (in an incompressible fluid) is

$$\psi = -\frac{\Gamma}{2\pi}\ln r + \text{const.} \qquad (3\text{-}92)$$

This follows from the introduction of Eq. 3-90 into Eq. 3-79. The term $\Gamma/2\pi$ is often referred to as the *strength of a free vortex.* If we want the streamline $\psi = 0$ to correspond to a circle $r = a$, we write

$$\psi = -\frac{\Gamma}{2\pi}\ln \frac{r}{a} \qquad (3\text{-}92\text{a})$$

Figure 3-20 shows the streamlines and the equipotential lines of a free vortex.

Observe that the streamlines of a two-dimensional vortex flow are circles (like the equipotential lines of a two-dimensional source flow) while the equipotential lines of a free vortex are straight lines passing through the center of the vortex (like the streamlines of a two-dimensional source flow).

Two-Dimensional Source-Sink Pair.   In Secs. 3-7 and 3-9 we discussed the velocity potential and the stream function obtained by combination of motions. From our discussion it follows that, for a flow of an incompressible fluid resulting from a two-dimensional source-sink pair

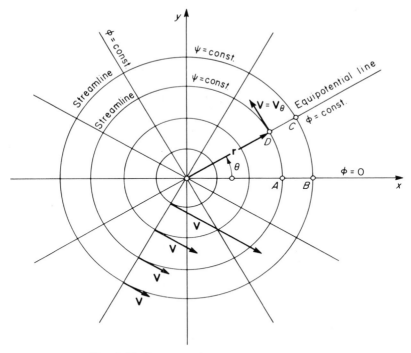

FIG. 3-20. Free vortex in an incompressible fluid.

shown in Fig. 3-21, the expression for the stream function is

$$\psi = \frac{Q_{S_+}}{2\pi}\theta_+ - \frac{Q_{S_-}}{2\pi}\theta_-$$

where Q_{S_+} and $-Q_{S_-}$ represent the strengths of the source and sink, respectively (Q_{S_-} being a positive quantity), and the angles θ_+ and θ_- represent the angles of inclination of the position vectors of a point $P(x, y)$ in the flow field (drawn from the source and the sink respectively) measured from the horizontal x-axis on which both the source and the sink lie. (We are choosing the arbitrary constants in the expressions for the stream functions to be zero.)

Assuming the absolute values of the strengths of the source and the sink to be the same, and denoting the strength of the source by Q, we can write

$$\psi = -\frac{Q}{2\pi}(\theta_- - \theta_+) \tag{3-93}$$

Since the locus of points P for which the angle $\theta_+ - \theta_-$ between the radii from two fixed points is constant is a circle, the streamlines of the flow under consideration are circles passing through the source and the sink.

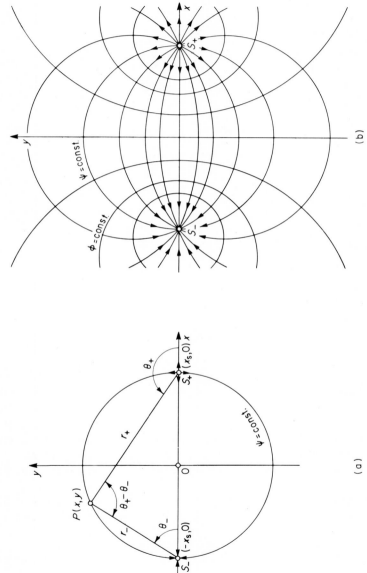

Fig. 3-21. A source-sink pair. (a) Construction of a streamline. (b) Streamlines and equipotential lines of a flow produced by a two-dimensional source-sink pair.

For the velocity potential we obtain in this case the expression

$$\phi = \frac{Q}{2\pi} \ln \frac{r_+}{r_-} + \text{const.} \tag{3-94}$$

where r_+ and r_- denote the magnitudes of the position radii of a point in the flow field from the source and sink respectively.

The streamlines and the equipotential lines for a flow produced by a two-dimensional source-sink pair are shown in Fig. 3-21b.

The expression for the stream function ψ can be transformed so that it involves the coordinates x, y, of a point in the flow field. This transformation will be utilized in the discussion of a doublet which follows. Denoting by x_s and $-x_s$ the values of the coordinate x corresponding to the sink and source respectively, we can write

$$\tan \theta_- = \frac{y}{x + x_s} \quad \text{and} \quad \tan \theta_+ = \frac{y}{x - x_s}$$

Therefore

$$\tan (\theta_- - \theta_+) = \frac{\tan \theta_- - \tan \theta_+}{1 + \tan \theta_- \tan \theta_+} = \frac{-2y\, x_s}{x^2 + y^2 - x_s^2}$$

and we can write

$$\tan \left(-\frac{2\pi\psi}{Q} \right) = \frac{-2y\, x_s}{x^2 + y^2 - x_s^2} \tag{3-95}$$

in view of Eq. 3-93. This equation can be transformed to

$$x^2 + \left[y + x_s \cot \left(-\frac{2\pi\psi}{Q} \right) \right]^2 = x_s^2 \csc^2 \left(-\frac{2\pi\psi}{Q} \right) \tag{3-96}$$

A corresponding equation can be derived for the velocity potential ϕ.

Two-Dimensional Doublet. A *doublet*, or a *dipole*, is defined as a point in the flow field resulting from a source-sink pair of equal (magnitudes of) strength obtained in the limit by allowing them to approach each other while keeping constant the product of the magnitude of their strength and the distance between them. The line on which lie the source and the sink from which a doublet is formed is known as the *axis of the doublet*. Its positive direction is from the sink toward the source (which corresponds to the positive direction of the x-axis in Fig. 3-22). The magnitude of the *strength of a doublet*, μ, is defined as the product of the strength Q of the source (or the magnitude of the strength of the sink) and the distance between them. If the source and the sink were initially separated by a distance $2x_s$, then the magnitude of the strength of the resulting doublet is $\mu = 2x_s Q$. The strength of a doublet can be positive or negative. It is positive when the positive direction of its axis corresponds to the positive direction of the x-axis (from which angle θ is measured.)

The expression for the stream function of a two-dimensional doublet shown in Fig. 3-22 [obtained from a sink located at $(-x_s, 0)$ and a source

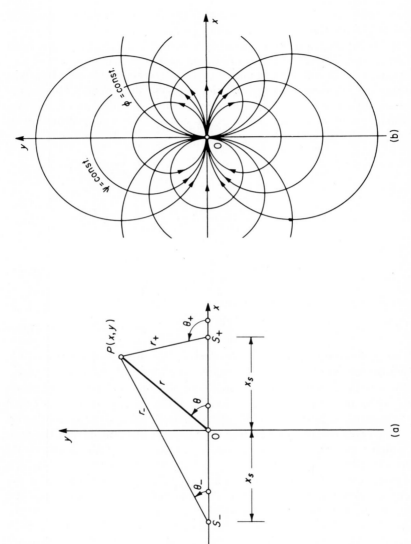

FIG. 3-22. A two-dimensional doublet. (a) Construction of a streamline. (b) Streamlines and equipotential lines of a flow produced by a two-dimensional doublet.

located at $(x_s, 0)$ in the (x, y) plane] can be derived as follows: For the source-sink pair shown in Fig. 3-22a we have

$$\psi = -\frac{Q}{2\pi} \tan^{-1} \left(\frac{-2x_s r \sin \theta}{r^2 - x_s^2} \right)$$

in view of Eq. 3-95, because $x^2 + y^2 = r^2$ and $y = r \sin \theta$ where r denotes the magnitude of the position radius of a point $P(x, y)$ in the flow field from the origin of the x, y coordinates and θ denotes its angle of inclination measured from the positive x-axis. For x_s tending to zero, we can substitute the value of the angle for the value of the tangent of the angle in the last equation. As a result, we obtain

$$\psi = \frac{Q}{2\pi} \frac{2x_s r \sin \theta}{r^2 - x_s^2}$$

which simplifies further to

$$\psi = \frac{2x_s Q}{2\pi} \frac{\sin \theta}{r}$$

$$= \frac{\mu}{2\pi} \frac{\sin \theta}{r} \tag{3-97}$$

Note that, in general, we have

$$\psi = \frac{\mu}{2\pi} \frac{\sin \theta}{r} + \text{const.} \tag{3-97a}$$

This is the expression for the stream function ψ of a flow produced by a two-dimensional doublet in an initially stationary incompressible fluid. The streamlines form circles which touch the x-axis at point O (as shown in Fig. 3-22b). Like the source and sink flows, this flow is irrotational and there exists the velocity potential ϕ. The expression for the velocity potential of a two-dimensional doublet can be derived as follows: We have $r_+^2 = (x - x_s)^2 + y^2$ and $r_-^2 = (x + x_s)^2 + y^2$, and, for a source-sink pair

$$\phi = \frac{Q}{2\pi} \ln \frac{r_+}{r_-} + \text{const.} = \frac{Q}{2\pi} \ln \left[\frac{(x - x_s)^2 + y^2}{(x + x_s)^2 + y^2} \right]^{1/2} + \text{const.}$$

or

$$\phi = \frac{Q}{2\pi} \left(-\frac{1}{2} \right) \ln \frac{r^2 + 2rx_s \cos \theta + x_s^2}{r^2 - 2rx_s \cos \theta + x_s^2} + \text{const.}$$

since $x = r \cos \theta$. For x_s tending to zero we can write

$$\phi = -\frac{Q}{2\pi} \left(\frac{1}{2} \right) \ln \frac{1 + \dfrac{2x_s \cos \theta}{r}}{1 - \dfrac{2x_s \cos \theta}{r}} + \text{const.}$$

Using the series expansion

$$\ln \frac{1 + x}{1 - x} = 2 \left(x + \frac{x^3}{3} + \cdots \right)$$

with $-1 < x < 1$, and retaining only the first term, we obtain

$$\phi = -\frac{Q}{2\pi}\frac{2x_s \cos\theta}{r} + \text{const.}$$

$$= -\frac{\mu}{2\pi}\frac{\cos\theta}{r} + \text{const.} \qquad (3\text{-}98)$$

The equipotential lines are also circles; they touch the y-axis at point O as shown in Fig. 3-22b.

The expressions for the velocity components of the flow produced by a doublet in an initially stationary incompressible fluid can be obtained either from Eq. 3-79 or Eq. 3-53. We have

$$V_\theta = -\frac{\partial\psi}{\partial r} = \frac{\partial\phi}{r\partial\theta} = \frac{\mu}{2\pi}\frac{\sin\theta}{r^2} \qquad (3\text{-}99)$$

and

$$V_r = \frac{\partial\psi}{r\partial\theta} = \frac{\partial\phi}{\partial r} = \frac{\mu}{2\pi}\frac{\cos\theta}{r^2} \qquad (3\text{-}100)$$

Two-Dimensional Source in a Uniform Stream. Consider the flow (of unit depth) resulting from combination of a uniform stream and a two-dimensional source flow, as shown in Fig. 3-23. The stream function of the combined flow is

$$\psi = -U_\infty y + \frac{Q}{2\pi}\theta = -U_\infty r\sin\theta + \frac{Q}{2\pi}\theta \qquad (0 \le \theta \le 2\pi) \quad (3\text{-}101)$$

where U_∞ denotes the speed of the uniform stream, if we assume the uniform flow to be in the direction of the negative x-axis. This follows from Eqs. 3-83 and 3-89, if we choose the arbitrary constant in the expression of the stream function of the combined flow to be zero.

The streamline $\psi = 0$ in the flow under consideration is in this case given by

$$\frac{\theta}{\pi} = \frac{2U_\infty}{Q}y = \frac{2U_\infty}{Q}r\sin\theta$$

It is indicated in Fig. 3-23a. The point P on the x-axis at which the flow velocity becomes equal to zero (as a result of cancellation of the velocity of the uniform stream and the velocity of the source flow) is known as a *stagnation point*. The value of the coordinate x of the stagnation point can be obtained either from the last equation evaluated for $\theta \to 0$, or by writing an expression for the resultant flow speed at the x-axis:

$$-U_\infty + \frac{Q}{2\pi x_P} = 0$$

Using either method we find that $x_P = Q/2\pi U_\infty$. For $\theta = \pm\pi$, $r = \infty$ and the value of y of the streamline $\psi = 0$ attains its maximum equal to $\pm Q/2U_\infty$.

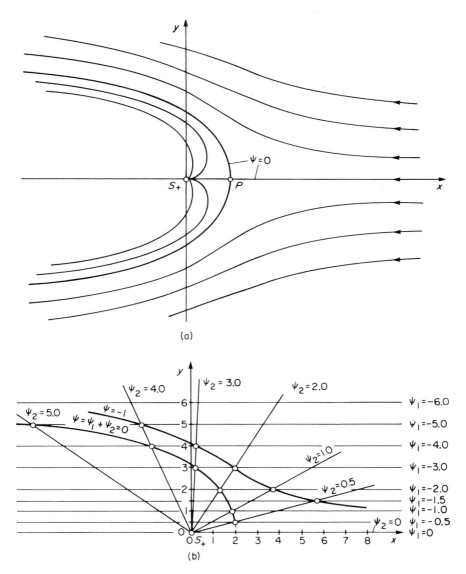

FIG. 3-23. (a) Potential flow resulting from combination of a uniform flow with
a two-dimensional source flow. (b) Construction of streamlines.

Figure 3-23a shows a number of streamlines for the flow under consideration. The method used in their determination is shown in Fig.
3-23b. The flow pattern shown corresponds to the chosen values $Q = 4\pi$
(unit of length)^2/(unit of time) and $U_\infty = 1$ (unit of length)/(unit of time).

Any of the streamlines can be considered to represent a contour of a solid body around which flows a nonviscous (that is, perfect) fluid. This is so because such flow is irrotational everywhere; in such flow the fluid slips freely along material surfaces. If we choose the streamline $\psi = 0$ to represent the contour of a (long) body perpendicular to the (x, y) plane, then the internal streamlines shown in Fig. 3-23a cease to exist. The point P represents the stagnation line on the body.

The expressions for the components of the fluid velocity for the flow under consideration studied in a rectangular cartesian coordinate system (in which $\mathbf{V} = u\mathbf{i} + v\mathbf{j}$), are

$$u = \frac{\partial \psi}{\partial y} = -U_\infty + \frac{Q}{2\pi} \frac{\partial \theta}{\partial y} = -U_\infty + \frac{Q}{2\pi} \frac{\cos \theta}{r} \qquad (3\text{-}102)$$

because $\partial \theta / \partial y = \cos \theta / r$ (see Fig. 3-24a), and

$$v = -\frac{\partial \psi}{\partial x} = -\frac{Q}{2\pi} \frac{\partial \theta}{\partial x} = \frac{Q}{2\pi} \frac{\sin \theta}{r} \qquad (3\text{-}103)$$

because $\partial \theta / \partial x = -\sin \theta / r$ (see Fig. 3-24b).

For the (circumferential and radial) components of the flow velocity we have expressions

$$V_\theta = -\frac{\partial \psi}{\partial r} = U_\infty \sin \theta \qquad (3\text{-}104)$$

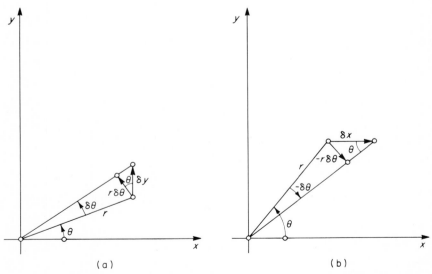

FIG. 3-24. Derivation of relationships involving changes in the angle θ and the corresponding changes in the coordinate y and x.

and

$$V_r = \frac{1}{r} \frac{\partial \psi}{\partial \theta} = -U_\infty \cos \theta + \frac{Q}{2\pi r} \tag{3-105}$$

These are the component of the flow velocity in a circular cylindrical co-ordinate system (in which $\mathbf{V} = V_r \mathbf{u}_r + V_\theta \mathbf{u}_\theta$).

The velocity potential of the flow under consideration is given by

$$\phi = -U_\infty x + \frac{Q}{2\pi} \ln r$$

$$= -U_\infty r \cos \theta + \frac{Q}{2\pi} \ln r \tag{3-106}$$

This example is one illustration of the usefulness of the artificial concept of a source. By considering a source in a uniform stream we learned about the velocity field in a potential flow (of an incompressible fluid) past a long blunt-nosed body. We can consider that we have only imagined the existence of the source.

Two-Dimensional Doublet in a Uniform Stream. A number of stream-lines of the flow obtained by combining a uniform flow with a two-dimensional doublet are shown in Fig. 3-25. If we identify the streamline denoted arbitrarily as $\psi = 0$ as a material surface, this flow pattern can be considered to represent the potential flow of an incompressible perfect fluid past an infinitely long circular cylinder placed in a uniform stream with its axis perpendicular to the direction of flow of the uniform stream.

The expression for the stream function of the combined flow (with the

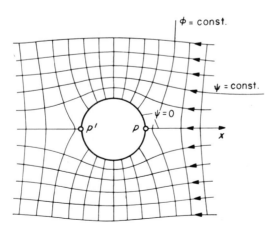

FIG. 3-25. Streamlines and equipotential lines of a potential incompressible flow resulting from a combination of a uniform flow with a two-dimensional doublet.

$\psi = 0$ streamline as shown in Fig. 3-25) is

$$\psi = -U_\infty r \sin \theta + \frac{\mu}{2\pi} \frac{\sin \theta}{r} \qquad (3\text{-}107)$$

if we assume the uniform flow to be in the direction of the negative x-axis, and the doublet corresponding to that shown in Fig. 3-22, or

$$\psi = \sin \theta \left(-U_\infty r + \frac{\mu}{2\pi r} \right) \qquad (3\text{-}107a)$$

The equation of the streamline $\psi = 0$ is therefore

$$\sin \theta \left(-U_\infty r + \frac{\mu}{2\pi r} \right) = 0$$

which is satisfied by $\theta = 0$, $\theta = \pi$, and $r_{\psi=0} = (\mu/2\pi U_\infty)^{1/2}$. Putting $r_{\psi=0} = a$ for convenience of notation, we can rewrite Eq. 3-107a in the form

$$\psi = -U_\infty \left(r - \frac{a^2}{r} \right) \sin \theta \qquad (3\text{-}107b)$$

The expressions for the circumferential and radial velocity components are

$$V_\theta = -\frac{\partial \psi}{\partial r} = U_\infty \sin \theta \left(1 + \frac{a^2}{r^2} \right)$$

and

$$V_r = \frac{\partial \psi}{r \partial \theta} = -U_\infty \cos \theta \left(1 - \frac{a^2}{r^2} \right)$$

(Note that the flow speed $V = \sqrt{V_\theta^2 + V_r^2}$.)

For the surface of the cylinder, since $r = a$ there, we obtain

$$\left. \begin{array}{l} (V_\theta)_{r=a} = 2U_\infty \sin \theta \\ (V_r)_{r=a} = 0 \end{array} \right\} \qquad (3\text{-}108)$$

There are two stagnation points P and P' in the (x, y) plane. [They correspond to $\theta = 0$ deg and 180 deg, since $(V_\theta)_{r=a} = (V)_{r=a} = 0$ there.] These points correspond to stagnation lines on the surface of the cylinder. The maximum flow velocity on the surface of the cylinder in this (potential) flow is $(V_\theta)_{max} = 2U_\infty$. It occurs at $\theta = \pm 90$ deg.

The expression for the velocity potential for this flow is

$$\phi = -U_\infty x - \frac{\mu}{2\pi} \frac{\cos \theta}{r}$$

$$= -U_\infty \left(r + \frac{a^2}{r} \right) \cos \theta \qquad (3\text{-}109)$$

Combined Two-Dimensional Doublet with a Free Vortex in a Uniform Stream. Superposition of a free vortex on a two-dimensional doublet, and additional combination with a uniform flow results in the following expression for the stream function of the resultant incompressible flow

$$\psi = -U_\infty r \sin\theta + \frac{\mu}{2\pi}\frac{\sin\theta}{r} - \frac{\Gamma}{2\pi}\ln\left(\frac{r}{a}\right) \qquad (3\text{-}110)$$

For $\Gamma = 0$ the above equation reduces to Eq. 3-107. The streamline $\psi = 0$ corresponds to the circle of radius $a = (\mu/2\pi U_\infty)^{1/2}$. The uniform flow is in the direction of the negative x-axis, the positive direction of the axis of the doublet corresponds to the positive direction of the x-axis (like for the doublet shown in Fig. 3-22), and the free vortex corresponds to that shown in Fig. 3-20 (that is, the vortex motion is counterclockwise).

Figure 3-26 shows some of the streamlines of this fluid motion.

If we consider the circular streamline to represent a cylinder, then this motion can be considered to represent the potential (that is, irrotational)

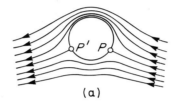

(a)

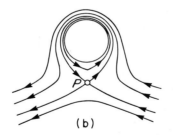

(b)

FIG. 3-26. Streamlines of a potential incompressible flow resulting from a combination of a uniform flow with a two-dimensional free vortex superimposed on a doublet.

motion of a perfect fluid past a cylinder with an added counterclockwise circulation Γ. Introducing the radius of the cylinder $a = r_{\psi=0} = (\mu/2\pi U_\infty)^{1/2}$, we can write

$$\psi = -U_\infty \sin\theta\left(r - \frac{a^2}{r}\right) - \frac{\Gamma}{2\pi}\ln\left(\frac{r}{a}\right) \qquad (3\text{-}111)$$

The expression for the circumferential velocity component V_θ at the surface of the cylinder ($V_r = 0$ there) becomes

$$(V_\theta)_{r=a} = -\left(\frac{\partial \psi}{\partial r}\right)_{r=a} = 2U_\infty \sin \theta + \frac{\Gamma}{2\pi a} \tag{3-112}$$

Therefore the stagnation points P and P', as long as they are on the surface of the cylinder, are located at angles θ which satisfy equation $(V_\theta)_{r=a} = (V)_{r=a} = 0$, that is, equation

$$\sin \theta = -\frac{\Gamma}{4\pi a U_\infty} \tag{3-113}$$

Two stagnation points on the surface of the cylinder, points P and P', are shown in Fig. 3-26a. When $\Gamma = 4\pi a U_\infty$, $\sin \theta = -1$ and the stagnation points coincide at the bottom of the cylinder. For $\Gamma > 4\pi a U_\infty$ the stagnation point in the flow does not lie on the surface of the cylinder; it is directly beneath it, as shown in Fig. 3-26b. There is a circulation of the fluid in the space between the cylinder and the side of the stream tube which passes through the stagnation point and which encloses the cylinder.

Figure 3-26 shows that the streamlines, which are drawn for approximately equal increments $\Delta \psi$, are much more closely spaced above than below the cylinder. As a result, the flow speed is larger above than below the cylinder. We shall return to the discussion of this flow pattern in Chapter 5.

Note that the analyses of various simple potential flows of an incompressible fluid made in this section represent studies of only the kinematics of fluid flow. For that reason they tell us nothing about the variation of the pressure in the flow fields considered. This information can be obtained by studying the dynamics of fluid flow (with the aid of the principle of conservation of linear momentum).

Apparent Mass. The velocity potential of the flow produced by a very long circular cylinder moving with a speed U_∞ in direction perpendicular to its axis in an incompressible perfect fluid of infinite extent which is at rest at infinity is given by

$$\phi = -\frac{\mu}{2\pi} \frac{\cos \theta}{r}$$

This equation is obtained from Eq. 3-109 by subtracting from it the term $-U_\infty x$ which is equivalent to superimposing velocity U_∞ on the flow illustrated in Fig. 3-25. As we have shown, the radius a of the cylinder is related to the constant μ by

$$\mu = 2\pi a^2 U_\infty$$

and therefore we can write

$$\phi = -a^2 U_\infty \frac{\cos \theta}{r}$$

As a result, we obtain the following expressions for the components of the flow velocity:

$$V_\theta = \frac{\partial \phi}{r \partial \theta} = a^2 U_\infty \frac{\sin \theta}{r^2}$$

$$V_r = \frac{\partial \phi}{\partial r} = a^2 U_\infty \frac{\cos \theta}{r^2}$$

$$V_w = 0$$

Since

$$V^2 = V_\theta^2 + V_r^2 + V_w^2 = a^4 U_\infty^2 \left(\frac{\sin^2 \theta}{r^4} + \frac{\cos^2 \theta}{r^4} \right)$$

$$= \frac{a^4 U_\infty^2}{r^4}$$

the kinetic energy of the fluid per unit depth is

$$\frac{1}{2} \rho \int_0^{2\pi} \int_a^\infty V^2 r d\theta \, dr = \frac{1}{2} \rho a^4 U_\infty^2 \int_a^\infty \left(\int_0^{2\pi} d\theta \right) \frac{dr}{r^3}$$

$$= \pi \rho a^4 U_\infty^2 \int_a^\infty \frac{dr}{r^3}$$

$$= \frac{\rho \pi a^2 U_\infty^2}{2}$$

$$= (\text{apparent mass}) \frac{1}{2} U_\infty^2$$

The effective mass of the moving long cylinder is therefore its own mass and the apparent mass which represents the mass of the fluid displaced by the circular cylinder. This indicates that objects move through a fluid with an increased interia. In general, for cylinders the apparent mass depends on the direction of motion. It can be represented by the expression

Apparent mass = K (mass of fluid displaced)

where, for simple objects, in general, the coefficient $K < 1$. For a sphere, the apparent mass is $\frac{2}{3} \pi \rho a^3$; that is, $K = \frac{1}{2}$.

3-11. APPROXIMATE METHODS OF DETERMINING STREAMLINES AND EQUIPOTENTIAL LINES

In our previous discussion we showed that in potential (that is, irrotational) flows of incompressible fluids the velocity potential ϕ obeys Laplace's equation

$$\nabla^2 \phi = 0 \qquad\qquad [3\text{-}54]$$

We further showed that in such flows the stream function ψ also obeys Laplace's equation

$$\nabla^2\psi = 0 \qquad\qquad [3\text{-}82]$$

provided that it can be introduced. Since the flow velocity $\mathbf{V}$ and the velocity potential ϕ are related by equation

$$\mathbf{V} = \nabla\phi \qquad\qquad [3\text{-}53]$$

we concluded (in Sec. 3-7) that the streamlines are normal to the equipotential surfaces. Therefore, in two-dimensional flows the lines of constant stream function (which represent streamlines) are normal to the equipotential lines. An inspection of the points of intersection of the ψ = constant lines with the ϕ = constant lines shown in the illustrations of simple flow patterns discussed in Sec. 3-10 shows agreement with this statement.

The exact analytical solutions of Laplace's equations for the stream function ψ and the velocity potential ϕ in potential flows of incompressible fluids exist only for a number of relatively simple flows. (The simplest of them were discussed in the last section.) For more complex flows, especially those which involve arbitrary (perhaps even geometrically irregular) boundary conditions, the analytical methods of solution (of Eqs. 3-54 and 3-82) are often quite difficult. An introduction to analysis of some such flows using the complex variables is given in Chapter 6.

Often we require only the knowledge of the approximate solution of a potential flow problem. In such case we determine the streamlines and the equipotential lines in the flow field either graphically, or using electrical analog field plotter. The net of ψ = constant and ϕ = constant lines of a potential flow is usually referred to as a *flux plot*.

In this section we will concern ourselves with the approximate methods of determining streamlines and equipotential lines in two-dimensional incompressible irrotational flows.

Graphical Method. In this method of solution of Laplace's equations for the velocity potential ϕ and the stream function ψ we usually decide, quite arbitrarily, to space all streamlines by the same increments $\Delta\psi$ and all potential lines by the same increments $\Delta\phi$. In addition, we usually take $\Delta\psi = \Delta\phi$.

If we denote the differential arc length along a streamline by ds and the differential arc length along an equipotential line by dn, as shown in Fig. 3-27, then we have

$$\mathbf{V} = V\mathbf{u}_s = \nabla\phi = \frac{\partial\phi}{\partial s}\mathbf{u}_s$$

where $\mathbf{u}_s$ denotes a unit vector having direction of the streamline at the point under consideration, or

$$V = \frac{\partial\phi}{\partial s} = \frac{d\phi}{ds} \qquad\qquad (3\text{-}114)$$

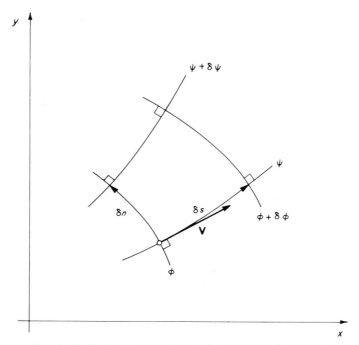

FIG. 3-27. Fluid element bounded by streamlines and equipotential lines.

This is so because the flow velocity is normal to the equipotential line, and therefore $\partial\phi/\partial n = 0$. In addition, we have

$$V = \frac{\partial\psi}{\partial n} = \frac{d\psi}{dn} \qquad (3\text{-}115)$$

because $\partial\psi/\partial s = 0$ since the velocity component normal to the streamline at a point is zero.

As a result of our choice of $\Delta\psi = \Delta\phi$ in the flux plot we have, therefore, for the increments $\Delta\psi$ and $\Delta\phi$ tending to zero

$$\frac{\Delta\psi}{\Delta\phi} = \frac{\Delta n}{\Delta s} = 1$$

which indicates that the net of the ψ = const. and ϕ = constant lines is one of squares in the limit as the size of the squares tends to zero.

Thus we follow two rules in the graphical flux plotting:

(a) the general rule that the streamlines are normal to the equipotential lines, and

(b) the arbitrary rule, which follows from our decision to space the streamlines and the equipotential lines by equal increments, that the net of the ψ = constant and ϕ = constant lines is, in the limit, one of squares ($\Delta n = \Delta s$).

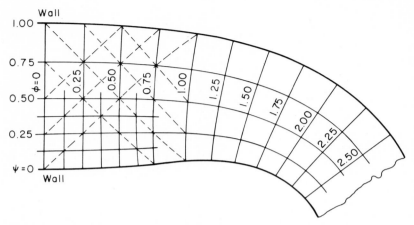

FIG. 3-28. Flux plot for a two-dimensional incompressible and irrotational channel flow.

When making a flux plot we usually start with a relatively large net and progressively decrease its size, as shown in Fig. 3-28. We help ourselves in the plotting by sketching in a diagonal network (shown with broken lines in Fig. 3-28) which is also an orthogonal network.

Once a flux plot is finished, we can estimate the flow speed at various points in the flow field using the relations

$$V \simeq \frac{\Delta\phi}{\Delta s} \tag{3-116}$$

or

$$V \simeq \frac{\Delta\psi}{\Delta n} \tag{3-117}$$

These relations indicate that in the flow regions in which the equipotential lines and streamlines are closely spaced, the flow speed is higher than in the regions in which they are widely spaced. [Note that these relations which follow from Eqs. 3-114 and 3-115, are generally valid, (although the above conclusion is not). That is, they are valid even if in the flux plot we do not space the streamlines and the equipotential lines by equal increments.] For the ratio of the flow speeds at different points in the flow region we can write

$$\frac{V}{V_1} \simeq \frac{\Delta s_1}{\Delta s} \simeq \frac{\Delta n_1}{\Delta n} \tag{3-118}$$

if the streamlines and the equipotential lines are spaced by equal increments (that is, if $\Delta\phi = \Delta\psi$).

Since the size of the squares in a flux plot is finite, they may turn out to be rather odd-looking. We often refer to them as "curvilinear squares." If we look closely at Fig. 3-25 in which equal increments between the values of the stream function ψ and velocity potential ϕ are employed, we notice that we may even encounter five-sided "squares" unless a very small net is used. In addition, at stagnation points and at points where the flow speed becomes infinitely large, at which points (known as singular points) the streamline changes its direction abruptly, the potential line intersects the streamline so that it halves the angle by which the streamline turns. This fact is illustrated in Figs. 3-29, 3-30, and 3-31.

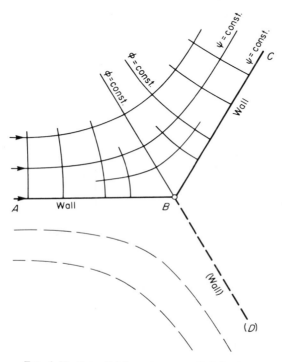

FIG. 3-29. Potential flow along a wall deflecting abruptly toward the flow.

Figure 3-29 shows a sketch of a potential flow pattern (that is, of streamlines and equipotential lines) in which the wall along which the fluid flows deflects abruptly toward the flow. In this case a stagnation point (which is a point at which the flow velocity relative to the wall is zero) forms at the point of the abrupt change of the direction of the wall, point B. The fluid decelerates along wall A–B, and accelerates along the wall B–C. Note that this flow net also corresponds to a symmetrical flow against the wall C–B–D, as indicated in Fig. 3-29 with broken lines.

Figure 3-30 illustrates the streamlines and the equipotential lines near a stagnation point on a blunt body in an irrotational flow.

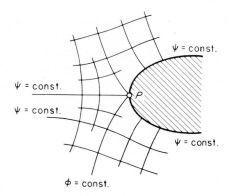

FIG. 3-30. Streamlines and equipotential lines near a stagnation
point in an irrotational flow.

Figure 3-31 illustrates a flux plot for a potential flow along a wall
which deflects abruptly away from the flow. At the vertex *B* (where the
radius of curvature of the wall is zero) the flow speed in a potential flow
would become infinite. The fluid is accelerated along the wall *A–B*, and
decelerated along the wall *B–C*. [In a flow of a real fluid, a separation of
flow may be expected downstream of point *B*. This separation would
change appreciably the flow pattern from that of a potential flow there.
In general, the potential flow analysis gives results which agree reasonably
with those observed in the flows of real fluids only for accelerating flows.
Such is not the case, however, when deceleration of flow occurs because,

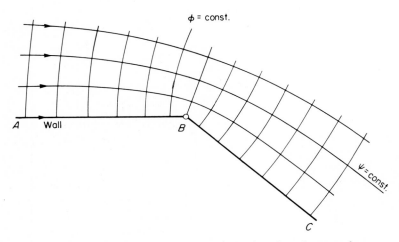

FIG. 3-31. Potential flow along a wall deflecting abruptly away from
the flow.

in a flow of a real fluid separation of the fluid from the wall takes place when the amount of deceleration is large enough. The point of separation of a real fluid from a wall depends, for a given decelerating flow, on whether the boundary layer is laminar or turbulent, the laminar boundary layer separating sooner than the turbulent boundary layer. The separation of flow was already briefly discussed in Chapter 1, (see Figs. 1-11, 1-12, and 1-16).]

Figure 3-32 shows the flux plot for a potential flow of an incompressible fluid in a two-dimensional channel. Note the rapid deceleration of the

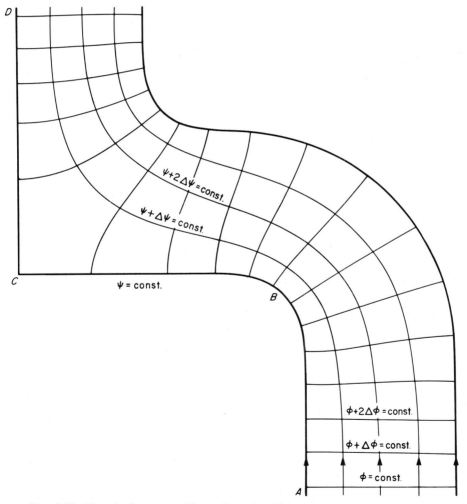

FIG. 3-32. Flux plot for a potential two-dimensional incompressible flow in a channel.

flow along the part *B–C* of the wall. Compare this figure with Fig. 1-12 showing the flow of a real fluid in a similar channel in which separation of flow occurs. This separation of flow, which starts in the vicinity of point *B* shown in Fig. 3-22 (a little downstream of it), affects significantly the velocity distribution in the flow field, making it differ substantially from that which Fig. 3-22 would indicate.

Figure 3-33 shows a flux plot for a two-dimensional potential flow of an incompressible fluid through a channel. Figure 3-34 shows the magnitudes and directions of the flow velocity at various locations in the flow field. Observe the existence of high flow velocities at the inner wall of the bend compared to those near the outer wall. Since the flow is irrotational, there is no deceleration of the fluid to zero velocity at the walls of the

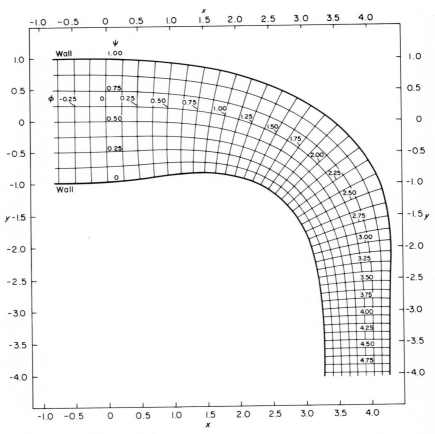

Fig. 3-33. Streamlines and equipotential lines in a two-dimensional potential flow of an incompressible fluid. (After J. D. Stanitz [10].)

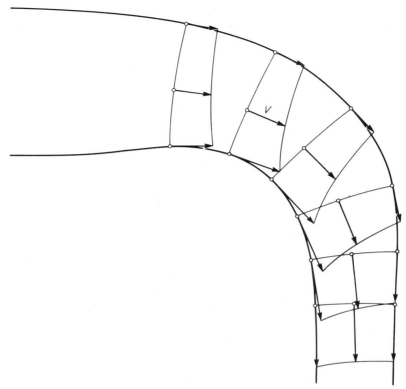

FIG. 3-34. Flow velocity at various points in the flow field
shown in Fig. 3-33.

channel such as would exist in a flow of a real fluid, and the fluid is
imagined to glide frictionlessly along the walls.

Electrical Analog Method. Since in the field involving steady electric
currents in a conducting medium the electric potential satisfies Laplace's
equation, we can use a geometrically similar electrical system to obtain
flux plot for a given flow problem.

Figure 3-35 illustrates the application of an electrical analog field
plotter to obtain streamlines of the flow field illustrated in Fig. 3-33.
The two-dimensional channel is represented by electrically conducting
"Teledeltos" paper (made of uniform thickness and therefore having
uniform resistance) cut to a shape which is geometrically similar to that
of the channel. The inner boundary of the solid conductor (usually dried
out silver paint) corresponds to the walls of the duct. The sides of the
"Teledeltos" paper which correspond to the inlet and exit from the duct
are insulated. In the example shown, the voltage (electrical potential)
drop between the solid conductors was divided into four equal parts. The

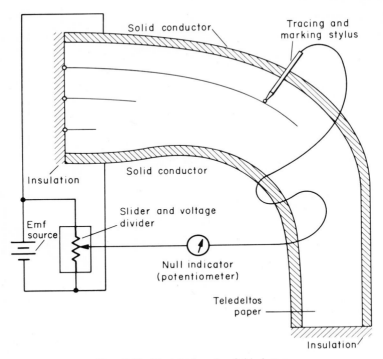

FIG. 3-35. Electrical-analog field plotter.

lines of constant electrical potential correspond in this case to the stream-lines in the flow field. To obtain the equipotential lines, the locations of the solid conductors and insulations should be interchanged.

If the flux plot obtained is made so that the streamlines and the equi-potential lines are spaced by unequal increments, the flow speed at a given location in the flow field can still be obtained from Eq. 3-116 (or Eq. 3-117). However, Eq. 3-118 cannot then be used.

Numerical Method. In addition to the methods just discussed, the solution of a potential flow problem can be obtained by solving numer-ically the Laplace equation. One of the popular numerical methods is known as the *relaxation method.* It is a method of finite differences, in which the differential equations are approximated by algebraic equations. A discussion of these methods can be found in Refs. 11, 12, 13, and 14.

Concluding Remarks. Observe that, since for the flows considered both the stream function ψ and the velocity potential ϕ obey Laplace's equation, a flux plot in which the ψ-lines are taken as the ϕ-lines, and the ϕ-lines as the ψ-lines also represents a flow pattern (although often such an exchange may not produce a physically meaningful flow.

In a flow of a real fluid, a part of the fluid may be in a motion which can be considered as irrotational, while another part may be in a rotational motion. The velocity potential ϕ exists only in the region of flow which is irrotational. On the other hand, as we showed in Sec. 3-9, the stream function ψ can exist in both rotational and irrotational fluid motions.

3-12. PATH LINES; STREAK LINES

A *path line* represents the path of a particular fluid element. At any instant, the path lines are tangent to the streamlines. In a steady flow, the path lines coincide with the streamlines. (In general, there is very little use for the concept of streamlines in unsteady flows.)

If a function f is constant along a path line, this fact can be expressed by writing

$$\frac{Df}{Dt} = \frac{\partial f}{\partial t} + \mathbf{V} \cdot \nabla f = 0 \qquad (3-119)$$

A *streak line* is defined as a line formed by the fluid elements which pass through a given location in the flow field. A streak line can be made visible by injecting a dye into the fluid at the given location. In a steady flow, the streak lines coincide with the path lines and the streamlines.

Construction of Path Lines. Figure 3-23a can be considered to represent a potential fluid flow past a long blunt-nosed object (drawn with a thick black line) immersed in a uniform stream. This flow is steady when studied in the reference frame of the object. The same flow pattern, but unsteady results when we consider the motion with a constant velocity (of equal magnitude but opposite direction to that of the uniform stream considered previously) of the object in the fluid which is (initially) stationary (that is, when we study the flow in the reference frame of the uniform stream). The instantaneous streamlines in this unsteady flow correspond to those of the source flow with the source located at point S_+. They move with the object, as shown in Fig. 3-36 which illustrates the construction of a path line in the unsteady flow produced by the moving object. The object, which moves with a constant speed U_∞ is shown in Fig. 3-36 at five instances: t_1, $t_2 = t_1 + \Delta t$, $t_3 = t_1 + 2\Delta t$, $t_4 = t_1 + 3\Delta t$, and $t_5 = t_1 + 4\Delta t$. During each time interval Δt the object (and the instantaneous streamlines) moves a distance $c = U_\infty \Delta t$. At every instant the direction of motion of the chosen fluid element corresponds to the direction of the streamline passing through it. As time goes on the fluid element finds itself on different streamlines. Since the flow speed in the flow field is, at every instant, inversely proportional to the distance from

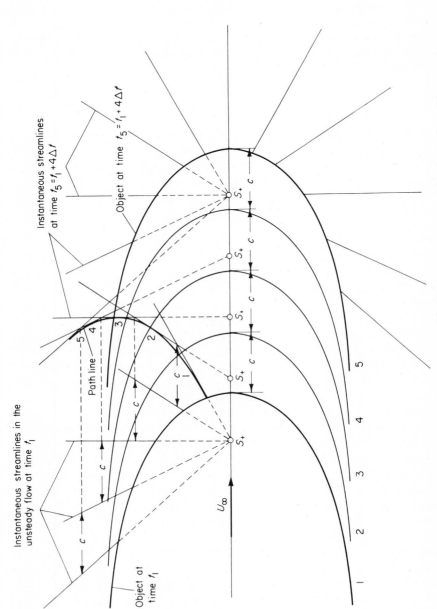

FIG. 3-36. Construction of a path line in an unsteady two-dimensional flow produced by the motion with a constant speed of a long object.

the corresponding point S_+, the distances traveled by the fluid element in each time interval Δt decrease progressively with time.

A streak line (in an unsteady flow) which passes through a given point in space can, at a given instant, be determined by finding the end points at that time of the path lines of the fluid elements which have previously passed through the chosen point.

3-13. KINEMATIC BOUNDARY CONDITIONS

When a fluid flows along a solid surface then, as long as the surface is impervious to the fluid and there is no cavitation present, the normal velocity of the fluid relative to the surface must be equal to zero in order to preserve the contact between the fluid and the surface. Denoting by **n** the unit vector normal to the surface, and by **V** the fluid velocity, we have therefore

$$\mathbf{n} \cdot \mathbf{V} = 0$$

at the surface.

For real fluids treated as continua we have, in addition, a physical condition on the tangential velocity relative to a solid surface which requires no slip of the fluid at the wall. This condition cannot be satisfied by an irrotational flow.

REFERENCES

1. C. Truesdell, *The Kinematics of Vorticity.* Bloomington: Indiana U. P., 1954.

2. J. Serrin, "Mathematical Principles of Classical Fluid Mechanics," in S. Flügge (ed.), *Encyclopedia of Physics.* Berlin: Springer, 1959, Vol. VIII/1.

3. A. Sommerfeld, *Mechanics of Deformable Bodies.* New York: Academic, 1950.

4. L. Prandtl and O. G. Tietjens, *Fundamentals of Hydro- and Aeromechanics.* (First published in 1934.) New York: Dover, 1957.

5. S. Goldstein, *Lectures on Fluid Mechanics*, Vol. II of *Lectures in Applied Mathematics.* London: Interscience, 1960.

6. R. Aris, *Vectors, Tensors, and the Basic Equations of Fluid Mechanics.* Englewood Cliffs, N.J.: Prentice-Hall, 1962.

7. J. A. Owczarek, *Fundamentals of Gas Dynamics.* Scranton, Pa.: International Textbook, 1964.

8. W. J. Duncan, A. S. Thom, and A. D. Young, *Mechanics of Fluids.* London: Arnold, 1960.

9. Theodor von Kármán, *Aerodynamics.* Ithaca: Cornell U. P., 1954.

10. J. D. Stanitz, "Design of Two-Dimensional Channels with Prescribed Velocity Distributions along the Channel Walls," *NACA Report* 1115, 1953.

11. R. Southwell, *Relaxation Methods in Theoretical Physics.* Oxford: Oxford U. P., 1946.

12. D. N. de G. Allen, *Relaxation Methods*. New York: McGraw-Hill, 1954.

13. F. S. Shaw, *Relaxation Methods*. New York: Dover, 1953.

14. R. Southwell, "Relaxation Methods: A Retrospect," *Chartered Mechanical Engineer*, Vol. 1, No. 2 (February 1954).

15. J. L. Lumley, "Deformation of Continuous Media" (Film). Wilmette, Ill.: Encyclopaedia Britannica Films, 1963.

16. S. J. Kline, "Flow Visualization" (Film). Wilmette, Ill.: Encyclopaedia Britannica Films, 1963.

PROBLEMS

3-1. With the aid of Eq. A-57 prove that

$$\mathbf{V} \cdot \mathbf{\nabla} \, \mathbf{V} = (\mathbf{\nabla} \times \mathbf{V}) \times \mathbf{V} + \mathbf{\nabla} \left(\frac{V^2}{2} \right)$$

note that $\nabla (V^2/2) = \frac{1}{2} \nabla (\mathbf{V} \cdot \mathbf{V})$. (Sec. 3-5.)

3-2. In Sec. 3-6 we learned that the fluid velocity in the immediate neighborhood of a point P can be represented by the relation

$$\mathbf{V} = \mathbf{V}_P + d\mathbf{V} = \mathbf{V}_P + d\mathbf{r} \cdot (\mathbf{\nabla} \, \mathbf{V})_{\text{at } P} \qquad \text{[3-31]}$$

The expression for $\mathbf{\nabla}\mathbf{V}$, in a rectangular cartesian coordinate system in which $\mathbf{V} = u\mathbf{i} + v\mathbf{j} + w\mathbf{k}$, can be written in the form of Eq. 3-35.

For the purpose of an exercise, let us assume that the above relation is valid not only in the immediate neighborhood of a point P, but throughout a finite region around P. Let us further assume that the translational velocity of point P, $\mathbf{V}_P$, is equal to zero. Then we can write

$$\mathbf{V} = \mathbf{r} \cdot (\mathbf{\nabla} \, \mathbf{V})_{\text{at } P}$$

where $\mathbf{r} = x\mathbf{i} + y\mathbf{j} + z\mathbf{k}$ represents the position vector from point P. Using this relation determine the velocity field when (a) $\mathbf{\nabla}\mathbf{V} = \dfrac{\partial u}{\partial x}\mathbf{ii}$, (b) $\mathbf{\nabla}\mathbf{V} = \dfrac{\partial v}{\partial x}\mathbf{ij}$, (c) $\mathbf{\nabla}\mathbf{V} = \dfrac{1}{2}\left(\dfrac{\partial v}{\partial x} + \dfrac{\partial u}{\partial y}\right)\mathbf{ij} + \dfrac{1}{2}\left(\dfrac{\partial u}{\partial y} + \dfrac{\partial v}{\partial x}\right)\mathbf{ji}$, and (d) $\mathbf{\nabla}\mathbf{V} = \dfrac{1}{2}\left(\dfrac{\partial v}{\partial x} - \dfrac{\partial u}{\partial y}\right)\mathbf{ij} + \dfrac{1}{2}\left(\dfrac{\partial u}{\partial y} - \dfrac{\partial v}{\partial x}\right)\mathbf{ji}$. Illustrate these velocity fields in the (x, y) plane. [For cases (c) and (d) indicate the velocities of fluid elements lying on the x- and y-axes.] (Sec. 3-6.)

3-3. Derive the irrotationality conditions for a flow studied in a rectangular cartesian coordinate system by considering circulations taken in the positive sense around the boundaries of the oriented positive elements of area shown in the sketch. (An oriented positive element of area in a given coordinate system has its normal unit vector **n**, which orients it, pointing in the positive direction of the coordinate axis normal to the area element.) Subsequently, compare these irrotationality conditions with those obtained by expressing the irrotationality condition $\boldsymbol{\omega} = \mathbf{\nabla} \times \mathbf{V} = \mathbf{0}$ in a rectangular cartesian coordinate system. (Sec. 3-7.)

3-4. Derive the expression for the spatial form of the continuity equation in a circular cylindrical coordinate system considering the flux of $\rho\mathbf{V}$ out of a volume element as shown in the accompanying sketch. (Sec. 3-8.)

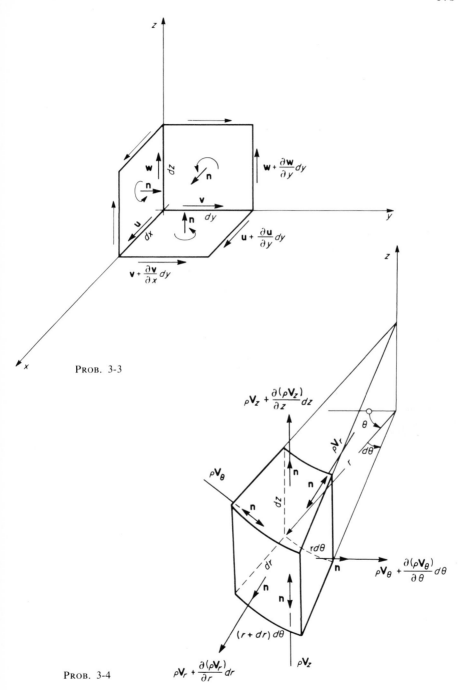

PROB. 3-3

PROB. 3-4

3-5. What is the expression for the velocity potential for a three-dimensional source flow? (Sec. 3-10.)

3-6. Show that the two-dimensional source flow is irrotational by considering the circulation about circuit $ABCD$ shown in Fig. 3-19. Make a similar proof for a circuit enclosing the source. (Sec. 3-10.)

3-7. By considering the circulation about the circuit $ABCD$ shown in Fig. 3-20, show that the flow induced by a free vortex is irrotational outside of the vortex. Further show that the circulation about an arbitrary circuit which encloses once the free vortex differs from zero, and is equal to $\Gamma = 2\pi r V_\theta$ = constant (since rV_θ = constant for a free vortex flow). (Sec. 3-10.)

3-8. Consider a two-dimensional free vortex motion. Draw a fluid element, which at some initial time has the form of a square whose two sides are perpendicular to a radius from the origin of the vortex, as shown in the sketch, in its initial position and after some small time interval Δt. By considering the motion of the initially perpendicular line segments connecting the nonadjacent angles of the fluid element, show that in this motion the fluid elements do not experience the motion of rotation (although they undergo distortion) and hence that this motion, outside of the origin, is irrotational. (Sec. 3-10.)

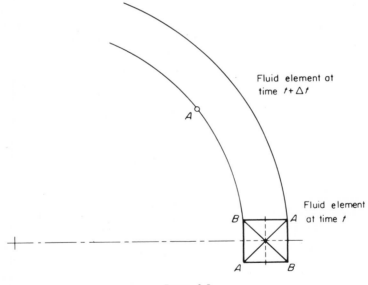

Fluid element at time $t + \Delta t$

Fluid element A at time t

PROB. 3-8

3-9. Derive Eqs. 3-102, 3-103, 3-104, and 3-105 using the expression for the velocity potential given by Eq. 3-106. (Sec. 3-10.)

3-10. Draw streamline $\psi = 0$ and a few external streamlines for a flow resulting from the combination of a uniform stream and a two-dimensional source-sink pair in an incompressible fluid. Assume that the uniform flow is in the direction of the negative x-axis and that its stream function $\psi = \psi_1 = 0$ for $y = 0$. The

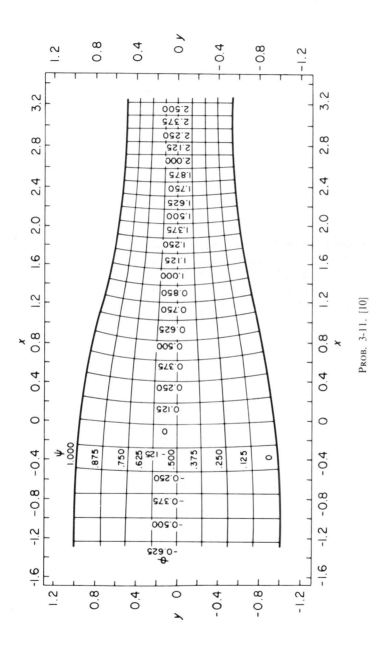

Prob. 3-11. [10]

coordinates of the source and the sink are $(2, 0)$ and $(-2, 0)$ respectively, and the expression for the stream function $\psi = \psi_2$ of the source-sink pair is given by Eq. 3-96. (The absolute values of $\psi = \psi_2$ should be limited to $0 \leq |\psi_2| \leq Q/4$ because of the nature of the function cosecant.) Further assume that $Q = 3\pi$ (unit of length)^2/(unit of time) and $U_x = 1$ (unit of length)/(unit of time). (The streamline $\psi = 0$ represents what is known as the *Rankine oval*.) (Sec. 3-10.)

3-11. Making use of Eq. 3-114, find and subsequently plot the variation of the dimensionless flow speed V/V_e along the wall of the two-dimensional duct shown in the sketch. V_e denotes here the flow speed at the wall of the duct near the exit. The flow is from left to right; the fluid is incompressible. Compare this variation with that obtained using Eq. 3-118. Which method is more accurate. Why? (Sec. 3-10.)

3-12. Finish the flux plot, started in the sketch, keeping $\Delta\phi = \Delta\psi$, for a two-dimensional irrotational flow of an incompressible fluid in a converging channel. (Sec. 3-10.)

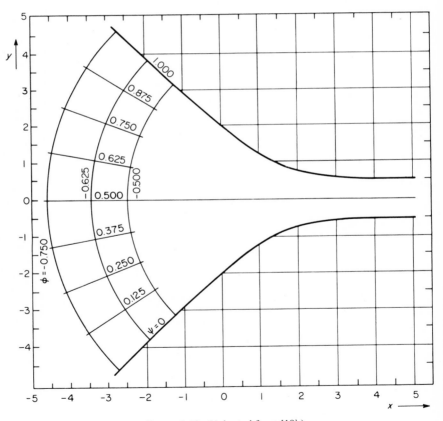

PROB. 3-12. (Adapted from [10].)

CHAPTER 4

Equations of Flow in Integral Form

4-1. INTRODUCTION

The equations which represent the mathematical formulations of the physical laws relevant to fluid flows are known as the *equations of flow*. The *principle of conservation of mass* represents one such law. Its mathematical formulation is known as the *continuity equation*. The continuity equation was discussed in Sec. 3-8. The fluid flows which we will consider obey the laws of the nonrelativistic, classical (Newtonian) mechanics. As a result, Newton's *principle of conservation of linear momentum* is applicable to them. The mathematical formulation of this law is known as the *momentum equation*. [In certain considerations of systems involving fluid flow (such as turbomachines) we may be interested in the torque exerted by the flowing fluid on the system. In such case we apply also the principle of conservation of angular momentum.] In addition, the flowing fluid must obey the *law of conservation of energy*, the mathematical formulation of which is known as the *energy equation*. The energy equation is of special importance in the study of flows of compressible fluids.

The laws of conservation of mass, momentum, and energy are the most important physical laws which flowing fluids obey. There is one additional law, the *second law of thermodynamics*, which puts additional restriction on the phenomena occurring in flowing fluids. This law is of particular importance in the study of high-speed flows of compressible fluids. We will not concern ourselves with it in our study.

Since the continuity equation was already discussed, in this chapter we will consider the (linear) momentum and energy equations and the angular momentum equation. These equations, which are valid for both the real and the (fictitious) perfect fluids, will be written in the integral form. In Chapter 5 the momentum and energy equations will be rewritten in a form valid for perfect fluids only. In addition, we will then write these equations also in the differential form. In such form they are valid at a point in the flow field. The momentum equation for the (real) Newtonian fluids written in the differential form will be derived in Chapter 7.

4-2. THE MOMENTUM EQUATION

For a *material volume* $\mathcal{V}$, the principle of conservation of linear momentum states that at any instant the rate of change of linear momentum of the material volume is equal to the resultant force acting on the volume. The momentum equation, which represents the mathematical formulation of this principle, can therefore be written as

$$\frac{D}{Dt} \int_{\bar{\mathcal{V}}} \rho \mathbf{V} \, d\mathcal{V} = \Sigma \, \mathbf{F} \tag{4-1}$$

Where the symbol $\Sigma \, \mathbf{F}$ represents the resultant external force acting on the fluid within the material volume.

The forces which, in general, always act on a material volume can be subdivided into two groups—the *surface forces* and the *body*, or *extraneous, forces*. The surface forces arise from the action of stresses at the surface of the volume. The body forces arise from action at a distance; they are proportional to mass or volume. The only body force which we will consider in our study is the gravitational force. Its effect can be quite important on the flows of liquids; it is, in general, negligible on the flows of gases. The electromagnetic force which acts on the electrically conducting fluids in magnetic fields is another example of a body force.

The momentum equation (in integral form) for a material volume can thus be written as

$$\frac{D}{Dt} \int_{\bar{\mathcal{V}}} \rho \mathbf{V} \, d\mathcal{V} = \int_{\bar{\mathcal{V}}} \rho \mathbf{f} \, d\mathcal{V} + \oint_{\bar{S}} \mathbf{t} \, dA \tag{4-2}$$

where $\mathbf{f}$ denotes the body force per unit mass of the fluid, and $\mathbf{t}$ denotes the stress which acts at each element of area of the surface $\bar{S}$ bounding the material volume $\mathcal{V}$. The stress $\mathbf{t}$ represents the action of the molecular forces exerted by the fluid outside the surface $\bar{S}$ on the fluid inside (see discussion in Sec. 1-3).

When applied to a *volume fixed in space* (relative to an inertial system) $\mathcal{V}$, the principle of conservation of linear momentum can be written as

$$\frac{\partial}{\partial t} \int_{\mathcal{V}} \rho \mathbf{V} \, d\mathcal{V} + \oint_{S} \rho \mathbf{V}(\mathbf{V} \cdot d\mathbf{A}) = \Sigma \mathbf{F} \tag{4-3}$$

This follows from Eq. 4-1 and the Reynolds transport theorem (Eq. 3-15a). Here the expression for the rate of change of linear momentum is made up of two terms: one term which accounts for the fact that the fluid velocity and density are, in general, functions of time (as well as position), and another term which accounts for the transfer of momentum taking place as a result of flow of the fluid across the boundary of the fixed volume.

For a volume fixed in space, the boundary may or may not be fully made up of a fluid surface; it may cross solid objects around which the fluid flows. *In such case, the force acting from outside on the solid surfaces forming a partial boundary must be included in the resultant force.*

The selection of the volume fixed in space (relative to the coordinate system in which the flow is studied) is the first step in an analysis of flow problems which are solved with the aid of equations of flow written in integral form.

As an example, consider a jet of a liquid lying in a plane and changing, without splashing, its direction by an angle α on a guide vane as shown in Fig. 4-1. Let us assume that the flow is steady and neglect the effects of gravity. In general, the average velocity of the liquid jet leaving the guide vane is less than the average velocity of the jet entering the guide vane as a result of viscous friction which the liquid jet experiences on the

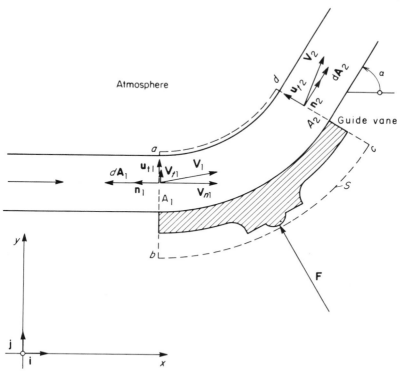

FIG. 4-1. A jet of liquid changing its direction on a guide vane.

deflecting surface of the guide vane. We are interested in deriving the expression for the components, in the x- and y-directions shown, of the force **R** exerted by the liquid jet on the guide vane.

For the volume fixed in space $a - b - c - d$ indicated with a broken line in Fig. 4-1, the momentum equation (Eq. 4-3) reads

$$\oint_S \rho \mathbf{V}(\mathbf{V} \cdot d\mathbf{A}) = \mathbf{F}$$

where $\mathbf{F} = -\mathbf{R}$ if we neglect the shearing force acting on the part $a - d$ of the boundary of the fixed volume (which is quite small if the density of the atmosphere is much smaller than the density of the liquid) because the (static) pressure is the same at the surface S of the fixed volume and therefore contributes nothing to the force acting on the volume. [We are assuming existence of normal forces only on the fluid surface which forms a part of the bounding surface S and which crosses the jet. For fluids having small viscosity, when the rate of change of velocity in the direction of flow is not very large (to be more exact, considering the flow in a rectangular cartesian coordinate system, when the terms $\mu \dfrac{\partial u}{\partial x}, \mu \dfrac{\partial v}{\partial y}, \mu \dfrac{\partial w}{\partial z}$ are small compared to P), the effect of viscosity on the normal stresses is negligible and we can consider the static pressure in their place. (This follows from Eq. 7-27 and subsequent discussion.) The static pressure is constant across the straight streamlines of the jet (this will be shown in Sec. 5-3).]

Denoting the cross sections of the jet along surfaces $a - b$ and $c - d$ by numbers 1 and 2 respectively, we can write

$$\rho \int_{A_2} \mathbf{V}(\mathbf{V} \cdot d\mathbf{A}) + \rho \int_{A_1} \mathbf{V}(\mathbf{V} \cdot d\mathbf{A}) = \mathbf{F} = -\mathbf{R}$$

Introducing the (outward) normal unit vectors **n**, and the tangent unit vectors $\mathbf{u}_t$ (which lie in the plane of vectors **n** and **V**) we have

$$\mathbf{n}_1 = -\mathbf{i}$$
$$\mathbf{u}_{t1} = \mathbf{j}$$
$$\mathbf{n}_2 = \mathbf{i}\cos\alpha + \mathbf{j}\sin\alpha$$
$$\mathbf{u}_{t2} = -\mathbf{i}\sin\alpha + \mathbf{j}\cos\alpha$$

where **i** and **j** denote the unit vectors in the x- and y-directions, respectively. The momentum equation can now be rewritten as

$$\rho \int_{A_2} (V_n\mathbf{n}_2 + V_t\mathbf{u}_{t2})V_n\,dA - \rho \int_{A_1} (V_n\mathbf{i} + V_t\mathbf{j})V_n\,dA = -\mathbf{R}$$

where V_n and V_t denote the normal and tangential components of the flow velocities $\mathbf{V}_1$ and $\mathbf{V}_2$, or

$$\left(\rho \int_{A_2} V_n^2 \, dA \right) (\mathbf{i} \cos \alpha + \mathbf{j} \sin \alpha) + \left(\rho \int_{A_2} V_t V_n \, dA \right) (-\mathbf{i} \sin \alpha + \mathbf{j} \cos \alpha)$$

$$- \left(\rho \int_{A_2} V_n^2 \, dA \right) \mathbf{i} - \left(\rho \int_{A_1} V_t V_n \, dA \right) \mathbf{j} = -R_x \mathbf{i} - R_y \mathbf{j}$$

As a result,

$$R_x = -\rho \cos \alpha \int_{A_2} V_n^2 \, dA + \rho \sin \alpha \int_{A_2} V_t V_n \, dA + \rho \int_{A_1} V_n^2 \, dA$$

$$R_y = -\rho \sin \alpha \int_{A_2} V_n^2 \, dA - \rho \cos \alpha \int_{A_2} V_t V_n \, dA + \rho \int_{A_1} V_t V_n \, dA$$

When the tangential velocity components V_t at sections 1 and 2 are negligibly small (the cross sections are then normal to the streamlines), $V_n \cong V$ and we obtain

$$R_x = -\rho \cos \alpha \int_{A_2} V^2 \, dA + \rho \int_{A_1} V^2 \, dA$$

$$R_y = -\rho \sin \alpha \int_{A_2} V^2 \, dA$$

[In most practical cases the sign of the tangential velocity component (which is small compared to the normal velocity component) changes sign across the jet and the term $\int V_t V_n \, dA$ is negligible when compared to the term $\int V_n^2 \, dA$.] In such a case, the average flow speed based on the rate of flow of an incompressible fluid is

$$\bar{V} = \frac{Q}{A} = \frac{\int_A \mathbf{V} \cdot d\mathbf{A}}{A} = \frac{\int_A V_n \, dA}{A} \cong \frac{\int_A V \, dA}{A}$$

Introducing the so-called *momentum correction factor*, which for an incompressible fluid is defined by

$$\beta = \frac{\int_A V^2 \, dA}{\bar{V}^2 A} \tag{4-4}$$

we can write

$$R_x = -\rho \beta_2 \bar{V}_2^2 A_2 \cos \alpha + \rho \beta_1 \bar{V}_1^2 A_1$$
$$R_y = -\rho \beta_2 \bar{V}_2^2 A_2 \sin \alpha$$

[While for a one-dimensional flow $\beta = 1$, for a laminar flow in a pipe of circular cross section $\beta = 4/3$, and for a turbulent flow in a pipe of circular cross section $\beta \cong 1.02$ (in such flow the velocity profile is much more uniform near the center of the pipe than in a laminar flow). Note that for turbulent velocity profiles the value of β is so close to unity that this correction can be neglected in most engineering calculations. Although the value of β for laminar velocity profiles is relatively large, the net effect of this correction on the acting forces is usually quite small because the magnitudes of the fluid velocity in laminar flows is very small.]

4-3. THE ENERGY EQUATION

The law of conservation of energy for a *material volume* $\overline{\mathscr{V}}$ states that at any instant the rate at which energy enters the volume in the form of heat is equal to the rate at which energy increases within the volume and to the rate at which work is done on the surroundings by the fluid within the boundary of the volume. The *energy equation*, which represents the mathematical formulation of the law of conservation of energy can be written as

$$\frac{D}{Dt} \int_{\overline{\mathscr{V}}} q_{\text{rad}} \rho d\mathscr{V} - \oint_{\overline{S}} \mathbf{n} \cdot \mathbf{q} \, dA$$

$$= \frac{D}{Dt} \int_{\overline{\mathscr{V}}} \left(e + \frac{V^2}{2} \right) \rho d\mathscr{V} - \int_{\overline{\mathscr{V}}} \mathbf{f} \cdot \mathbf{V} \rho d\mathscr{V} - \oint_{\overline{S}} \mathbf{t} \cdot \mathbf{V} \, dA \qquad (4\text{-}5)$$

Where q_{rad} denotes the heat transferred by radiation from the outside to the material volume per unit mass of the fluid, $\mathbf{q}$ represents the vector of heat flux by conduction (the sign ahead of the term involving $\mathbf{q}$ is negative because $\mathbf{n}$ denotes an outward unit vector orienting an area element of the boundary surface of the material volume), V denotes the magnitude of the velocity of the fluid, and e denotes the *specific internal energy* of the fluid (that is, the internal energy of the fluid per unit mass).

The term $-\int_{\overline{\mathscr{V}}} \mathbf{f} \cdot \mathbf{V} \rho \, d\mathscr{V}$ represents the negative of the rate at which work is being done by the body forces $\mathbf{f}$ on the fluid within the material volume, and therefore the rate at which work is being done on the surroundings by the fluid within the material volume as a result of the action of the body forces.

The term $-\oint_{\overline{S}} \mathbf{t} \cdot \mathbf{V} \, dA$ represents the rate at which work is being done on the surroundings by the fluid within the material volume as a result of the surface forces acting on the boundary of the material volume (see the definition of the stress $\mathbf{t}$ acting across a surface at a point in a fluid in Sec. 1-3).

The internal energy of a substance represents the energy of its molecules. This energy represents, in general, the sum of the kinetic energy of translatory motion of the molecules, the kinetic rotational energy of the atoms about the center of the mass of the molecules, the vibrational energy of the atoms, the internal atomic energy, and the potential energy due to intermolecular forces. The specific internal energy of a substance is a thermodynamic property and depends, in general, on temperature and pressure.

For a *volume fixed in space* (relative to an inertial system) $\mathscr{V}$ whose *boundary is made up wholly of a fluid surface*, the energy equation has the form

$$\int_{\mathscr{V}} \dot{q}_{rad}\, d\mathscr{V} - \oint_{S} \mathbf{n} \cdot \mathbf{q}\, dA$$

$$= \frac{\partial}{\partial t}\, \int_{\mathscr{V}} \left(e + \frac{V^2}{2}\right)\rho\, d\mathscr{V} + \oint_{S} \left(e + \frac{V^2}{2}\right)\rho\, \mathbf{V} \cdot d\mathbf{A}$$

$$- \int_{\mathscr{V}} \mathbf{f} \cdot \mathbf{V}\rho\, d\mathscr{V} - \oint_{S} \mathbf{t} \cdot \mathbf{V}\, dA \qquad (4\text{-}6)$$

where $\dot{q}_{rad} = \dfrac{\partial(q_{rad}\,\rho)}{\partial t}$ represents the rate of heat transfer per unit volume by radiation to the fluid instantaneously in the fixed volume. This follows from Eq. 4-5 and Reynolds transport theorem. Writing the above equation, we omitted the radiant heat convection term $\oint_{S} q_{rad}\, \rho\, \mathbf{V} \cdot d\mathbf{A}$ because the absorbed radiant heat appears as the internal energy of the fluid.

In the case when the boundary of the volume fixed in space $\mathscr{V}$ crosses a solid object, such as a turbine or compressor shaft through which work W_{shaft} is transmitted from or to the fluid, the term representing the rate at which work due to the surface forces is being done on the surroundings by the fluid has to be written as

$$- \int_{S'} \mathbf{t} \cdot \mathbf{V}\, dA + \frac{dW_{shaft}}{dt}$$

where S' denotes the fluid surface forming a partial boundary of the volume fixed in space $\mathscr{V}$ (which surface is smaller than the surface S bounding the fixed volume $\mathscr{V}$ by the cross section of the solid object at the boundary), and W_{shaft} represents the shaft work done by the fluid within the fixed volume on the surroundings. Denoting, as an abbreviation, by dQ/dt the rate of heat transfer to the fluid instantaneously occupying volume $\mathscr{V}$, we can write the energy equation in the form

$$\frac{dQ}{dt} = \frac{\partial}{\partial t}\, \int_{\mathscr{V}'} \left(e + \frac{V^2}{2}\right)\rho\, d\mathscr{V} + \int_{S'} \left(e + \frac{V^2}{2}\right)\rho\, \mathbf{V} \cdot d\mathbf{A}$$

$$- \int_{\mathscr{V}'} \mathbf{f} \cdot \mathbf{V}\rho\, d\mathscr{V} - \int_{S'} \mathbf{t} \cdot \mathbf{V}\, dA + \frac{dW_{shaft}}{dt} \qquad (4\text{-}7)$$

where $\mathscr{V}'$ denotes the volume filled with the fluid.

For a conservative field of body force, $\mathbf{f} = -\nabla\Omega$ where Ω denotes the potential energy per unit mass, and

$$- \int_{V} \mathbf{f} \cdot \mathbf{V} \rho \, dV \; = \; \int_{V} \mathbf{V} \cdot \boldsymbol{\nabla} \Omega \rho \, dV$$

If the conservative body forces are represented by the force of gravitational attraction of the earth, then

$$\Omega \; = \; -g(r)r \; = \; -g_0 \frac{r_0^2}{r} \tag{4-8}$$

Where r denotes the radial distance coordinate pointing outward from the center of gravity of the earth, $g(r) = |\mathbf{f}| = g_0(r_0/r)^2$ denotes the magnitude of gravitational acceleration at r, and g_0 is the value of g at $r = r_0$. As a result,

$$\boldsymbol{\nabla} \Omega \; = \; \frac{\partial \Omega}{\partial n} \, \mathbf{n} \; = \; \frac{d\Omega}{dr} \, \mathbf{u}_r \; = \; g_0 \frac{r_0^2}{r^2} \, \mathbf{u}_r \; = \; g(r) \mathbf{u}_r \tag{4-9}$$

When the assumption is made that the magnitude of gravitational acceleration g is constant (this is permissible when the change in the elevation in the flow system under consideration is such that $r_1/r_2 \approx 1$, where r_1 denotes the initial and r_2 the final value of the distance coordinate r), then, since

$$d\Omega \; = \; g_0 \frac{r_0^2}{r^2} \, dr \; = \; g(r) \, dr$$

we now have

$$d\Omega \; = \; g \, d\zeta \tag{4-10}$$

or

$$\Omega_2 - \Omega_1 \; = \; g(\zeta_2 - \zeta_1) \tag{4-10a}$$

or

$$\Omega \; = \; g\zeta + \text{const.} \tag{4-10b}$$

if we use the vertical coordinate ζ as the new distance variable. We usually take const. $= 0$ in the above equation. (Observe that the coordinate axis ζ points in direction opposite to that of the coordinate axis h used in Sec. 1-6.) Therefore, in such case,

$$\boldsymbol{\nabla} \Omega \; = \; \frac{\partial \Omega}{\partial n} \, \mathbf{n} \; = \; \frac{\partial \Omega}{\partial \zeta} \, \mathbf{u}_\zeta \; = \; g \mathbf{u}_\zeta \tag{4-11}$$

where g is now a constant and $\mathbf{u}_\zeta$ denotes a unit vector in the direction of the positive vertical ζ-axis pointing away from the surface of the earth, as shown in Fig. 4-2.

In the case of flows of fluids having small viscosity, when the rate of change of velocity in the direction of flow is not very large, viscosity has very small effect on the normal stresses and we can consider the static pressure in their place. This we shall now assume to be the case. If the fluid surface S' which forms a partial boundary of the volume fixed in space V is either normal to the streamlines or follows solid walls, then the

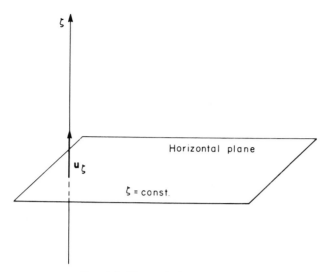

FIG. 4-2. The vertical coordinate ζ.

shear work done at this surface is zero. This is so because then the fluid velocity is either normal to the shearing force or it is zero. *The net result, as it affects the viscous stress term in the energy equation, is then equivalent to the assumption that the state of stress in the fluid at the fluid surface S' is hydrostatic* (although in fact it is not). Writing

$$\mathbf{t} = -P\mathbf{n} \qquad [1\text{-}1]$$

we have

$$-\int_{S'} \mathbf{t} \cdot \mathbf{V} \, dA = \int_{S'} \mathbf{n} \cdot (P\mathbf{V}) \, dA = \int_{S'} P\mathbf{V} \cdot d\mathbf{A} \qquad (4\text{-}12)$$

and, in such case, the energy equation for a volume fixed in space (relative to an inertial system) (Eq. 4-7) can be written as

$$\frac{dQ}{dt} = \frac{\partial}{\partial t} \int_{\mathcal{V}'} \left(e + \frac{V^2}{2} \right) \rho \, d\mathcal{V} + \int_{S'} \left(e + \frac{V^2}{2} \right) \rho \mathbf{V} \cdot d\mathbf{A}$$

$$+ \int_{\mathcal{V}'} \mathbf{V} \cdot \nabla \Omega \rho \, d\mathcal{V} + \int_{S'} P\mathbf{V} \cdot d\mathbf{A} + \frac{dW_{\text{shaft}}}{dt} \qquad (4\text{-}13)$$

if we assume conservative body force. Since

$$\rho \mathbf{V} \cdot \nabla \Omega = \nabla \cdot (\rho \Omega \mathbf{V}) - \Omega \nabla \cdot (\rho \mathbf{V})$$

and

$$\int_{\mathcal{V}'} \nabla \cdot (\rho \Omega \mathbf{V}) \, d\mathcal{V} = \oint_{S'} \Omega \rho \mathbf{V} \cdot d\mathbf{A}$$

in view of the divergence theorem of Gauss, for a *steady flow* Eq. 4-13 reduces to

$$\frac{dQ}{dt} = \int_{S'} \left(e + \frac{P}{\rho} + \frac{V^2}{2} + g\zeta \right) \rho \mathbf{V} \cdot d\mathbf{A} + \frac{dW_{\text{shaft}}}{dt} \qquad (4\text{-}14)$$

if the only body force is a constant gravitational field, because $\nabla \cdot (\rho \mathbf{V}) = 0$ in such flow (this is the continuity equation). Introducing enthalpy h defined by

$$h = e + \frac{P}{\rho}$$

We can rewrite Eq. 4-14 as

$$\frac{dQ}{dt} = \int_{S'} \left(h + \frac{V^2}{2} + g\zeta \right) \rho \mathbf{V} \cdot d\mathbf{A} + \frac{dW_{\text{shaft}}}{dt} \qquad (4\text{-}14a)$$

This is the energy equation for a steady flow written for a volume fixed in space (relative to an inertial system) *whose boundary crosses a solid object such as a turbine or compressor shaft and whose fluid surface S' is normal to the streamlines and may follow solid walls.*

For a volume fixed in space (relative to an inertial system) *whose boundary is made up wholly of a fluid surface, the energy equation for a steady flow in which the surface S bounding the volume is normal to the streamlines and may follow solid walls* reads

$$\frac{dQ}{dt} = \oint_{S} \left(e + \frac{P}{\rho} + \frac{V^2}{2} + g\zeta \right) \rho \mathbf{V} \cdot d\mathbf{A} \qquad (4\text{-}15)$$

or

$$\frac{dQ}{dt} = \oint_{S} \left(h + \frac{V^2}{2} + g\zeta \right) \rho \mathbf{V} \cdot d\mathbf{A} \qquad (4\text{-}15a)$$

We shall return to our discussion of the energy equation in Chapter 5 when considering flows of perfect fluids, and in Chapter 9 when applying the hydraulic approach to the solution of various flow problems.

4-4.   THE PRINCIPLE OF CONSERVATION OF ANGULAR MOMENTUM

The principle of conservation of angular momentum for a *material volume* $\mathcal{V}$ states that the rate of increase of the angular momentum of the fluid within the volume about a fixed point is equal to the moment of the external forces about the point.   The mathematical formulation of this principle can be written as

$$\frac{D}{Dt} \int_{\overline{\mathcal{V}}} \mathbf{r} \times \mathbf{V} \rho \, d\mathcal{V} = \Sigma(\mathbf{r} \times \mathbf{F}) \qquad (4\text{-}16)$$

where $\Sigma(\mathbf{r} \times \mathbf{F}) = \mathbf{T}$ represents the moment of the external forces, and $\mathbf{r}$ denotes a position vector from the origin of a fixed frame of reference.

In view of Eq. 3-58, it can be rewritten as

$$\int_{\mathcal{V}} \mathbf{r} \times \frac{D\mathbf{V}}{Dt}\, \rho\, d\mathcal{V} = \Sigma(\mathbf{r} \times \mathbf{F}) \qquad (4\text{-}16a)$$

because $D\mathbf{r}/Dt = \mathbf{V}$.

For a *volume fixed in space* $\mathcal{V}$, the principle of conservation of angular momentum can be written as

$$\frac{\partial}{\partial t}\int_{\mathcal{V}} \mathbf{r} \times \mathbf{V}\rho\, d\mathcal{V} + \oint_{S} \mathbf{r} \times \mathbf{V}(\rho\mathbf{V} \cdot d\mathbf{A}) = \Sigma(\mathbf{r} \times \mathbf{F}) \qquad (4\text{-}17)$$

in view of the Reynolds transport theorem.

The main engineering application of the principle of conservation of angular momentum is in the study of turbomachinery. Of special interest there is the magnitude of the moment about the axis of rotation of the rotor, or the torque. If we place this axis along the z-coordinate of the circular cylindrical coordinate system $\curvearrowright, \theta, z$ from whose origin the position vector $\mathbf{r}$ emanates, as shown in Fig. 4-3, then it is the z-component

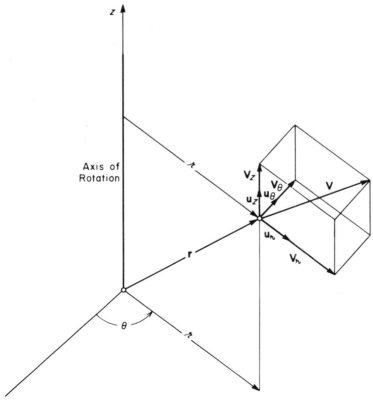

FIG. 4-3. Axis of rotation oriented along the z-coordinate.

of the total moment $\mathbf{T} = \Sigma(\mathbf{r} \times \mathbf{F})$ that is of special interest. Since, in this case, for any fluid element at some arbitrary location $\curvearrowright, \theta, z$

$$\mathbf{r} \times \mathbf{V} = (\curvearrowright\mathbf{u}_\curvearrowright + z\mathbf{u}_z) \times (V_\curvearrowright \mathbf{u}_\curvearrowright + V_\theta\mathbf{u}_\theta + V_z\mathbf{u}_z)$$
$$= -V_\theta z\mathbf{u}_\curvearrowright + (V_\curvearrowright z - V_z \curvearrowright)\mathbf{u}_\theta + V_\theta\curvearrowright\mathbf{u}_z$$

the z-component of $\mathbf{T}$ is given by

$$T_z = \frac{D}{Dt} \int_{\overline{V}} V_\theta\curvearrowright\rho\, d\mathcal{V} \qquad (4\text{-}18)$$

Where V_θ represents the circumferential component of the flow velocity about the axis of rotation. This follows from Eq. 4-16.

For a *volume fixed in space* $\mathcal{V}$ we have

$$T_z = \frac{\partial}{\partial t} \int_V V_\theta\curvearrowright\rho\, d\mathcal{V} + \oint_S V_\theta\curvearrowright\rho(\mathbf{V} \cdot d\mathbf{A}) \qquad (4\text{-}19)$$

For a steady flow the last equation reduces to

$$T_z = \oint_S V_\theta\curvearrowright\rho(\mathbf{V} \cdot d\mathbf{A}) \qquad (4\text{-}20)$$

EXAMPLE 4-1.   As an example of application of the principle of conservation of angular momentum, we will derive now equation for the torque developed in a turbine by a cylindrical stream filament indicated in Fig. 4-4. We will assume that the flow is steady.

A turbine is a device in which an expanding fluid is forced to undergo changes in direction of flow in consecutive rows of stationary and rotating blades. As a result of the change of the angular momentum of the fluid in the rotating blades, torque is exerted by the fluid on the shaft of the turbine, and external work is done.

In Fig. 4-4, W denotes the peripheral speed of the rotor. $\mathbf{V}_1$ and $\mathbf{V}_2$ denote the absolute fluid velocities at the entrance and exit from the rotor blades respectively. The primes refer to the velocities relative to the rotor. $V_{\theta 2}$ as indicated is a positive quantity.

Equation 4-20 applied to the fixed annular volume indicated with broken lines in Fig. 4-4a becomes

$$\delta T_z = V_{\theta 2}\curvearrowright_2\rho_2 V_2 \cos \delta\, 2\pi\curvearrowright_2\delta\curvearrowright_2 - V_{\theta 1}\curvearrowright_1\rho_1 V_1 \sin \alpha\, 2\pi\curvearrowright_1\delta\curvearrowright_1$$

Since the continuity equation applied to the stream filament under consideration reads

$$\delta\dot{m} = \rho_1 V_1 \sin \alpha\, 2\pi\curvearrowright_1\delta\curvearrowright_1 = \rho_2 V_2 \cos \delta\, 2\pi\curvearrowright_2\delta\curvearrowright_2$$

we can write

$$\delta T_z = 2\pi V_1 \sin \alpha\rho_1\curvearrowright_1 \delta\curvearrowright_1(V_{\theta 2}\curvearrowright_2 - V_{\theta 1}\curvearrowright_1)$$

or

$$\delta T_z = \delta\dot{m}(V_{\theta 2}\curvearrowright_2 - V_{\theta 1}\curvearrowright_1)$$

For a turbine the torque exerted by the rotor on the fluid, δT_z, is negative, indicating that it is the fluid that exerts the torque on the rotor. For a compressor, δT_z is positive.

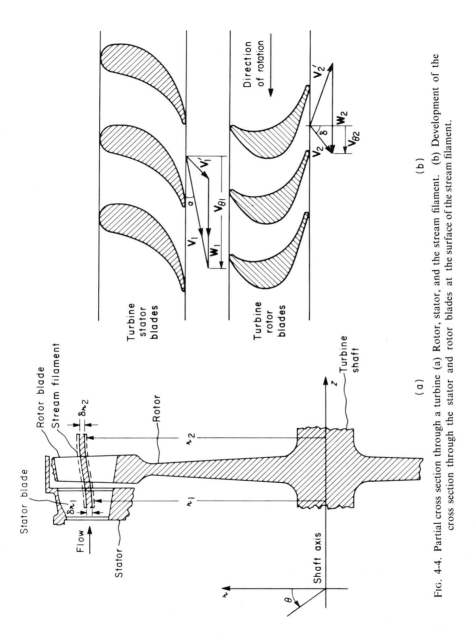

Fig. 4-4. Partial cross section through a turbine (a) Rotor, stator, and the stream filament. (b) Development of the cross section through the stator and rotor blades at the surface of the stream filament.

PROBLEMS

4-1. A rocket is held in position as shown in the sketch. If the atmospheric pressure is P_a, and the pressure, density, and flow speed at the exit from the nozzle are P_e, ρ_e, and V_e respectively (one-dimensional steady flow at the exit from the nozzle is assumed), what is the expression for the magnitude of the force **F** acting in excess of the weight of the rocket, which is necessary to hold the rocket in position (that is, for the thrust of the rocket, or the magnitude of the force which would normally be accelerating the rocket)? The state of stress in the jet leaving the rocket should be considered as hydrostatic. Explain why. (When the state of stress is hydrostatic $\mathbf{t} = -P\mathbf{n}$; see Eq. 1-1.) Consider the term $\dfrac{\partial}{\partial t} \displaystyle\int_{V} \rho \mathbf{V}\, dV$ in the momentum equation to be negligible. Discuss validity of this assumption. (Sec. 4-2.)

PROB. 4-1

4-2. Consider a very long object of constant cross section, such as a strut, immersed in a stream of an incompressible fluid flowing with speed V_1 as shown in the sketch. The stream, whose direction is perpendicular to the axis of the strut, is large enough so that the pressure is uniform on the fluid surface bounding the volume fixed in space V shown. Surface S bounding the fixed volume V intersects the strut in two sections, and on its upstream and downstream ends is normal to the streamlines. The fixed volume is bounded laterally by streamlines as shown. By applying the momentum equation to the fixed volume V, show that the expression for the drag experienced by the strut is

$$\mathbf{D} = \rho \int_{A_2} (\mathbf{V}_1 - \mathbf{V}_2) V_2\, dA$$

where V_2 denotes the flow speed on the downstream end of the surface S. (Sec. 4-2.)

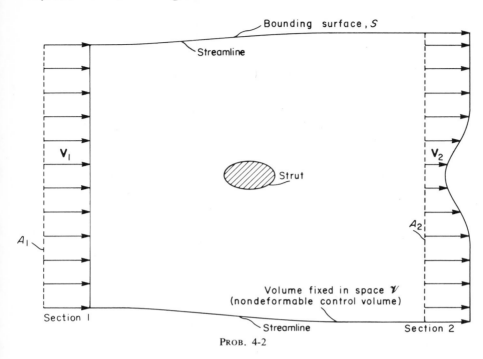

PROB. 4-2

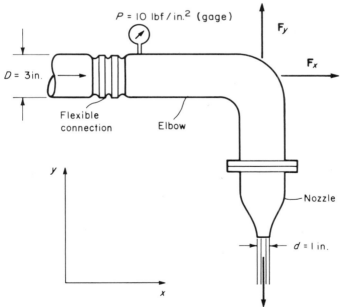

PROB. 4-3

4-3. Water at 60°F flows through a 90-deg elbow which is followed by a nozzle, as shown in the sketch. Upstream of the elbow is a flexible connection which does not transmit any force. If the rate of mass flow of water is 12 lbm/sec, find the magnitudes and directions of the forces $\mathbf{F}_x$ and $\mathbf{F}_y$ necessary to hold the elbow in position. Assume a one-dimensional steady flow and neglect the gravity forces. Consider static pressure in place of normal stresses in the stream. (Sec. 4-2.)

4-4. Consider a steam turbine, as shown in the sketch, through which steam flows at a rate of 300,000 lbm/hr. Assume the flow at section 1 of the inlet duct and section 2 of the exhaust duct to be one-dimensional. The enthalpies and flow speeds at sections 1 and 2 are: $h_1 = 1280$ Btu/lbm, $h_2 = 1050$ Btu/lbm, and $V_1 = 100$ ft/sec, $V_2 = 500$ ft/sec. The flow at sections 1 and 2 can be considered to be steady. If the rate of heat loss from the turbine is negligible, find the power output of the turbine (dW_{shaft}/dt) in kilowatts. (Sec. 4-3.)

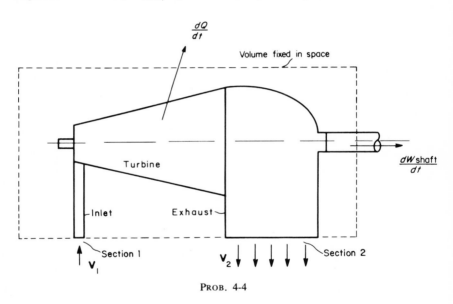

PROB. 4-4

4-5. A jet of water enters a water wheel with a speed V_1 as shown in the sketch. If the wheel buckets have cross sections indicated, show that the power developed by the wheel is given by

$$\text{Power} = Q\rho \hbar \omega(V_1 - \omega \hbar)(1 + \cos \beta)$$

where Q denotes the volumetric rate of flow of the water, and ω the magnitude of the angular velocity of the wheel. In the derivation make the approximating assumption that the speed of the water relative to the bucket remains unchanged, that is, $V_2' = V_1 - \hbar \omega$. What is the relation between ω and V_1 for maximum power? (Sec. 4-4.)

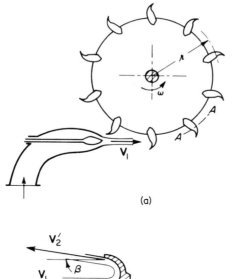

(a)

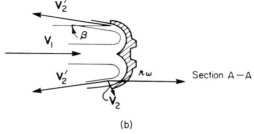

β

Section A—A

(b)

PROB. 4-5

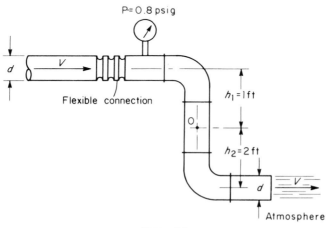

P= 0.8 psig

d

V

Flexible connection

$h_1 = 1$ ft

O

$h_2 = 2$ ft

d

V

Atmosphere

PROB. 4-6

4-6. Water at 60°F flows with an (average) speed of 10 ft/sec through the pipe system shown in the sketch. If the diameter of the pipes is $d = 4$ in., calculate the moment acting on the support located at 0. It can be assumed that the flexible connection does not transmit any force. Assume a steady flow and uniform velocity distribution in the pipe. (Sec. 4-4.)

4-7. Consider a steady flow of a liquid through a rotating pipe as shown in the sketch. The (average) flow speed of the liquid, whose density is 60 lbm/ft³, is 10 ft/sec. If the diameter of the pipe $d = 2$ in., and the magnitude of the angular

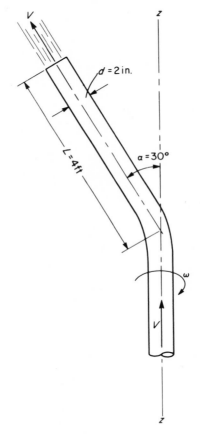

Prob. 4-7

velocity $\omega = 10$ radians/sec, find the torque necessary to rotate the pipe. Assume a uniform velocity distribution at the exit from the pipe, and that the incoming fluid possesses no angular momentum. (Sec. 4-4.)

4-8. Water flows steadily through the pipe system shown in the sketch. If the diameter of the horizontal pipes is $d = 3$ in., determine the torque acting on the vertical support. Assume the density of the water to be 62.35 lbm/ft^3. (Sec. 4-4.)

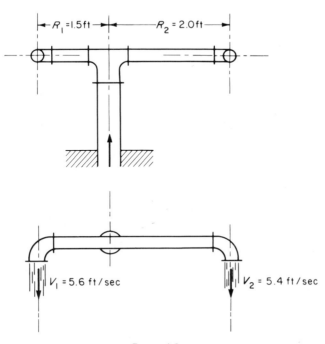

PROB. 4-8

CHAPTER 5

Equations of Flow of Perfect Fluids

5-1. INTRODUCTION

In this chapter we will discuss the momentum and energy equations, in integral and differential forms, which are valid for perfect fluids. The continuity equation, which was discussed in Sec. 3-8, will not be discussed here because its validity is quite general and does not depend on the physical model of the fluid used in the analysis.

The assumption that the fluid is perfect will allow us to obtain general integrals of the momentum equation and the circulation theorem known as the law of conservation of circulation.

5-2. THE MOMENTUM EQUATION

As was discussed in Chapter 1, in flowing perfect fluids the stress acting across a fluid surface at a point is normal to the surface—that is, the state of stress is hydrostatic. The magnitude of this normal stress at a point is the same in all directions, the magnitude of the negative normal stress being called the static pressure and being denoted by the letter P. Since the stress t is defined as the force per unit area of the fluid surface in the limit as the surface tends to zero, which is exerted by the fluid toward which the normal unit vector n, orienting the area element of the surface, is directed, we have for perfect fluids

$$t = -Pn \qquad [1\text{-}1]$$

As a result of the fact that the static pressure P at a point is independent of direction, it can be considered a scalar-field function just like the density or temperature of the fluid.

For perfect fluids we have therefore

$$\oint_S t\, dA = -\oint_S P\, d\mathbf{A} \qquad (5\text{-}1)$$

where $d\mathbf{A} = \mathbf{n}\,dA$ with $\mathbf{n}$ denoting the outward normal unit vector orienting an element of area of surface S.

Making use of Eq. 5-1 we can transform the momentum equation for a *material volume* $\mathcal{V}$ (Eq. 4-2) into

$$\int_{\mathcal{V}} \frac{D\mathbf{V}}{Dt}\,\rho\,d\mathcal{V} = \int_{\mathcal{V}} \rho\mathbf{f}\,d\mathcal{V} - \oint_{S} \mathbf{n}\,P\,dA \qquad (5\text{-}2)$$

valid for perfect fluids. (The form of the first term follows from Eq. 3-59.) In view of Eq. A-60, this equation can be rewritten in the form

$$\int_{\mathcal{V}} \left(\frac{D\mathbf{V}}{Dt} + \frac{1}{\rho}\,\nabla P - \mathbf{f} \right) \rho\,d\mathcal{V} = 0$$

Since the material volume $\mathcal{V}$ is arbitrary, the integrand of the above equation must vanish everywhere in the flow field, and we obtain the differential form of the momentum equation for perfect fluids

$$\frac{D\mathbf{V}}{Dt} + \frac{1}{\rho}\,\nabla P - \mathbf{f} = 0 \qquad (5\text{-}3)$$

which, in view of Eq. 3-3, can also be written as

$$\frac{\partial\mathbf{V}}{\partial t} + \mathbf{V}\cdot\nabla\mathbf{V} + \frac{1}{\rho}\,\nabla P - \mathbf{f} = 0 \qquad (5\text{-}3\text{a})$$

This equation, which represents the spatial form of the momentum equation in differential form, is known as *Euler's momentum equation*.

When only conservative body forces act on the fluid, Euler's momentum equation can be written as

$$\frac{D\mathbf{V}}{Dt} = -\frac{1}{\rho}\,\nabla P - \nabla\Omega \qquad (5\text{-}4)$$

an equation due to Euler (1752, 1755) [1].

The acceleration of a fluid element $D\mathbf{V}/Dt$ can be represented in form of equation

$$\frac{D\mathbf{V}}{Dt} = \frac{\partial\mathbf{V}}{\partial t} + \nabla\left(\frac{V^2}{2}\right) - \mathbf{V}\times(\nabla\times\mathbf{V}) \qquad (5\text{-}5)$$

which is known as *Lagrange's acceleration formula* (1781) [1]. It follows from Eqs. 3-7 and 3-30. Therefore Euler's momentum equation (Eq. 5-4) can be rewritten as

$$\frac{\partial\mathbf{V}}{\partial t} - \mathbf{V}\times(\nabla\times\mathbf{V}) = -\left[\frac{1}{\rho}\,\nabla P + \nabla\Omega + \nabla\left(\frac{V^2}{2}\right)\right] \qquad (5\text{-}6)$$

For a *volume fixed in space* (relative to an inertial system) $\mathcal{V}$ whose boundary is made up fully of a fluid surface, the momentum equation valid for perfect fluids can be written as

$$\frac{\partial}{\partial t}\int_{\mathcal{V}} \rho\mathbf{V}\,d\mathcal{V} + \oint_{S} \rho\mathbf{V}(\mathbf{V}\cdot d\mathbf{A}) = \int_{\mathcal{V}} \rho\mathbf{f}\,d\mathcal{V} - \oint_{S} \mathbf{n}\,P\,dA \qquad (5\text{-}7)$$

in view of Eq. 5-1.

If the boundary of the fixed volume is not made up fully of a fluid surface, but crosses solid objects around which the fluid flows, then the force acting from the outside on the solid surfaces forming a partial boundary must be included in the resultant force—that is, it must be added to the right-hand side of Eq. 5-7.

Euler's Momentum Equation for a Constant Field of Gravitational Attraction. In Chapter 4 we showed that *when we assume that the magnitude of the gravitational acceleration is constant*, and the gravitational force is only body force which we consider, we have

$$\mathbf{f} = -\nabla \Omega = -g\mathbf{u}_\zeta \tag{5-8}$$

where g denotes the (constant) magnitude of the gravitational attraction, and $\mathbf{u}_\zeta$ is a unit vector perpendicular to horizontal planes and pointing away from the earth.

In a rectangular cartesian coordinate system, the Euler's momentum equation (Eq. 5-4) can be written in the form of the following three equations. Momentum equation in the x-direction:

$$\frac{\partial u}{\partial t} + u\frac{\partial u}{\partial x} + v\frac{\partial u}{\partial y} + w\frac{\partial u}{\partial z} = -\frac{1}{\rho}\frac{\partial P}{\partial x} - g\frac{\partial \zeta}{\partial x}$$

Momentum equation in the y-direction:

$$\frac{\partial v}{\partial t} + u\frac{\partial v}{\partial x} + v\frac{\partial v}{\partial y} + w\frac{\partial v}{\partial z} = -\frac{1}{\rho}\frac{\partial P}{\partial y} - g\frac{\partial \zeta}{\partial y} \tag{5-9}$$

Momentum equation in the z-direction:

$$\frac{\partial w}{\partial t} + u\frac{\partial w}{\partial x} + v\frac{\partial w}{\partial y} + w\frac{\partial w}{\partial z} = -\frac{1}{\rho}\frac{\partial P}{\partial z} - g\frac{\partial \zeta}{\partial z}$$

in view of Eqs. 3-3, 5-8, and A-84, where u, v, and w denote the components of the flow velocity $\mathbf{V}$ in the x-, y-, and z-direction respectively ($\mathbf{V} = u\mathbf{i} + v\mathbf{j} + w\mathbf{k}$), because

$$\nabla \Omega = \frac{\partial \Omega}{\partial x}\mathbf{i} + \frac{\partial \Omega}{\partial y}\mathbf{j} + \frac{\partial \Omega}{\partial z}\mathbf{k}$$

with

$$\Omega = g\zeta + \text{const.} \tag{4-10b}$$

Observe that the terms $\frac{\partial \zeta}{\partial x}$, $\frac{\partial \zeta}{\partial y}$, and $\frac{\partial \zeta}{\partial z}$ represent the rates of increase of elevation in the x-, y-, and z-directions respectively. They are constant for a given orientation of the x-, y-, z-axes with respect to the ζ-axis. The terms

$$\frac{\partial u}{\partial t} + u\frac{\partial u}{\partial x} + v\frac{\partial u}{\partial y} + w\frac{\partial u}{\partial z} = a_x$$

$$\frac{\partial v}{\partial t} + u\frac{\partial v}{\partial x} + v\frac{\partial v}{\partial y} + w\frac{\partial v}{\partial z} = a_y \tag{5-10}$$

$$\frac{\partial w}{\partial t} + u\frac{\partial w}{\partial x} + v\frac{\partial w}{\partial y} + w\frac{\partial w}{\partial z} = a_z$$

represent the components of the acceleration of fluid elements $\mathbf{a} = D\mathbf{V}/Dt$ in the directions of the x-, y-, and z-axes respectively.

If we orient the x-, y-, z-coordinate axes so that the *z-axis is vertical and pointing away from the earth*, that is, when the z-axis corresponds with the ζ-axis, then Eqs. 5-9 reduce to the following equations:

$$\left.\begin{array}{l} \dfrac{\partial u}{\partial t} + u\,\dfrac{\partial u}{\partial x} + v\,\dfrac{\partial u}{\partial y} + w\,\dfrac{\partial u}{\partial z} = -\dfrac{1}{\rho}\,\dfrac{\partial P}{\partial x} \\[2mm] \dfrac{\partial v}{\partial t} + u\,\dfrac{\partial v}{\partial x} + v\,\dfrac{\partial v}{\partial y} + w\,\dfrac{\partial v}{\partial z} = -\dfrac{1}{\rho}\,\dfrac{\partial P}{\partial y} \\[2mm] \dfrac{\partial w}{\partial t} + u\,\dfrac{\partial w}{\partial x} + v\,\dfrac{\partial w}{\partial y} + w\,\dfrac{\partial w}{\partial z} = -\dfrac{1}{\rho}\,\dfrac{\partial P}{\partial z} - g \end{array}\right\} \quad \text{(5-9a)}$$

In a circular cylindrical coordinate system r, θ, z, the base unit vectors $\mathbf{u}_r, \mathbf{u}_\theta$, and $\mathbf{u}_z$ can be represented by equations

$$\left.\begin{array}{l} \mathbf{u}_r = \mathbf{i}\cos\theta + \mathbf{j}\sin\theta \\[1mm] \mathbf{u}_\theta = -\mathbf{i}\sin\theta + \mathbf{j}\cos\theta \\[1mm] \mathbf{u}_z = \mathbf{k} \end{array}\right\} \quad \text{(5-11)}$$

where $\mathbf{i}$, $\mathbf{j}$, and $\mathbf{k}$ are the base unit vectors in a rectangular cartesian coordinate system (see Fig. 5-1). In such a coordinate system, in which $\mathbf{V} = V_r\mathbf{u}_r + V_\theta\mathbf{u}_\theta + V_z\mathbf{u}_z$, the Euler's momentum equation (Eq. 5-4),

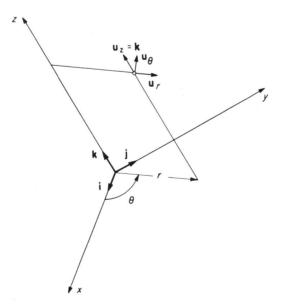

FIG. 5-1. Circular cylindrical coordinate system r, θ, z and the rectangular cartesian coordinate system x, y, z.

which is valid at a point in the flow field, can be written in the form of the following three equations. Momentum equation in the r-direction:

$$\frac{\partial V_r}{\partial t} + V_r \frac{\partial V_r}{\partial r} + \frac{V_\theta}{r} \frac{\partial V_r}{\partial \theta} + V_z \frac{\partial V_r}{\partial z} - \frac{V_\theta^2}{r} = -\frac{1}{\rho} \frac{\partial P}{\partial r} - g \frac{\partial \zeta}{\partial r}$$

Momentum equation in the θ-direction:

$$\frac{\partial V_\theta}{\partial t} + V_r \frac{\partial V_\theta}{\partial r} + \frac{V_\theta}{r} \frac{\partial V_\theta}{\partial \theta} + V_z \frac{\partial V_\theta}{\partial z} + \frac{V_r V_\theta}{r} = -\frac{1}{\rho r} \frac{\partial P}{\partial \theta} - \frac{g}{r} \frac{\partial \zeta}{\partial \theta} \qquad (5\text{-}12)$$

Momentum equation in the z-direction:

$$\frac{\partial V_z}{\partial t} + V_r \frac{\partial V_z}{\partial r} + \frac{V_\theta}{r} \frac{\partial V_z}{\partial \theta} + V_z \frac{\partial V_z}{\partial z} = -\frac{1}{\rho} \frac{\partial P}{\partial z} - g \frac{\partial \zeta}{\partial z}$$

if again the magnitude of gravitational attraction is assumed constant. The derivation of the above equations is left as a problem assignment. Observe that, in general, the terms $\partial \zeta / \partial r$ and $(1/r)\partial \zeta / \partial \theta$ are not constant but are functions of angle θ. (See Prob. 5-3.)

Concluding Remarks. Observe that since Euler's momentum equation is valid only for perfect fluids, we can expect it to be of value in a study of flows of real fluids having small viscosity only outside of the regions in which the effects of viscosity are large. It cannot be used in the analysis of flow within the boundary layer. In addition, we cannot expect Euler's momentum equation to hold for highly turbulent flows. (See our discussion in Sec. 1-4.)

5-3. GENERAL INTEGRALS OF MOMENTUM EQUATION

General Integral Along a Streamline in a Steady Barotropic Flow. A fluid flow is said to be *barotropic* if the density of the flowing fluid is a function of pressure [that is, if $\rho = \rho(P)$] or, in the special case, if the fluid behaves as though it were incompressible [that is, if $\rho = $ const.]. In a barotropic flow the changes in the fluid density, if any, depend only on the local changes of the (static) pressure.

When the body forces acting on a flowing fluid are conservative and flow is barotropic, it is possible to obtain a general line integral of Euler's momentum equation *along a streamline*. Assuming a *steady flow* and forming a line integral of Eq. 5-4 we obtain

$$\int (\mathbf{V} \cdot \boldsymbol{\nabla} \mathbf{V}) \cdot d\mathbf{r} = -\int \frac{1}{\rho} \boldsymbol{\nabla} P \cdot d\mathbf{r} - \int \boldsymbol{\nabla} \Omega \cdot d\mathbf{r} + \text{const.}$$

From Eq. A-34 it follows that

$$\int \boldsymbol{\nabla} \Omega \cdot d\mathbf{r} = \int d\Omega = \Omega + \text{const.}$$

and

$$\int \frac{1}{\rho} \boldsymbol{\nabla} P \cdot d\mathbf{r} = \int \frac{dP}{\rho}$$

Since the integration is performed along a streamline, $d\mathbf{r}$ has the direction of $\mathbf{V}$, and therefore

$$(\mathbf{V} \cdot \nabla \mathbf{V}) \cdot d\mathbf{r} = V \frac{\partial \mathbf{V}}{\partial r} \cdot d\mathbf{r} = V \frac{\partial V}{\partial r} dr = V dV = d\left(\frac{V^2}{2}\right)$$

where dV denotes the differential of the flow speed along the streamline. As a result,

$$\int (\mathbf{V} \cdot \nabla \mathbf{V}) \cdot d\mathbf{r} = \frac{V^2}{2} + \text{const.}$$

and the *line integral of Euler's momentum equation along a streamline in a field of conservative body forces for a steady and continuous flow* becomes

$$\frac{V^2}{2} + \int \frac{dP}{\rho} + \Omega = \text{const.} \tag{5-13}$$

Observe that for this integral to exist the flow must be barotropic. For an incompressible fluid flow the above equation becomes

$$\frac{V^2}{2} + \frac{P}{\rho} + \Omega = \text{const.} \tag{5-14}$$

along every streamline in the flow. This equation is known as *Bernoulli's equation.*

If subscripts 1 and 2 denote two locations on a streamline, and Ω represents the potential energy of the gravitational field (which field is considered to be constant), then the Bernoulli's equation can be written as

$$\frac{V_1^2}{2} + \frac{P_1}{\rho} + g\zeta_1 = \frac{V_2^2}{2} + \frac{P_2}{\rho} + g\zeta_2$$

$$= \text{const. along a streamline} \tag{5-15}$$

in view of Eq. 4-10a.

Equation 5-15 can be rewritten in the form

$$\frac{V^2}{2g} + \frac{P}{g\rho} + \zeta = \text{const. along a streamline} \tag{5-15a}$$

where $g\rho = \gamma$ represents the specific weight of the fluid. All terms in the above equation have the dimension of length. The term $V^2/2g$ is known as the *velocity head*, while the term $P/g\rho$ is known as the *pressure head.* The term ζ, which represents the elevation of the point on a given streamline, is referred to as the *position head.* The sum of the pressure head and the position head is called the *piezometric head*, while the sum of the velocity head, pressure head, and the position head is known as the *total head.*

The Bernoulli equation applied to a fluid flow in a gravitational field can therefore be stated in words by saying that the *total head is constant along a streamline in a steady incompressible flow of a perfect fluid.*

Note that Bernoulli's equation, since it is derived from Euler's momentum equation, is valid only for perfect fluids. Therefore, in the study of flow of real fluids having small viscosity, we can expect it to hold only in the flow regions outside of the boundary layers since there the effects of viscosity are large. From our discussion in Sec. 1-4 it should also be clear that Bernoulli's equation cannot be applied to highly turbulent flows.

Application of Bernoulli's Equation. Consider a flow of a liquid from a large container through a small opening, as shown in Fig. 5-2. Since the container is large and the opening is small, the change in the elevation of the free surface of the liquid in the container is very slow and, for a brief period of time, the flow can be considered as steady. If the small viscous effects and the effects of the curvature of the jet of the liquid issuing from the opening are neglected, then the flow variables such as the fluid velocity and pressure can be assumed to be constant across the jet at the opening (section 2 in Fig. 5-2) because the jet is thin and therefore the effect of the gravitational force on them is small.

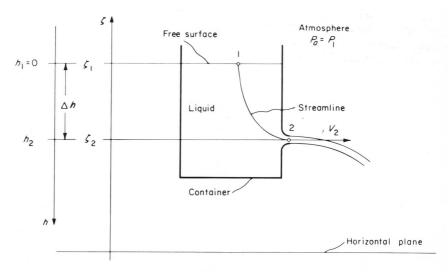

FIG. 5-2. Flow of a liquid from a container through a small opening.

Observe that, strictly speaking, the flow variables in a steady fluid flow can be constant across streamlines only if the streamlines are straight and parallel. This follows from the momentum equation in direction of the principal normal to a streamline having radius of curvature R:

$$\frac{V_\theta^2}{R} = \frac{1}{\rho} \frac{\partial P}{\partial R} + g \frac{\partial \zeta}{\partial R}$$

where V_θ^2/R represents the normal component of acceleration of fluid elements, which equation follows from the first equation of Eq. 5-12. When the streamlines are straight, in which case $R = \infty$, and the flow incompressible,

$$\frac{P}{\rho} + g\zeta = \text{const.} \tag{5-16}$$

across them. If $\zeta = \text{const.}$, we have $P = \text{const.}$ across the straight streamlines.

Making use of Bernoulli's equation we can derive an equation for the magnitude of the flow velocity at the exit from the small opening. For the streamline indicated in Fig. 5-2 we can write

$$\frac{V_2^2}{2} + \frac{P_2}{\rho} + g\zeta_2 = \frac{P_1}{\rho} + g\zeta_1$$

because $V_1 \simeq 0$. In view of our assumptions we also have $P_2 \simeq P_1$, if the hydrostatic pressure difference of the atmosphere $g(\rho_{\text{atm}} \zeta)_1 - g(\rho_{\text{atm}} \zeta)_2$ is negligible when compared to the hydrostatic pressure difference of the liquid $g\rho(\zeta_1 - \zeta_2)$. As a result we obtain expression

$$V_2 = \sqrt{2g(\zeta_1 - \zeta_2)}$$

$$= \sqrt{2g\,\Delta h} \tag{5-17}$$

where $\Delta h = h_2 - h_1 = \zeta_1 - \zeta_2$, with h denoting the vertical coordinate used in Sec. 1-6. This equation is known as *Toricelli's equation*. (Observe that the magnitude of the fluid velocity as given by Toricelli's equation is quite independent of the direction of flow leaving the surface. That is, the opening may point upward, downward, or in any other direction.)

The expression for the volumetric rate of flow of an incompressible fluid escaping from a large container through an opening can thus be written as

$$Q = A\sqrt{2g\,\Delta h} \tag{5-18}$$

where A denotes the cross-sectional area of the opening.

To account for the fact that the cross-sectional area of the jet issuing from the opening can be smaller than that of the opening (this is true when the opening is in the form of a sharp-edged orifice) and for the viscous effects which are present in flows of real fluids, we introduce a correction factor c_d, known as the *discharge coefficient*, to Eq. 5-18 and write

$$Q = c_d A\sqrt{2g\,\Delta h} \tag{5-18a}$$

The discharge coefficient depends on the shape of the opening and the Reynolds number (based on the diameter of the opening if the opening is round).

Note that the dimensional analysis would yield, for a perfect fluid, the relation

$$\frac{Q}{A} = \text{const.}\,\sqrt{g\,\Delta h}$$

when applied to this flow system.

Bernoulli's Equation for a Flow Through a Duct. Let subscripts 1 and 2 denote normal cross sections of a duct through which flows a fluid considered to be incompressible and perfect. (By a normal cross section we mean that cross section which is normal to the streamlines.) The flow is steady, and the duct has varying cross-sectional area, as shown in Fig. 5-3. In view of Bernoulli's equation (Eq. 5-15) we can write the following equation for an elementary stream tube in such flow

$$\left(\frac{V_1^2}{2} + \frac{P_1}{\rho} + g\zeta_1\right)V_1\,dA_1 = \left(\frac{V_2^2}{2} + \frac{P_2}{\rho} + g\zeta_2\right)V_2\,dA_2 = \text{const.}$$

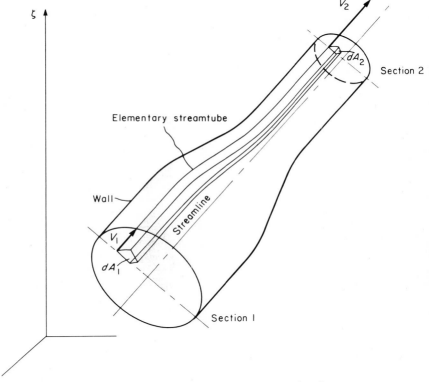

FIG. 5-3. Flow in a duct of varying cross-sectional area.

for any cross section of the stream tube. In this equation dA represents a normal cross-sectional area of the elementary stream tube, while $V\,dA$ represents the constant volumetric rate of flow of the fluid through the stream tube. That the volumetric rate of fluid flow is constant follows from the continuity equation.

Since the fluid is assumed to be perfect (it is assumed to glide without friction along the walls of the duct), the last equation is valid for any elementary stream tube of the flow, and we can write

$$\int_{A_1} \frac{V_1^3}{2} dA + \int_{A_1} \left(\frac{P_1}{\rho} + g\zeta_1\right) V_1\, dA = \int_{A_2} \frac{V_2^3}{2} dA + \int_{A_2} \left(\frac{P_2}{\rho} + g\zeta_2\right) V_2\, dA$$

$$(5\text{-}19)$$

If the normal cross sections 1 and 2 of the duct are so chosen that the streamlines are essentially straight and parallel there, then the term

$$\frac{P}{\rho} + g\zeta = \text{const.} \qquad (5\text{-}20)$$

across the sections. This follows from Eq. 5-16. The last relation is valid even when large variation of the pressure P and elevation ζ exists over the cross section. As a result we obtain relation

$$\frac{P}{\rho} + g\zeta + \frac{\int_A \frac{V^3}{2} dA}{\int_A V\, dA} = \text{const.} \qquad (5\text{-}19a)$$

across the sections. The term $\int_A V\, dA$ can be written as

$$\int_A V\, dA = \int_A \mathbf{V} \cdot d\mathbf{A} = Q = A\overline{V} \qquad (5\text{-}21)$$

where $\overline{V}$ represents the average flow speed at a given cross section based on the rate of flow of the fluid.

Introducing the so-called *kinetic energy correction factor* α which for an incompressible fluid flow is defined by

$$\alpha = \frac{\int_A \left(\frac{V^2}{2}\right) V\, dA}{\left(\frac{\overline{V}^2}{2}\right)\overline{V} A} = \frac{\int_A V^3\, dA}{\overline{V}^3 A} \qquad (5\text{-}22)$$

we can write Eq. 5-19a as

$$\frac{P}{\rho} + g\zeta + \alpha \frac{\overline{V}^2}{2} = \text{const.} \qquad (5\text{-}23)$$

for each normal cross section of the duct at which the streamlines are straight and parallel.

Equation 5-23 can be considered as a form of Bernoulli's equation valid for a normal cross section of a duct (in which flows a perfect and incompressible fluid).

The term $\alpha\, \overline{V}^2/2$ represents the average kinetic energy per unit mass of the fluid at a given cross section. When the flow is one-dimensional, in which case the flow velocity is uniform across the normal cross sections of the duct, the kinetic energy correction factor $\alpha = 1$. Observe that Eq. 5-23 cannot in general be applied to flows of real fluids without introducing a correction factor for the pressure drop resulting from viscous friction. Such a correction factor will be introduced in Sec. 9-2.

From Eq. 5-23 and the continuity equation

$$Q = A_1\overline{V_1} = A_2\overline{V_2}$$

we can obtain the following expression for the volumetric rate of flow of an incompressible perfect fluid through a horizontal duct having variable cross-sectional area if we assume that the flow is one-dimensional (that is, $\alpha_1 = \alpha_2 = 1.0$):

$$Q = \frac{A_2}{\sqrt{1 - \left(\dfrac{A_2}{A_1}\right)^2}} \sqrt{\frac{2(P_1 - P_2)}{\rho}} \qquad (5\text{-}24)$$

Equation 5-24 indicates a simple relation between the volumetric rate of flow through a duct of variable cross-sectional area, the fluid density, cross-sectional areas, and the corresponding pressure difference. This fact allows us to use such a duct of variable cross section to measure rates of fluid flow. The rate-of-flow measuring instrument in which the cross-sectional area decreases and then increases is known as a *Venturi tube*. We shall return to the discussion of Venturi tubes in Chapter 9. Since Eq. 5-24 is valid only for perfect fluids, when applied to the Venturi tubes it is modified by introduction of the *discharge coefficient* c_d by writing

$$Q = c_d \frac{A_2}{\sqrt{1 - \left(\dfrac{A_2}{A_1}\right)^2}} \sqrt{\frac{2(P_1 - P_2)}{\rho}} \qquad (5\text{-}25)$$

The discharge coefficient depends on the Reynolds number (which is usually based on the duct diameter ahead of the contraction) and the geometry of the Venturi tube.

Remark Concerning Bernoulli's Equation. If we do not assume a steady flow in the derivation of Bernoulli's equation, we end up with equation

$$\int \frac{\partial \mathbf{V}}{\partial t} \cdot d\mathbf{r} + \frac{V^2}{2} + \frac{P}{\rho} + g\zeta = \text{const. along a streamline}$$

This equation, although valid in an unsteady flow, holds in general only at a definite instant. This is so because, in general, in unsteady motions the streamlines are at different times made up of different fluid elements, and therefore the values of the "constant" change. Even in the case of an unsteady flow in which streamlines retain their shape, the "constant" is a function of time because $\mathbf{V} = \mathbf{V}(t)$ and $P = P(t)$.

General Integral Along an Arbitrary Line in an Irrotational Barotropic Flow. For an irrotational flow, Euler's momentum equation reduces to

$$\frac{\partial \mathbf{V}}{\partial t} = -\left[\frac{1}{\rho}\nabla P + \nabla \Omega + \nabla \left(\frac{V^2}{2}\right)\right] \qquad (5\text{-}26)$$

This follows from Eq. 5-6, since in an irrotational flow $\nabla \times \mathbf{V} = \mathbf{0}$.
Writing $\mathbf{V} = \nabla \phi$ and assuming a barotropic flow, we have

$$\nabla \left(\frac{\partial \phi}{\partial t} + \int \frac{dP}{\rho} + \frac{V^2}{2} + \Omega \right) = \mathbf{0}$$

because then $\nabla \int (1/\rho)\, dP = (1/\rho)\nabla P$ which can be verified by forming
the scalar product of these vectors with the differential of the position
vector $d\mathbf{r}$. Performing integration of the last equation *along an arbitrary
line* in the flow field, we obtain the equation

$$\frac{\partial \phi}{\partial t} + \int \frac{dP}{\rho} + \frac{V^2}{2} + \Omega = C(t) \tag{5-27}$$

where $C(t)$ is a function of time having the same value everywhere in the
flow field at a given instant. This equation represents the mathematical
formulation of the so-called *Bernoulli-Euler theorem for potential flow.*

For a steady irrotational and incompressible fluid flow, the Bernoulli-
Euler equation reduces to

$$\frac{V^2}{2} + \frac{P}{\rho} + \Omega = \text{const.} \tag{5-28}$$

along an arbitrary line in the flow field.

If subscripts 1 and 2 denote any two arbitrary points in a steady irrotational and incompressible flow field, and if Ω represents the potential
energy of the gravitational field (which field is considered to be constant),
then the Bernoulli-Euler equation (in view of Eq. 4-10) becomes

$$\frac{V_1^2}{2} + \frac{P_1}{\rho} + g\zeta_1 = \frac{V_2^2}{2} + \frac{P_2}{\rho} + g\zeta_2 = \text{const. along an arbitrary line}$$

$$\tag{5-29}$$

The Bernoulli-Euler equation is much more powerful than Bernoulli's
equation which it includes as a special case. It is valid only in a potential
(that is, irrotational) flow.[1]

Application of Bernoulli-Euler Equation. The Bernoulli-Euler equation
allows us to determine the variation of pressure in an incompressible flow
field of a fluid whose motion is irrotational, once the velocity variation is
known. Introducing the *pressure coefficient C_p* defined by

$$C_P = \frac{P - P_\infty}{\frac{1}{2}\, \rho U_\infty^2} \tag{5-30}$$

---

[1] As will be shown in Sec. 7-4, for irrotational and incompressible flows the momentum
equation of Newtonian fluids reduces to Euler's momentum equation. For that reason,
Eq. 5-29 also applies to such viscous-fluid flows. However, since in general the flows of
viscous fluids are rotational, it has little usefulness in their study. For an irrotational
flow of a viscous fluid, see Prob. 7-6.

where P_∞ and U_∞ respectively denote the (static) pressure and flow speed in the free stream (that is, the undisturbed uniform stream) and utilizing the Bernoulli-Euler equation written in the form $P + \dfrac{\rho V^2}{2} = P_\infty + \dfrac{\rho U_\infty^2}{2}$, that is, not concerning ourselves with the effects of the gravitational attraction if any between the points considered, we have

$$C_P = 1 - \frac{V^2}{U_\infty^2} \tag{5-31}$$

[The gravitational effects are negligible for gases. They do not exist for liquids if the points in the flow field between which the Bernoulli-Euler equation is used lie in the same horizontal planes (for the constant gravitational field). When the gravity effects exist, then we should look upon P in Eq. 5-30 as representing the sum $(P + g\rho\zeta)$.]

In Sec. 3-10 we derived equations for the velocity components in a number of potential incompressible flows. For the flow obtained by placing a two-dimensional source in a uniform stream we obtained

$$u = \frac{\partial \psi}{\partial y} = -U_\infty + \frac{Q}{2\pi} \frac{\cos \theta}{r} \tag{3-102}$$

and

$$v = -\frac{\partial \psi}{\partial x} = \frac{Q}{2\pi} \frac{\sin \theta}{r} \tag{3-103}$$

from which it follows that

$$V^2 = u^2 + v^2 = U_\infty^2 + \frac{Q^2}{4\pi^2 r^2} - \frac{Q U_\infty}{\pi} \frac{\cos \theta}{r}$$

As a result, in such flow

$$C_P = 1 - \frac{V^2}{U_\infty^2} = \frac{Q}{2\pi r U_\infty}\left(2\cos\theta - \frac{Q}{2\pi r U_\infty}\right) \tag{5-32}$$

The equation for the streamline $\psi = 0$ indicated in Fig. 3-23 was shown in Sec. 3-10 to be

$$\frac{\theta}{\pi} = \frac{2U_\infty}{Q} r \sin \theta$$

which can be rewritten as

$$\frac{Q}{2\pi r U_\infty} = \frac{\sin \theta}{\theta}$$

As a result, the pressure distribution over the surface of the solid body represented by the streamline $\psi = 0$ in an inviscid and incompressible flow is given by

$$C_P = \frac{P - P_\infty}{\frac{1}{2}\rho U_\infty^2} = \left(\frac{\sin \theta}{\theta}\right)^2 (2\theta \cot \theta - 1) \tag{5-33}$$

The pressure on this solid body in the potential flow under consideration is equal to the free-stream pressure P_∞ for $\theta \cot \theta = \frac{1}{2}$, or for $\theta = \pm 66.8°$. At the nose of the body the pressure attains a maximum value of $P_\infty + \frac{1}{2} \rho U_\infty^2$, since for $\theta = 0$ the pressure coefficient becomes unity. For the values of θ larger than 66.8 deg the pressure decreases at first with increasing θ and then increases back to P_∞, since for $\theta = \pi$ we have $C_p = 0$. Figure 5-4 shows the pressure distribution on the surface of the object.

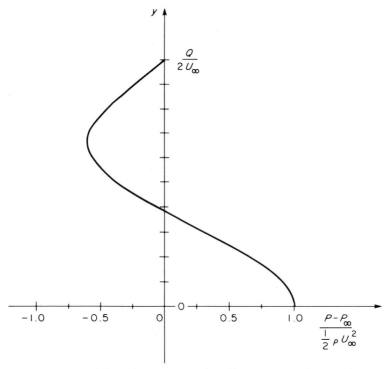

FIG. 5-4. Variation of pressure on the object corresponding to the streamline $\psi = 0$ shown in Fig. 3-23 in a steady two-dimensional potential incompressible flow of a perfect fluid.

For a potential (that is irrotational) flow of a perfect fluid, the knowledge of the pressure distribution on the surface of an object immersed in a fluid of infinite extent allows us to calculate the drag, or resistance to motion, experienced by the object. (There is no skin-friction drag in such a flow.) For the body under consideration, the expression for the drag in such a flow can be written in the form of integral

$$D = \int (P - P_\infty) \, dy$$

with the integration performed over the surface of the object. In this case

$$D = 2 \int_0^{Q/2U_\infty} (P - P_\infty)\, dy = \rho U_\infty^2 \int_0^{Q/2U_\infty} \frac{Q}{2\pi U_\infty} \left(2\frac{\cos\theta}{r} - \frac{Q}{2\pi U_\infty}\frac{1}{r^2}\right) dy$$

$$= \frac{\rho U_\infty Q}{2\pi} \left[\int_0^\pi \frac{2\cos\theta\sin\theta}{\theta}\, d\theta - \int_0^\pi \frac{\sin^2\theta}{\theta^2}\, d\theta\right]$$

because, for the surface of the object $\theta = 2\pi U_\infty y/Q$, while $r = y/\sin\theta$. Since

$$\int_0^\pi \frac{\sin^2\theta}{\theta^2}\, d\theta = -\frac{\sin^2\theta}{\theta}\Big|_0^\pi + 2\int_0^\pi \frac{\cos\theta\sin\theta}{\theta}\, d\theta$$

we obtain for the drag

$$D = \frac{\rho U_\infty Q}{2\pi}\left(-\frac{\sin^2\theta}{\theta}\Big|_0^\pi\right) = 0 \tag{5-34}$$

because

$$\lim_{\theta\to 0} \frac{\sin^2\theta}{\theta} = \lim_{\theta\to 0} \frac{2\sin\theta\cos\theta}{1} = 0$$

The reason why the calculated resistance of the object to the flow is zero is the result of our assumption that the flow is irrotational and ships freely on the surface of the object (the fluid is perfect). In the flow of a real fluid the object would experience a drag as a result of viscosity of the fluid. The calculated pressure distribution for an irrotational flow is nevertheless a valid approximation near the nose of the object (and up to the point of minimum pressure) which is placed symmetrically with respect to the incoming stream.

For a two-dimensional flow about a cylinder immersed in a stream of an incompressible perfect fluid of infinite extent flowing with a speed U_∞ we obtained, in Sec. 3-10, the following expressions for the velocity components on the surface of the cylinder:

$$V_\theta = 2U_\infty \sin\theta \qquad \text{and} \qquad V_r = 0$$

As a result, in this case

$$C_P = 1 - 4\sin^2\theta \tag{5-35}$$

Figure 5-5 shows a plot of the pressure distribution on the surface of the cylinder. Angles $\theta = 0$ and $\theta = \pi$ correspond to the forward and rear stagnation points (or lines, since the cylinders possess certain height). Figure 5-6 shows another representation of the same pressure distribution. As in the previous example, the drag acting on the cylinder in an irrotational flow of a perfect fluid is zero. This result follows directly from inspection of the pressure distribution shown in Fig. 5-5 or Fig. 5-6. We shall return to the discussion of drag acting on objects immersed in flowing fluids when considering the flow of real fluids in Chapter 8.

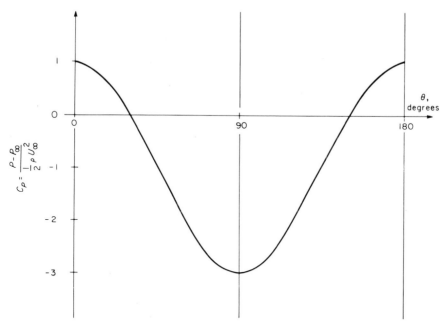

FIG. 5-5. Variation of pressure on the surface of a cylinder in a two-dimensional steady-potential flow of a perfect incompressible fluid.

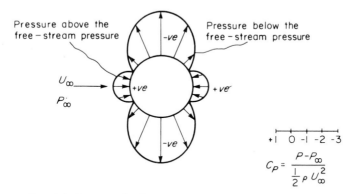

FIG. 5-6. Pressure distribution on the surface of a circular cylinder in a two-dimensional incompressible flow of a perfect fluid presented in form of values of the pressure coefficient.

The term $\frac{1}{2}\rho V^2$ is usually known as the *dynamic pressure* (sometimes called also the *kinetic pressure*). We found that for the objects immersed in an incompressible fluid flowing with the speed U_∞ the difference between the static pressure P and P_∞ at the stagnation points was equal to $\frac{1}{2}\rho U_\infty^2$. A general statement can be made that for a flow of an incompressible fluid, the (static) pressure at the stagnation points, which is known as the *stagnation pressure* or the *total pressure*, is given by

$$P_t = P_\infty + \frac{1}{2} \rho U_\infty^2 \qquad (5\text{-}36)$$

From the Bernoulli-Euler equation it follows that *the total pressure (as defined above) is constant throughout a steady potential flow of an incompressible fluid.* [Observe that the more general definition of the total pressure would include the term $g\rho\zeta$ in it. (See the definition of the total head following Eq. 5-15a.)]

Lift Acting on a Cylinder with Circulation. For flows of a perfect fluid, knowledge of the variation of pressure on the surface of an object allows us to determine the components of the force acting on the object. In the case of an irrotational flow of an incompressible fluid past a circular cylinder we found that the drag acting on the cylinder was zero. From the symmetry of the pressure distribution it also follows that there is no force acting at right angle to the direction of flow of the free stream.

In the case of a potential flow past a circular cylinder with circulation, the symmetry of the distribution of streamlines (and therefore also of the pressure distribution) with respect to the axis perpendicular to the direction of flow of the undisturbed (free) stream and passing through the axis of the cylinder indicates that, as in other potential flow examples, the drag acting on the cylinder is zero. Since there is no symmetry in the distribution of streamlines with respect to an axis having direction of flow of the undisturbed stream and passing through the axis of the cylinder, we can expect existence of a force acting on the cylinder in direction perpendicular to the direction of flow of the undisturbed stream. For the direction of flow of the undisturbed stream and the circulation corresponding to that illustrated in Fig. 3-26 we can expect an upward force acting on the cylinder because, since the streamlines, which were drawn for approximately equal increments $\Delta\psi$, are more closely spaced near the upper side of the cylinder than near the lower side, the flow speeds are higher there. As a result, the pressure is lower near the upper side than at the lower side. This follows from the Bernoulli-Euler equation. A force acting on an object in direction perpendicular to the direction of flow of the undisturbed (free) stream is called the *lift*.

In Sec. 3-10 we showed that the velocity components on the surface of a cylinder of radius a placed in a perfect incompressible fluid flowing with speed U_∞, with circulation present, are

$$V_\theta = 2 U_\infty \sin\theta + \frac{\Gamma}{2\pi a}$$

$$V_r = 0 \qquad\qquad [3\text{-}112]$$

Hence

$$C_P = \frac{P - P_\infty}{\frac{1}{2}\rho U_\infty^2} = 1 - 4\sin^2\theta - \frac{2\Gamma\sin\theta}{\pi a U_\infty} - \frac{\Gamma^2}{4\pi^2 a^2 U_\infty^2} \qquad (5\text{-}37)$$

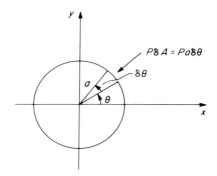

FIG. 5-7. Force acting on an element of surface of a cylinder of unit height around which flows a perfect fluid.

The expression for the lift L acting on a cylinder of unit height is

$$L = -\int_0^{2\pi} Pa \sin \theta \, d\theta = -\int_0^{2\pi} (P - P_\infty) a \sin \theta \, d\theta$$

(see Fig. 5-7) because P_∞ = const. As a result we obtain

$$L = -\frac{1}{2} \rho U_\infty^2 a \int_0^{2\pi} \left(\sin \theta - 4 \sin^3\theta - \frac{2\Gamma \sin^2\theta}{\pi a U_\infty} - \frac{\Gamma^2 \sin \theta}{4\pi^2 a^2 U_\infty^2} \right) d\theta$$

$$= \frac{\rho U_\infty \Gamma}{\pi} \int_0^{2\pi} \sin^2\theta \, d\theta = \rho U_\infty \Gamma \qquad (5\text{-}38)$$

For the lift coefficient, for a cylinder of unit height, we obtain

$$C_L = \frac{L}{\frac{1}{2} \rho U_\infty^2 \, 2a} = \frac{\Gamma}{a U_\infty} \qquad (5\text{-}39)$$

The result which we just obtained is quite significant. It shows that the lift is independent of the size (radius a) of the cylinder, and is proportional to the circulation Γ. Hence it is the action of the (free) vortex which is responsible for the generation of the lift in the flow under consideration. It is left as a homework assignment to show that Eq. 5-38 is valid for a free vortex held in place in a uniform flow.

A flow with circulation of a real fluid past a cylinder can be obtained in practice by providing rotation about its axis to the cylinder which is in relative translatory motion with respect to the fluid. The circulation in such flow results from the action of viscosity at the surface of the cylinder. Such flow is not wholly irrotational. The lifting force acting on rotating cylinders or spheres traveling through a fluid is known as the *Magnus effect*. Figure 5-8 is a photograph of a flow of water past a rotating cylin-

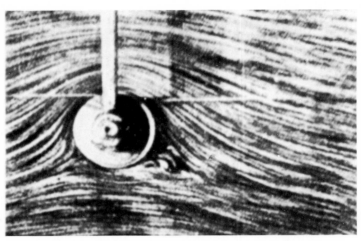

FIG. 5-8. Photograph of a flow of a fluid past a rotating cylinder.
Direction of flow is from left to right. (After L. Prandtl)

der. Observe the similarity of the shape of the streamlines shown in this photograph and those in Fig. 3-26a. Observe also the region of separated flow.

Although we may be justified to consider a potential flow past a cylinder with circulation, when studying flows of a perfect fluid, as a result of the fact that a nonviscous fluid slips on solid surfaces, no vortex motion would be produced in a perfect fluid by a rotating cylinder.

The above discussion should provide us with an appreciation of the effect of circulation which results in the generation of lift on bodies traveling through a fluid. Equation 5-38 is valid for a cylinder of an arbitrary shape which travels through a fluid with circulation present. (This can be rigorously proven with the aid of the *Blasius theorem* in whose derivation we make use of the theory of functions of complex variable.) It is often referred to as the *Kutta–Joukowski law*. As was already pointed out, the origin of circulation in fluid flows over objects can be traced to the viscosity, however small, of the fluid. In the next section we shall discuss briefly the process of generation of circulation (and therefore also of lift) in a flow past an airfoil in a fluid having small viscosity.

Calculations show that for any object immersed in a fluid which is in a steady motion relative to the object and uniform far upstream there would be no forces acting on the object if the fluid had zero viscosity (this we take here to imply absence of circulation) and the flow were subsonic everywhere. This is known as the *d'Alembert paradox*, which remained unexplained until the importance of viscosity, however small, of the fluid which is responsible for the generation of circulation in flows over lifting bodies and for the formation of the boundary layers and wakes, and the phenomenon of separation of flow became recognized. (By lifting bodies we mean objects which are nonsymmetrical or are nonsymmetrically placed with respect to the incoming flow, or, when symmetrical like cylinders or spheres, which are in rotation as well as translation with respect to the fluid.)

5-4. THE LAW OF CONSERVATION OF CIRCULATION

In Sec. 3-4 we showed that the equation for the rate of change with time of circulation for a material line C is given by

$$\frac{D\Gamma}{Dt} = \oint_C \frac{D\mathbf{V}}{Dt} \cdot d\mathbf{r} \qquad\qquad [3\text{-}18]$$

For perfect fluids the expression for the acceleration of fluid elements, $D\mathbf{V}/Dt$, is given by Euler's momentum equation. Assuming that the body forces are conservative, like the force due to gravitational attraction, we can introduce Eq. 5-4 into Eq. 3-18. We obtain the expression

$$\frac{D\Gamma}{Dt} = -\oint_C \frac{1}{\rho} \nabla P \cdot d\mathbf{r} - \oint_C \nabla \Omega \cdot d\mathbf{r} \qquad (5\text{-}40)$$

For barotropic fluid flows, that is for the flows in which either the density of the fluid is a function of pressure only or the density is constant, since both the potential energy Ω and the pressure P are single-valued scalar-field functions, both integrals on the right-hand side of Eq. 5-40 vanish. As a result, we obtain

$$\frac{D\Gamma}{Dt} = 0 \qquad\qquad (5\text{-}41)$$

This result can be expressed in words by saying that a flow of a perfect fluid in a field of conservative body forces is circulation preserving only if it is barotropic. This is known as the *Hankel–Kelvin circulation theorem* (1861, 1869)[1], or the *law of conservation of circulation*.

Observe that Eqs. 3-18, 5-40, and 5-41 indicate that for any barotropic flow of a perfect fluid in a field of conservative body forces we can express the acceleration of the fluid elements as $\mathbf{a} = D\mathbf{V}/Dt = \nabla \phi^*$ where ϕ^* denotes a single-valued potential.

The restrictions which we had to put on a fluid flow to which the law of conservation of circulation applies allow us to enumerate the effects which are responsible for generation of vorticity in a fluid. These are as follows: the viscous effects, the effects resulting from the fact that the flow may not be barotropic, and the effects resulting when the body forces are not conservative. The action of viscosity on generation of vorticity was already discussed in Sec. 3-4. As a result of viscosity, vorticity is generated *at the boundary* of the fluid and spreads to other flow regions by diffusion. The lack of barotropy in a fluid flow, such as may exist in the vicinity of a lit candle (in the presence of gravitational attraction), can result in generation vorticity *within* the fluid. (By considering the circulation about a closed rectangular circuit with horizontal and vertical sides having one vertical side passing through the region in which the heated fluid moves upward as a result of buoyancy and one vertical side outside of this region, we can easily show that the circulation is not zero and therefore that vortices must pass through the circuit. The vortices in this case are ring-shaped and lie in horizontal planes.) Since the force of gravitational attraction is conservative, the restriction placed on the body forces in the derivation of the law of conservation loses its importance from the practical point of view in this study.

In the derivation of the law of conservation of circulation we made a tacit restriction that the flow is continuous, since only for such perfect-fluid flow we can use the Euler's momentum equation (which involves spatial derivatives). This restriction is important in the study of high-speed flows of gases treated as perfect fluids in which discontinuity in the form of a curved shock wave is present. One effect of such discontinuity is generation of vorticity within the fluid at the discontinuity surface.

It is important to realize that the law of conservation of circulation does not preclude formation of vortex sheets or concentrated vortices (line vortices) in a perfect fluid. However, in such a fluid, once a vortex sheet or a vortex line is formed they persist and do not diffuse.

Figure 5-9 illustrates the law of conservation of circulation and the generation of circulation in a flow of a (real) fluid possessing very small viscosity past an airfoil (which circulation is responsible for the lift which acts on the airfoil). It shows the development of flow around an airfoil suddenly brought into motion relative to the surrounding water and subsequently suddenly brought to rest. Figure 5-9a shows the streamlines (made visible by spraying aluminium powder on the water) at the moment the airfoil is brought into motion relative to the water. Observe that the rear stagnation point (better: line, since the airfoil of finite length) is on the upper surface of the airfoil and the fluid tends to flow around the trailing edge. This flow requires very large velocities (infinitely large for a fluid model assumed to be nonviscous) at the sharp trailing edge. As a result of viscous effects in the thin boundary layer present near the surface of the airfoil, the fluid, flowing at high speed upward past the trailing edge (in a region of rising pressure), separates from the airfoil and forms what can be described as a surface of separation in the form of a vortex layer which rolls up and forms a vortex. This vortex, which is known as the *starting vortex*, is washed away with the fluid. The shedding of the starting vortex is shown in Fig. 5-9b. Once the starting vortex is shed, if the trailing edge is of zero thickness, the velocity of the fluid leaving the upper and lower airfoil surfaces equalizes. If the trailing edge

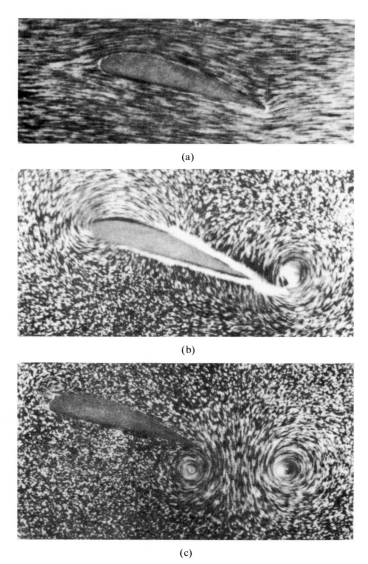

(a)

(b)

(c)

FIG. 5-9. Flow around an airfoil suddenly brought into motion and subsequently suddenly brought to rest relative to a
fluid having very small viscosity. (a) Photograph showing
streamlines at the moment the airfoil is brought impulsively
into motion (camera moving with the airfoil). (b) Shedding
of the starting vortex (camera at rest relative to the undisturbed fluid). (c) Shedding of the vortex, having equal
strength but opposite direction of rotation of the fluid to that
of the starting vortex, as the airfoil is brought suddenly to rest
(camera at rest relative to the undisturbed fluid). (From Ref. 6
by permission of United Engineering Trustees, Inc.)

has a finite vertex angle, it forms the rear stagnation line. This final flow pattern corresponds to the so-called *Kutta–Joukowski condition.*

To conserve the circulation in the fluid, as the starting vortex forms, circulation of the sense opposite to that of the starting vortex is created in the fluid around the airfoil and moves with it. (This is so because, even in this case of a flow in a real fluid having very small viscosity, the law of conservation of circulation is valid for a large circuit embracing both the airfoil and the starting vortex, since the viscous effects are confined to the vicinity of the airfoil and elsewhere the fluid behaves as though it were a perfect fluid.) This circulation can be thought of as being produced by a vortex which, unlike an ordinary vortex which moves with the fluid, is bound to the airfoil. [Since in real fluids having small viscosity a boundary layer forms near the surface of the airfoil, the bound vorticity (responsible for the circulation in the approximately irrotational flow outside the airfoil) is equal to the net boundary-layer vorticity.] If the airfoil is suddenly brought to rest, this bound vorticity is shed in the form of a concentrated vortex from the airfoil. Figure 5-9c shows the starting vortex and the vortex shed when the airfoil was brought to rest. In a perfect fluid, these vortices, to which correspond opposite directions of rotation, would have the same strength since there is no diffusion of vorticity in such a fluid.

Figure 5-10 illustrates the fluid motions corresponding to the potential flow without circulation and the pure circulatory flow (or the bound vortex which moves with the airfoil) which, when superimposed, result in the flow pattern of a perfect fluid around the airfoil after the starting vortex has been shed. (The flow of a real fluid possessing small viscosity past an airfoil is illustrated in Figs. 1-11a, 8-1, and 8-2. Observe formation of the boundary layers and of the wake in real-fluid flows.)

Each time the angle of attack of an airfoil in a steady motion is changed, the strength of the bound vorticity changes, and a vortex is shed from the airfoil. The same is also true, in general, when the speed of the flow around an airfoil is changed.

The fundamental importance of the Kutta–Joukowski condition is that it provides us with means to compute the lift (per unit span) on a two-dimensional lifting body such as a wing in a perfect fluid by proper choice of the circulation Γ. When the trailing edge of the lifting body is of zero thickness, this circulation results in a tangential, and therefore also finite, velocity at the trailing edge; when the trailing edge has a finite vertex angle, it results in a stagnation line there. The fact that the starting vortex in a real fluid eventually becomes dissipated has no effect on the flow pattern around the lifting body and therefore also on the forces acting on it. [In a real fluid possessing small viscosity, such as air, as a result of formation of the boundary layer and of the wake, the flow and the pressure distribution around the airfoil differ from that in a perfect

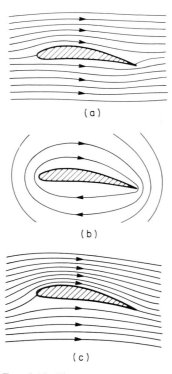

(a)

(b)

(c)

FIG. 5-10. Flow around an airfoil.
(a) Potential flow without circulation. (b) Pure circulatory flow, or
the bound vortex which moves
with the airfoil. (c) Potential flow
with circulation. (After L. Prandtl.)

fluid (see Fig. 8-39) and, as a consequence, the lift in a real fluid is always somewhat less than that calculated for a potential flow satisfying the Kutta–Joukowski condition.]

5-5. THE ENERGY EQUATION

Since the expression for the stress acting in perfect fluids is

$$\mathbf{t} = -P\mathbf{n} \qquad [1\text{-}1]$$

we have

$$-\oint_S \mathbf{t} \cdot \mathbf{V} \, dA = \oint_S \mathbf{n} \cdot (P\mathbf{V}) \, dA \qquad [4\text{-}12]$$

where $\mathbf{n}$ is the outward normal unit vector to an element of area of the fluid surface S. Making use of the divergence theorem of Gauss, we can rewrite the last equation in the form

$$-\oint_S \mathbf{t} \cdot \mathbf{V} \, dA \;=\; \int_{\mathcal{V}} \boldsymbol{\nabla} \cdot (P\mathbf{V}) \, d\mathcal{V} \tag{5-42}$$

As a result, the energy equation for a *material volume* $\overline{\mathcal{V}}$ (Eq. 4-5) valid for perfect fluids has the form

$$\frac{D}{Dt} \int_{\overline{\mathcal{V}}} q_{\text{rad}} \, \rho \, d\mathcal{V}$$

$$= \frac{D}{Dt} \int_{\overline{\mathcal{V}}} \left(e + \frac{V^2}{2}\right) \rho \, d\mathcal{V} \;-\; \int_{\overline{\mathcal{V}}} \mathbf{f} \cdot \mathbf{V}\rho \, d\mathcal{V} \;+\; \int_{\overline{\mathcal{V}}} \boldsymbol{\nabla} \cdot (P\mathbf{V}) \, d\mathcal{V} \tag{5-43}$$

We have omitted the term representing the heat transfer by conduction to the material volume $\overline{\mathcal{V}}$ because we are considering perfect fluids. [Observe that if a fluid is considered to be nonviscous, it must also be considered thermally nonconducting (see our discussion of viscosity and heat conductivity in Sec. 1-2).]   In view of Eq. 3-59,

$$\frac{D}{Dt} \int_{\overline{\mathcal{V}}} q_{\text{rad}} \, \rho \, d\mathcal{V} \;=\; \int_{\overline{\mathcal{V}}} \frac{Dq_{\text{rad}}}{Dt} \rho \, d\mathcal{V}$$

and

$$\frac{D}{Dt} \int_{\overline{\mathcal{V}}} \left(e + \frac{V^2}{2}\right) \rho \, d\mathcal{V} \;=\; \int_{\overline{\mathcal{V}}} \frac{D\left(e + \dfrac{V^2}{2}\right)}{Dt} \rho \, d\mathcal{V}$$

If we assume the body forces to be conservative and make use of the above relations, then Eq. 5-43 can be rewritten as

$$\int_{\overline{\mathcal{V}}} \left[\frac{D\left(e + \dfrac{V^2}{2} + \Omega\right)}{Dt} + \frac{1}{\rho} \boldsymbol{\nabla} \cdot (P\mathbf{V}) - \frac{Dq_{\text{rad}}}{Dt} \right] \rho \, d\mathcal{V} \;=\; 0$$

if we consider $\partial\Omega/\partial t = 0$. (The potential energy of gravitational attraction is not a function of time, only of position in space.)

Since the material volume $\overline{\mathcal{V}}$ is arbitrary, the integrand of this equation must vanish everywhere in the flow field, and we obtain the spatial form of the energy equation for a perfect fluid in a field of conservative body forces

$$\frac{Dq_{\text{rad}}}{Dt} \;=\; \frac{D\left(e + \dfrac{V^2}{2} + \Omega\right)}{Dt} + \frac{1}{\rho} \boldsymbol{\nabla} \cdot (P\mathbf{V}) \tag{5-44}$$

(The material time derivatives can be eliminated with the aid of Eq. 3-3).

For a *volume fixed in space* (relative to an inertial system) $\mathcal{V}$ the energy equation Eq. 4-23 is valid, since it was derived assuming hydrostatic state of stress on the fluid surface S' bounding the volume. (If the boundary of the fixed volume is made up wholly of a fluid surface, then the term involving the shaft work should be omitted.) For a steady flow Eq. 4-14 and 4-15 are also valid for perfect fluids.

Since

$$\nabla \cdot (PV) = V \cdot \nabla P + P \nabla \cdot V \tag{5-45}$$

by introducing the continuity equation (Eq. 3-56b) we obtain

$$\nabla \cdot (PV) = V \cdot \nabla P - \frac{P}{\rho} \frac{D\rho}{Dt}$$

$$= \frac{DP}{Dt} - \frac{\partial P}{\partial t} - \frac{P}{\rho} \frac{D\rho}{Dt}$$

$$= \rho \frac{D}{Dt} \left(\frac{P}{\rho} \right) - \frac{\partial P}{\partial t}$$

in view of Eq. 3-3. As a result, the energy equation (Eq. 5-44) can be rewritten as

$$\frac{Dq_{rad}}{Dt} = \frac{D \left(e + \dfrac{P}{\rho} + \dfrac{V^2}{2} + \Omega \right)}{Dt} - \frac{1}{\rho} \frac{\partial P}{\partial t} \tag{5-46}$$

For a steady flow in the field of constant gravitational forces the energy equation becomes

$$\frac{D}{Dt} \left(e + \frac{P}{\rho} + \frac{V^2}{2} + g\zeta - q_{rad} \right) = 0 \tag{5-47}$$

Eq. 5-47 can also be written in the form

$$\left(e + \frac{P}{\rho} + \frac{V^2}{2} + g\zeta \right)_2 - (q_{rad})_{1-2} = \left(e + \frac{P}{\rho} + \frac{V^2}{2} + g\zeta \right)_1 \tag{5-47a}$$

or

$$\left(h + \frac{V^2}{2} + g\zeta \right)_2 - (q_{rad})_{1-2} = \left(h + \frac{V^2}{2} + g\zeta \right)_1 \tag{5-47b}$$

where points 1 and 2 lie on the same streamline. In general, the heat transfer by radiation to a flowing fluid is negligible and the term involving it can be omitted.

For compressible fluids the energy equation (say in form of Eq. 5-47) differs from the equation

$$\frac{V^2}{2} + \int \frac{dP}{\rho} + g\zeta = \text{const. along a streamline} \tag{5-13a}$$

which may be called the Bernoulli's equation for compressible fluids. Eq. 5-13a can be transformed into Eq. 5-47 with the aid of the *first law of thermodynamics* which, for the continuous changes of state of a perfect fluid, can be written as

$$q_{1-2} = e_2 - e_1 + \int_1^2 P dv$$

$$= h_2 - h_1 - \int_1^2 \frac{dP}{\rho} \tag{5-48}$$

where q_{1-2} denotes the heat transferred (in this case by radiation) to the fluid (per unit mass) during the change of state from some state 1 to state 2.

For incompressible (perfect) *fluids* it follows from Eq. 5-48 that

$$q_{1-2} = e_2 - e_1$$

As a result, Eq. 5-47 can be written in the form

$$\frac{V^2}{2} + \frac{P}{\rho} + g\zeta = \text{const. along a streamline} \qquad (5\text{-}49)$$

Hence *the energy equation for a steady flow of an incompressible perfect fluid is equivalent to Bernoulli's equation.*

5-6. EQUATIONS OF FLOW IN MOVING REFERENCE FRAMES[2]

Consider a volume fixed in the set of axes x', y', z' which rotate with an angular velocity $\boldsymbol{\omega}_P$ relative to the set of axes x,y,z which represent an inertial system, as shown in Fig. 5-11. Let a particle P within the volume be in motion relative to the x',y',z' axes. The position of the particle P in space can be represented by the position vector $\mathbf{r}$ drawn from the origin

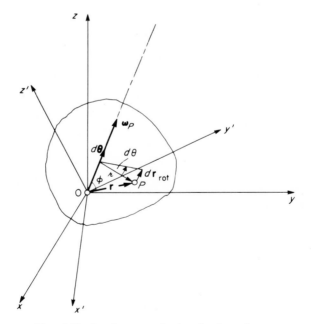

FIG. 5-11. A volume rotating in a fixed set of axes x, y, z.

[2] This section corresponds to Sec. 3-15 of Ref. 8 by the author.

of the axes, which is only a function of time and the initial position of the particle. The difference between the change of the vector $\mathbf{r}$ with time, as measured in the x,y,z axes $d\mathbf{r}$ and in the x',y',z' axes $d'\mathbf{r}$, is due to rotation. We have

$$d\mathbf{r} - d'\mathbf{r} = d\mathbf{r}_{\text{rot}} \qquad (5\text{-}50)$$

In this section the prime will refer to the derivatives and quantities measured in the x',y',z' system.

The change in the magnitude of the position vector $\mathbf{r}$ owing to rotation of the x',y',z' axes is

$$| d\mathbf{r}_{\text{rot}} | = r \sin \phi \, d\theta \qquad (5\text{-}51)$$

Therefore we can write

$$d\mathbf{r}_{\text{rot}} = d\theta \times \mathbf{r} \qquad (5\text{-}52)$$

where $d\theta$ represents a vector along the instantaneous axis of rotation whose magnitude is equal to the differential change of the angle of rotation θ and whose direction is that in which a right-handed screw advances when rotated in the direction considered. Equation 5-50 can thus be rewritten as

$$d\mathbf{r} = d'\mathbf{r} + d\theta \times \mathbf{r} \qquad (5\text{-}53)$$

The time rate of change of the position vector $\mathbf{r}$ of the particle is

$$\frac{D\mathbf{r}}{Dt} = \frac{D'\mathbf{r}}{Dt} + \boldsymbol{\omega}_P \times \mathbf{r} \qquad (5\text{-}54)$$

where $\boldsymbol{\omega}_P(t) = d\theta/dt$ denotes the angular velocity (a vector) whose direction is that of vector $d\theta$. The above equation can be rewritten as

$$\mathbf{V} = \mathbf{V}' + \boldsymbol{\omega}_P \times \mathbf{r} \qquad (5\text{-}55)$$

where $\mathbf{V} = D\mathbf{r}/Dt$ is the velocity of particle P in the inertial system and $\mathbf{V}' = D'\mathbf{r}/Dt$ is the velocity of particle P relative to the axes x',y',z'.

Equation 5-53 is valid in its form for any vector, not for the position vector $\mathbf{r}$ only. This is so because Eqs. 5-50 and 5-52 are valid for any vector. We may conclude, therefore, that for a rotating system there exists an operator

$$\frac{d}{dt} = \frac{d'}{dt} + \boldsymbol{\omega}_P \times \qquad (5\text{-}56)$$

with which we can operate on a vector to obtain the relation between its time rate of change in fixed axes and in the rotating system.

The expression for the acceleration acting on particle P can be obtained by operating with the operator (Eq. 5-56) on the velocity $\mathbf{V}$,

$$\mathbf{a} = \frac{D\mathbf{V}}{Dt} = \frac{D'\mathbf{V}}{Dt} + \boldsymbol{\omega}_P \times \mathbf{V}$$

$$= \frac{D'\mathbf{V}'}{Dt} + \frac{d\boldsymbol{\omega}_P}{dt} \times \mathbf{r} + \boldsymbol{\omega}_P \times \frac{D'\mathbf{r}}{Dt} + \boldsymbol{\omega}_P \times (\mathbf{V}' + \boldsymbol{\omega}_P \times \mathbf{r})$$

in view of Eq. 5-55 and because $d'\boldsymbol{\omega}_P/dt = d\boldsymbol{\omega}_P/dt$, which follows from Eq. 5-56. The above equation can be rewritten as

$$\mathbf{a} = \frac{D'\mathbf{V}'}{Dt} + 2\,\boldsymbol{\omega}_P \times \mathbf{V}' + \boldsymbol{\omega}_P \times (\boldsymbol{\omega}_P \times \mathbf{r}) + \frac{d\boldsymbol{\omega}_P}{dt} \times \mathbf{r} \qquad (5\text{-}57)$$

where $D'\mathbf{V}'/Dt = \mathbf{a}'$ represents the acceleration of particle P in the reference frame x',y',z'.

If the reference frame x',y',z' in which the volume containing particle P is fixed is in a translatory as well as a rotating motion with respect to the axes of the inertial frame, as shown in Fig. 5-12, then

$$\mathbf{r} = \mathbf{R} + \mathbf{r}' \qquad (5\text{-}58)$$

$$\mathbf{V} = \mathbf{V}' + \boldsymbol{\omega}_P \times \mathbf{r}' + \dot{\mathbf{R}} \qquad (5\text{-}59)$$

$$\mathbf{a} = \frac{D\mathbf{V}}{Dt}$$

$$= \frac{D'\mathbf{V}'}{Dt} + 2\,\boldsymbol{\omega}_P \times \mathbf{V}' + \boldsymbol{\omega}_P \times (\boldsymbol{\omega}_P \times \mathbf{r}') + \frac{d\boldsymbol{\omega}_P}{dt} \times \mathbf{r}' + \ddot{\mathbf{R}} \qquad (5\text{-}60)$$

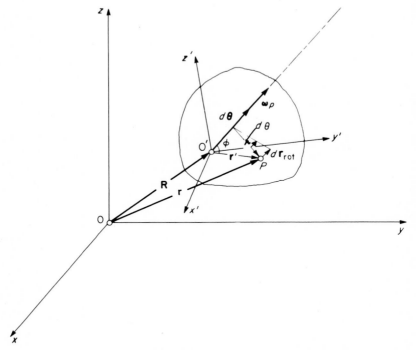

Fig. 5-12. General motion of a volume with respect to a fixed set of axes x, y, z.

where the dots over the position vector **R** denote differentiation with respect to time. The last formula for the acceleration of a material particle in a moving reference frame was derived by Coriolis in 1835. The term $2\,\omega_P \times \mathbf{V}'$ represents the Coriolis acceleration, which exists only when the particle possesses relative velocity $\mathbf{V}'$ in the rotating system. The term $\omega_P \times (\omega_P \times \mathbf{r}')$ represents the centripetal acceleration, which acts inward and whose magnitude is $\omega_P^2\, r'\sin\phi$. We can write $\omega_P \times (\omega_P \times \mathbf{r}') = -\omega_P^2\,\boldsymbol{\kappa}$ where $\boldsymbol{\kappa}$ is a vector perpendicular to the instantaneous axis of rotation and extending from this axis to point P. This is an easily recognizable form of the centripetal acceleration of a particle rotating about an axis. The term $(d\omega_P/dt) \times \mathbf{r}'$ is known as the Euler acceleration.

To an observer in the moving reference system, it appears as though the force acting on a particle of mass m is

$$\mathbf{F}' = \mathbf{F} - m\left[\ddot{\mathbf{R}} + 2\,\omega_P \times \mathbf{V}' + \omega_P \times (\omega_P \times \mathbf{r}') + \frac{d\omega_P}{dt} \times \mathbf{r}'\right] = m\mathbf{a}'$$

where $\mathbf{F} = m\mathbf{a}$ denotes the force in the inertial frame, $-m\omega_P \times (\omega_P \times \mathbf{r}')$ is the centrifugal force which acts outward, $-2m\omega_P \times \mathbf{V}'$ is the Coriolis force, and the whole term $-m[2\omega_P \times \mathbf{V}' + \omega_P \times (\omega_P \times \mathbf{r}') + (d\omega_P/dt) \times \mathbf{r}']$ represents the inertia force produced by the rotation of the system considered relative to the inertial system.

In view of Eqs. 5-3 and 5-60, the momentum equation for perfect fluids in a moving reference frame can be written in the form

$$\frac{D'\mathbf{V}'}{Dt} + 2\,\omega_P \times \mathbf{V}' + \omega_P \times (\omega_P \times \mathbf{r}') + \frac{d\omega_P}{dt} \times \mathbf{r}' + \ddot{\mathbf{R}}$$

$$= \frac{D\mathbf{V}}{Dt} = -\frac{1}{\rho}\,\nabla'P + \mathbf{f} \qquad (5\text{-}61)$$

The momentum equation for perfect fluids, written for a fixed volume in the moving reference frame whose boundary is made up wholly of a fluid surface, can be written as

$$\frac{\partial'}{\partial t}\int_V \mathbf{V}'\rho\,d\mathcal{V} + \oint_S \rho\mathbf{V}'(\mathbf{V}' \cdot d\mathbf{A})$$

$$+ \int_V \left[2\omega_P \times \mathbf{V}' + \omega_P \times (\omega_P \times \mathbf{r}') + \frac{d\omega_P}{dt} \times \mathbf{r}' + \ddot{\mathbf{R}}\right]\rho\,d\mathcal{V}$$

$$= \int_V \mathbf{f}\rho\,d\mathcal{V} - \oint_S \mathbf{n}P\,dA \qquad (5\text{-}62)$$

with $d\mathbf{A} = \mathbf{n}dA$, in view of Reynolds' transport theorem (Eq. 3-15) and Eq. 3-59.

Note that in writing Eq. 5-61 we have written the prime over the nabla sign. Whether we put the prime there or not makes no difference, because the rotation and translation of the axes do not affect the form of the expressions for the gradient, divergence, or curl; that is,

$$\nabla f = \nabla' f$$
$$\nabla \cdot \mathbf{F} = \nabla' \cdot \mathbf{F}$$
$$\nabla \times \mathbf{F} = \nabla' \times \mathbf{F}$$

For the divergence of the flow velocity $\mathbf{V}$, we get the expression

$$\nabla \cdot \mathbf{V} = \nabla' \cdot \mathbf{V} = \nabla' \cdot (\mathbf{V}' + \boldsymbol{\omega}_P \times \mathbf{r}' + \dot{\mathbf{R}}) = \nabla' \cdot \mathbf{V}'$$

in view of Eqs. A-46 and A-70.

Since the material time derivative of a scalar-field function is independent of the motion of the axes, we have

$$\frac{D'\rho}{Dt} = \frac{D\rho}{Dt}$$

As a result, the continuity equation becomes

$$\frac{D'\rho}{Dt} + \rho \nabla' \cdot \mathbf{V}' = 0 \tag{5-63}$$

For a fixed volume in the moving reference frame, it can be written in the form

$$-\frac{\partial'}{\partial t} \int_{\mathcal{V}} \rho \, d\mathcal{V} = \oint_S \mathbf{n} \cdot (\rho \mathbf{V}') \, dA \tag{5-64}$$

To derive the energy equation which includes terms that have to do with the work of the forces arising when considering motion in a moving coordinate system, we form the scalar product of the flow velocity $\mathbf{V}'$ with the vectors in the momentum equation (Eq. 5-61). Assuming conservative body forces, as

$$\mathbf{V}' \cdot \frac{D'\mathbf{V}'}{Dt} = \frac{D'\left(\dfrac{V'^2}{2}\right)}{Dt}$$

we obtain

$$\frac{D'\left(\dfrac{V'^2}{2}\right)}{Dt} + \mathbf{V}' \cdot \left[\boldsymbol{\omega}_P \times (\boldsymbol{\omega}_P \times \mathbf{r}') + \frac{d\boldsymbol{\omega}_P}{dt} \times \mathbf{r}' + \ddot{\mathbf{R}} \right]$$
$$= -\frac{1}{\rho} \mathbf{V}' \cdot \nabla P - \mathbf{V}' \cdot \nabla \Omega \tag{5-65}$$

The first law of thermodynamics can be written as

$$\frac{D'q_{\mathrm{rad}}}{Dt} = \frac{D'h}{Dt} - \frac{1}{\rho} \frac{D'P}{Dt} \tag{5-66}$$

Adding Eqs. 5-65 and 5-66 yields the energy equation for perfect fluids in the form

$$\frac{D'q_{rad}}{Dt} = \frac{D'\left(h + \frac{V'^2}{2} + \Omega\right)}{Dt}$$

$$+ \mathbf{V'} \cdot \left[\boldsymbol{\omega}_P \times (\boldsymbol{\omega}_P \times \mathbf{r'}) + \frac{d\boldsymbol{\omega}_P}{dt} \times \mathbf{r'} + \ddot{\mathbf{R}}\right] - \frac{1}{\rho}\frac{\partial'P}{\partial t} \qquad (5\text{-}67)$$

because we assume that $\partial\Omega/\partial t = 0$.

For a fixed volume in the moving reference frame, whose boundary is made up wholly of a fluid surface, the above equation can be written as

$$\int_{\mathcal{V}} \dot{q}_{rad} d\mathcal{V}$$

$$= \frac{\partial'}{\partial t} \int_{\mathcal{V}} \left(e + \frac{V'^2}{2}\right)\rho \, d\mathcal{V} + \oint_S \left(e + \frac{V'^2}{2}\right)\rho \mathbf{V'} \cdot d\mathbf{A} + \int_{\mathcal{V}} \mathbf{V'} \cdot \boldsymbol{\nabla}\Omega\rho \, d\mathcal{V}$$

$$+ \int_{\mathcal{V}} \mathbf{V'} \cdot \left[\boldsymbol{\omega}_P \times (\boldsymbol{\omega}_P \times \mathbf{r'}) + \frac{d\boldsymbol{\omega}_P}{dt} \times \mathbf{r'} + \ddot{\mathbf{R}}\right]\rho \, d\mathcal{V}$$

$$+ \oint_S \mathbf{n} \cdot (P\mathbf{V'}) \, dA \qquad (5\text{-}68)$$

in view of Eqs. 3-59, 3-15, and 3-56, where $\dot{q}_{rad} = \partial(q_{rad}\,\rho)/\partial t$ represents the rate of heat transfer per unit volume by radiation to the fluid instantaneously in the fixed volume. (See comment following Eq. 4-6.)

REFERENCES

1. C. Truesdell, *The Kinematics of Vorticity*. Bloomington: Indiana U. P., 1954.

2. L. Prandtl and O. G. Tietjens, *Fundamentals of Hydro- and Aeromechanics*. (First published in 1934). New York: Dover, 1957.

3. W. H. Li and S. H. Lam, *Principles of Fluid Mechanics*. Reading, Mass.: Addison-Wesley, 1964.

4. W. J. Duncan, A. S. Thom, and A. D. Young, *Mechanics of Fluids*. London: Arnold, 1960.

5. W. M. Swanson, "The Magnus Effect: a Summary of Investigations to Date," *J. Basic Engng., Trans. ASME*, Vol 83 D, No. 3 (September 1961), pp. 461–470.

6. L. Prandtl and O. G. Tietjens, *Applied Hydro- and Aeromechanics*. (First published in 1934), New York: Dover, 1957.

7. J. C. Hunsaker and B. G. Rightmire, *Engineering Applications of Fluid Mechanics*. New York: McGraw-Hill, 1947.

8. J. A. Owczarek, *Fundamentals of Gas Dynamics*. Scranton, Pa.: International Textbook, 1964.

PROBLEMS

5-1. Consider a two-dimensional liquid jet striking an inclined plate as shown in the sketch. Assuming that the fluid is perfect, that is, neglecting frictional

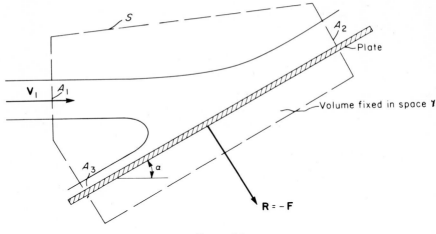

PROB. 5-1

effects, find the expression for the magnitude of the force **R** acting on the plate. Will there be a tangential component of this force relative to the plate? Why? Find also the expressions for the cross-sectional areas A_2 and A_3 of the deflected jets as functions of the cross-sectional area A_1 of the impinging jet and angle α. (Sec. 5-2.)

5-2. Derive Eqs. 5-11. Subsequently, using Eqs. 5-4 and A-109, derive Eqs. 5-12. (Sec. 5-2.)

5-3. (a) If a (right-handed) rectangular cartesian coordinate system x, y, z is oriented in such a way that the z-axis is horizontal while the x-axis is inclined at an angle α to the horizontal plane, what are the expressions for the terms $\partial \zeta/\partial x$ and $\partial \zeta/\partial y$? (b) What are the expressions for the terms $\partial \zeta/\partial r$ and $\partial \zeta/\partial \theta$ for a circular cylindrical coordinate system r, θ, z if the z-axis and the axis from which angle θ is measured are horizontal? (Sec. 5-2.)

5-4. As explained in Sec. 3-10, by a two-dimensional vortex motion we mean a steady fluid motion in which the fluid moves about a vertical axis with an angular velocity ω which is some function of the distance r from the axis. The paths of the fluid elements are circles which lie in horizontal planes. The speed of the fluid elements is $V = V_\theta = r\omega$ (it is independent of the angle θ), and the centripetal acceleration which acts inward has a magnitude of $\omega^2 r = V_\theta^2/r$. If the only body force is a constant field of gravitational attraction, then the momentum equations (Eq. 5-12) written in the circular cylindrical coordinate system r, θ, z in which the z-axis corresponds to the vertical axis of the vortex become:

$$\frac{V_\theta^2}{r} = \frac{1}{\rho}\frac{\partial P}{\partial r}$$

$$\frac{1}{\rho}\frac{\partial P}{\partial z} + g = 0$$

Assuming $\rho = $ const., that is, assuming an incompressible flow, show that in the so-called *Rankine combined vortex* which is composed of a forced vortex of radius

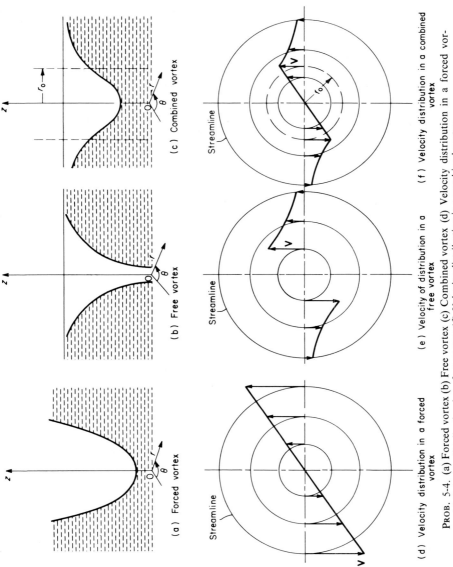

PROB. 5-4. (a) Forced vortex (b) Free vortex (c) Combined vortex (d) Velocity distribution in a forced vortex (e) Velocity distribution in a free vortex (f) Velocity distribution in a combined vortex.

r_0, in which the fluid rotates like a solid with a constant angular velocity ω, and a free vortex at $r > r_0$ (the flow speed changes continuously across $r = r_0$), the pressure at $r < r_0$ is given by

$$P = P_0 + \frac{1}{2}\rho r^2 \omega^2 - g\rho z$$

while at $r > r_0$

$$P = P_0 + \rho r_0^2 \omega^2 \left(1 - \frac{r_0^2}{2r^2}\right) - g\rho z$$

where P_0 represents the pressure at the origin of the coordinate axes. The Rankine combined vertex is illustrated in the sketch. [4, 7]. [HINT: First integrate the differential equations and obtain relation

$$P = \rho F(r) - g\rho z + \text{const.}$$

(Sec. 5-2.)]

5-5. What is the instantaneous horizontal force acting on the large stationary vessel shown in the sketch from which a fluid escapes through an opening, if the fluid is water, the height of the free surface of the water above the opening is $\Delta h = 10$ ft, and the cross-sectional area of the jet leaving the opening is 2 in.^{2}? The actual mean speed of the water jet leaving the opening should be calculated by multiplying by the velocity coefficient $c_v = 0.98$ the flow speed determined from Toricelli's equation. (Sec. 5-3.)

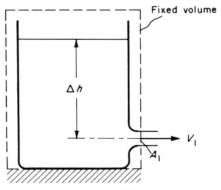

PROB. 5-5

5-6. Consider a vessel filled with a liquid and having an orifice shown in the sketch. Such an orifice is known as the *Borda mouthpiece*. Assuming that the fluid is perfect and incompressible, determine the contraction coefficient, C_c, for this orifice. By a contraction coefficient we mean the ratio of the cross-sectional area of the issuing jet to the cross-sectional area of the orifice. That is, $C_c = A_e/A_0$. Since the flow leaving the orifice is horizontal consider, in the momentum equation, only the horizontal components of the forces acting in the system. Also write the expression for the volumetric rate of discharge Q as a function of the cross-sectional area of the orifice and the elevation Δh of the free surface above the orifice. (Sec. 5-3.)

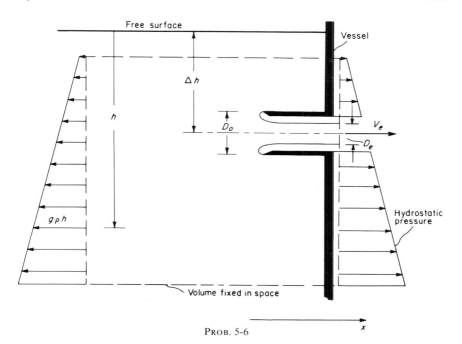

PROB. 5-6

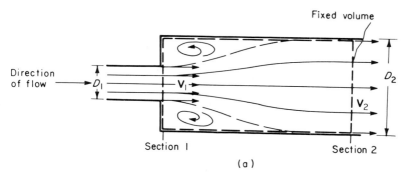

(a)

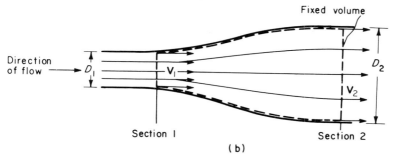

(b)

PROB. 5-7

5-7. Consider two steady flows, one in which an incompressible fluid flowing through a tube expands as a result of a sudden change in the cross-sectional area of the tube with the accompanying flow separation and generation of highly turbulent flow, and one in which the same fluid expands gradually, as shown in the sketch [the streamlines in figure (a) represent mean streamlines of the flow.] In both cases the cross-sectional areas of the ducts before and after the expansion are the same, the rates of flow are the same, and so are the pressures before the expansions. Assuming one-dimensional flow and hydrostatic state of stress at sections 1 and 2 in both cases, show that the pressure difference

$$P_{2,b} - P_{2,a} = \frac{\rho}{2} (V_1 - V_2)^2$$

where the subscripts a and b refer to the two cases as shown in the sketch. Assume that in case (b) the fluid is perfect. [2]. (Sec. 5-3.)

5-8. Consider a two-dimensional free vortex in an incompressible perfect fluid flowing with a uniform speed U_∞ as shown in the sketch. Calculate the x- and y-components of the force which would be necessary to hold the vortex in position by considering the forces acting on a cylindrical volume of radius r whose axis coincides with the axis of the vortex and which is fixed in space. Assume that the flow is of unit depth. (Observe that the cylindrical volume fixed in space is *not* a solid cylinder through whose surface fluid cannot flow.) (Sec. 5-3.)

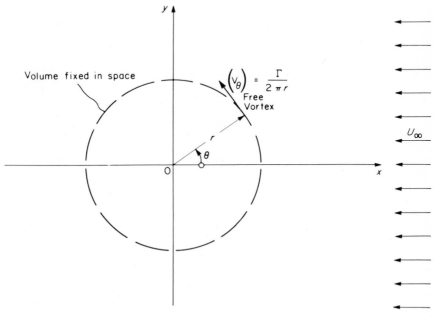

PROB. 5-8

5-9. Consider two points in a one-dimensional steady flow of a liquid in a field of constant gravitational attraction: point 1 at an elevation $\zeta = \zeta_1$ and point 2 at an elevation $\zeta = \zeta_2$. Assume that these two points lie in one cross section normal to the direction of flow. Making use of the equation for the hydrostatic pressure difference, show that the Bernoulli-Euler equation (Eq. 5-29) applies between points 1 and 2. Explain why in the region of flow under consideration hydrostatic state of stress can be assumed. (Sec. 5-3.)

5-10. Consider a two-dimensional steady incompressible and irrotational fluid flow for which the expression for the velocity potential is

$$\phi = \frac{k}{2} (x^2 - y^2)$$

Derive the equation for the streamlines and the expression for the pressure in a horizontal z = const. plane, if the pressure at $x = 0$, $y = 0$ in that plane is P_0. Sketch a few streamlines in a z = constant plane. (Sec. 5-3.)

5-11. Consider an incompressible steady flow whose velocity potential is $\phi = a(x^2 + y^2 - 2z^2)$. The constant a is a real and positive number. The coordinate axis z is vertical. Verify that this flow satisfies the continuity equation and the irrotationality conditions. Derive the equation of the streamlines in the $y = 0$ plane. Sketch a few streamlines in the $y = 0$ plane. Describe this flow. If at $x = y = z = 0$ the pressure $P = P_0$, what is the expression for the pressure P as a function of position in space? (Sec. 5-3.)

5-12. In the study of flows in turbomachinery, we require equations of fluid motion written for a rotating coordinate system. Consider a cylindrical coordinate system $\curlywedge$, θ, z shown on the accompanying sketch to represent a moving system relative to an inertial system whose origin is at point 0. Assume that the moving coordinate system rotates with a constant angular velocity ω_P about the z axis, that $\mathbf{R}$ = const., and that there are no body forces acting on the fluid. Making use of Eqs. 5-61, 5-63, and 5-67, show that the equations of fluid flow in the rotating coordinate system are as follows:

The momentum equation is

$$\frac{D'\mathbf{V}'}{Dt} + 2\,\omega_P \times \mathbf{V}' - \omega_P^2\,\curlywedge = \frac{D\mathbf{V}}{Dt} = -\frac{1}{\rho}\,\nabla P$$

The continuity equation is

$$\frac{D'\rho}{Dt} + \rho\,\nabla' \cdot \mathbf{V}' = 0$$

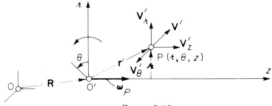

PROB. 5-12

The energy equation is

$$\frac{D'q_{rad}}{Dt} = \frac{D'\left[h + \dfrac{V'^2}{2} - \dfrac{(\omega_P \curlywedge)^2}{2}\right]}{Dt} - \frac{1}{\rho}\frac{\partial' P}{\partial t}$$

Subsequently, show that

$$h + \frac{V'^2}{2} - \frac{(\omega_P \curlywedge)^2}{2} = h + \frac{V^2}{2} - \curlywedge \omega_P V_\theta$$

where V denotes the magnitude of the flow velocity in the inertial system (stator) which is sometimes referred to as the absolute velocity, and V_θ denotes the component of V in direction θ, and obtain the so-called *Euler's turbine equation*

$$\frac{Dh_t}{Dt} = \omega_P \frac{D(\curlywedge V_\theta)}{Dt}$$

valid for an adiabatic steady flow (steady in the rotating coordinate system), where

$$h_t = h + \frac{V^2}{2}$$

and where $D(\curlywedge V_\theta)/Dt$ represents the rate of change of angular momentum of the fluid with respect to the axis of rotation, per unit mass, $[\omega_P D(\curlywedge V_\theta)/Dt$ representing the rate at which work is done on the fluid per unit mass along a streamline]. (Sec. 5-6.)

5-13. Write the three momentum equations in the $\curlywedge$, θ, and z directions represented by the vectorial momentum equation of Prob. 5-12:

$$\frac{D'\mathbf{V}'}{Dt} + 2\,\omega_P \times \mathbf{V}' - \omega_P^2\,\curlywedge = -\frac{1}{\rho}\,\nabla P$$

(Sec. 5-6.)

CHAPTER 6

Plane Irrotational and Incompressible Fluid Flows; Introduction to Wing Theory

6-1. INTRODUCTION

In Secs. 6-2 and 6-3 of this chapter we will discuss the elements of the theory of complex function and its use in finding expressions for the velocity potentials and the stream functions (and therefore also for the velocity components) of various steady two-dimensional irrotational (that is, potential) incompressible fluid flows. The main object of this study is to introduce the student to the powerful methods of the theory of complex functions and to show how it can be applied to a study of incompressible flow of perfect fluids. The last section of this chapter represents an introduction to the wing theory.

6-2. FUNCTIONS OF A COMPLEX VARIABLE

Complex Numbers. By a *complex number* we mean a quantity of the form

$$z = x + iy \tag{6-1}$$

where both x and y are real numbers and i is defined by

$$i = \sqrt{-1}, \qquad i^2 = -1 \tag{6-2}$$

The number x represents the so-called *real part* of the complex number, while the number y represents the *imaginary part*.

The complex numbers are conveniently represented geometrically as points in the (x, y) plane as shown in Fig. 6-1. Such plane is then called

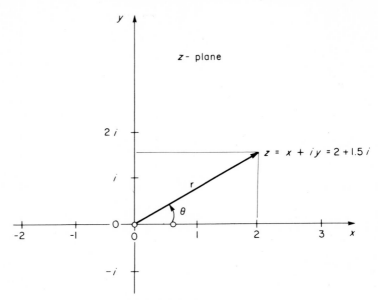

FIG. 6-1. Geometrical representation of a complex number.

the *complex plane* or the *z-plane*. It is often referred to as the *Argand diagram*. The *x*-axis represents the real parts and the *y*-axis the imaginary parts of complex numbers. From Fig. 6-1 it follows that we can represent a complex number in *polar form*

$$z = r(\cos \theta + i \sin \theta) \qquad (6\text{-}3)$$

if we introduce the polar coordinates r and θ. The (positive) number r is known as the *modulus*, or the *absolute value*, of the complex number. It is related to the numbers x and y by

$$r = |z| = \sqrt{x^2 + y^2} \qquad (6\text{-}4)$$

The angle θ, which is the angle the radius vector r makes with the positive direction of the *x*-axis, and which is measured positive in the counter-clockwise direction, is called the *argument*, or the *angle*, of the complex number. We have

$$\theta = \tan^{-1} \frac{y}{x} = \arg z \qquad (6\text{-}5)$$

The angle θ is usually restricted to the range $-\pi \le \theta \le \pi$ or $0 \le \theta \le 2\pi$. Since the Maclaurin expansions of $\cos \theta$, $\sin \theta$, and e^x are

$$\cos \theta = 1 - \frac{\theta^2}{2!} + \frac{\theta^4}{4!} - \frac{\theta^6}{6!} + \cdots$$

$$\sin \theta = \theta - \frac{\theta^3}{3!} + \frac{\theta^5}{5!} - \frac{\theta^7}{7!} + \cdots$$

$$e^x = 1 + x + \frac{x^2}{2!} + \frac{x^3}{3!} + \cdots$$

we have

$$\cos \theta + i \sin \theta = \left(1 - \frac{\theta^2}{2!} + \frac{\theta^4}{4!} - \frac{\theta^6}{6!} + \cdots\right)$$

$$+ i\left(\theta - \frac{\theta^3}{3!} + \frac{\theta^5}{5!} - \frac{\theta^7}{7!} + \cdots\right)$$

$$= 1 + i\theta - \frac{\theta^2}{2!} - i\frac{\theta^3}{3!} + \frac{\theta^4}{4!}$$

$$+ i\frac{\theta^5}{5!} - \frac{\theta^6}{6!} - i\frac{\theta^7}{7!} + \cdots$$

$$= e^{i\theta} \tag{6-6}$$

Similarly,

$$\cos \theta - i \sin \theta = e^{-i\theta} \tag{6-7}$$

As a result, we obtain another convenient form for expressing a complex number, namely $z = re^{i\theta}$. The three forms in which a complex number can be expressed are therefore

$$z = x + iy = r(\cos \theta + i \sin \theta) = re^{i\theta} \tag{6-8}$$

Observe that a complex number remains unchanged if any integral multiple of 2π is added to angle θ. Thus

$$z = r(\cos \theta + i \sin \theta) = re^{i\theta}$$

$$= r[\cos(\theta + 2k\pi) + i \sin(\theta + 2k\pi)] = re^{i(\theta + 2k\pi)} \tag{6-9}$$

where k is an arbitrary integer.

From Eq. 6-8 it follows that

$$z^n = r^n e^{in\theta} = r^n(\cos n\theta + i \sin n\theta) \tag{6-10}$$

A complex number is zero only when the numbers x and y are both zero. The complex numbers obey the laws of algebra. Therefore

$$z_1 \pm z_2 = (x_1 \pm x_2) + i(y_1 \pm y_2) \tag{6-11}$$

Since a complex number may be thought of as a vector from the origin to some point whose coordinates are (x, y), the addition (or subtraction) of two complex numbers corresponds to that of two vectors, as illustrated in Fig. 6-2.

The product of two complex numbers is a complex number. We can write

$$z_1 z_2 = (x_1 + iy_1)(x_2 + iy_2) = (x_1 x_2 - y_1 y_2) + i(x_1 y_2 + x_2 y_1) \tag{6-12}$$

Also,

$$z_1 z_2 = r_1 r_2 e^{i(\theta_1 + \theta_2)} \tag{6-12a}$$

Observe that multiplication of a complex number z_1 by z_2 results in multiplication of the modulus of z_1 by the modulus of z_2 and anticlockwise

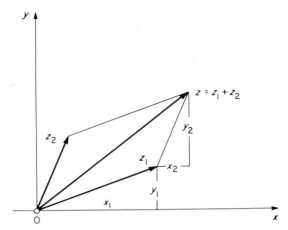

FIG. 6-2. Addition of two complex numbers.

rotation through angle θ_2. Since

$$e^{i(\pi/2)} = \cos\left(\frac{\pi}{2}\right) + i\sin\left(\frac{\pi}{2}\right) = i \qquad (6\text{-}13)$$

multiplication of a complex number by i results in anticlockwise rotation of the vector $\mathbf{r}$ representing the complex number through the angle of 90 degrees leaving the modulus unchanged.

The division of two complex numbers results in another complex number. We have

$$\frac{z_1}{z_2} = \frac{x_1 + iy_1}{x_2 + iy_2} = \frac{(x_1 + iy_1)(x_2 - iy_2)}{(x_2 + iy_2)(x_2 - iy_2)}$$

$$= \frac{x_1 x_2 + y_1 y_2}{x_2^2 + y_2^2} + i\,\frac{x_2 y_1 - x_1 y_2}{x_2^2 + y_2^2}. \qquad (6\text{-}14)$$

Also,

$$\frac{z_1}{z_2} = \frac{r_1 e^{i\theta_1}}{r_2 e^{i\theta_2}} = \frac{r_1}{r_2}\,e^{i(\theta_1 - \theta_2)} \qquad (6\text{-}14a)$$

Conjugate of a Complex Number. The conjugate of a complex number $z = x + iy$ is the complex number

$$\bar{z} = x - iy$$

The points z and $\bar{z}$ are symmetrically located with respect to the x-axis, as shown in Fig. 6-3. The following are the relations for the product, sum and difference between a complex number and its conjugate:

$$z\bar{z} = (x + iy)(x - iy) = x^2 + y^2 \qquad (6\text{-}15)$$

$$z\bar{z} = re^{i\theta} re^{-i\theta} = r^2 = x^2 + y^2 \qquad (6\text{-}15a)$$

because

$$\bar{z} = r(\cos\theta - i\sin\theta) = re^{-i\theta}$$

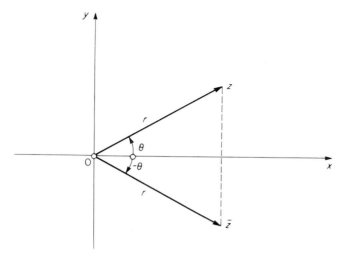

FIG. 6-3. Conjugate of a complex number.

in view of Eq. 6-7,

$$z + \bar{z} = (x + iy) + (x - iy) = 2x \qquad (6\text{-}16)$$

$$z - \bar{z} = (x + iy) - (x - iy) = 2iy \qquad (6\text{-}17)$$

Logarithm of a Complex Number. Since $z = re^{i\theta}$

$$\ln z = \ln r + i\theta \qquad (6\text{-}18)$$

or

$$\ln z = \frac{1}{2} \ln (x^2 + y^2) + i \tan^{-1} \frac{y}{x} \qquad (6\text{-}18a)$$

which indicates that the logarithm of a complex number is another complex number whose real part is equal to logarithm of the modulus and whose imaginary part is equal to the argument of that number.

In view of Eq. 6-9, the imaginary part of the logarithm of a complex number is undefined to the extent of $2k\pi$.

Functions of a Complex Variable. When the real and imaginary parts of a complex number z are variables—that is, when z denotes one of a set of complex numbers—then z is called a *complex variable*. If to each complex variable z corresponds another complex variable w, then w is a *function of the complex variable z*. In our considerations we will assume that this function is single-valued, that is, that there is only one complex number w corresponding to each complex number z. We can write

$$w = f(z) = \phi + i\psi \qquad (6\text{-}19)$$

with

$$z = x + iy, \qquad i = \sqrt{-1}$$

where $\phi = \phi(x, y)$ is the real part and $\psi = \psi(x, y)$ the imaginary part of the complex number w.

A function of a complex variable $f(z)$ is said to be *analytic in a region* of the z-plane if it is single-valued and if its derivative $f'(z) = \dfrac{dw}{dz}$ exists at every point in that region. If a function $f(z)$ is analytic in the neighborhood of a point z_0, but not at z_0, then z_0 is called the *singular point*, or *singularity*, of the function.

A necessary condition for a function of a complex variable to be analytic in a region is that it must be continuous there. The necessary and sufficient conditions for a function $f(z)$ to be analytic include in addition the relations which ensure that $f(z)$ has a *unique derivative* for a given value of z. We shall now derive these relations following the treatment given in Ref. 2.

The definition of the derivative $f'(z)$ is

$$f'(z) = \frac{dw}{dz} = \lim_{q \to 0} \frac{f(z + q) - f(z)}{q}$$

where q is given by

$$q = \Delta z = \Delta x + i\Delta y$$

Since

$$\Delta w = \Delta\phi + i\Delta\psi$$

then, if the functions ϕ and ψ have continuous first derivatives,

$$\Delta\phi = \left(\frac{\partial \phi}{\partial x} + \epsilon_1\right) \Delta x + \left(\frac{\partial\phi}{\partial y} + \epsilon_2\right) \Delta y$$

$$\Delta\psi = \left(\frac{\partial\psi}{\partial x} + \epsilon_3\right) \Delta x + \left(\frac{\partial\psi}{\partial y} + \epsilon_4\right) \Delta y$$

with

$$\lim_{\substack{\Delta x \to 0 \\ \Delta y \to 0}} \epsilon_j = 0, \qquad j = 1,2,3,4$$

As a result we obtain

$$f'(z) = \frac{dw}{dz} = \lim_{\Delta z \to 0} \frac{\Delta w}{\Delta z} = \frac{\left(\dfrac{\partial\phi}{\partial x} + i\dfrac{\partial\psi}{\partial x}\right) + \left(\dfrac{\partial\phi}{\partial y} + i\dfrac{\partial\psi}{\partial y}\right)\dfrac{dy}{dx}}{1 + i\dfrac{dy}{dx}}$$

$$= \frac{C + Dm}{1 + im} \tag{6-20}$$

where

$$C = \frac{\partial\phi}{\partial x} + i\frac{\partial\psi}{\partial x}$$

$$D = \frac{\partial \phi}{\partial y} + i \frac{\partial \psi}{\partial y}$$

$$m = \frac{dy}{dx}$$

For the derivative $f'(z) = dw/dz$ to be unique, it must be independent of the direction from which Δz approaches zero—that is, it must be independent of m. This is so when

$$\frac{\partial [f'(z)]}{\partial m} = \frac{(1 + im)D - (C + Dm)i}{(1 + im)^2} = 0$$

or when

$$D = iC \tag{6-21}$$

that is, when

$$\frac{\partial \phi}{\partial y} + i \frac{\partial \psi}{\partial y} = i\left(\frac{\partial \phi}{\partial x} + i \frac{\partial \psi}{\partial x}\right)$$

Equating the real and imaginary parts we obtain the following conditions for the uniqueness of the derivative $f'(z) = dw/dz$:

$$\frac{\partial \phi}{\partial x} = \frac{\partial \psi}{\partial y}, \qquad \frac{\partial \phi}{\partial y} = -\frac{\partial \psi}{\partial x} \tag{6-22}$$

These conditions are known as the *Cauchy–Riemann conditions.*

Conformal Mapping. The transformation of points in the z-plane into points in the w-plane (in which the complex numbers $w = \phi + i\psi$ are represented as points) by the function $f(z)$ is known as *mapping.* As a simple example of mapping, consider the functional relation

$$w = z^n$$

where n is a positive integer. In this case the angular region $r \geq 0$, $0 \leq \theta \leq \pi/n$ in the z-plane, maps into the upper half of the w-plane, (see Eq. 6-10). This is illustrated in Fig. 6-4.

In mapping—that is, under transformation $w = f(z)$—the direction of a curve at some point $z = z_0$ changes. We assume that the function $f(z)$ is analytic and that the derivative $f'(z) = dw/dz$ at $z = z_0$ is finite. That is,

$$f'(z_0) = \frac{dw}{dz} = \lim_{\Delta z \to 0} \frac{\Delta w}{\Delta z} \neq 0$$

Since

$$\Delta w = \Delta z \left(\frac{\Delta w}{\Delta z}\right)$$

the argument of Δw is equal to the sum of the argument of Δz and the argument of $\Delta w/\Delta z$, which we can write in the form

$$\arg \Delta w = \arg \Delta z + \arg \frac{\Delta w}{\Delta z}$$

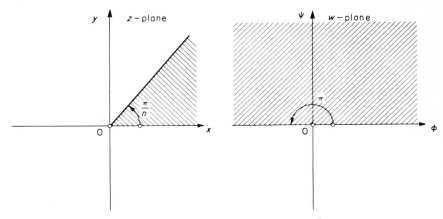

FIG. 6-4. Mapping with a function $w = z^n$.

For $\Delta z \to 0$, arg $\Delta w \to \beta$, arg $\Delta z \to \alpha$ (see Fig. 6-5), and arg $(\Delta w / \Delta z)$ tends to some limit δ_0 which represents the argument of the number $f'(z_0)$. Therefore

$$\beta = \alpha + \delta_0 \qquad (6\text{-}23)$$

and the directed tangent to a curve at z_0 is rotated through the angle $\delta_0 = \text{arg } f'(z)$ by the transformation $w = f(z)$ [subject to the restrictions that $f(z)$ is analytic and $f'(z) \neq 0$].

Since all curves passing through a point z_0 are rotated through the same angle δ_0 by the transformation $w = f(z)$ for which Eq. 6-23 holds, such mapping preserves the angles between the curves passing through a point, as shown in Fig. 6-6. We call such mapping, or transformation, *conformal*. The terms *conformal mapping*, or *conformal transformation*,

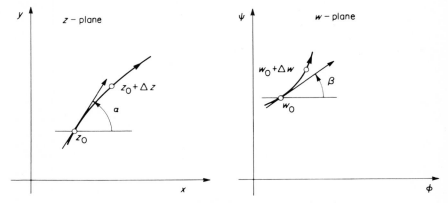

FIG. 6-5. Rotation of tangents in mapping.

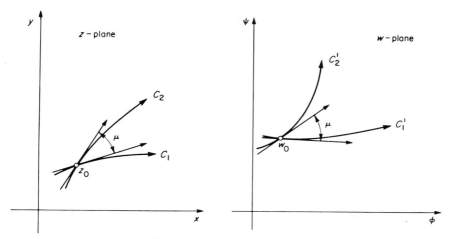

FIG. 6-6. Conformal mapping.

refer to the transformations by means of analytic functions with non-vanishing derivatives.

In conformal mapping infinitesimal figures are transformed, subject to rotation and change in size, with no distortion. Finite figures are subject to distortion, although the angles between intersecting lines are preserved.

6-3. APPLICATION OF FUNCTIONS OF COMPLEX VARIABLE TO A STUDY OF PLANE IRROTATIONAL FLOWS

If we consider, in Eq. 6-19, the function ϕ to represent the velocity potential and the function ψ to represent the stream function of a plane irrotational and incompressible fluid flow, then the Cauchy–Riemann conditions are satisfied in view of the fact that

$$\left.\begin{array}{ll} \dfrac{\partial \phi}{\partial x} = u, & \dfrac{\partial \phi}{\partial y} = v \\[2mm] \dfrac{\partial \psi}{\partial y} = u, & \dfrac{\partial \psi}{\partial x} = -v \end{array}\right\} \tag{6-24}$$

where u and v denote the velocity components in the x- and y-directions respectively.

Differentiating the first and second Cauchy–Riemann conditions (Eq. 6-22) with respect to x and y respectively, and adding we obtain equation

$$\frac{\partial^2 \phi}{\partial x^2} + \frac{\partial^2 \phi}{\partial y^2} = 0 \tag{6-25}$$

which is the Laplace equation involving the velocity potential (Eq. 3-54) for a two-dimensional irrotational and incompressible flow studied in a rectangular cartesian coordinate system.

Differentiating the first and second Cauchy–Riemann conditions with respect to y and x respectively, and subtracting the second equation from the first we obtain equation

$$\frac{\partial^2 \psi}{\partial x^2} + \frac{\partial^2 \psi}{\partial y^2} = 0 \tag{6-26}$$

which is the Laplace equation involving the stream function (Eq. 3-82) for a two-dimensional irrotational incompressible fluid flow studied in a rectangular cartesian coordinate system.

Therefore the real and imaginary parts of any analytic function of a complex variable represent the velocity potential and the stream function of a possible (at least mathematically, if not physically) two-dimensional irrotational incompressible fluid flow. Both these functions ensure that the continuity equation and the irrotationality conditions are satisfied. (Observe that every function of a complex variable defines in fact two different irrotational flows because the streamlines and the equipotential lines of one flow can be interchanged to represent another flow since both the stream function and the velocity potential independently satisfy Laplace's equation.) We can also say that every plane irrotational and incompressible flow defines an analytic function of a complex variable.

Since the Cauchy–Riemann conditions are linear, the sum of two analytic functions is also an analytic function. As a result, two-dimensional irrotational and incompressible flow patterns can be obtained by superposition of two or more flow patterns. This we already concluded in Chapter 3.

In the discussion which follows we shall apply the theory of the function of complex variables (which involves the mapping) to a study of plane irrotational incompressible fluid flow.

The Complex Velocity. The analytic function

$$w = f(z) = \phi(x, y) + i\psi(x, y)$$

where the functions ϕ and ψ represent the velocity potential and the stream function is called the *complex potential*. The derivative of the complex potential

$$\begin{aligned}
\frac{dw}{dz} &= \frac{\partial \phi}{\partial x} + i \frac{\partial \psi}{\partial x} \\
&= \frac{\partial \psi}{\partial y} - i \frac{\partial \phi}{\partial y} \\
&= u - iv
\end{aligned} \tag{6-27}$$

in view of the Cauchy–Riemann conditions. This follows from Eqs. 6-20 and 6-21. The term dw/dz is called the *complex velocity*. The modulus of the complex velocity is the flow speed V. The complex velocity can be looked upon as the complex conjugate of the flow velocity vector represented in form of a complex number on the Argand diagram. Since the derivatives of analytic functions are also analytic, and we assume the function w to be such, the complex velocity is an analytic function.

At stagnation points in a flow, since both velocity components u and v vanish there, $dw/dz = 0$.

Complex Potentials of Simple Flows. Since every analytic function of a complex variable represents a possible two-dimensional irrotational and incompressible fluid flow, we can choose some such functions and see what the corresponding flows are. This we shall do now.

The function $w = f(z) = Az$ *where A is a complex number* $A = B + iC.$ We have

$$\frac{dw}{dz} = u - iv = B + iC$$

or

$$u = B, \qquad v = -C$$

The flow represented by this function is a uniform flow inclined to the x-axis at an angle $\alpha = \tan^{-1} \dfrac{v}{u} = \tan^{-1}\left(-\dfrac{C}{B}\right)$, as shown in Fig. 6-7.

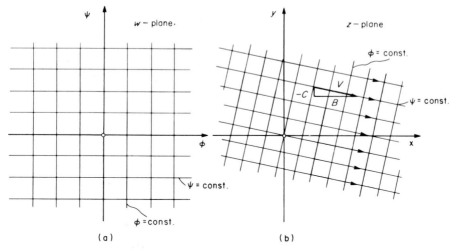

FIG. 6-7. The transformation $w = Az$ with $A = B + iC$.   (a) w-plane. (b) z-plane.

Since $w = \phi + i\psi = Az = (B + iC)(x + iy)$, we have

$$\phi = Bx - Cy \quad \text{and} \quad \psi = Cx + By$$

The function $w = f(z) = Az^2$ *where A is a real number.* In this case, since

$$w = Az^2 = A(x + iy)^2 = A(x^2 - y^2) + i2Axy$$

we have

$$\phi = A(x^2 - y^2) \quad \text{and} \quad \psi = 2Axy$$

Therefore the streamlines and the equipotential lines are two orthogonal families of hyperbolas as shown in Fig. 6-8a. Since

$$\frac{dw}{dz} = u - iv = 2Az = 2A(x + iy)$$

the expressions for the velocity components are

$$u = 2Ax \quad \text{and} \quad v = -2Ay$$

At the origin of the x,y-coordinates is a stagnation point ($u = v = 0$ there). This complex potential represents the (two-dimensional) flow in

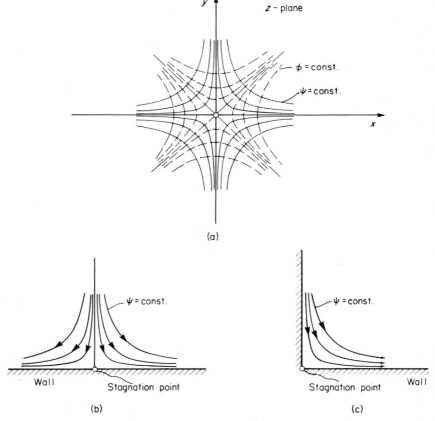

Fig. 6-8. The transformation $w = f(z) = Az^2$ where A is a real number. (a) z-plane. (b) Stagnation flow normal to a surface. (c) Flow in a right-angle corner.

which the fluid impinges at right angle on a flat surface, or the flow in a right-angle corner. (This is so because any streamline in the flows under consideration can be replaced by a solid boundary.) These flows are illustrated in Figs. 6-8b and 6-8c.

The function $w = f(z) = Az^n$ *where* A *is a real number, and* n *is real and positive.* We have

$$\phi = Ar^n \cos n\theta \quad \text{and} \quad \psi = Ar^n \sin n\theta$$

in view of Eq. 6-10. The stream function ψ is constant (it is equal to zero) for $\theta = k \dfrac{\pi}{n}$ where $k = 0,1,2,\ldots$. For $n > 1$ this function represents the flow in a corner (Fig. 6-8c illustrates this for $n = 2$). Figure 6-9a illustrates such flow for $n = 4$. For $n < 1$ this function represents the flow around an exterior corner. Figure 6-9b illustrates such flow for $n = \frac{2}{3}$.

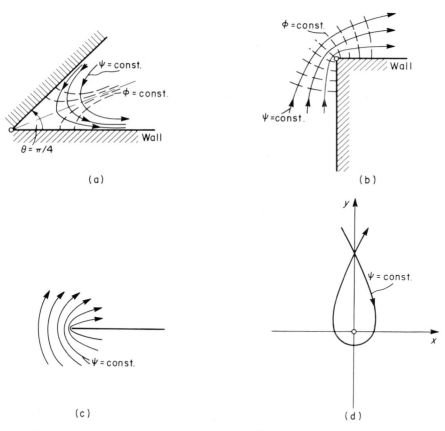

FIG. 6-9. The transformation $w = f(z) = Az^n$, where A is a real number
(a) $n = 4$. (b) $n = 2/3$. (c) $n = 1/2$. (d) $n = 1/3$.

For $n = \frac{1}{2}$ this function represents the flow around the edge of a plate, as shown in Fig. 6-9c. For $n < \frac{1}{2}$ the streamlines cross and the flow loses physical significance.

The function $w = f(z) = A \ln(z - z_0)$ *where A is a real number and* z_0 *is a (constant) complex number.* The term $(z - z_0)$ represents a complex number which can be obtained by subtraction of vectors whose initial point is the origin of the x,y-coordinates and the final points are z and z_0 respectively, as shown in Fig. 6-10. Writing

$$z - z_0 = r_1 e^{i\theta_1}$$

we obtain

$$w = A \ln r_1 + i A \theta_1$$

Therefore

$$\phi = A \ln r_1 \quad \text{and} \quad \psi = A\theta_1$$

Also

$$\frac{dw}{dz} = \frac{A}{z - z_0}$$

from which it follows that

$$|V| = \left|\frac{dw}{dz}\right| = \left|\frac{A}{z - z_0}\right| = \frac{A}{r_1}$$

This flow corresponds to a (two-dimensional) source flow with the source located at point z_0 in the (x, y) plane. (See our discussion in Sec. 3-10.) We have, in this case, $A = Q/2\pi$.

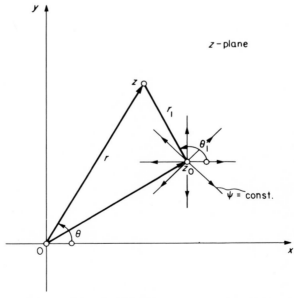

FIG. 6-10. Function $A \ln (z - z_0)$, where A is a real positive number.

The function $w = f(z) = iA \ln (z - z_0)$ where A is a real number and z_0 is a (constant) complex number. Writing, as before, $z - z_0 = r_1 e^{i\theta_1}$ we obtain

$$w = -A\theta_1 + iA \ln r_1$$

from which it follows that

$$\phi = -A\theta_1 \quad \text{and} \quad \psi = A \ln r_1$$

As in the case of the source flow, we have in this case

$$|V| = \frac{A}{r_1}$$

This flow corresponds to the free vortex flow with the vortex located at point z_0 in the (x, y) plane. The real constant A is equal to $-\Gamma/2\pi$ (see Sec. 3-10).

The function $w = f(z) = \dfrac{A}{z}$ where A is a real number. In this case

$$w = \phi + i\psi = \frac{A}{x + iy} = \frac{A(x - iy)}{(x + iy)(x - iy)} = \frac{Ax}{x^2 + y^2} - i\frac{Ay}{x^2 + y^2}$$

As a result

$$\phi = \frac{Ax}{x^2 + y^2} = \frac{A \cos \theta}{r} \quad \text{and} \quad \psi = -\frac{Ay}{x^2 + y^2} = -\frac{A \sin \theta}{r}$$

This flow corresponds to a doublet located at the origin of the x, y coordinates. The positive direction of its axis corresponds to that of the x-axis if we put $A = -\mu/2\pi$ (see Sec. 3-10). (For reversed positive direction of the axis the sign is reversed.) A doublet located at point z_0 in the (x, y) plane, whose axis is rotated by an angle β with respect to the x-axis is given by the function.

$$w = -\frac{\mu e^{i\beta}}{2\pi(z - z_0)}$$

Flow Past a Cylinder. As was shown in Chapter 3, the combination of a two-dimensional doublet with a uniform flow resulted in a flow pattern corresponding to an irrotational flow past a circular cylinder. [In real fluids, such flow exists only during the initial moments after the motion of the fluid relative to the cylinder has begun (see Fig. 1-16a).] The complex potential for the uniform flow in the direction of the negative x axis and a two-dimensional doublet with its axis in the direction of the positive x-axis is given by

$$w = (w)_{\text{uniform flow}} + (w)_{\text{doublet}}$$

$$= -U_\infty z - \frac{\mu}{2\pi z}$$

$$= -U_\infty \left(z + \frac{a^2}{z}\right) \tag{6-28}$$

where $a = (\mu/2\pi U_\infty)^{1/2}$ denotes the radius of the cylinder (see Sec. 3-10). At very large values of z the complex potential tends to $-U_\infty z$ which represents the uniform flow. The complex velocity $dw/dz = 0$ at $z = \pm a$ indicating that these are the stagnation points of the flow. The expression for the complex potential can be rewritten in the form

$$w = \phi + i\psi = -U_\infty\left(re^{i\theta} + \frac{a^2}{r}e^{-i\theta}\right)$$

$$= -U_\infty\left(r\cos\theta + ir\sin\theta + \frac{a^2}{r}\cos\theta - i\frac{a^2}{r}\sin\theta\right)$$

$$= -U_\infty\left(r + \frac{a^2}{r}\right)\cos\theta - iU_\infty\left(r - \frac{a^2}{r}\right)\sin\theta$$

and therefore the expression for the velocity potential and the stream function for the flow under consideration are

$$\phi = -U_\infty\left(r + \frac{a^2}{r}\right)\cos\theta \qquad [3\text{-}109]$$

$$\psi = -U_\infty\left(r - \frac{a^2}{r}\right)\sin\theta \qquad [3\text{-}107b]$$

This is in agreement with the results obtained in Chapter 3.

Flow Past a Cylinder with Circulation. The complex potential for a potential flow past a circular cylinder with counterclockwise circulation, located at the origin of the x, y axes is

$$w = -U_\infty\left(z + \frac{a^2}{z}\right) - i\frac{\Gamma}{2\pi}\ln\left(\frac{z}{a}\right) \qquad (6\text{-}29)$$

This follows from Eq. 6-28 and our analysis of the function $w = f(z) = iA \ln(z - z_0)$, if we take $\psi = 0$ to correspond to the circle of radius a. The uniform flow, far away from the cylinder, is in the direction of the negative x-axis. The expressions for the velocity potential and the stream functions are, in this case,

$$\phi = -U_\infty\left(r + \frac{a^2}{r}\right)\cos\theta + \frac{\Gamma}{2\pi}\theta$$

$$\psi = -U_\infty\left(r - \frac{a^2}{r}\right)\sin\theta - \frac{\Gamma}{2\pi}\ln\left(\frac{r}{a}\right) \qquad [3\text{-}111]$$

Use of Conformal Transformation. The w-plane always represents a rectangular network of the equipotential lines and streamlines, as was shown in Fig. 6-7a. With the aid of an analytic function of a complex variable $w = f(z)$ these equipotential lines and streamlines are mapped onto the z-plane.

Instead of mapping directly from the w-plane to the z-plane, we can perform the transformation in stages using one or more intermediate planes. In such case the functional relationship $w = f(z)$ includes a set of successive transformation equations. The expression for the complex velocity (which gives the expressions for the velocity components in the z-plane) can then be obtained by differentiation. For example, if

$$w = f(z_1) = -U_\infty \left(z_1 + \frac{a^2}{z_1} \right)$$

and

$$z_1 = ze^{i\alpha}$$

then

$$\frac{dw}{dz} = \frac{dw}{dz_1} \frac{dz_1}{dz} = -U_\infty \left(1 - \frac{a^2}{z_1^2} \right) e^{i\alpha}$$

$$= -U_\infty \left(1 - \frac{a^2}{z^2 e^{2i\alpha}} \right) e^{i\alpha} = u - iv$$

where $z = x + iy$.

The use of successive conformal transformation enables us to obtain expressions for the velocity potential and the stream function (and hence also for the velocity components) of complicated flows from the known expressions for these functions corresponding to relatively simple flows. One of its application, which we will now study, has to do with the determination of the flow past such objects as elliptical cylinders and airfoils from the known (irrotational) flow in the neighborhood of a cylinder.

Transformations of a Circle. In what follows we shall concern ourselves with successive transformations involving a transformation from the w-plane to an intermediate z_1-plane, in which the (irrotational) flow past a circular cylinder is represented, followed by additional transformations to the z-plane. Therefore the transformation

$$w = -\left(z_1 + \frac{a^2}{z_1} \right) \tag{6-30}$$

where a denotes the radius of a circle (projection of the circular cylinder) in the z_1-plane is considered as the first transformation from the w-plane. Note, by comparing this complex potential with that given by Eq. 6-28 that, for simplicity, we are assuming here the magnitude of the uniform flow velocity $U_\infty = 1$. The flow in the z_1-plane corresponds to that illustrated in Fig. 3-25.

One of the successive transformations which we will utilize will be the transformation of the type

$$z = z_1 + \frac{b^2}{z_1} \tag{6-31}$$

where b, just like a, is a positive real number. There exists a simple graphical method which allows us to determine the shape of a line in the z-plane

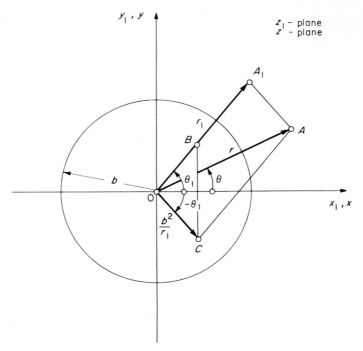

FIG. 6-11. Graphical construction corresponding to the transformation $z = z_1 + b^2/z_1$. Point A_1 in the z_1-plane is transformed to point A in the z-plane.

which corresponds to some chosen line in the z_1-plane. We shall now discuss this method. Let point A_1, shown in Fig. 6-11, represent a point in the z_1-plane. That is, let it represent the complex number $z_1 = r_1 e^{i\theta_1}$. Point B, lying on line OA_1, is so located that the distance $OB = b^2/OA_1$. Point B thus defined is known as the *inverse of point* A_1 with respect to the circle of radius b. Point C represents the image of point B in the x-axis. Therefore distance $OC = OB = b^2/OA_1 = b^2/r_1$. Point C represents the complex number $\dfrac{b^2}{r_1} e^{-i\theta_1}$. Since the addition of two complex numbers corresponds to the addition of two vectors (see Fig. 6-2), the sum of vectors OA_1 and OC, which is equal to the vector OA, represents the complex number

$$re^{i\theta} = r_1 e^{i\theta_1} + \frac{b^2}{r_1} e^{-i\theta_1}$$

Denoting $re^{i\theta} = z$, it follows that the complex number z represented by point A is related to the complex number z_1 represented by point A_1 by the Eq. 6-31. And so to find a point A in the z-plane which corresponds to some point A_1 in the z_1-plane, for the transformation given by Eq. 6-31, we find first the inverse of point A_1 with respect to the circle of radius b. Subsequently we determine the image of the inverse of point A_1 and add it vectorially to the complex number z_1.

When point A_1 is so chosen that it lies on the circle of radius b then the corresponding point A lies on the x-axis, because then $OB = OA_1 = b$, point B coincides with point A_1, and point C also lies on the circle. As a result, the circle of radius b in the z_1-plane transforms into a straight line in the z-plane. This line falls on the x-axis and its length is $4b$ as shown in Fig. 6-12.

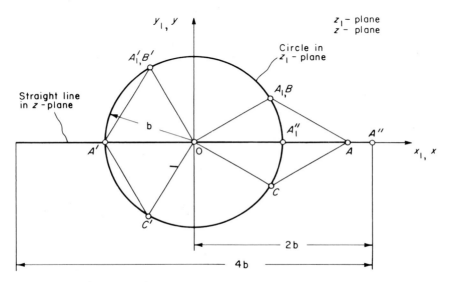

FIG. 6-12. Transformation of a circle of radius b into a straight line according to relation $z = z_1 + b^2/z_1$.

Flow Past an Elliptical Cylinder. Consider the flow defined by successive transformations

$$
\left.
\begin{aligned}
w &= z_1 + \frac{a^2}{z_1} \\
z &= z_1 + \frac{b^2}{z_1}
\end{aligned}
\right\}
\qquad (6\text{-}32)
$$

where $b < a$. As shown in Fig. 6-13, this mapping results in an irrotational flow past an elliptic cylinder whose major axis has the direction of the undisturbed flow. Observe that since the transformation function $w = f(z_1)$ has sign opposite to that in Eq. 6-30, the flow is in the direction of the positive x-axis.

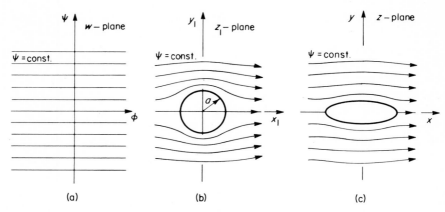

FIG. 6-13. Irrotational flow past an elliptical cylinder resulting from the successive transformations $w = z_1 + a^2/z_1, z = z_1 + b^2/z_1$ with $b < a$.

The graphical method which can be used to obtain the elliptical contour from the circle of radius a representing the circular cylinder corresponds to that illustrated in Fig. 6-11. For the contour $r_1 = a = $ const., the locus of points B and C is a circle of radius b^2/a as shown in Fig. 6-14. The half-length of the major axis of the ellipse is $r = a + b^2/a$ because

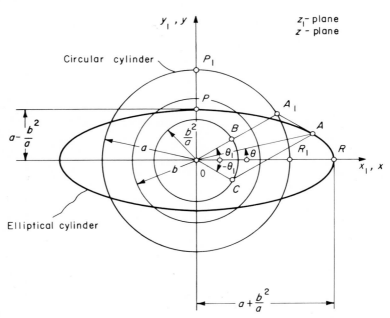

FIG. 6-14. Graphical construction of the elliptical cylinder transformed from a circular cylinder of radius a according to transformation illustrated in Fig. 6-13.

the transformed point R (which corresponds to point R_1) represents the complex number $z = a + b^2/a$ since point R_1 is given by $z_1 = a$. The half-length of the minor axis of the ellipse is $a - b^2/a$ because the complex number represented by point P, which corresponds to the complex number represented by point P_1 (that is, to $z_1 = ia$), is $z = ia - ib^2/a$.

Observe that the circle of radius b in the z_1-plane (which is inside the circle of radius a) transforms into a straight line of length $4b$ in the z-plane. (This line is inside the elliptical profile.) This follows from our discussion illustrated in Fig. 6-12.

Flow Past a Streamlined Strut. By a streamlined object we mean an object which possesses a rounded nose and a thin trailing edge. The flow past a streamlined strut can be represented by the transformations used in the last example with a modification which ensures lack of symmetry with respect to the y-axis. This effect is produced by moving the circle of radius a with respect to the circle of radius b along the x-axis. To achieve a sharp trailing edge, the two circles must touch as shown in Fig. 6-15 (point E).

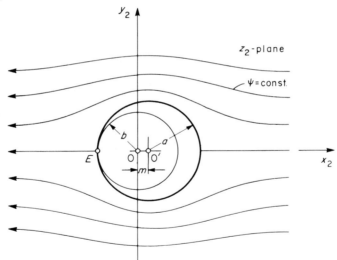

FIG. 6-15. Successive transformation from z_1-plane to z_2-plane resulting in a sharp trailing edge of the strut.

The successive transformations which result in an irrotational flow past a streamlined strut at zero angle of attack are:

$$
\left.
\begin{aligned}
w &= -\left(z_1 + \frac{a^2}{z_1}\right) \\
z_2 &= z_1 + m \\
z &= z_2 + \frac{b^2}{z_2}
\end{aligned}
\right\} \qquad (6\text{-}33)
$$

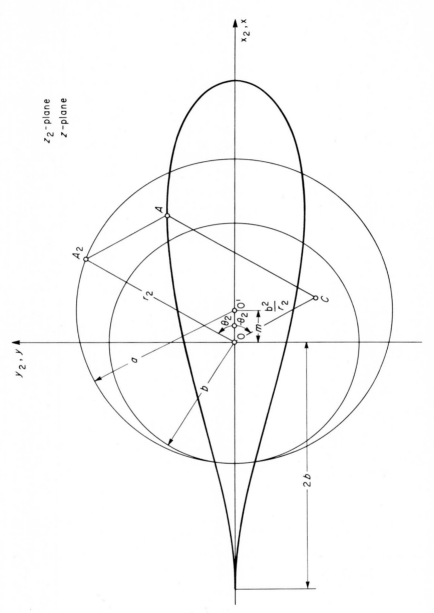

FIG. 6-16. Graphical construction of the streamlined strut.

with $b = a - m$. We assume, for a change, that the flow is in the direction of the negative x-axis. As before, we take the magnitude of the uniform flow velocity to be unity (that is, $U_\infty = 1$). The graphical construction of the profile of the strut is shown in Fig. 6-16. The streamlines can be constructed using the method explained with the aid of Fig. 6-11.

Observe that at point $z = -2b$, which represents the trailing edge of the strut, there is a cusp, while there is no cusp at the corresponding point in the z_2-plane. This indicates that there the transformation is not conformal, and therefore the derivative dz_2/dz must be equal to 0 or ∞ at that point. We have

$$\frac{dz_2}{dz} = \frac{1}{\dfrac{dz}{dz_2}} = \frac{1}{1 - \dfrac{b^2}{z_2^2}}$$

which is equal to ∞ at $z = -2b$ because the complex number z_2 corresponding to $z = -2b$ is $-b$. (Note that in this case, since the trailing edge corresponds to the point $z_1 = -b - m = -a$, $\dfrac{dw}{dz} = \dfrac{dw}{dz_1}\dfrac{dz_1}{dz_2}\dfrac{dz_2}{dz} = \dfrac{0}{0}$ there.)

Flow Past an Airfoil. The successive transformations which result in an irrotational flow past an airfoil are

$$\left.\begin{array}{c} w = -\left(z_1 + \dfrac{a^2}{z_1}\right) \\[2mm] z_2 = z_1 + me^{i\delta} \\[2mm] z = z_2 + \dfrac{b^2}{z_2} \end{array}\right\} \qquad (6\text{-}34)$$

The circles of radii a and b must intersect, with one of the points of intersection lying on the x_2-axis (point E), as shown in Fig. 6-17. This point transforms into the trailing edge of the airfoil. (Points P and P' in Fig. 6-17, denote the forward and the rear stagnation points respectively.) Again we assume that the flow is in the direction of the negative x-axis, and take the magnitude of the uniform flow velocity to be unity. Fig. 6-17 shows the effect of the successive transformations (Eq. 6-34) on the resulting flows, while Fig. 6-18 illustrates the graphical construction of the airfoil, known as *Joukowski airfoil*, produced by these transformations. As in the case of the strut, there is a cusp at the trailing edge of the airfoil. The complex velocity dw/dz is infinite there since

$$\frac{dw}{dz} = \frac{dw}{dz_1}\frac{dz_1}{dz_2}\frac{dz_2}{dz}$$

$$= -\left(1 - \frac{a^2}{z_1^2}\right)(1)\frac{1}{1 - \dfrac{b^2}{z_2^2}}$$

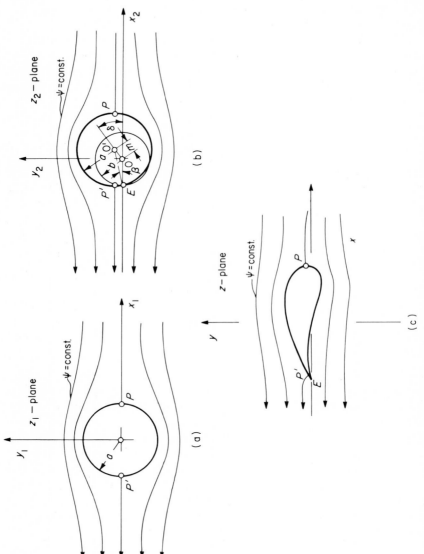

FIG. 6-17. Irrotational flow past a Joukowski airfoil. (No circulation.)

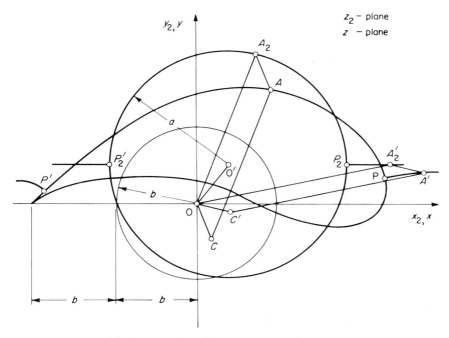

FIG. 6-18. Graphical construction of the Joukowski airfoil and of the streamlines passing through the stagnation points in an irrotational flow.

and the trailing edge corresponds to point $z = -2b$, $z_2 = -b$, $z_1 = -b - me^{i\delta}$. This indicates that the flow speed is infinite at the trailing edge of a Joukowski airfoil (in a flow with no circulation). The airfoil differs from the strut considered previously in that it possesses camber, that is, its *mean line* (which is the line equidistant from the upper and lower surfaces) deviates from the chord line. The *chord line* is usually defined as the straight line which joins the intersections of the mean line with the airfoil surface. For definitions of various terms relating to airfoils, see Fig. 6-19.

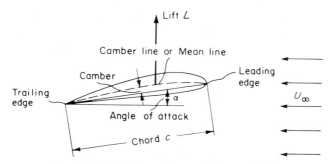

FIG. 6-19. Definition of terms relating to airfoils.

The thickness and the camber of the Joukowski airfoil depends on the location of the center O' of the circle of radius a in the z_2-plane. [Conventional airfoil sections are obtained for small angles β (see Fig. 6-17b) and radii a only slightly larger than $b \sec \beta$.]

The irrotational flow past an airfoil shown in Fig. 6-17c corresponds to the flow illustrated in Figs. 5-9a and 5-10a. Observe the rear stagnation point on the upper surface of the airfoil.

The transformation

$$z = z_2 + \frac{b^2}{z_2}$$

can be written as

$$\frac{z + 2b}{z - 2b} = \left(\frac{z_2 + b}{z_2 - b}\right)^2 \tag{6-35}$$

Von Kármán and Trefftz modified this transformation by writing

$$\frac{z + nb}{z - nb} = \left(\frac{z_2 + b}{z_2 - b}\right)^n \tag{6-36}$$

where $n = 2 - \dfrac{\lambda}{\pi}$, with λ denoting the vertex angle of the airfoil at the trailing edge. This transformation is useful from the practical point of view since it removes the cusp from the trailing edge of the airfoil. Such airfoils are called the *extended Joukowski airfoils* (see Ref. 7).

6-4. INTRODUCTION TO WING THEORY

In this section we will consider the circulation theory of lift for wings of infinite and finite span. The treatment will be of introductory character only, the flow will be assumed steady, and the compressibility effects will not be considered.

Wing of Infinite Span. In the case of the two-dimensional irrotational flow past an airfoil illustrated in Fig. 6-17c there is no lift acting because there is no circulation present. This should be obvious from our discussion of lift in Sec. 5-3. As was made clear in Sec. 5-4, for a real fluid such flow [in which very large (infinitely large for a fluid model assumed to be nonviscous) flow speed is required to move the fluid around the sharp trailing edge] can exist only during the initial moment when the airfoil is brought into motion relative to the surrounding fluid. In the established flows past airfoils, the Kutta–Joukowski condition is satisfied and the flow speed at the trailing edge is finite when the trailing edge is of zero thickness (that is, when the airfoil possesses a cusp there) or is zero (that is, a stagnation point is formed) when the trailing edge has a finite vertex angle. During the establishment of the flow, circulation around the airfoil is produced, and a starting vortex shed. This was explained with the aid of Fig. 5-9.

The Kutta–Joukowski condition allows us to determine the magnitude of circulation present in a flow past an airfoil, and therefore also the lifting force which acts at right angle to the direction of flow of the free (that is, undisturbed) stream whose speed is U_∞, and whose magnitude is $\rho U_\infty \Gamma$ (see our discussion in Sec. 5-3). It forms the basis of what is known as the *circulation theory of lift*.

Use of Functions of Complex Variable to Determine the Flow Past a Joukowski Airfoil. The potential flow past a Joukowski airfoil at an angle of attack α, with circulation present, can be obtained with the aid of the following successive transformations:

$$w = -U_\infty \left(z_1 + \frac{a^2}{z_1}\right) - i\,\frac{\Gamma}{2\pi}\,\ln\left(\frac{z_1}{a}\right) \qquad [6\text{-}29]$$

which represents the complex potential for a flow past a circular cylinder of radius a with counterclockwise circulation (the flow is in the direction of the negative x-axis),

$$z_2 = z_1 e^{-i\alpha} \qquad (6\text{-}37)$$

which rotates the flow pattern through angle $-\alpha$ so that the uniform stream is at an angle α to the x-axis,

$$z_3 = z_2 + m e^{i\delta} \qquad (6\text{-}38)$$

which shifts, in the z_3-plane, the center O' of the circle of radius a from the origin of the coordinate axes a distance m and locates it at an angle δ with respect to the x_3-axis, and finally

$$z = z_3 + \frac{b^2}{z_3} \qquad (6\text{-}39)$$

which transforms the circle of radius a (which represents the circular cylinder) into the Joukowski airfoil. (The magnitude of b is such that the circles of radii a and b intersect, with one point of intersection lying on the x_3-axis.) The Kutta-Joukowski condition is satisfied, and an infinite flow speed at the trailing edge avoided, if the circulation Γ is such that point E in the z_3-plane (which lies on the x_3 axis and which transforms into the trailing edge of the airfoil) coincides with the stagnation point P' of the flow past the circular cylinder in that plane, that is, if the complex velocity $dw/dz_3 = 0$ there. Such circulation has been assumed for the flows illustrated in Fig. 6-20. (The w-plane is not shown in Fig. 6-20.) Since at point P'

$$\frac{dw}{dz_3} = \frac{dw}{dz_1}\frac{dz_1}{dz_2}\frac{dz_2}{dz_3}$$

$$= \left[-U_\infty\left(1 - \frac{a^2}{z_1^2}\right) - \frac{i\Gamma}{2\pi z_1}\right]e^{i\alpha} = 0$$

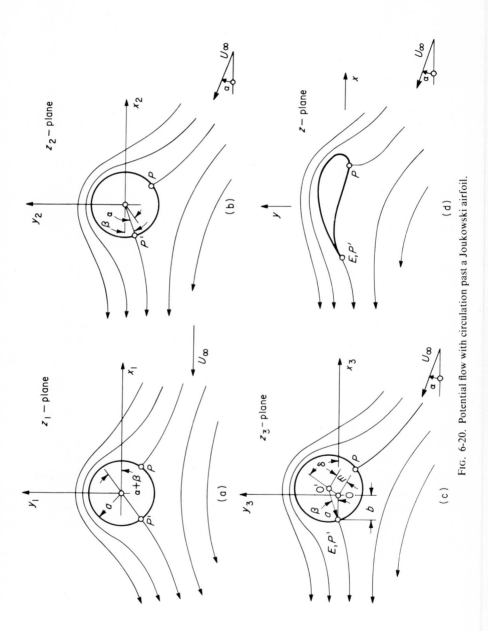

Fig. 6-20. Potential flow with circulation past a Joukowski airfoil.

with $z_1 = -ae^{i(\alpha + \beta)}$ (which follows from Fig. 6-20a), the magnitude of the circulation which results in a flow which satisfies the Kutta–Joukowski condition can be determined from the equation

$$U_\infty[1 - e^{-2i(\alpha+\beta)}] = \frac{i\Gamma}{2\pi a} e^{-i(\alpha+\beta)}$$

It is

$$\Gamma = 4\pi a U_\infty \sin(\alpha + \beta) \qquad (6\text{-}40)$$

The lift L per unit length of the airfoil is

$$L = \rho U_\infty \Gamma = 4\pi a \rho U_\infty^2 \sin(\alpha + \beta) \qquad (6\text{-}41)$$

and the lift coefficient based on the area $A = $ (chord) $\times$ (length) is

$$C_L = \frac{L}{\frac{1}{2}\rho U_\infty^2 c} = 8\pi \frac{a}{c} \sin(\alpha + \beta) \qquad (6\text{-}42)$$

where c denotes the chord. For small angle β the chord $c \simeq 4a$ (see Ref. 7), and the expression for the life coefficient becomes

$$C_L = 2\pi \sin(\alpha + \beta) \qquad (6\text{-}43)$$

The lift of the airfoil vanishes at an angle of incidence of the free stream $\alpha = -\beta$. Angle β, which is related to the camber, is always positive for an airfoil. Therefore, the angle $(\alpha + \beta)$ can be looked upon as the angle of attack measured with relation to the line of vanishing lift. Since $\sin x = x - \frac{x^3}{3!} + \cdots$, for small angles $(\alpha + \beta)$ the lift is approximately linearly dependent on $(\alpha + \beta)$.

The lift L is the only force which acts on a two-dimensional airfoil in a potential flow. The drag is equal to zero.

Wing of Finite Span. For wings of finite span the two-dimensional wing theory must be modified to account for the three-dimensional end effects near the tips. Since, as we have concluded in Sec. 3-5, vortex tubes (and therefore also vortices) are either closed in space or extend between the boundaries of the flow field, the bound vortex cannot end at the tips of the wing but must extend into the fluid. The theory of wings of finite span must explain two things: (1) the shape of the vortex which is not bound to the wing, and (2) the fact that the lift, and therefore also the circulation, decreases to zero as we approach the wing tips, which seems to contradict the first vortex theorem of Helmholtz (in the form given by Kelvin).

The first ideas on the flow past wings of finite span were advanced by F. W. Lanchester in England in 1907. It was he who suggested that the wing be replaced by a bound vortex which extends to the tips of the wing and which continues outside each wing tip as a free vortex extending downstream. This free vortex is known as the *trailing vortex*. Figure 6-21 shows Lanchester's drawing of the vortex system near a wing tip. Figure

FIG. 6-21. Vortex system near the
wing tip. (After W. F. Lanchester.)

6-22 shows a recent photograph of an airplane spraying insecticide from
the trailing edge of its wing. The edges of the spray sheet are rolled up
indicating presence of the trailing vortices which extend downstream from
the vicinity of the wing tips.

FIG. 6-22. An airplane spraying insecticide from the trailing edge of
its wing. (Courtesy of U. S. Forest Service.)

The ideas of Lanchester were extended by L. Prandtl in Germany who formulated the modern circulation theory of wings of finite span. In its simplest form, the wing is replaced by the bound vortex which extends downstream in form of trailing vortices (forming what is called a horse-shoe vortex) which join the starting vortex (discussed in Sec. 5-4), as shown in Fig. 6-23. This closed vortex loop induces a downward velocity

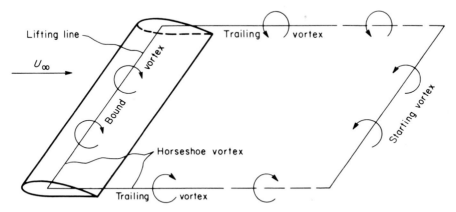

FIG. 6-23. Representation of a wing of finite span by a horseshoe vortex.

component. As a result, along the lifting line, which replaced the wing, the flow velocity corresponds to the velocity U_∞ of the forward motion and the *downwash velocity* $\mathbf{w}$ produces by the trailing vortices. (The starting vortex is either too far from the wing to affect it, or has already been dissipated as a result of viscosity of the fluid.) Note that if the flow were two-dimensional, that is, if the wing were of an infinite span, the effect of the trailing vortices would be absent and the downwash velocity $\mathbf{w}$ would be zero. (Although, as a result of circulation produced by the bound vortex, the Kutta–Joukowski condition at the trailing edge of the airfoil would be satisfied.)

Figure 6-24 represents an illustration, for a wing of finite span, of the flow velocities and forces acting on the wing. The vector $\mathbf{U}$ represents the velocity of the so-called "induced wind." It is obtained by summation of vectors U_∞ and $\mathbf{w}$. Vector $\mathbf{w}$ represents the downwash velocity known also as the *induced velocity*. Angle α_a is the *absolute angle of attack* of the wing, that is, the angle between the flight path and the line of zero lift ($\alpha_a = \alpha + \beta$). Angle α_i is the *induced angle of attack*, which is the angle between the direction of the induced wind and the flight path. Note that $\alpha_i \cong w/U_\infty$. Angle $\alpha_0 (= \alpha_a - \alpha_i)$ is the *effective angle of attack*, which is the angle between the induced wind and the zero-lift line of the wing. In accordance with the Kutta–Joukowski law, the bound vortex (and

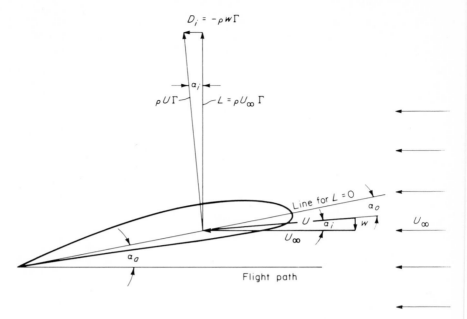

FIG. 6-24. Wing of finite span.

therefore the wing) experiences a force $\rho U_\infty \Gamma$ at right angle to $\mathbf{U}_\infty$, and a force $\rho w \Gamma$ at right angle to $\mathbf{w}$. The total force acting on the wing is equal to $\rho U \Gamma$. It is perpendicular to the velocity of the induced wind $\mathbf{U}$.

By lift and drag of an object we mean the components of the resultant force that are, respectively, perpendicular and parallel to the direction of flow of the undisturbed fluid; that is, to the direction of the flight path in the case of an object in motion relative to a stationary fluid. As a result, the magnitudes of the lift L and the drag D_i per unit span, acting on the wing are given by

$$L = \rho \Gamma U \cos \alpha_i = \rho U_\infty \Gamma \qquad (6\text{-}44)$$

and

$$D_i = -\rho \Gamma U \sin \alpha_i = -\rho w \Gamma \qquad (6\text{-}45)$$

The drag D_i is known as the *induced drag*, since it exists as a result of the induced velocity.

The effect of the downwash is to reduce the effective angle of attack of a wing compared to a wing of infinite span and to produce the induced drag. Observe that, since the circulation Γ increases with increasing angle of attack of a wing, so does the induced drag. The work in overcoming this drag goes into the kinetic energy of the trailing vortices left behind the wing. In a real fluid, in addition to the induced drag, there is the skin friction and the form drag acting on a wing. We shall return to the discussion of drag in Chapter 8.

This simple theory of wings of finite span does not explain the decrease of the circulation as the wing tips are approached. Prandtl refined it by assuming that, since the circulations about parallel vortex filaments may be superimposed, any distribution of circulation can be built up by superimposing a number of horseshoe vortices in the manner illustrated in Fig. 6-25. (This way a trailing vortex sheet is produced in place of

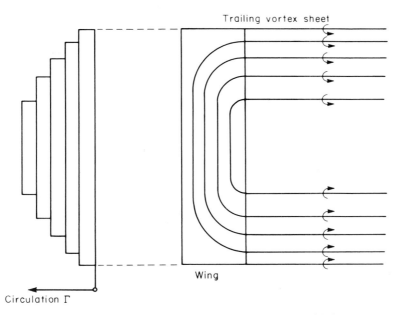

FIG. 6-25. Stepwise distribution of circulation in a wing of finite span.

trailing vortices.) For each section of the wing the lift $L = \rho U_\infty \Gamma$, but now Γ is a function of distance from the axis of symmetry of the wing. This, then, is the foundation of the modern wing theory.

REFERENCES

1. R. V. Churchill, *Complex Variables and Applications.* New York: McGraw-Hill, 1960.

2. L. A. Pipes, *Applied Mathematics for Engineers and Physicists.* New York: McGraw-Hill, 1958.

3. V. L. Streeter, *Fluid Dynamics.* New York: McGraw-Hill, 1948.

4. J. C. Hunsaker and B. G. Rightmire, *Engineering Applications of Fluid Mechanics.* New York: McGraw-Hill, 1947.

5. W. R. Sears, *Theoretical Aerodynamics. Part I: Introduction to Theoretical Hydrodynamics.* Ithaca: Cornell University Graduate School of Aeronautical Engineering, 1960.

6. H. R. Vallentine, *Applied Hydrodynamics.* London: Butterworth, 1959.

7. H. Glauert, *The Elements of Aerofoil and Airscrew Theory.* 2nd ed. London: Cambridge U. P., 1959.

8. L. Prandtl and O. G. Tietjens, *Applied Hydro- and Aeromechanics.* (First published in 1934.) New York: Dover, 1957.

9. Theodor von Kármán, *Aerodynamics.* Ithaca: Cornell U. P., 1954.

10. A. M. Kuethe and J. D. Schetzer, *Foundation of Aerodynamics.* New York: Wiley, 1950.

11. W. F. Durand, "Application of Conformal Transformation to Fields of Flow," in: W. F. Durand (ed), *Aerodynamic Theory*, Vol. 1. Pasadena, Calif.: California Institute of Technology, 1943, pp. 171–184.

12. D. O. Dommasch, *Principles of Aerodynamics*, New York: Pitman, 1953.

13. M. Rauscher, *Introduction to Aeronautical Dynamics.* New York: Wiley, 1953.

PROBLEMS

6-1. Verify the following: (a) $(2 - i) + i(2 + i) = 1 + i$; (b) $(1 + i)(3 + i) = 2 + 4i$; (c) $\dfrac{5}{2 + i} = 2 - i$; (d) $\ln(2i) = \ln 2 + i\dfrac{\pi}{2}$; (e) $e^{\pi i} = -1$. (Sec. 6-2.)

6-2. Verify the expressions for the velocity potential and stream function for the following complex potentials: (a) $w = \ln z^3$; (b) $w = \dfrac{1}{z}$. For (a) $\phi = \ln (x^2 + y^2)^{3/2}$, $\psi = 3 \tan^{-1}\dfrac{y}{x}$; for (b) $\phi = \dfrac{x}{x^2 + y^2}$, $\psi = \dfrac{y}{x^2 + y^2}$. (Sec. 6-3.)

6-3. Write the expression for the complex potential w of a flow produced by superposition of a free vortex on a sink at $z = z_0$ in the z-plane. Subsequently, writing $z - z_0 = r_1 e^{i\theta_1}$, derive the expressions for the velocity potential, stream function, and the radial and tangential velocity components (V_r and V_θ) for this flow. Sketch a few streamlines of this flow. (Sec. 6-3.)

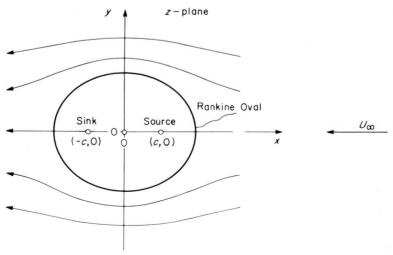

PROB. 6-4

6-4. What is the expression for the complex potential of a two-dimensional flow past a Rankine oval, shown in the sketch? This flow can be obtained by combination of a uniform flow with a source and a sink of equal strength, as shown. Determine the expressions for the velocity components u and v in the flow field and the location of the stagnation points. (Sec. 6-3.)

6-5. What flow is represented by the successive transformations $w = z_1 + (a^2/z_1)$, $z_2 = -iz_1$, $z = z_2 + (a^2/z_2)$? Sketch streamlines of the flows in the z_1-, z_2-, and z-planes. In addition, sketch the streamlines which you would expect in a flow of a real fluid. (Sec. 6-3.)

6-6. Sketch streamlines in the z-plane corresponding to the flow past a streamlined strut at zero angle of attack. (The streamlines in the z_2-plane are shown in Fig. 6-15.) (Sec. 6-3.)

6-7. Sketch a few streamlines (including the streamlines passing through the stagnation points) of the flows in the z_1-, z_2-, z_3-, and z-planes corresponding to the successive transformations

$$w = -\left(z_1 + \frac{a^2}{z_1}\right)$$

$$z_2 = z_1 e^{-i\alpha}$$

$$z_3 = z_2 + im$$

$$z = z_3 + \frac{b^2}{z_3}$$

with $b = \sqrt{a^2 - m^2}$, where a, b, and m are positive real numbers. (Sec. 6-3.)

6-8. Construct graphically the Joukowski airfoil and a few streamlines above and below the airfoil, including the streamlines passing through the stagnation points, taking $\delta = 50°$ and $m = 0.3a$. Assume that there is no circulation present; that is, draw a figure similar to that shown in Fig. 6-17c. For the flow past a circular cylinder of radius a use the streamlines as drawn in the accompanying sketch. (Sec. 6-3.)

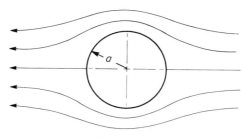

PROB. 6-8

6-9. State what flow is represented by the successive transformations

$$w = -\left(z_1 + \frac{a^2}{z_1}\right), \quad z_2 = z_1 e^{-i\alpha}, \quad z = z_2 + \frac{b^2}{z_2} \quad \text{with} \quad b < a$$

Sketch a few streamlines in the z_1-, z_2-, and z-planes. Indicate, among others, also the streamlines passing through the stagnation points. (Sec. 6-3.) What would the flow look like if the final transformation were $z = z_2 + a^2/z_2$?

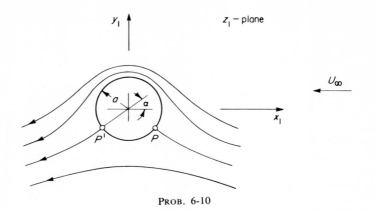

PROB. 6-10

6-10. Consider a two-dimensional irrotational and incompressible flow with circulation past a cylinder of radius a, as shown in the sketch. If the successive transformations to the z_2-plane and, finally, to the z-plane are

$$z_2 = z_1 e^{-i\alpha}$$

and

$$z = z_2 + \frac{a^2}{z_2}$$

sketch the streamlines in the z_2-plane and the z-plane. Also, verify that in this case the circulation Γ is given by $\Gamma = 4\pi a U_\infty \sin \alpha$. (Sec. 6-4.)

CHAPTER 7

Navier–Stokes Equation;
Hydrodynamic Stability;
Turbulence

7-1. INTRODUCTION

In the first part of this chapter we concern ourselves with the momentum equation, written in differential form, which is valid for real Newtonian fluids (which are also Stokesian) whose flow is laminar. This momentum equation is known as the *Navier–Stokes equation.* In our discussion we will limit ourselves to flows in which the density of the fluid is essentially constant. The velocity and pressure fields of such flows can be analyzed utilizing only the continuity and momentum equations. These solutions are valid for fluid flows in which the flow speed is everywhere much smaller than the local speed of sound in the fluid. These solutions are therefore valid for flows of liquids (in which the flow Mach number is very small everywhere in the flow field under normal conditions of practical interest) and for flows of gases in which the flow Mach number is small everywhere in the flow field. As was mentioned in Sec. 1-4, we will consider the fluids flowing at small Mach numbers as incompressible, and such flows will be referred to as *incompressible flows*; in the analysis of such flows we will use the physical model of a fluid whose density is constant. In addition, in our analyses in this chapter and in Chapter 8, we consider the temperature of the fluid to be also essentially constant. That is, we assume no appreciable heat transfer between the fluid and the surroundings. For that reason we will not need the energy equation (of viscous fluids) in our analyses. (The energy equation would allow us to determine the temperature field once the flow velocity field of the incompressible flow has been determined.) Since in Sec. 9-1, in which we consider the effects of compressibility on fluid flow, only an introductory, phenomenological, treatment will be given, there is no need to consider the energy equation of viscous fluids in this course of study.

In our further discussion in this chapter we consider some of the fluid flows that can be analyzed with the aid of the Navier–Stokes equation. The computational difficulties are responsible for the fact that only a handful of such solutions exists. We show how the dynamic similarity parameters (such as the Reynolds number) can be obtained from the Navier–Stokes equation, and consider briefly the problem of stability of the laminar flow.

The chapter ends with a brief discussion of turbulence. The effect of turbulence necessitates modification of the Navier–Stokes equation. Since our knowledge of the mechanism of turbulence is quite limited, we cannot solve these equations and must use semiempirical equations instead.

7-2. THE NAVIER—STOKES EQUATION[1]

The Stress Tensor. Cauchy's Equation of Motion. In Chapter 4 we showed that the momentum equation, in integral form, for a material volume $\overline{\mathcal{V}}$ can be written as

$$\frac{D}{Dt} \int_{\overline{\mathcal{V}}} \rho \mathbf{V} \, d\mathcal{V} = \int_{\overline{\mathcal{V}}} \rho \mathbf{f} \, d\mathcal{V} + \oint_{\overline{S}} \mathbf{t} \, dA \qquad [4\text{-}2]$$

where $\mathbf{t}$ denotes the stress acting at each element of area of the fluid surface $\overline{S}$ bounding the material volume (which, once the direction of the unit normal vector orienting the element of area is specified can be considered as a vector), defined as a force (due to molecular action) per unit area of the surface in the limit as the surface tends to zero, which is exerted by the fluid toward which the normal unit vector $\mathbf{n}$, orienting the area element of the surface, is directed. (In our considerations, the area elements of closed surfaces are oriented by the outward normal unit vectors.)

The component of $\mathbf{t}$ in direction normal to the surface $\overline{S}$ is a measure of tension in the fluid when the normal stress is positive (in which case the normal resolute of $\mathbf{t}$ points in the direction of $\mathbf{n}$) and of compression when it is negative. Since fluids in stable equilibrium do not support tension, it is the compression stress that concerns us.

In view of Eq. 3-59, Eq. 4-2 can be written in the form

$$\int_{\overline{\mathcal{V}}} \frac{D\mathbf{V}}{Dt} \rho \, d\mathcal{V} = \int_{\overline{\mathcal{V}}} \rho \mathbf{f} \, d\mathcal{V} + \oint_{\overline{S}} \mathbf{t} \, dA \qquad (7\text{-}1)$$

---

[1] This section represents essentially an abbreviated version of Secs. 10–5 to 10–7 of Ref. 6 by the author.

If we allow the material volume $\overline{\mathscr{V}}$ to tend to zero, thus shrinking its boundary surface $\bar{S}$ to a point, the above equation reduces to

$$\lim_{\overline{\mathscr{V}} \to 0} \oint_S \mathbf{t}\, dA = 0 \tag{7-2}$$

which indicates that the stresses at a point in a fluid are in equilibrium.

Consider a small tetrahedron of fluid, as shown in Fig. 7-1. Let us define stresses $\mathbf{t}_1$, $\mathbf{t}_2$, and $\mathbf{t}_3$ as the forces per unit area acting on surfaces

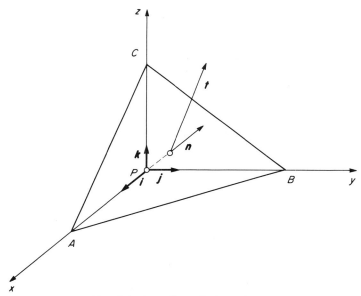

FIG. 7-1. A small tetrahedron of fluid.

PCB, PAC, and PAB of the tetrahedron, associated with the positive directions of the x-, y-, and z-axes. Writing in the component form, we have

$$\left. \begin{aligned} \mathbf{t}_1 &= \sigma_x \mathbf{i} + \tau_{xy}\mathbf{j} + \tau_{xz}\mathbf{k} \\ \mathbf{t}_2 &= \tau_{yx}\mathbf{i} + \sigma_y \mathbf{j} + \tau_{yz}\mathbf{k} \\ \mathbf{t}_3 &= \tau_{zx}\mathbf{i} + \tau_{zy}\mathbf{j} + \sigma_z \mathbf{k} \end{aligned} \right\} \tag{7-3}$$

These equations indicate that the directions of the stresses $\mathbf{t}_1$, $\mathbf{t}_2$, and $\mathbf{t}_3$ are, in general, different than the directions of the x-, y-, and z-axes. Denoting the area of the surface ABC by A, the areas of the surfaces PCB, PAC, and PAB are $A \cos \sphericalangle (n, x) = \mathbf{n} \cdot \mathbf{i}A$, $A \cos \sphericalangle (n, y) = \mathbf{n} \cdot \mathbf{j}A$, and $A \cos \sphericalangle (n, z) = \mathbf{n} \cdot \mathbf{k}A$ respectively. If the volume of the tetrahedron is allowed to tend to zero then, making use of Eq. 7-2, we obtain

$$\lim_{\mathscr{V} \to 0} \oint_{\bar{S}} \mathbf{t}\, dA = \mathbf{t}A - \mathbf{n} \cdot \mathbf{i}A\mathbf{t}_1 - \mathbf{n} \cdot \mathbf{j}A\mathbf{t}_2 - \mathbf{n} \cdot \mathbf{k}A\mathbf{t}_3 = 0$$

from which it follows that

$$\mathbf{t} = \mathbf{n} \cdot \mathbf{it}_1 + \mathbf{n} \cdot \mathbf{jt}_2 + \mathbf{n} \cdot \mathbf{kt}_3$$
$$= \mathbf{n} \cdot (\mathbf{it}_1 + \mathbf{jt}_2 + \mathbf{kt}_3)$$

As a result, the expression for the stress $\mathbf{t}$ can be written as

$$\mathbf{t} = \mathbf{n} \cdot \mathbf{T} \tag{7-4}$$

where the capital Greek letter tau

$$\mathbf{T} = \mathbf{it}_1 + \mathbf{jt}_2 + \mathbf{kt}_3 \tag{7-5}$$

denotes the *stress dyadic* or *stress tensor*. [Observe that the scalar (or inner) product of a vector and a dyadic is a vector.]

The concept of a dyadic, or a tensor of the second order, was introduced in Sec. 3-6. There dyadics were written in a form involving nine coefficients. The stress dyadic can be written in such form if we introduce Eq. 7-3 into Eq. 7-5. This we shall do later (see Eq. 7-13).

Making use of the divergence theorem of Gauss (Eq. A-59) and writing

$$\mathbf{F} = \mathbf{T} \cdot \mathbf{b}$$

where $\mathbf{b}$ denotes an arbitrary constant vector field, and $\mathbf{T}$ denotes the stress dyadic, we obtain

$$\int_{\mathscr{V}} \boldsymbol{\nabla} \cdot (\mathbf{T} \cdot \mathbf{b})\, d\mathscr{V} = \oint_{S} \mathbf{n} \cdot (\mathbf{T} \cdot \mathbf{b})\, dA$$

Since $\mathbf{b}$ represents a constant vector field

$$\boldsymbol{\nabla} \cdot (\mathbf{T} \cdot \mathbf{b}) = (\boldsymbol{\nabla} \cdot \mathbf{T}) \cdot \mathbf{b}$$

and therefore

$$\int_{\mathscr{V}} \boldsymbol{\nabla} \cdot \mathbf{T}\, d\mathscr{V} = \oint_{S} \mathbf{n} \cdot \mathbf{T}\, dA \tag{7-6}$$

Introducing Eqs. 7-4 and 7-6 into Eq. 7-1 gives equation

$$\int_{\mathscr{V}} \left(\rho \frac{D\mathbf{V}}{Dt} - \boldsymbol{\nabla} \cdot \mathbf{T} - \rho \mathbf{f} \right) d\mathscr{V} = 0$$

As the material volume $\mathscr{V}$ is arbitrary, the integrand vanishes everywhere in the flow field and we obtain the equation

$$\rho \frac{D\mathbf{V}}{Dt} = \rho \mathbf{f} + \boldsymbol{\nabla} \cdot \mathbf{T} \tag{7-7}$$

known as *Cauchy's equation of motion* (1828). Observe that no assumptions as to the form of the stress tensor were made in the derivation of this equation.

The divergence of a dyadic $\mathbf{T}$ is defined by

$$\boldsymbol{\nabla} \cdot \mathbf{T} = \mathbf{i} \cdot \frac{\partial \mathbf{T}}{\partial x} + \mathbf{j} \cdot \frac{\partial \mathbf{T}}{\partial y} + \mathbf{k} \cdot \frac{\partial \mathbf{T}}{\partial z} \tag{7-8}$$

In view of Eq. 7-5 we can write

$$\boldsymbol{\nabla} \cdot \mathbf{T} = \frac{\partial \mathbf{t}_1}{\partial x} + \frac{\partial \mathbf{t}_2}{\partial y} + \frac{\partial \mathbf{t}_3}{\partial z} \tag{7-9}$$

The Cauchy equation of motion can also be derived by considering the forces acting on a cubical fluid element in a rectangular cartesian co-ordinate system, such as shown in Fig. 7-2. We are assuming that the

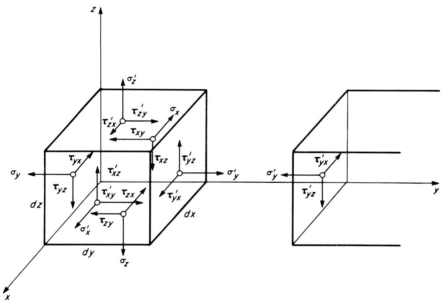

FIG. 7-2. Stresses acting on a fluid element.

stresses acting on each surface of the fluid element represent the average stresses acting on these faces. In the notation used for the shearing stresses, the second subscript refers to the direction of the stresses. The sign convention for the shearing stress is as follows: stress $\tau_{\alpha\beta}$, when acting on an element of surface whose normal unit vector (which orients it) has direction of the positive coordinate α, is taken as positive when acting in the positive direction of the axis β. By the principle of action and reaction, the (positive) shearing stress acting on a surface whose normal unit vector (which orients it) has direction opposite to that of the positive axis α acts in the direction of the negative β-axis. In Fig. 7-2 the stresses acting on the faces whose outward normal unit vectors point in the positive directions of the coordinate axes are denoted by primes to indicate that their magnitudes differ, in general, by infinitesimal amounts from the magnitudes of the corresponding stresses acting on the opposite faces of the fluid elements. For example, the relationships between the primed and unprimed components of stress acting on the faces of the fluid element normal to the x-axis are

$$\sigma_x' = \sigma_x + \frac{\partial \sigma_x}{\partial x} dx$$

$$\tau_{xy}' = \tau_{xy} + \frac{\partial \tau_{xy}}{\partial x} dx$$

$$\tau_{xz}' = \tau_{xz} + \frac{\partial \tau_{xz}}{\partial x} dx$$

The net surface force acting in the direction of the x-axis is

$$\left(\frac{\partial \sigma_x}{\partial x} dx\right) dy\, dz + \left(\frac{\partial \tau_{yx}}{\partial y} dy\right) dx\, dz + \left(\frac{\partial \tau_{zx}}{\partial z} dz\right) dx\, dy$$

and the momentum equation in the x-direction for the fluid element becomes

$$\rho \frac{Du}{Dt} = \rho f_x + \frac{\partial \sigma_x}{\partial x} + \frac{\partial \tau_{yx}}{\partial y} + \frac{\partial \tau_{zx}}{\partial z} \tag{7-10}$$

where f_x denotes the x-compoent of the body force. Similarly, we can derive the momentum equation in the y-direction:

$$\rho \frac{Dv}{Dt} = \rho f_y + \frac{\partial \tau_{xy}}{\partial x} + \frac{\partial \sigma_y}{\partial y} + \frac{\partial \tau_{zy}}{\partial z} \tag{7-11}$$

and the momentum equation in the z-direction:

$$\rho \frac{Dw}{Dt} = \rho f_z + \frac{\partial \tau_{xz}}{\partial x} + \frac{\partial \tau_{yz}}{\partial y} + \frac{\partial \sigma_z}{\partial z} \tag{7-12}$$

That these equations follow from Eq. 7-7 can be demonstrated by introducing to it Eq. 7-9 and Eq. 7-3.

Making use of Eq. 7-3, we can rewrite Eq. 7-5 in the form

$$\begin{aligned} \mathbf{T} = \;& \sigma_x \mathbf{ii} + \tau_{xy} \mathbf{ij} + \tau_{xz} \mathbf{ik} \\ &+ \tau_{yx} \mathbf{ji} + \sigma_y \mathbf{jj} + \tau_{yz} \mathbf{jk} \\ &+ \tau_{zx} \mathbf{ki} + \tau_{zy} \mathbf{kj} + \sigma_z \mathbf{kk} \end{aligned} \tag{7-13}$$

By comparing to zero the moment of the forces parallel to the z-axis and passing through the center of gravity of the fluid element shown in Fig. 7-2 we obtain equation

$$\Sigma M = (\tau_{xy} dy\, dz)\frac{dx}{2} + \left[\left(\tau_{xy} + \frac{\partial \tau_{xy}}{\partial x} dx\right) dy\, dz\right]\frac{dx}{2}$$

$$- (\tau_{yx} dx\, dz)\frac{dy}{2} - \left[\left(\tau_{yx} + \frac{\partial \tau_{yx}}{\partial y} dy\right) dx\, dz\right]\frac{dy}{2} = 0$$

from which it follows that

$$\tau_{xy} = \tau_{yx}$$

Similarly we can show that

$$\tau_{xz} = \tau_{zx}$$

and

$$\tau_{yz} = \tau_{zy}$$

This indicates that the *stress tensor* **T** is *symmetric*. As a result, there exist principal directions ξ, η, ζ in which the stress tensor takes the form

$$\mathbf{T} = \sigma_1 \mathbf{i}'\mathbf{i}' + \sigma_2 \mathbf{j}'\mathbf{j}' + \sigma_3 \mathbf{k}'\mathbf{k}' \qquad (7\text{-}14)$$

where $\mathbf{i}'$, $\mathbf{j}'$, and $\mathbf{k}'$ are the base unit vectors along the ξ-, η-, and ζ-axes respectively. The stresses acting in the directions of the ξ-, η-, and ζ-axes, whose magnitudes are σ_1, σ_2, and σ_3 respectively, are normal to the stress ellipsoid corresponding to the stress tensor **T** and are known as the *principal stresses*.

In a *fluid at rest* (as well as in the perfect fluids, whether at rest or in motion) the state of stress is hydrostatic; that is, the stress (across a surface at a point) is proportional to the unit normal vector **n** (orienting the surface) and we have $\sigma_x = \sigma_y = \sigma_z = \sigma_1 = \sigma_2 = \sigma_3 = -P$ and $\tau_{xy} = \tau_{yx} = \tau_{xz} = \tau_{zx} = \tau_{yz} = \tau_{zy} = 0$. In such case, we can write

$$\mathbf{t} = -P\mathbf{n}, \qquad \mathbf{t}_1 = -P\mathbf{i}, \qquad \mathbf{t}_2 = -P\mathbf{j}, \qquad \mathbf{t}_3 = -P\mathbf{k}$$

and the expression for the stress tensor becomes

$$\mathbf{T} = -P(\mathbf{ii} + \mathbf{jj} + \mathbf{kk}) = -P\mathbf{I} \qquad (7\text{-}15)$$

where

$$\mathbf{I} = \mathbf{ii} + \mathbf{jj} + \mathbf{kk} \qquad (7\text{-}16)$$

is a tensor known as the *unit dyadic*. It corresponds to the set of quantities δ_{ij} known as the *Kronecker delta*, such that

$$\delta_{11} = \delta_{22} = \delta_{33} = 1$$

$$\delta_{12} = \delta_{13} = \delta_{21} = \delta_{23} = \delta_{31} = \delta_{32} = 0$$

Using index notation, the above relationship can be written briefly as

$$\delta_{ij} = \left. \begin{array}{l} 1 \\ 0 \end{array} \right\} \begin{array}{l} i = j \\ i \neq j \end{array} \qquad (7\text{-}17)$$

and we can write

$$\tau_{ij} = -P\delta_{ij} \qquad (7\text{-}18)$$

where τ_{ij} represents the typical component of the stress tensor **T**.

The stress tensor **T** is usually represented as a sum of two tensors, the tensor representing the hydrostatic state of stress and the so-called *viscous stress tensor*:

$$\mathbf{T} = -P\mathbf{I} + \boldsymbol{\Pi} \qquad (7\text{-}19)$$

which, in the index notation, can be written in the form

$$\tau_{ij} = -P\delta_{ij} + \pi_{ij} \qquad (7\text{-}19a)$$

where π_{ij} represents the typical component of the viscous stress tensor Π. Equation 7-19 can be considered as the definition of the viscous stress tensor Π.

Constitutive Equations of Stokesian Fluids. The constitutive equations of viscous fluids relate their response to motion. Such equations have been first postulated by G. G. Stokes, and the fluids which obey his constitutive equations are called *Stokesian fluids*. Our present knowledge indicates that all gases which can be considered as a continuum and most common liquids can be considered Stokesian.

Stokes's postulates can be formulated as follows:

1. The fluid is a continuous medium in which the stress tensor **T** depends only on the rate-of-strain tensor **E** and the thermodynamic state of the fluid. Thus only the rate of deformation (and not the translation or the rotation of a fluid at a point) induces resisting stresses. This postulate can be expressed by the constitutive equation

$$\mathbf{T} = f(\mathbf{E}) \qquad (7\text{-}20)$$

with **T** depending also on the thermodynamic state of the fluid.

2. The fluid is homogeneous and, as a result, the stress tensor **T** is independent of position.

3. The fluid is isotropic; that is, its physical properties do not depend on direction and therefore the response function f in Eq. 7-20 does not depend on the orientation of the coordinate axes in which it is expressed.

4. When the fluid is at rest, in which case there is no deformation, the viscous stress tensor Π vanishes, and the stress tensor **T** reduces to

$$\mathbf{T} = -P\mathbf{I}$$

that is, the state of stress is hydrostatic.

The assumption of isotropy of the fluid implies that the principal axes of the rate-of-strain tensor **E** and of the stress tensor **T** coincide, because in an isotropic fluid the purely linear rates of deformation can be accompanied only by the principal (normal) stresses.

Momentum Equation of Newtonian Stokesian Fluids; Navier-Stokes Equation. Generalizing Newton's concept for the motion of simple shear, we use the name *Newtonian fluid* to describe a fluid in which the components of stress at a point are linearly dependent on the rates of strain (deformation) of the fluid (see discussion in Sec. 1-4). For such fluids, the magnitudes of the principal stresses can be expressed as linear functions of the principal rates of strain. Thus, in view of Eq. 7-19, we can write

$$\sigma_1 = -P + \lambda_1\epsilon_1 + \lambda_2\epsilon_2 + \lambda_3\epsilon_3$$

where ϵ_1, ϵ_2, and ϵ_3 are the principal (normal) rates of strain, σ_1 is the principal stress component acting in the direction of ϵ_1 and λ_1, λ_2, and λ_3 are coefficients which depend on the physical properties of the fluid.[2]

For a Stokesian fluid, in view of the isotropy of the medium, $\lambda_2 = \lambda_3$, and we can write

$$\sigma_1 = -P + \lambda_2(\epsilon_1 + \epsilon_2 + \epsilon_3) + (\lambda_1 - \lambda_2)\epsilon_1$$

Similarly, we can write

$$\sigma_2 = -P + \lambda_1'\epsilon_1 + \lambda_2'\epsilon_2 + \lambda_3'\epsilon_3$$

which equation, in view of the isotropy of the fluid ($\lambda_1' = \lambda_3'$) can be rewritten as

$$\sigma_2 = -P + \lambda_1'(\epsilon_1 + \epsilon_2 + \epsilon_3) + (\lambda_2' - \lambda_1')\epsilon_2$$

Comparing the equations for σ_1 and σ_2 we note that, in view of isotropy of the fluid,

$$\lambda_1' = \lambda_2 \quad (= \lambda_3' = \lambda_3)$$

and

$$\lambda_2' - \lambda_1' = \lambda_1 - \lambda_2$$

Therefore, for the Newtonian Stokesian fluids with which we will concern ourselves, (that is, for fluids which are Newtonian as well as Stokesian), the principal stresses and the principal rates of strain can be related by

$$\left.\begin{array}{l} \sigma_1 = -P + \mu'(\epsilon_1 + \epsilon_2 + \epsilon_3) + 2\mu\epsilon_1 \\ \sigma_2 = -P + \mu'(\epsilon_1 + \epsilon_2 + \epsilon_3) + 2\mu\epsilon_2 \\ \sigma_3 = -P + \mu'(\epsilon_1 + \epsilon_2 + \epsilon_3) + 2\mu\epsilon_3 \end{array}\right\} \qquad (7\text{-}21)$$

where μ' and μ are coefficients which depend on the physical properties of the fluid. [Observe that for Stokesian fluids, in general, the relation between the stress and the rate of deformation can be nonlinear.]

As shown previously in Sec. 3-6,

$$\epsilon_1 + \epsilon_2 + \epsilon_3 = \nabla \cdot \mathbf{V} \qquad [3\text{-}50]$$

Therefore, one third of the sum of the three components of the normal stresses, usually devoted as $-\bar{P}$, is equal to

$$\frac{1}{3}(\sigma_1 + \sigma_2 + \sigma_3) = -\bar{P} = -P + \left(\mu' + \frac{2}{3}\mu\right)\nabla \cdot \mathbf{V}$$

indicating that, for incompressible fluids, the hydrostatic pressure P can be looked upon as the negative of the arithmetic mean of the components of the three normal stresses, $\bar{P}$, because for such fluids $\nabla \cdot \mathbf{V} = 0$.

---

[2]Note that for a Newtonian isotropic and homogeneous fluid, Stokes's postulate (that stress is independent of the rotation of the fluid) can be justified by noting that the stress and rate-of-strain tensors are symmetric, while the vorticity tensor is antisymmetric.

For compressible fluids the difference between the hydrostatic pressure P, which is identified with the thermodynamic pressure, and $\bar{P}$ is

$$P - \bar{P} = \left(\mu' + \frac{2}{3} \mu \right) \boldsymbol{\nabla} \cdot \mathbf{V} = \kappa \boldsymbol{\nabla} \cdot \mathbf{V} \qquad (7\text{-}22)$$

where

$$\boldsymbol{\nabla} \cdot \mathbf{V} = \frac{1}{d\mathcal{V}} \frac{D(d\mathcal{V})}{Dt} \qquad [3\text{-}13]$$

is the (time) rate of relative local dilatation, and the proportionality coefficient

$$\kappa = \mu' + \frac{2}{3} \mu \qquad (7\text{-}23)$$

is known as the *coefficient of bulk viscosity*, while

$$\mu' = \kappa - \frac{2}{3} \mu \qquad (7\text{-}23a)$$

is called the *dilatational coefficient of viscosity*, or the *second coefficient of viscosity*.[3]

Introducing κ into Eq. 7-21 we obtain

$$\left. \begin{aligned}
\sigma_1 &= -P + \left(\kappa - \frac{2}{3} \mu \right) \boldsymbol{\nabla} \cdot \mathbf{V} + 2\mu\epsilon_1 \\
\sigma_2 &= -P + \left(\kappa - \frac{2}{3} \mu \right) \boldsymbol{\nabla} \cdot \mathbf{V} + 2\mu\epsilon_2 \\
\sigma_3 &= -P + \left(\kappa - \frac{2}{3} \mu \right) \boldsymbol{\nabla} \cdot \mathbf{V} + 2\mu\epsilon_3
\end{aligned} \right\} \qquad (7\text{-}24)$$

Denoting the direction cosines of the x-axis with respect to the principal axes ξ, η, ζ by l_1, m_1, n_1, the direction cosines of the y-axis with respect to the ξ-, η-, ζ-axes by l_2, m_2, n_2, and the direction cosines of the z-axis with respect to the ξ, η, ζ-axes by l_3, m_3, n_3, we have the following relations between the normal and tangential stresses (acting on a fluid element in the x,y,z-coordinate system) and the principal stresses:

$$\left. \begin{aligned}
\sigma_x &= \sigma_1 l_1^2 + \sigma_2 m_1^2 + \sigma_3 n_1^2 \\
\sigma_y &= \sigma_1 l_2^2 + \sigma_2 m_2^2 + \sigma_3 n_2^2 \\
\sigma_z &= \sigma_1 l_3^2 + \sigma_2 m_3^2 + \sigma_3 n_3^2 \\
\tau_{xy} = \tau_{yx} &= \sigma_1 l_1 l_2 + \sigma_2 m_1 m_2 + \sigma_3 n_1 n_2 \\
\tau_{xz} = \tau_{zx} &= \sigma_1 l_1 l_3 + \sigma_2 m_1 m_3 + \sigma_3 n_1 n_3 \\
\tau_{yz} = \tau_{zy} &= \sigma_1 l_2 l_3 + \sigma_2 m_2 m_3 + \sigma_3 n_2 n_3
\end{aligned} \right\} \qquad (7\text{-}25)$$

[3] We are using the notation and terminology advocated by Rosenhead[3], which differs from that used by Lamb[2].

Similarly, the relations between the normal and shear rates of strain and the principal rates of strain are

$$
\left.
\begin{aligned}
\epsilon_{11} &= \epsilon_x = \epsilon_1 l_1^2 + \epsilon_2 m_1^2 + \epsilon_3 n_1^2 \\
\epsilon_{22} &= \epsilon_y = \epsilon_1 l_2^2 + \epsilon_2 m_2^2 + \epsilon_3 n_2^2 \\
\epsilon_{33} &= \epsilon_z = \epsilon_1 l_3^2 + \epsilon_2 m_3^2 + \epsilon_3 n_3^2 \\
\epsilon_{12} &= \epsilon_{21} = \tfrac{1}{2} \gamma_{xy} = \epsilon_1 l_1 l_2 + \epsilon_2 m_1 m_2 + \epsilon_3 n_1 n_2 \\
\epsilon_{13} &= \epsilon_{31} = \tfrac{1}{2} \gamma_{zx} = \epsilon_1 l_1 l_3 + \epsilon_2 m_1 m_3 + \epsilon_3 n_1 n_3 \\
\epsilon_{23} &= \epsilon_{32} = \tfrac{1}{2} \gamma_{yz} = \epsilon_1 l_2 l_3 + \epsilon_2 m_2 m_3 + \epsilon_3 n_2 n_3
\end{aligned}
\right\}
\quad (7\text{-}26)
$$

Multiplying the equation for σ_1 (Eq. 7-24) by l_1^2, the equation for σ_2 by m_1^2 and the equation for σ_3 by n_1^2, and adding, we obtain

$$
\sigma_x = -P + \left(\kappa - \frac{2}{3} \mu \right) \nabla \cdot V + 2\mu \epsilon_x
$$

in view of relation $l_1^2 + m_1^2 + n_1^2 = 1$ between the direction cosines and the fact that $\epsilon_x = \epsilon_1 l_1^2 + \epsilon_2 m_1^2 + \epsilon_3 n_1^2$. Similar equations are obtained in this way for σ_y and σ_z.

Multiplying the equation for σ_1 (Eq. 7-24) by $l_1 l_2$, for σ_2 by $m_1 m_2$, and for σ_3 by $n_1 n_2$, and adding, we obtain

$$
\tau_{xy} = \tau_{yx} = 2\mu(\epsilon_1 l_1 l_2 + \epsilon_2 m_1 m_2 + \epsilon_3 n_1 n_2) = 2\mu \epsilon_{12} = \mu \gamma_{xy}
$$

in view of the relation $l_1 l_2 + m_1 m_2 + n_1 n_2 = 0$ between the direction cosines, and the fourth equation of the set of Eq. 7-26. Similar equations are obtained in this way for $\tau_{yz} = \tau_{zy}$ and $\tau_{zx} = \tau_{xz}$.

In a rectangular cartesian coordinate system the nine components of the stress tensor T (see Eq. 7-13) can thus be written as

$$
\left.
\begin{aligned}
\sigma_x &= -P + \left(\kappa - \frac{2}{3} \mu \right) \nabla \cdot V + 2\mu \epsilon_x \\
\sigma_y &= -P + \left(\kappa - \frac{2}{3} \mu \right) \nabla \cdot V + 2\mu \epsilon_y \\
\sigma_z &= -P + \left(\kappa - \frac{2}{3} \mu \right) \nabla \cdot V + 2\mu \epsilon_z \\
\tau_{xy} &= \tau_{yx} = \mu \gamma_{xy} \\
\tau_{yz} &= \tau_{zy} = \mu \gamma_{yz} \\
\tau_{zx} &= \tau_{xz} = \mu \gamma_{zx}
\end{aligned}
\right\}
\quad (7\text{-}27)
$$

For monatomic gases that are sufficiently rarefied, yet can be treated as a continuum, Maxwell's kinetic theory indicates that the bulk coefficient of viscosity is

$$
\kappa = \mu' + \frac{2}{3} \mu = 0 \quad (7\text{-}28)
$$

The general validity of this equation, often referred to as the *Stokes relation*, has been assumed by Stokes. Taking $\kappa = 0$ is equivalent to assuming that $P = \bar{P}$.

The coefficient μ, which can now easily be identified from the last three equations of the set (Eq. 7-27), is the *shear*, or *first*, *coefficient of viscosity* sometimes referred to as the (coefficient of) absolute, or dynamic, viscosity.

A great amount of attention has been directed recently toward better understanding of the limitations of the Stokes relation (Eq. 7-28) and of the second coefficient of viscosity. As the second coefficient of viscosity μ' drops out of Eq. 7-27 for incompressible fluids, it does not enter the well-known phenomena of hydrodynamics. The experimental, indirect, determination of μ' is very difficult and is subject to much controversy concerning the validity of the theories underlying the experiments. The measured values of absorption and attenuation of acoustic waves in gases and in liquids (whose dilatation, which is responsible for the absorption of sound energy, however small, is nevertheless finite) seem to indicate that there is no correlation between the first and the second coefficients of viscosity, and that the ratio of viscosities μ'/μ for most liquids investigated, has a positive value rather than $-\frac{2}{3}$ suggested by Maxwell's theory for the ideal monatomic gas [3]. However, many questions still remain to be answered before these experimental results can be accepted. One of them relates to the correctness of the hydrodynamic interpretation of acoustic streaming and energy absorption. Maxwell's justification of the Stokes relation depends so strongly on the definition of stress and temperature that, quoting Truesdell [7]: "...One may say that the kinetic theory assumes rather than proves that $3\mu' + 2\mu = 0$, or $3\mu' + 2\mu \neq 0$, as the case may be."

The coefficient of bulk viscosity can be looked upon as a parameter which describes some relaxation process. With each transport phenomenon (such as heat, mass, and momentum transfer) we can associate certain relaxation phenomena whenever the transfer phenomenon does not have enough time to reach a stationary state. In the case of momentum transfer by pure shear, the "lag" required for a molecule to adjust its translational energy represents only a few collisions. If this "lag" is very short compared with the time constant of the macroscopic process under consideration, then such a thermodynamically irreversible process can be represented by a coefficient.

It appears that the coefficient of bulk viscosity is of importance only in the study of the structure of the shock waves and in the study of the absorption and attenuation of acoustic waves.

In view of the results of our discussion in Sec. 3-6, and Eqs. 7-5, 7-3, 7-16, and 7-27, or Eqs. 7-14, 7-24, and 7-16, the stress tensor can be expressed in equation form as:

$$\mathbf{T} = \left[-P + \left(\kappa - \frac{2}{3}\mu\right)\nabla \cdot \mathbf{V}\right]\mathbf{I} + \mu[\nabla\mathbf{V} + (\nabla\mathbf{V})_c] \tag{7-29}$$

where

$$[\nabla\mathbf{V} + (\nabla\mathbf{V})_c] = 2\mathbf{E}$$

(**E** being the rate-of-strain dyadic) or, using the index notation, as

$$\tau_{ij} = \left[-P + \left(\kappa - \frac{2}{3}\mu\right)\nabla \cdot \mathbf{V}\right]\delta_{ij} + 2\mu\epsilon_{ij} \tag{7-30}$$

Introducing Eq. 7-29 into Cauchy's equation of motion results in the momentum equation of Newtonian Stokesian fluids:

$$\rho\frac{D\mathbf{V}}{Dt} = \rho\mathbf{f} + \nabla \cdot \left\{-P\mathbf{I} + \left[\left(\kappa - \frac{2}{3}\mu\right)\nabla \cdot \mathbf{V}\right]\mathbf{I} + \mu[\nabla\mathbf{V} + (\nabla\mathbf{V})_c]\right\} \tag{7-31}$$

With the aid of appropriate vector relations (see Ref. 6) this equation can be transformed into the equation

$$\rho\frac{D\mathbf{V}}{Dt} = \rho\mathbf{f} - \nabla P + \nabla\left[\left(\kappa - \frac{2}{3}\mu\right)\nabla \cdot \mathbf{V}\right]$$
$$+ (\nabla\mu) \cdot [\nabla\mathbf{V} + (\nabla\mathbf{V})_c] + \mu[\nabla^2\mathbf{V} + \nabla(\nabla \cdot \mathbf{V})] \tag{7-31a}$$

Making the assumption that the bulk coefficient of viscosity $\kappa = 0$, the last equation transforms into the so-called *Navier-Stokes equation*. For incompressible fluids and constant shear coefficient of viscosity the Navier–Stokes equation becomes

$$\rho\frac{D\mathbf{V}}{Dt} = \rho\mathbf{f} - \nabla P + \mu\nabla^2\mathbf{V} \tag{7-32}$$

In a rectangular cartesian coordinate system, with the body force representing the field of constant gravity—that is, with $\mathbf{f} = -\nabla\Omega$ and $\Omega = g\zeta + \text{const.}$—Eq. 7-32 transforms into the following three equations.

Momentum equation in the x-direction:

$$\frac{Du}{Dt} = \frac{\partial u}{\partial t} + u\frac{\partial u}{\partial x} + v\frac{\partial u}{\partial y} + w\frac{\partial u}{\partial z}$$
$$= -g\frac{\partial\zeta}{\partial x} - \frac{1}{\rho}\frac{\partial P}{\partial x} + \frac{\mu}{\rho}\left(\frac{\partial^2 u}{\partial x^2} + \frac{\partial^2 u}{\partial y^2} + \frac{\partial^2 u}{\partial z^2}\right) \tag{7-33}$$

Momentum equation in the y-direction:

$$\frac{Dv}{Dt} = \frac{\partial v}{\partial t} + u\frac{\partial v}{\partial x} + v\frac{\partial v}{\partial y} + w\frac{\partial v}{\partial z}$$
$$= -g\frac{\partial\zeta}{\partial y} - \frac{1}{\rho}\frac{\partial P}{\partial y} + \frac{\mu}{\rho}\left(\frac{\partial^2 v}{\partial x^2} + \frac{\partial^2 v}{\partial y^2} + \frac{\partial^2 v}{\partial z^2}\right) \tag{7-34}$$

Momentum equation in the z-direction:

$$\frac{Dw}{Dt} = \frac{\partial w}{\partial t} + u\frac{\partial w}{\partial x} + v\frac{\partial w}{\partial y} + w\frac{\partial w}{\partial z}$$

$$= -g\frac{\partial \zeta}{\partial z} - \frac{1}{\rho}\frac{\partial P}{\partial z} + \frac{\mu}{\rho}\left(\frac{\partial^2 w}{\partial x^2} + \frac{\partial^2 w}{\partial y^2} + \frac{\partial^2 w}{\partial z^2}\right) \qquad (7\text{-}35)$$

These equations can also be obtained by introducing Eq. 7-27 (with $\nabla \cdot V = 0$ since the fluid is assumed to be incompressible) and Eq. 3-48 together with the continuity equation into Eqs. 7-10, 7-11, and 7-12. For vanishing shear coefficient of viscosity the above equations reduce to Eq. 5-9.

With the assumption that the flow is incompressible, the expressions for the stresses become (see Eqs. 7-27 and 3-48):

$$\left.\begin{array}{l} \sigma_x = -P + 2\mu\dfrac{\partial u}{\partial x} \\[2mm] \sigma_y = -P + 2\mu\dfrac{\partial v}{\partial y} \\[2mm] \sigma_z = -P + 2\mu\dfrac{\partial w}{\partial z} \\[2mm] \tau_{xy} = \tau_{yx} = \mu\left(\dfrac{\partial u}{\partial y} + \dfrac{\partial v}{\partial x}\right) \\[2mm] \tau_{yz} = \tau_{zy} = \mu\left(\dfrac{\partial v}{\partial z} + \dfrac{\partial w}{\partial y}\right) \\[2mm] \tau_{zx} = \tau_{xz} = \mu\left(\dfrac{\partial u}{\partial z} + \dfrac{\partial w}{\partial x}\right) \end{array}\right\} \qquad (7\text{-}36)$$

Observe that in the momentum equations of fluids whose density and temperature (and therefore also shear coefficient of viscosity) can be considered as constant there are only four dependent variables: u, v, w (that is, the x-, y-, and z-components of the flow velocity) and pressure P. Since the continuity equation

$$\nabla \cdot V = \frac{\partial u}{\partial x} + \frac{\partial v}{\partial y} + \frac{\partial w}{\partial z} = 0$$

represents the fourth equation (which involves u, v, and w) only the momentum and continuity equations need be considered in an analysis of flows of such fluids (see discussion in Sec. 7-1).

Making use of Eqs. A-101 and A-104, and of Eq. 5-11, the Navier–Stokes equation for incompressible fluids with constant viscosity (Eq. 7-32) in a circular cylindrical coordinate system becomes as follows.

Momentum equation in the r-direction:

$$\frac{\partial V_r}{\partial t} + V_r \frac{\partial V_r}{\partial r} + \frac{V_\theta}{r} \frac{\partial V_r}{\partial \theta} + V_z \frac{\partial V_r}{\partial z} - \frac{V_\theta^2}{r} = -g \frac{\partial \zeta}{\partial r} - \frac{1}{\rho} \frac{\partial P}{\partial r}$$

$$+ \frac{\mu}{\rho} \left[\frac{1}{r} \frac{\partial}{\partial r} \left(r \frac{\partial V_r}{\partial r} \right) + \frac{1}{r^2} \frac{\partial^2 V_r}{\partial \theta^2} + \frac{\partial^2 V_r}{\partial z^2} - \frac{V_r}{r^2} - \frac{2}{r^2} \frac{\partial V_\theta}{\partial \theta} \right] \quad (7\text{-}37)$$

Momentum equation in the θ-direction:

$$\frac{\partial V_\theta}{\partial t} + V_r \frac{\partial V_\theta}{\partial r} + \frac{V_\theta}{r} \frac{\partial V_\theta}{\partial \theta} + V_z \frac{\partial V_\theta}{\partial z} + \frac{V_r V_\theta}{r} = -\frac{g}{r} \frac{\partial \zeta}{\partial \theta} - \frac{1}{\rho r} \frac{\partial P}{\partial \theta}$$

$$+ \frac{\mu}{\rho} \left[\frac{1}{r} \frac{\partial}{\partial r} \left(r \frac{\partial V_\theta}{\partial r} \right) + \frac{1}{r^2} \frac{\partial^2 V_\theta}{\partial \theta^2} + \frac{\partial^2 V_\theta}{\partial z^2} - \frac{V_\theta}{r^2} + \frac{2}{r^2} \frac{\partial V_r}{\partial \theta} \right] \quad (7\text{-}38)$$

Momentum equation in the z-direction:

$$\frac{\partial V_z}{\partial t} + V_r \frac{\partial V_z}{\partial r} + \frac{V_\theta}{r} \frac{\partial V_z}{\partial \theta} + V_z \frac{\partial V_z}{\partial z}$$

$$= -g \frac{\partial \zeta}{\partial z} - \frac{1}{\rho} \frac{\partial P}{\partial z} + \frac{\mu}{\rho} \left[\frac{1}{r} \frac{\partial}{\partial r} \left(r \frac{\partial V_z}{\partial r} \right) + \frac{1}{r^2} \frac{\partial^2 V_z}{\partial \theta^2} + \frac{\partial^2 V_z}{\partial z^2} \right] \quad (7\text{-}39)$$

For vanishing shear coefficient of viscosity, the last three equations reduce to Eq. 5-12.

The expressions for the stresses in a circular cylindrical coordinate system, in incompressible flows, are

$$\left. \begin{aligned}
\sigma_{rr} &= -P + 2\mu \epsilon_{rr} \\
&= -P + 2\mu \frac{\partial V_r}{\partial r} \\
\sigma_{\theta\theta} &= -P + 2\mu \epsilon_{\theta\theta} \\
&= -P + 2\mu \left(\frac{1}{r} \frac{\partial V_\theta}{\partial \theta} + \frac{V_r}{r} \right) \\
\sigma_{zz} &= -P + 2\mu \epsilon_{zz} \\
&= -P + 2\mu \frac{\partial V_z}{\partial z} \\
\tau_{r\theta} = \tau_{\theta r} &= 2\mu \epsilon_{r\theta} = \mu \left(\frac{\partial V_\theta}{\partial r} + \frac{1}{r} \frac{\partial V_r}{\partial \theta} - \frac{V_\theta}{r} \right) \\
\tau_{\theta z} = \tau_{z\theta} &= 2\mu \epsilon_{\theta z} = \mu \left(\frac{\partial V_\theta}{\partial z} + \frac{1}{r} \frac{\partial V_z}{\partial \theta} \right) \\
\tau_{rz} = \tau_{zr} &= 2\mu \epsilon_{rz} = \mu \left(\frac{\partial V_z}{\partial r} + \frac{\partial V_r}{\partial z} \right)
\end{aligned} \right\} \quad (7\text{-}40)$$

The boundary conditions which are taken when analyzing a motion of a viscous fluid relative to a solid surface in contact with the fluid are that there should be no slip of the fluid at the surface and no normal velocity relative to the surface.

In Sec. 3-4 we derived equation for the rate of change of circulation for a material line

$$\frac{D\Gamma}{Dt} = \oint_C \frac{D\mathbf{V}}{Dt} \cdot d\mathbf{r} \qquad [3\text{-}18]$$

In Sec. 5-4 we showed that for a barotropic flow of a perfect fluid in the field of conservative body forces

$$\frac{D\Gamma}{Dt} = 0 \qquad [5\text{-}41]$$

If we introduce the Navier–Stokes equation for incompressible fluids (Eq. 7-32) into Eq. 3-18 then, for conservative body forces, we obtain

$$\frac{D\Gamma}{Dt} = \frac{\mu}{\rho} \oint_C (\nabla^2 \mathbf{V}) \cdot d\mathbf{r}$$

Making use of Stokes's theorem, this equation can be rewritten in the form

$$\frac{D\Gamma}{Dt} = \frac{\mu}{\rho} \int_S (\nabla^2 \boldsymbol{\omega}) \cdot d\mathbf{A}$$

This is the expression relating the rate of change of circulation for a material line with the vorticity (distributed as a result of viscosity) and viscosity for an incompressible fluid.

7-3. DYNAMIC SIMILARITY PARAMETERS

The dynamic similarity parameters for fluid flows were discussed in Chapter 2. The purpose of the discussion which follows is to show how these parameters can be obtained from the equations of motion.

For a flow of an incompressible fluid studied in a rectangular cartesian coordinate system the continuity equation reads

$$\frac{\partial u}{\partial x} + \frac{\partial v}{\partial y} + \frac{\partial w}{\partial z} = 0 \qquad (7\text{-}41)$$

while the momentum equation in the x-direction is

$$\frac{\partial u}{\partial t} + u\frac{\partial u}{\partial x} + v\frac{\partial u}{\partial y} + w\frac{\partial u}{\partial z} = -g\frac{\partial \zeta}{\partial x} - \frac{1}{\rho}\frac{\partial P}{\partial x} + \nu\left(\frac{\partial^2 u}{\partial x^2} + \frac{\partial^2 u}{\partial y^2} + \frac{\partial^2 u}{\partial z^2}\right)$$

$$[7\text{-}33]$$

where $\nu = \mu/\rho$ represents the kinematic viscosity. Only one momentum equation is needed in this discussion. We shall make Eqs. 7-41 and 7-33 dimensionless by introducing proper reference quantities. Since for similarity of two flows the solutions utilizing dimensionless flow variables must be the same, it follows that the differential equations of flow expressed in dimensionless terms must also be the same for these flows, and that the boundary conditions expressed in dimensionless terms must be identical. The necessity for identity of the boundary conditions of two similar flows expressed in dimensionless terms is important.   These boundary conditions involve such things as solid walls and their roughness. (As was mentioned in Chapter 2, in general, the turbulence, which we do not consider in this discussion, should also be considered in similarity studies.)

Let us denote the reference flow speed by V_0, the reference pressure by P_0, and the reference length by L. The reference time is then $t_0 = L/V_0$. The reference quantities V_0, P_0 and L should be some characteristic quantities of the flow field (see our discussion in Chapter 2). Denoting the dimensionless flow variables by a superscript asterisk, we have

$$u = V_0 u^*, \quad v = V_0 v^*, \quad w = V_0 w^*, \quad P = P_0 P^*$$

$$x = L x^*, \quad y = L y^*, \quad z = L z^*, \quad t = \frac{L}{V_0} t^*$$

$$\zeta = L \zeta^*$$

Introducing the above relations into the continuity equation (Eq. 7-41) and the momentum equation (Eq. 7-33) results in the following dimensionless equations:

$$\frac{\partial u^*}{\partial x^*} + \frac{\partial v^*}{\partial y^*} + \frac{\partial w^*}{\partial z^*} = 0 \tag{7-42}$$

$$\frac{\partial u^*}{\partial t^*} + u^* \frac{\partial u^*}{\partial x^*} + v^* \frac{\partial u^*}{\partial y^*} + w^* \frac{\partial u^*}{\partial z^*}$$

$$= -\left(\frac{gL}{V_0^2}\right)\frac{\partial \zeta^*}{\partial x^*} - \left(\frac{P_0}{\rho V_0^2}\right)\frac{\partial P^*}{\partial x^*} + \left(\frac{\nu}{V_0 L}\right)\left\{\frac{\partial^2 u^*}{\partial x^{*2}} + \frac{\partial^2 u^*}{\partial y^{*2}} + \frac{\partial^2 u^*}{\partial z^{*2}}\right\} \tag{7-43}$$

The continuity equation expressed in dimensionless terms, Eq. 7-42, involves only the dimensionless flow variables and therefore is independent of the reference quantities. For that reason it is the same for all flows, and provides us with no conditions which must be satisfied if any two flows are to be similar. However, the momentum equation expressed in dimensionless terms is the same for two flows only if the dimensionless parameters gL/V_0^2, $P_0/\rho V_0^2$, and $\nu/V_0 L$ are the same for them. We encountered these parameters in Chapter 2 when we studied the conditions which must be satisfied if two flow systems are to be similar. The parameter gL/V_0^2 we modified to $V_0/\sqrt{gL}$ and called it the Froude number (Fr), the parameter $P_0/\rho V_0^2$ we denoted by symbol $\sqcap$, and the reciprocal of the parameter $\nu/V_0 L_0$ we called the Reynolds number.

In Sec. 2-2, when discussing the Froude number, it was stated that when a flowing liquid does not possess a free surface then the Froude number can be omitted from considerations when studying physical similarity of flow systems. We shall now show that this is so provided that a modified dimensionless pressure is used in the momentum equations. For this purpose let us introduce the dimensionless pressure P_{rest}^* which would exist if the liquid were at rest. The relation between this pressure and the dimensionless vertical coordinate ζ^* is

$$\left(\frac{P_0}{\rho V_0^2}\right)\frac{\partial P_{rest}^*}{\partial x^*} = -\left(\frac{gL}{V_0^2}\right)\frac{\partial \zeta^*}{\partial x^*} \tag{7-44}$$

Subtracting this equation from the momentum equation in the x-direction gives

$$\frac{\partial u^*}{\partial t^*} + u^* \frac{\partial u^*}{\partial x^*} + v^* \frac{\partial u^*}{\partial y^*} + w^* \frac{\partial u^*}{\partial z^*}$$

$$= -\left(\frac{P_0}{\rho V_0^2}\right)\frac{\partial(P^* - P_{rest}^*)}{\partial x^*} + \left(\frac{\nu}{V_0 L}\right)\left\{\frac{\partial^2 u^*}{\partial x^{*2}} + \frac{\partial^2 u^*}{\partial y^{*2}} + \frac{\partial^2 u^*}{\partial z^{*2}}\right\} \tag{7-45}$$

Thus if the dimensionless pressure ($P^* - P_{rest}^*$) is used in the momentum equations, then the Froude number ceases to affect the similarity conditions requirement concerning identity of the differential equations. If, in addition, the boundary conditions do not involve pressure (as is *not* the case for flows with a free surface), then the similarity of such flows depends only on the Reynolds number and the dimensionless pressure parameter $\Pi = P_0/\rho V_0^2$. If there is no possibility of cavitation then the pressure parameter Π loses its importance (see discussion in Sec. 2-2) and the Reynolds number remains the only parameter on which similarity of such flows depends.

The above discussion indicates that for incompressible fluid flows, as long as the boundary conditions do not involve pressure, we can omit the gravitational body force term from the momentum equations (and use P instead of $P + g\rho\zeta$ in them). (The action of gravity on the individual fluid elements is eliminated by their buoyancy.) We must only remember to add at the end the hydrostatic pressure to the calculated pressure. This procedure is in general always used in analyses of flows past bodies immersed in an infinite fluid.

In addition, we may conclude that the Reynolds number is the most important parameter for incompressible flows without a free surface. As we shall see in Chapter 8, the flow fields may experience very significant changes at some quite high values of the Reynolds number. This fact indicates that we should be very careful when trying to extrapolate the flow characteristics from one range of the Reynolds number to another. The experiments further show that at high Reynolds numbers the effects of the dimensionless parameter based on the height of the roughness elements of the wall and of the turbulence intensity are quite large, even when the magnitudes of these parameters are very small.

7-4. SOME SOLUTIONS OF LAMINAR FLOW PROBLEMS

Introduction. With the flow velocity $\mathbf{V}$ taking the place of the vector field $\mathbf{U}$ we can rewrite Eq. A-58 in the form

$$\nabla^2 \mathbf{V} = \nabla (\nabla \cdot \mathbf{V}) - \nabla \times (\nabla \times \mathbf{V})$$

For an incompressible flow, the above equation reduces to

$$\nabla^2 \mathbf{V} = - \nabla \times (\nabla \times \mathbf{V})$$

in view of the continuity equation $\nabla \cdot \mathbf{V} = 0$ valid for such flows. As a result, the Navier–Stokes equation for incompressible fluids with constant shear coefficient of viscosity, Eq. 7-32, can be rewritten as

$$\rho \frac{D\mathbf{V}}{Dt} = \rho \mathbf{f} - \nabla P - \mu \nabla \times (\nabla \times \mathbf{V}) \tag{7-32a}$$

This equation indicates that the wholly irrotational flows of incompressible fluids calculated using the perfect-fluid model, satisfy the equations of motion of viscous fluids. This is so because for such flows, since the vorticity $\boldsymbol{\omega} = \nabla \times \mathbf{V} = \mathbf{0}$ in them, the momentum equation (Eq. 7-32a) reduces to Euler's momentum equation (Eq. 5-3). What they do not satisfy, however, are the boundary conditions of real fluids at solid walls. While in a flow of a real fluid both the normal and tangential components of the velocity relative to a solid surface are zero, in an irrotational flow of a perfect fluid (as a result of the fact that the order of the differential momentum equation is lowered by one when the viscous terms vanish) only the boundary condition of zero normal velocity component on the solid surface is utilized, and we cannot put any restriction on the tangential velocity component. As a result, the flow fields determined using the Navier–Stokes equations—that is, the flow fields of viscous fluids—differ from the corresponding flow fields of perfect fluids. An inspection of Eq. 7-43 or Eq. 7-45 indicates, however, that for very large Reynolds numbers the difference between the flow fields of the real (viscous) fluids and those of perfect fluids should be small. Nevertheless, we should expect large differences in regions which are affected by the separation of the (real) fluid from the solid surface.

Solutions for Very Small Reynolds Number. For flows at very small Reynolds number (in such flows about an object either the flow speed and the size of the object is very small or the fluid viscosity very large), the magnitudes of the inertia forces in the fluid are much smaller than the magnitudes of the viscous forces. As the first approximation for such flows, we can, therefore, neglect the inertia force terms in the Navier–Stokes equations. This approach was first used by Stokes (1851), who obtained this way the solution for the flow field around a sphere at low Reynolds numbers. He found that the drag of a sphere in such a flow was

$$D = 3\pi\mu U_\infty d$$

where d denotes the diameter of the sphere and U_∞ the speed of the sphere or the flow speed of the undisturbed fluid relative to the sphere. The drag coefficient based on the projected area of the sphere is in the case

$$C_D = \frac{D}{\frac{1}{2}\rho U_\infty^2 A} = \frac{D}{\frac{1}{2}\rho U_\infty^2 \left(\frac{\pi d^2}{4}\right)} = \frac{24}{\dfrac{U_\infty d}{\nu}}$$

or

$$C_D = \frac{24}{\mathrm{Re}_d} \qquad (7\text{-}46)$$

As Fig. 7-3 indicates, the experiments show that this solution is adequate only for the values of $\mathrm{Re}_d < 1$.

The solution of Stokes past a sphere at low Reynolds number has been improved by C. W. Oseen (in 1910) who assumed that the sphere caused a small perturbation in the uniform parallel flow. He retained only the first-order perturbation velocities, thus accounting to a limited extent for the inertia terms. The corresponding drag coefficient is

$$C_D = \frac{24}{\mathrm{Re}_d}\left(1 + \frac{3\mathrm{Re}_d}{16}\right) \qquad (7\text{-}47)$$

Recently the Oseen's solution of his linearized equation has been improved by a number of investigators. However, these solutions, which are based on the linearizing approximations, prove to be inadequate for the

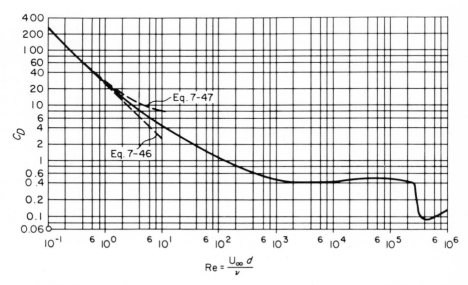

FIG. 7-3. Experimentally determined drag coefficient for spheres as a function of the Reynolds number.

values of the Reynolds number $\mathrm{Re}_d > 2$. Solutions valid for $\mathrm{Re}_d < 40$ have been obtained by V. G. Jensen in 1959[8], who in his paper gives a list of references dealing with the slow-speed flows past spheres.

Another interesting solution for low Reynolds numbers is that for a flow between two parallel and very closely spaced flat plates. This flow is known as the *Hele–Shaw flow* (1898). Its usefulness lies in the fact that its streamlines, as viewed from above the plates, are the same as those corresponding to a potential flow and for that reason can be used in a study of two-dimensional irrotational flow past obstacles of arbitrary shapes. The streamlines in such an apparatus, in which the top plate is made out of glass, are made visible by injection of a dye into the fluid between the plates. That the velocity components in the Hele–Shaw flow are derivable from a potential can be shown as follows: The equations of a steady horizontal motion of a viscous fluid with negligible inertia forces studied in the coordinate system shown in Fig. 7-4 are

$$
\left.
\begin{aligned}
\frac{\partial P}{\partial x} &= \mu\left(\frac{\partial^2 u}{\partial x^2} + \frac{\partial^2 u}{\partial y^2} + \frac{\partial^2 u}{\partial z^2}\right) \\[2mm]
\frac{\partial P}{\partial y} &= \mu\left(\frac{\partial^2 v}{\partial x^2} + \frac{\partial^2 v}{\partial y^2} + \frac{\partial^2 v}{\partial z^2}\right) \\[2mm]
\frac{\partial P}{\partial z} &= -g\rho + \mu\left(\frac{\partial^2 w}{\partial x^2} + \frac{\partial^2 w}{\partial y^2} + \frac{\partial^2 w}{\partial z^2}\right) \\[2mm]
\frac{\partial u}{\partial x} &+ \frac{\partial v}{\partial y} + \frac{\partial w}{\partial z} = 0
\end{aligned}
\right\}
\qquad (7\text{-}48)
$$

The first three of these equations follow from Eqs. 7-33, 7-34 and 7-35. The last one is the continuity equation. Since the two plates between which the fluid flows are very closely spaced, the component of the flow velocity in the z-direction $w \approx 0$, and the third equation reduces to

$$
\frac{\partial P}{\partial z} = -g\rho
$$

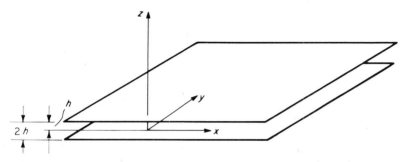

FIG. 7-4. Two horizontal flat plates a small distance apart.

from which it follows that

$$P = -g\rho z + f(x, y)$$

which indicates that the derivatives $\partial P/\partial x$ and $\partial P/\partial y$ are independent of z. Since the flow speed is zero at the walls of the passage formed by the flat plates and the width of the passage is very small, we can expect that the derivatives of the flow velocity components with respect to x and y are much smaller than those with respect to z. Therefore the first two equations of Eq. 7-48 reduce to

$$\frac{\partial P}{\partial x} = \mu \frac{\partial^2 u}{\partial z^2} \quad \text{and} \quad \frac{\partial P}{\partial y} = \mu \frac{\partial^2 v}{\partial z^2}$$

from which, by integration, it follows that

$$u = \frac{1}{\mu} \frac{\partial P}{\partial x} \frac{z^2}{2} + C_1 z + C_2$$

$$v = \frac{1}{\mu} \frac{\partial P}{\partial y} \frac{z^2}{2} + C_3 z + C_4$$

The boundary conditions are $u = v = 0$ at $z = \pm h$. Also, we have $\partial u/\partial z = 0$ and $\partial v/\partial z = 0$ at $z = 0$. As a result, we find that $C_1 = C_3 = 0$, while

$$C_2 = -\frac{1}{\mu} \frac{\partial P}{\partial x} \frac{h^2}{2}$$

and

$$C_4 = -\frac{1}{\mu} \frac{\partial P}{\partial y} \frac{h^2}{2}$$

and we obtain

$$u = \frac{1}{2\mu} \frac{\partial P}{\partial x} (z^2 - h^2)$$

$$v = \frac{1}{2\mu} \frac{\partial P}{\partial y} (z^2 - h^2) \tag{7-49}$$

In any plane $z = z_0 = $ constant, we have

$$u = \frac{\partial}{\partial x} \left[\frac{(z_0^2 - h^2)}{2\mu} P \right]$$

$$v = \frac{\partial}{\partial y} \left[\frac{(z_0^2 - h^2)}{2\mu} P \right]$$

which indicates that the velocity components u and v are derivable from a potential $\phi(x, y) = \dfrac{(z_0^2 - h^2)}{2\mu} P$ and therefore the streamlines of the Hele–Shaw flow correspond to those of a potential flow. We must realize, of course, that the Hele–Shaw flow is rotational and there is no slip of the

fluid at the solid walls. That there exist the vorticity components in the
x- and y-directions follows immediately from the expressions for the
velocity components u and v, Eq. 7-49. Since the expression for the
vorticity in a rectangular cartesian coordinate system is

$$\boldsymbol{\omega} = \nabla \times \mathbf{V} = \left(\frac{\partial w}{\partial y} - \frac{\partial v}{\partial z}\right)\mathbf{i} + \left(\frac{\partial u}{\partial z} - \frac{\partial w}{\partial x}\right)\mathbf{j} + \left(\frac{\partial v}{\partial x} - \frac{\partial u}{\partial y}\right)\mathbf{k}$$

and $w = 0$ in this case, only the vorticity components in the z-direction
vanish in the flow field everywhere except, of course, on the surface of
the object around which the fluid flows.

Figure 7-5 shows the streamlines of the Hele–Shaw flow past a two-
dimensional airfoil. These streamlines approximate quite well those of a

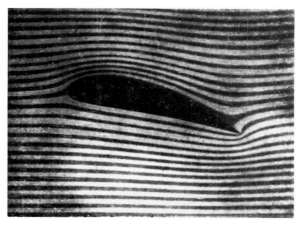

FIG. 7-5. Hele–Shaw flow past an airfoil. (By permission from Ref. 9.)

potential two-dimensional flow past such an airfoil. For a comparison,
see Figs. 5-9a, 5-10a, and 6-17c.

Some Other Solutions. Two of the most important exact solutions of
the Navier–Stokes equations are those for the steady two-dimensional
(parallel) laminar and incompressible flow between parallel plates in
which the upper plate is in a uniform motion parallel to the other plate,
and the (fully-developed) steady parallel axisymmetrical laminar and incompressible flow through a straight pipe. These flows are called the
(plane) *Couette flow* and the *Poiseuille* (pipe) *flow* respectively.

Couette Flow. Since for a parallel flow only one velocity component
differs from zero, for the flow illustrated in Fig. 7-6 we have the components of the flow velocity in the y- and z-direction equal to zero. That is,
$v = w = 0$. As a result, from the continuity equation it follows that

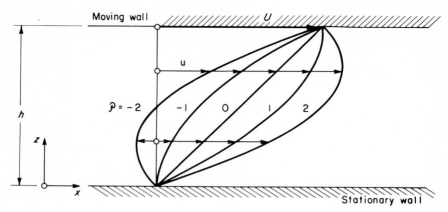

FIG. 7-6. The Couette flow.

$\partial u / \partial x = 0$ which indicates that the component of the flow velocity in the x-direction (which is the only nonvanishing velocity component) is independent of the distance x. The Navier–Stokes equations for a flow in which the shear coefficient of viscosity can be assumed to be constant (Eqs. 7-33, 7-34, and 7-35) reduce to the following

$$\frac{\partial (P + g\rho\varsigma)}{\partial x} = \mu \frac{\partial^2 u}{\partial z^2} \tag{7-50}$$

because u is independent of y for a parallel flow in the x-direction, and

$$\frac{\partial (P + g\rho\varsigma)}{\partial y} = 0, \qquad \frac{\partial (P + g\rho\varsigma)}{\partial z} = 0$$

(Observe that all inertia terms vanished in this steady parallel flow.) Since $\partial(P + g\rho\varsigma)/\partial z = 0$, Eq. 7-50 can be integrated. The result is

$$u = \frac{1}{\mu} \frac{d(P + g\rho\varsigma)}{dx} \frac{z^2}{2} + C_1 z + C_2$$

where the pressure gradient in the direction of flow is constant. The boundary conditions are $u = 0$ for $z = 0$, and $u = U$ for $z = h$ where U denotes the magnitude of the velocity of the moving plate. Hence $C_2 = 0$ and

$$C_1 = \frac{U}{h} - \frac{1}{\mu} \frac{d(P + g\rho\varsigma)}{dx} \frac{h}{2}$$

and we obtain expression

$$u = \frac{z}{h} U - \frac{h^2}{2\mu} \frac{d(P + g\rho\varsigma)}{dx} \frac{z}{h} \left(1 - \frac{z}{h}\right) \tag{7-51}$$

In the case in which the pressure gradient $d(P + g\rho\varsigma)/dx = 0$, the expression for the flow speed becomes

$$u = U \frac{z}{h}$$

This is the simple shear flow which we discussed in Sec. 1-4. (The vertical coordinate z is employed here in place of coordinate y used in the example discussed in Sec. 1-4.) In the general case of a Couette flow with a pressure gradient the velocity distribution is that illustrated in Fig. 7-6. The parameter $\mathscr{P}$ is given by

$$\mathscr{P} = -\frac{h^2}{2\mu U}\frac{d(P + g\rho\zeta)}{dx}$$

When the pressure decreases in the direction of flow, that is when $d(P + g\rho\zeta)/dx < 0$ and $\mathscr{P} > 0$, the velocity component u is positive over the whole width of the passage between the plates. For flows with increasing pressure in the direction of flow the velocity component u can become negative over a part of the width of the passage. This "backflow" occurs for $\mathscr{P} < -1$. The Couette flow is of importance in the study of lubrication.

Poiseuille Flow. In this case the velocity components in the radial and tangential directions, V_r and V_θ, are zero. As a result, from the continuity equation

$$\nabla \cdot V = \frac{1}{r}\frac{\partial}{\partial r}(rV_r) + \frac{1}{r}\frac{\partial V_\theta}{\partial \theta} + \frac{\partial V_z}{\partial z} = 0$$

it follows that $\partial V_z/\partial z = 0$ and therefore also that the velocity component V_z depends on the radius only, as shown in Fig. 7-7. The Navier–Stokes

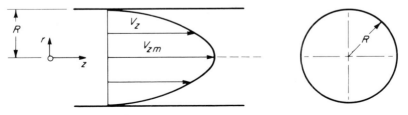

FIG. 7-7. The Poiseuille flow.

equations for a flow in which the shear coefficient of viscosity can be assumed to be constant (Eqs. 7-37, 7-38, and 7-39) reduce to equations

$$\frac{\partial(P + g\rho\zeta)}{\partial r} = 0, \qquad \frac{\partial(P + g\rho\zeta)}{\partial \theta} = 0$$

and

$$\frac{\partial(P + g\rho\zeta)}{\partial z} = \mu\frac{1}{r}\frac{\partial}{\partial r}\left(r\frac{\partial V_z}{\partial r}\right)$$

(Observe that, as in the case of Couette flow, the inertia terms vanished from the momentum equations.) The last equation can be rewritten as

$$\frac{d(P + g\rho\zeta)}{dz} = \mu\frac{1}{r}\frac{d}{dr}\left(r\frac{dV_z}{dr}\right)$$

It indicates that the pressure gradient $d(P + g\rho\zeta)/dz$ is independent of the distance z, and therefore can be expressed in the form $d(P + g\rho\zeta)/dz = [(P + g\rho\zeta)_2 - (P + g\rho\zeta)_1]/L$ where $L = z_2 - z_1$ denotes the length of the pipe between sections 1 and 2. The last equation can be integrated twice with respect to r. The boundary conditions are $V_z = 0$ at $r = R$. We also have $dV_z/dr = 0$ at $r = 0$. The result is

$$V_z = -\frac{R^2}{4\mu} \frac{d(P + g\rho\zeta)}{dz} \left[1 - \left(\frac{r}{R}\right)^2\right] \tag{7-52}$$

which is the equation of a paraboloid of revolution. The maximum value of V_z, which occurs at $r = 0$ is

$$V_{z,m} = -\frac{R^2}{4\mu} \frac{d(P + g\rho\zeta)}{dz}$$

while the average flow speed is

$$\overline{V} = \frac{\int_0^R V_z 2\pi r \, dr}{\pi R^2} = -\frac{R^2}{8\mu} \frac{d(P + g\rho\zeta)}{dz} = \frac{1}{2} V_{z,m}$$

and the expression for the volumetric rate of flow is

$$Q = \pi R^2 \overline{V} = \frac{\pi R^4}{8\mu} \left[-\frac{d(P + g\rho\zeta)}{dz}\right] \tag{7-53}$$

Observe that combining Eqs. 7-53 and 7-52 we can write the expression for the flow speed $V_z = V$ in the form

$$V = 2\overline{V} \left[1 - \left(\frac{r}{R}\right)^2\right]$$

If the pipe is horizontal, and therefore the effect of the gravitational attraction on the flow negligible, we can omit the term $g\rho\zeta$ in Eq. 7-53 and rewrite it, in the integrated form, as

$$P_1 - P_2 = 8\mu \frac{L\overline{V}}{R^2} \tag{7-54}$$

where $P_1 - P_2 = -\Delta P$ and $L = \Delta z = z_2 - z_1$, subscripts 1 and 2 referring to sections of the pipe. (Otherwise, we should continue using the term $P + g\rho\zeta$ instead of P.) This equation is known as the Hagen–Poiseuille equation. (See discussion in Sec. 1-4.) If we introduce the *resistance coefficient for pipe flow* f defined by

$$f = \frac{-\dfrac{\Delta P}{\Delta z}}{\dfrac{1}{2} \rho \overline{V}^2} d \tag{7-55}$$

where d denotes the (inside) diameter of the pipe (we have $\Delta P/\Delta z = \Delta P/L = $ constant), then

$$f = \frac{32\mu}{\rho \overline{V} R}$$

or

$$f = \frac{64}{\text{Re}_d} \qquad (7\text{-}56)$$

This result is in very good agreement with the experimental observations for the laminar flow range.

The only nonvanishing shearing stress in this flow is

$$\tau = \tau_{zr} = \mu\left(\frac{\partial V_z}{\partial r} + \frac{\partial V_r}{\partial z}\right)$$

(see Eq. 7-40) which reduces to

$$\tau = \mu \frac{\partial V_z}{\partial r}$$

since $V_r = 0$. Hence we have

$$\frac{d(P + g\rho\zeta)}{dz} = \frac{1}{r}\frac{d}{dr}(r\tau)$$

and the equation for the shearing stress becomes

$$\tau = \frac{r}{2}\frac{d(P + g\rho\zeta)}{dz} \qquad (7\text{-}57)$$

which indicates that the shearing stress is proportional to radius from the center of the pipe. We can also write

$$\tau = \tau_w \frac{r}{R} \qquad (7\text{-}58)$$

where τ_w denotes the shearing stress at the wall $\tau(r = R)$. In view of Eq. 7-53 we can also write

$$c_f' = \frac{\tau_w}{\frac{1}{2}\rho \bar{V}^2} = \frac{8\mu}{\rho\bar{V}R} = \frac{16\mu}{\rho\bar{V}d} = \frac{16}{\text{Re}_d} \qquad (7\text{-}59)$$

where the coefficient c_f' is the *resistance coefficient based on the wall shearing stress*. Observe that from our discussion it follows that for laminar incompressible flows in pipes

$$4c_f' = f \qquad (7\text{-}60)$$

(Since for incompressible flows in pipes in general $\pi dL\tau_w = -\Delta P\pi d^2/4$, this relation is valid also for turbulent incompressible flows in pipes.)

From the discussion in Sec. 1-4 it should be clear that this laminar Poiseuille flow can occur in practice only for the values of the Reynolds number $\text{Re}_d = \bar{V}d/\nu$ (where $d = 2R$) smaller than the critical value $\text{Re}_{d,\text{crit}}$ which is approximately 2300 (this number represents the average of the critical values observed by Reynolds), in spite of the fact that the above solution is an exact solution of the Navier–Stokes equations involving arbitrary pressure gradient. When the value of the Reynolds number $\text{Re}_d > \text{Re}_{d,\text{crit}}$, the flow becomes turbulent and the velocity profile is then different than that for the laminar flow (being much flatter at the center of the pipe). In addition, Eqs. 7-53 and 7-54 are valid only for a fully developed laminar flow, and therefore only a sufficient distance from the entrance to the pipe.

Figure 7-8 shows a comparison of the experimental results of G. Hagen for a fully developed laminar flow in a pipe and a line corresponding to Eq. 7-56. The agreement is very good.

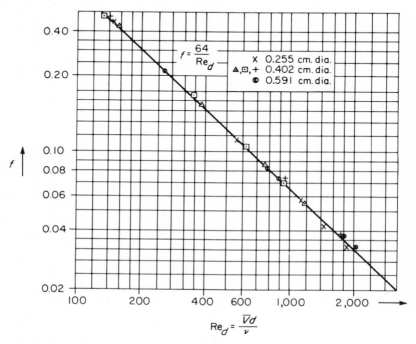

FIG. 7-8. The resistance coefficient for a laminar flow through a pipe as a function of the Reynolds number. The experimental results of G. Hagen. (Adapted from Ref. 10.)

The term "length of transition" for a laminar flow in a pipe is used to denote the length of the pipe from the (rounded) entrance for which the velocity distribution differs so little from the parabolic distribution given by Eq. 7-52 that the maximum values of the flow speed in the middle of the pipe differ by only one percent. For the length of transition which is necessary for a fully developed laminar flow to be established in a pipe, J. Boussinesq gave the formula (Ref. 10, p. 22)

$$x_{tr} = 0.26R\left(\frac{\bar{V}R}{\nu}\right)$$

$$= 0.065\,d\,\mathrm{Re}_d \tag{7-61}$$

And so, for a flow of water through a pipe of 0.5 in. diameter at the Reynolds number $\mathrm{Re}_d = 2000$ the length of transition is 54 ft, and the

Hagen–Poiseuille law, as expressed by Eq. 7-54, holds only at distances larger than 54 ft in this case.

Figure 7-9 shows the development of the laminar velocity profile in the entrance region of a pipe as measured by J. Nikuradse.

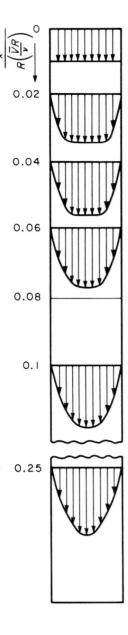

FIG. 7-9. Laminar velocity distribution near the entrance to a pipe. (After J. Nikuradse.)

The pressure drop per unit length at the entrance to the pipe is larger than that given by Eq. 7-54 because a part of this pressure drop is utilized in accelerating the inner layers of the fluid and therefore also in increasing the kinetic energy of the fluid. The corrected expression for the pressure drop, as calculated by H. L. Langhaar (in 1942, Ref. 11) is

$$P_1 - P_2 = 8\mu \frac{L\bar{V}}{R^2} + 2.28 \frac{\rho \bar{V}^2}{2} \tag{7-62}$$

L. Schiller (in 1932) computed the kinetic-energy correction factor to be $2.16 \rho \bar{V}^2/2$, while Boussinesq (in 1890) found it to be $2.24 \rho \bar{V}^2/2$. Additional information on this topic can be found in Ref. 12.

A solution of the Navier–Stokes equation for a laminar parallel flow through a circular annulus is also known. Its derivation is left as a problem assignment.

7-5. HYDRODYNAMIC STABILITY

As was pointed out in Sec. 7-4, the solutions of the Navier–Stokes equations cease to be of value in an analysis of a fluid flow when the turbulent form of fluid motion occurs. The experimental evidence indicates that laminar flow occurs at low Reynolds numbers. At such conditions, as a result of viscosity, all irregular fluid motions which characterize a turbulent flow are damped out and the laminar flow is stable. At high Reynolds numbers turbulent fluid motion is observed, a laminar flow is in general unstable and it may in certain instances be produced only by a careful elimination of all, even extremely small, disturbances.

An instability of a laminar flow does not necessarily result in a turbulent motion, however. It may result in a transformation of a simple laminar motion into another, more complex, but nevertheless still laminar motion.

In this section we will discuss briefly the general problem of stability of certain fluid flows. The discussion of the transition of the two-dimensional boundary layer flow from laminar to turbulent will be continued in Sec. 8-2.

The three basic types of instability of fluid flows are as follows [14]: (a) the instability produced by centrifugal forces (such as occurs in a flow between rotating concentric cylinders), (b) the thermal instability (such as occurs when a fluid is heated in the field of gravitational attraction), and (c) the instability of two-dimensional parallel flows.

The Instability Produced by Centrifugal Forces. The instability of flow between rotating concentric cylinders was first studied by G. I. Taylor in 1923. He observed the flow instability in form of closed ring vortices uniformly spaced along the axis of the cylinders. These rings, which can be observed not only when the flow is laminar but also when it is turbulent, are called the *Taylor instability*. When plotted on a graph in which the values on the ordinate axis represent the Reynolds number $Re_i = \omega_i r_i^2 / \nu$ and those on the abscissa axis the Reynolds number $Re_0 = \omega_0 r_0^2 / \nu$, where ω denotes the magnitude of the angular velocity and r the radius of a cylinder while the subscripts i and 0 refer to the inner and outer cylinder respectively, the limit below which the flow is laminar and free of the instability (nonperiodic flow) is called the *Taylor stability boundary*. It is indicated by open circles in Fig. 7-10 which represents results of recent experiments by D. Coles [15]. The negative values of the Reynolds number Re_0 indicate opposite directions of rotation of the cylinders. The radius ratio in the experiments of Coles was $r_0 / r_i = 1.135$.

Figure 7-10c shows clearly that two distinct instabilities of the laminar flow can occur: the so-called *singly periodic flow* which is characterized by flat ring vortices and which occurs between the Taylor stability boundary and the "second" stability boundary (which appears to be not unique for the same direction of rotation of both cylinders, but depends on the number of Taylor ring vortices or cells), and the *doubly periodic flow* which is characterized by a rotating pattern of tangential waves superimposed on the original cellular motion. (This doubly periodic flow was also observed by Taylor in 1923.)

Figures 7-11 to 7-14 show photographs obtained by Coles of the singly and doubly periodic laminar flows, and of the turbulent flows which show disappearance of residual periodicity. (In his experiments, Coles used a silicon oil with a small amount of aluminium paint pigment to accomplish flow visualization.)

The experiments of Coles indicate that two distinct processes of transition from laminar to turbulent flow take place in a flow between concentric cylinders. One, which he calls the *catastrophic transition*, is typical of the flows dominated by rotation of the outer cylinder (the region to the left of the origin of the coordinates in Fig. 7-10). It is characterized by intermittent fluctuations of the flow velocity depending on whether turbulent or laminar parts of the fluid pass the observation point. The flow is observed to divide itself into finite regions which are either laminar or turbulent. These regions are separated by well-defined interfaces. A configuration called *spiral turbulence* occurs generally throughout the transition region. This region is indicated in Fig. 7-10, on which γ denotes the *intermittency factor* defined as the average fraction of the fluid participating in the turbulent motion. (Usually the intermittency factor is defined as that fraction of time during which the flow at a given position remains turbulent [18].) The photographs of the spiral turbulence are shown in Fig. 7-14a, 7-14b, and 7-14c. The second process of transition to turbulent flow, called *transition by spectral evolution*, is typical of the flows dominated by rotation of the inner cylinder (the region above

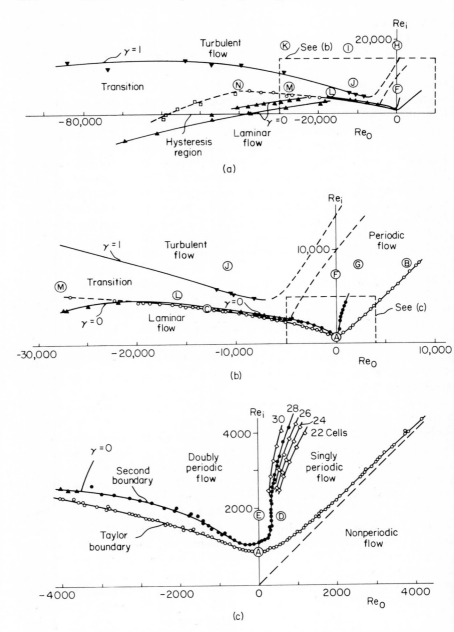

FIG. 7-10. Various regions in a flow between rotating cylinders. (After Prof. Donald Coles. First published in an article by Prof. Coles, "Transition in Circular Couette Flow," *Journal of Fluid Mechanics,* Vol. 21, part 3, Cambridge University Press, London, pp. 385–425.)

FIG. 7-11. Singly periodic laminar flow between rotating cylinders. (a) Flow
at A in Figs. 7-10b and 7-10c. (b) Flow at B in Fig. 7-10b. (c) Flow at C in
Fig. 7-10b. (d) Flow at D in Fig. 7-10c. (Photographs courtesy of Prof. Donald Coles. First published in an article by Prof. Coles, "Transition in Circular
Couette Flow," *Journal of Fluid Mechanics,* Vol. 21, part 3, Cambridge University Press, London, pp. 385–425.)

the origin of coordinates in Fig. 7-10). As the speed of the inner cylinder
increases, the Taylor instability is followed by a second instability characterized by the appearance of a tangential wave pattern which rotates at
approximately the mean speed of the two cylinders. For a time this

FIG. 7-12. Doubly periodic flow between rotating cylinders. (e) Flow at E in Fig. 7-10c. (f) Flow at F in Figs. 7-10a and 7-10b. (g) Flow at G in Fig. 7-10b. (Photographs courtesy of Prof. Donald Coles. First published in an article by Prof. Coles, "Transition in Circular Couette Flow," *Journal of Fluid Mechanics*, Vol. 21, part 3, Cambridge University Press, London, pp. 385–425.)

motion remains laminar until at sufficiently high speeds irregularities begin to appear. They increase with speed until a fully turbulent flow appears. The essential feature of this transition process is the absence of the intermittency.

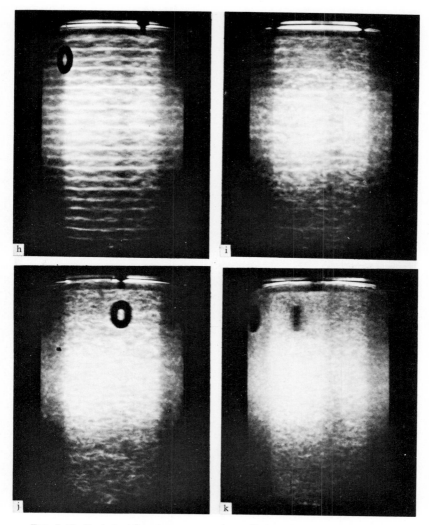

FIG. 7-13. Turbulent flow between rotating cylinders showing disappearance of residual periodicity. The outer cylinder rotates in opposite direction to that of the inner cylinder. (h) Flow at *H* in Fig. 7-10a. (i) Flow at *I* in Fig. 7-10a. (j) Flow at *J* in Figs. 7-10a and 7-10b. (k) Flow at *K* in Fig. 7-10a. (Photographs courtesy of Prof. Donald Coles. First published in an article by Prof. Coles, "Transition in Circular Couette Flow," *Journal of Fluid Mechanics,* Vol. 21, part 3, Cambridge University Press, London, pp. 385–425.)

In fluid mechanics, by a *secondary flow* we mean a cross flow superimposed on a mean flow. The ring vortices (the Taylor instability), which may occur in a flow between rotating cylinders, represent one type of a secondary flow.

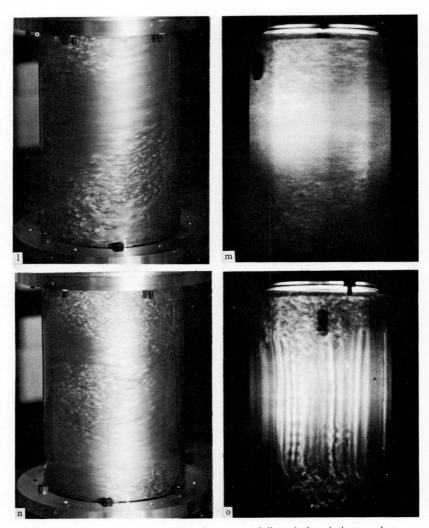

FIG. 7-14. Intermittently turbulent flows, especially spiral turbulence, when the outer cylinder rotates in opposite direction to that of the inner cylinder. (l) Flow at L in Figs. 7-10a and 7-10b. (m) Flow at M in Figs. 7-10a and 7-10b. (n) Flow at N in Fig. 7-10a. (o) Instability following start-stop motion of the outer cylinder. (Photographs courtesy of Prof. Donald Coles. First published in an article by Prof. Coles, "Transition in Circular Couette Flow," *Journal of Fluid Mechanics,* Vol. 21, part 3, Cambridge University Press, London, pp. 385–425.)

An instability of flow resulting from the action of centrifugal forces occurs also in boundary-layer flows along concave walls, in flows in curved channels, and in flows on rotating disks.

The instability of laminar boundary layer on a concave wall was analyzed by H. Görtler in 1940 [16] who predicted that vortices whose axes are parallel to the main flow should occur in such flow. These vortices are shown in Fig. 7-15. The existence of this instability was confirmed experimentally in 1950 by N. Gregory and W. S. Walker [33].

The instability of laminar flow in curved channels was investigated by W. R. Dean in 1928 [17]. He showed that such flow is unstable with respect to disturbances in form of vortices whose axes are parallel to the direction of flow. He has found that this type of instability occurs when the dimensionless parameter (sometimes called the *Dean number*) $(\bar{V}h/\nu)\sqrt{h/r}$ reaches a value of 36. In this parameter $\bar{V}$ denotes the mean speed, h is the distance between the walls, and r is the radius of the inner wall. When the channel is in form of a pipe, the vortices have the form

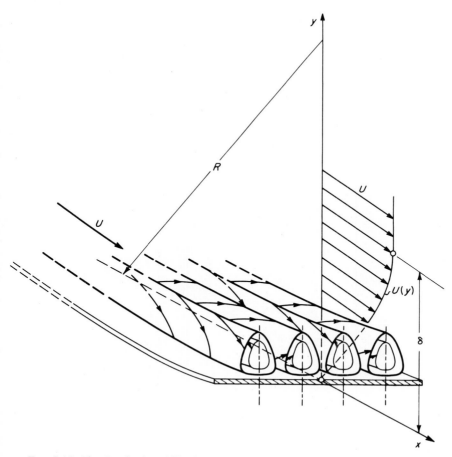

FIG. 7-15. The Görtler instability in a boundary layer flow on a concave wall. (After H. Görtler.)

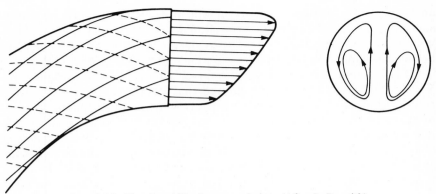

FIG. 7-16. Flow instability in a curved pipe. (After L. Prandtl.)

shown in Fig. 7-16. Figure 7-17 shows the direction of flow at the inner wall of a curved pipe. The direction of the flow approaching the elbow is from right to left. (The direction of flow at a wall is usually made visible by coating the wall with a mixture of lampblack and oil.) Figure 7-17 illustrates clearly the formation of the secondary flow (vortices shown in Fig. 7-16). W. R. Hawthorne in 1951 [20] showed that the secondary flow in bent pipes and ducts is oscillatory, the direction of the circulation changing periodically. The formation of secondary flows in curved channels is very important in the study of flow through cascades of blades in turbomachines.

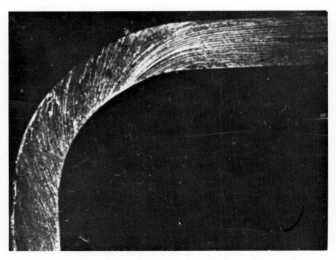

FIG. 7-17. Secondary flow in a curved pipe. (By permission from Ref. 9.)

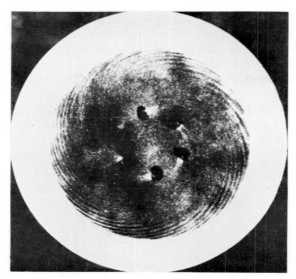

Fig. 7-18. China-clay record showing the flow instability and transition on a rotating disk. The direction of rotation of the disk was counter-clockwise, the rotational speed 3,200 rpm, the disk radius was 6 in. (Photograph by N. Gregory, J. T. Stuart and N. S. Walker [34]. Reproduced by permission from the Royal Society, London.)

The instability of laminar boundary layer on a rotating disk was investigated, in 1955, by N. Gregory, J. T. Stuart, and W. S. Walker [34]. Figure 7-18 shows a china-clay record of the boundary-layer flow instability on a rotating disk.[4] The flow near the center of the disk is laminar. The flow instability is in form of spiral vortices which cause transition of flow from laminar to turbulent near the rim. In the turbulent boundary-layer region the disk shown in the photograph is white; there the rate of evaporation of methyl salicylate is larger than in the laminar boundary-layer region.

The Thermal Instability. The experiments indicate that when a fluid, which is initially at rest, is heated from below or cooled from above, a number of vertical cells having polygonal sections are formed. These are known as the Bénard cells [14]. This type of instability is of main interest in meteorology. A review of this field can be found in Ref. 26.

The Instability of Two-Dimensional Parallel Flows. The study of stability of parallel laminar flows is an investigation of stability of such flows with respect to small disturbances (which are always present in flowing fluids). Since the boundary-layer flows do not differ much from

[4] The china-clay flow visualization technique is described in Sec. 9-4.

parallel flows, the results of such study are approximately valid also for the laminar boundary layers. The importance of such study lies in the light which it throws on the problem of transition of laminar motion to turbulent. We attribute the onset of turbulence (in localized regions of laminar flow) to the instability of the laminar flow caused by the disturbances.

The results of an analysis of stability of a laminar boundary–layer flow are usually presented in form of curves of neutral stability, such as shown in Fig. 7-19. In this figure, δ denotes the boundary-layer thickness,

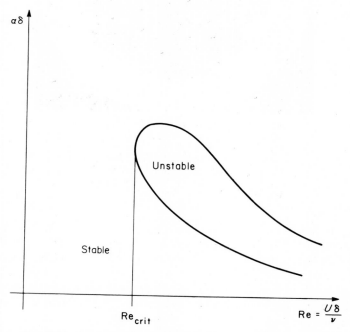

Fig. 7-19. Curve of neutral stability for a two-dimensional boundary-layer flow.

the parameter $\alpha = 2\pi/\lambda$ where λ is the wavelength of the disturbance, and U denotes the flow speed outside the boundary layer. The smallest value of the Reynolds number for the curve is known as the *critical Reynolds number*, Re_{crit}.

A flow can become unstable to small disturbances but still be laminar for some distance because of the time necessary for the disturbances to become amplified sufficiently to cause transition to turbulence.

The stability theory of laminar parallel flows, especially the relation between the instability of the flow and the transition to turbulence, is still incomplete owing mainly to the mathematical difficulties involved. For that reason we are still unable to predict the transition Reynolds numbers for the laminar boundary layers. We shall return to this topic in Sec. 8-2. The topic of transition of laminar flow to turbulent in a pipe (in particular the experiments of O. Reynolds) has already been considered in Sec. 1-4.

7-6. INTRODUCTION TO A STUDY OF TURBULENT MOTION

The phenomenon of turbulent fluid motion has been briefly discussed in Sec. 1-4. In most fluid flows of practical interest the Reynolds number (based on such significant physical quality in the flow field as the length of the object about which the fluid flows, the chord of an aircraft wing, or the diameter in case of a flow through a pipe) is large enough so that the fluid motion is turbulent. At a given point in a steady turbulent-flow field the velocity of the fluid exhibits random fluctuations about the (temporal) mean flow speed $\overline{U}$ defined by

$$\overline{U} = \frac{1}{T} \int_t^{t+T} U \, dt \qquad (7\text{-}63)$$

where U denotes the actual flow speed and T the time interval which is long enough so that the mean flow speed is independent of time (T is of the order of 1 sec; the variations in the mean flow speed for $T > 1$ sec would normally be considered as indications that the flow is unsteady). By turbulence we mean the random fluctuations about this mean within the frequency range of 10 to 10^5 cycles per second (cps). The magnitude of turbulence is usually very small when compared with the mean flow speed, say 5×10^{-2} to 10^{-4} of the mean flow speed. Higher relative magnitudes of turbulence can occur in the wake flows downstream of blunt bodies. (Note that the vortex streets are not random and are not classified as turbulence.) They can also occur in the motion of atmospheric air masses (in which case the turbulence is referred to as the large-scale turbulence).

In our discussion we will limit ourselves to the so-called *wall turbulence* which, unlike the *free turbulence*, takes place in flows near a solid boundary or boundaries. That is, we will consider the most important case of *shear flow* in which turbulent motions arise and sustain themselves, and not with free shear layers produced by jets nor the flows having no mean shear in which the turbulent motions represent the decay of the turbulence produced in some shear flow upstream.

The outstanding features of turbulent fluid motion are: (a) the randomness of turbulent fluctuations, (b) its diffusive nature, and (c) the rapid dissipation of mechanical (kinetic) energy into heat.

Figure 7-20a shows the fluctuations of a single velocity component which are characteristic of a fully (or nearly fully) turbulent flow.

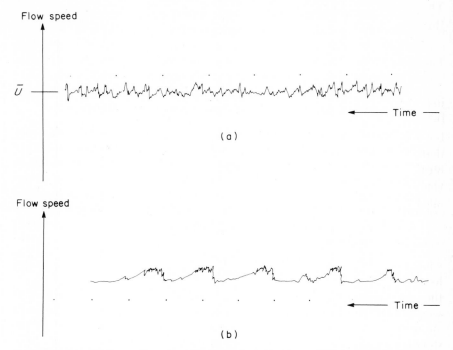

FIG. 7-20. Typical traces of a single velocity component variation. (a) Fully turbulent flow. (b) Intermittent turbulence. Time interval between dots is 1/60 sec. (Adapted from Fig. 5 of Ref. 29.)

Figure 7-20b shows the fluctuations of a single velocity component in the region of intermittent turbulence which exists downstream of laminar flow region and upstream of fully turbulent region. The flow in that region changes intermittently between laminar and turbulent, and the intermittent bursts of turbulence correspond to the passage of turbulent spots over the hot-wire probe which was used in these measurements. (We shall discuss these turbulent spots in Sec. 8-2.)

In the presence of mean stress, the turbulent motions generate shearing stress and thus extract energy from the mean flow. The present view is that the (kinetic) energy is fed into the turbulence through the larger eddies and that it is converted into heat by the damping action of viscosity, which action is large only among the very small eddies. Hence there must be transfer of energy from the larger to the smaller eddies. We think that this energy transfer takes place progressively from one size of eddies to the next one, and that the number of sizes of the eddies (and therefore also the number of stages of energy transfer) increases with the Reynolds number. When the Reynolds number of the flow is high enough so that the flow is fully turbulent (that is, the intermittency of the velocity fluctuations has already disappeared), the chain in the energy transfer is already long enough so that a further increase in the Reynolds number has very little effect on the character of the turbulent flow. That is, the mean flow velocity distribution, or profile, shows little dependence on the Reynolds number, and so do the ratios of the magnitudes of the turbulent velocity fluctuations to the mean flow speed at given distances from the wall. This observed lack of direct effect of viscosity on the flow in the turbulent flow region is referred to as the *Reynolds number similarity*. [The turbulent flow region, in flows along walls, excludes a very thin region at the wall, known as the *viscous sublayer* (see Sec. 8-3).] In addition, a fully turbulent flow exhibits preservation of form from one flow section to another which is known as *self-preservation*. Both the Reynolds number similarity and self-preservation are very important characteristics of turbulent shear flows because they allow formulation of certain laws of behavior of such flows.

The measure of the magnitude of the eddies in a turbulent flow is usually expressed with the aid of the characteristic length known as the *scale of turbulence*. The structure of turbulence is described with the aid of the intensity (which will be defined later in this section) and the scale of turbulence.

As far as the diffusive nature of turbulent motion is concerned, the turbulent diffusiveness is much larger than the molecular diffusiveness of a laminar motion. In the fully turbulent flow region the molecular diffusion is usually neglected. In regions in which this cannot be done, these two effects are assumed to be additive. As was already mentioned in Sec. 1-4, in analogy to laminar motion we often endow a fluid whose motion is turbulent with the *eddy viscosity* and *eddy heat conductivity*, which are usually much higher than the (shear) viscosity and the (molecular) heat conductivity, and which are not properties of the fluid but depend on a number of factors such as the size of the flow field and on the particular location in it.

The fact that the turbulent fluctuations are random led to statistical treatment of turbulence. The experiments on fully turbulent flows have shown that certain empirical laws can be advanced for the distribution of the mean flow speed in flows through pipes and in (turbulent) boundary layers on flat surfaces. This fact suggests existence of a definite statistical state of the fluid. We shall not concern ourselves with the statistical theory of fully developed turbulent flows, but will concentrate our discussion on the concept of stresses in the fluid resulting from turbulence and on the empirical and semiempirical laws.

Reynolds Stresses. When velocity fluctuations are present in a fluid flow, we analyze it by considering separately the mean flow speed $\bar{U}$ and the fluctuating components whose mean values are zero. If we denote the three mean velocity components of a flow studied in a rectangular cartesian coordinate system x, y, z as $\bar{u}, \bar{v}$, and $\bar{w}$ and the velocity components of the random fluctuations (turbulence) as u', v', and w' respectively, then we can write the following expressions for the velocity components at a point in a turbulent flow:

$$u = \bar{u} + u', \qquad v = \bar{v} + v', \qquad w = \bar{w} + w' \qquad (7\text{-}64)$$

with $u = u(t), u' = u'(t), v = v(t), v' = v'(t), w = w(t), w' = w'(t)$. We have

$$\bar{u} = \frac{1}{T} \int_t^{t+T} u \, dt \qquad (7\text{-}65)$$

and

$$\overline{u'} = \frac{1}{T} \int_t^{t+T} u' \, dt = 0 \qquad (7\text{-}66)$$

etc., the bar over a symbol denoting a mean value. For the pressure we can write

$$P(t) = \bar{P} + P'(t) \qquad (7\text{-}67)$$

The continuity equation $\nabla \cdot \mathbf{V} = 0$ (we assume the flow to be incompressible) expressed in rectangular cartesian coordinate system is

$$\frac{\partial u}{\partial x} + \frac{\partial v}{\partial y} + \frac{\partial w}{\partial z} = 0 \qquad (7\text{-}68)$$

can, for a turbulent flow, be written as

$$\frac{\partial (\bar{u} + u')}{\partial x} + \frac{\partial (\bar{v} + v')}{\partial y} + \frac{\partial (\bar{w} + w')}{\partial z} = 0 \qquad (7\text{-}69)$$

Averaging the terms in Eq. 7-68 we obtain

$$\frac{\overline{\partial u}}{\partial x} + \frac{\overline{\partial v}}{\partial y} + \frac{\overline{\partial w}}{\partial z} = 0$$

or

$$\frac{\partial \bar{u}}{\partial x} + \frac{\partial \bar{v}}{\partial y} + \frac{\partial \bar{w}}{\partial z} = 0 \qquad (7\text{-}70)$$

which is the continuity equation for the mean flow, since

$$\frac{\overline{\partial u}}{\partial x} = \frac{1}{T} \int_t^{t+T} \frac{\partial u}{\partial x} \, dt = \frac{\partial}{\partial x} \left[\frac{1}{T} \int_t^{t+T} u \, dt \right] = \frac{\partial \bar{u}}{\partial x}$$

because integration with respect to time and differentiation with respect to distance are independent operations, etc. As a result, from Eqs. 7-69 and 7-70 it follows that the equation of continuity involving the fluctuating velocity components is

$$\frac{\partial u'}{\partial x} + \frac{\partial v'}{\partial y} + \frac{\partial w'}{\partial z} = 0 \qquad (7\text{-}71)$$

For a turbulent incompressible flow, the Navier–Stokes equation in the x-direction (Eq. 7-33) can be written as

$$\frac{\partial u}{\partial t} + u \frac{\partial u}{\partial x} + v \frac{\partial u}{\partial y} + w \frac{\partial u}{\partial z} =$$

$$-g \frac{\partial \zeta}{\partial x} - \frac{1}{\rho} \frac{\partial \bar{P}}{\partial x} + \frac{\mu}{\rho} \left(\frac{\partial^2 \bar{u}}{\partial x^2} + \frac{\partial^2 \bar{u}}{\partial y^2} + \frac{\partial^2 \bar{u}}{\partial z^2} \right) \qquad (7\text{-}72)$$

when the terms are averaged. Since

$$\overline{\frac{\partial u}{\partial t}} = \frac{1}{T} \int_t^{t+T} \frac{\partial u}{\partial t} \, dt = \frac{1}{T} \left[u(t + T) - u(t) \right]$$

and

$$\frac{\partial \bar{u}}{\partial t} = \frac{\partial}{\partial t} \left[\frac{1}{T} \int_t^{t+T} u \, dt \right] = \frac{1}{T} \left[u(t + T) - u(t) \right]$$

we have

$$\overline{\frac{\partial u}{\partial t}} = \frac{\partial \bar{u}}{\partial t}$$

The term vanishes for quasi-steady flows (which we call steady turbulent flows), since $\bar{u}$ is independent of time in them. The term $\overline{u \dfrac{\partial u}{\partial x}}$ becomes

$$\overline{u \frac{\partial u}{\partial x}} = \overline{(\bar{u} + u') \frac{\partial (\bar{u} + u')}{\partial x}} = \overline{\bar{u} \frac{\partial \bar{u}}{\partial x}} + \overline{\bar{u} \frac{\partial u'}{\partial x}} + \overline{u' \frac{\partial \bar{u}}{\partial x}} + \overline{u' \frac{\partial u'}{\partial x}}$$

$$= \bar{u} \frac{\partial \bar{u}}{\partial x} + \bar{u} \overline{\frac{\partial u'}{\partial x}} + \overline{u'} \frac{\partial \bar{u}}{\partial x} + \overline{u' \frac{\partial u'}{\partial x}}$$

$$= \bar{u} \frac{\partial \bar{u}}{\partial x} + \overline{u' \frac{\partial u'}{\partial x}}$$

because, in general

$$\overline{f + g} = \bar{f} + \bar{g}$$

where f and g represent arbitrary functions whose sum is being averaged. Also, $\bar{u}$ is unaffected by the process of averaging with respect to time, while $\overline{u'} = 0$ (see Eq. 7-66) and

$$\overline{\frac{\partial u'}{\partial x}} = \frac{\partial}{\partial x} \overline{u'} = 0$$

Making similar transformations on the other terms on the left-hand side of Eq. 7-72 we obtain the equation

$$\frac{\partial \bar{u}}{\partial t} + \bar{u} \frac{\partial \bar{u}}{\partial x} + \bar{v} \frac{\partial \bar{u}}{\partial y} + \bar{w} \frac{\partial \bar{u}}{\partial z} + \overline{u' \frac{\partial u'}{\partial x}} + \overline{v' \frac{\partial u'}{\partial y}} + \overline{w' \frac{\partial u'}{\partial z}}$$

$$= -g \frac{\partial \zeta}{\partial x} - \frac{1}{\rho} \frac{\partial \bar{P}}{\partial x} + \frac{\mu}{\rho} \left(\frac{\partial^2 \bar{u}}{\partial x^2} + \frac{\partial^2 \bar{u}}{\partial y^2} + \frac{\partial^2 \bar{u}}{\partial z^2} \right) \qquad (7\text{-}73)$$

We can write

$$u' \frac{\partial u'}{\partial x} + v' \frac{\partial u'}{\partial y} + w' \frac{\partial u'}{\partial z}$$

$$= \frac{\partial(u'u')}{\partial x} + \frac{\partial(u'v')}{\partial y} + \frac{\partial(u'w')}{\partial z} - u'\left(\frac{\partial u'}{\partial x} + \frac{\partial v'}{\partial y} + \frac{\partial w'}{\partial z}\right)$$

$$= \frac{\partial(u'^2)}{\partial x} + \frac{\partial(u'v')}{\partial y} + \frac{\partial(u'w')}{\partial z}$$

in view of Eq. 7-71. As a result, we can rewrite Eq. 7-73 in the form

$$\frac{\partial \bar{u}}{\partial t} + \bar{u} \frac{\partial \bar{u}}{\partial x} + \bar{v} \frac{\partial \bar{u}}{\partial y} + \bar{w} \frac{\partial \bar{u}}{\partial z}$$

$$= -g \frac{\partial \zeta}{\partial x} - \frac{1}{\rho} \frac{\partial \bar{P}}{\partial x} + \frac{1}{\rho} \frac{\partial}{\partial x}\left(\mu \frac{\partial \bar{u}}{\partial x} - \rho \overline{u'^2}\right) + \frac{1}{\rho} \frac{\partial}{\partial y}\left(\mu \frac{\partial \bar{u}}{\partial y} - \rho \overline{u'v'}\right)$$

$$+ \frac{1}{\rho} \frac{\partial}{\partial z}\left(\mu \frac{\partial \bar{u}}{\partial z} - \rho \overline{u'w'}\right) \qquad (7\text{-}74)$$

Similar expressions can be obtained from the Navier–Stokes equations in the y- and z-directions (Eqs. 7-34 and 7-35). Equation 7-74 is just like the Navier–Stokes equation written for the mean flow variables except for the terms $\rho\overline{u'^2}$, $\rho\overline{u'v'}$, and $\rho\overline{u'w'}$. When the fluctuating velocity components vanish, that is, when the flow is laminar, the last equation transforms into the Navier–Stokes equation. The additional terms are equivalent to additional stresses acting in the fluid and are called *turbulent stresses* or *Reynolds stresses* (after O. Reynolds, who published a paper on the subject in 1895). As the equations show, they exist in addition to the viscous stresses whenever oscillating disturbances are present in the flow field. For example, the expression for the magnitude of the shearing stress τ_{xy} in a two-dimensional parallel flow ($\bar{v} = 0$ in such flow):

$$\tau_{xy} = \tau_{yx} = \mu \frac{\partial \bar{u}}{\partial y} - \rho \overline{u'v'}$$

(compare Eqs. 7-74 and 7-10).

The expressions for the magnitudes of the (normal and tangential) Reynolds stresses in a rectangular cartesian coordinate system are

$$\sigma_x = -\rho\overline{u'^2}, \qquad \tau_{yx} = -\rho\overline{u'v'}, \qquad \tau_{xz} = -\rho\overline{u'w'}$$
$$\tau_{xy} = -\rho\overline{u'v'}, \qquad \sigma_y = -\rho\overline{v'^2}, \qquad \tau_{yz} = -\rho\overline{v'w'}$$
$$\tau_{xz} = -\rho\overline{u'w'}, \qquad \tau_{yz} = -\rho\overline{v'w'}, \qquad \sigma_z = -\rho\overline{w'^2}$$

The Reynolds stresses represent the mean rates of momentum transfer per unit area across a fluid surface caused by the velocity fluctuations.

The shearing Reynolds stresses $-\rho\overline{u'v'}$, $-\rho\overline{u'w'}$, and $-\rho\overline{v'w'}$ would vanish if the turbulence were perfectly random. Their existence depends on the existence of correlations between the fluctuating velocity components at any given point. Such correlations can be expected whenever the flow experiences mean shear.

In the study of two-dimensional turbulent boundary layers the Reynolds stress $\tau_{yx} = -\rho\overline{u'v'}$ is of special importance. In such boundary layers, except in the thin viscous layer which exists at the surface, this stress is very much larger than the viscous stress $\mu\,\partial u/\partial y$. It is a positive stress since if v' is positive (that is, the fluid motion associated with turbulence is away from the wall) it gives rise to a negative value of u' (because at large distance from the wall, within the turbulent boundary layer, the magnitude of $\bar{u}$ is larger than that which exists at the level from which the fluid having velocity component v' comes), while if v' is negative it gives rise to positive values of u'.

Figures 7-21 and 7-22 show the distribution of the fluctuating velocity components u', v', and w' and the distribution of the turbulent shearing stress factor, $-\overline{u'v'} = \tau_{yx}/\rho$ in a turbulent boundary layer with zero pressure gradient on a flat plate. Observe the relative magnitudes of the fluctuating velocity components. (The u' component rises to 11 percent of the flow speed outside the boundary layer before it drops to zero at the wall.)

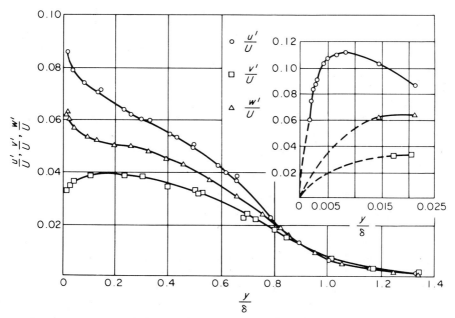

Fig. 7-21. Distribution of fluctuating velocity components u', v', and w' in a turbulent boundary layer with zero pressure gradient on a flat plate. U denotes the flow speed outside the boundary layer, and δ denotes the boundary-layer thickness. (By P. S. Klebanoff, Ref. 31.)

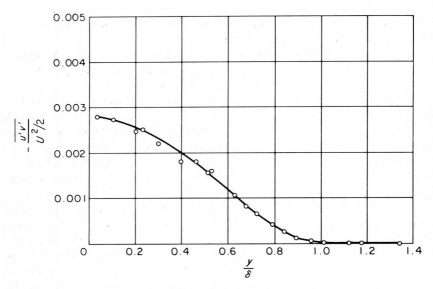

FIG. 7-22. Distribution of the turbulent shearing stress factor $-u'v' = \tau_{xy}/\rho$ in a turbulent boundary layer with zero pressure gradient on a flat plate. U denotes the flow speed outside the boundary layer, and δ denotes the boundary-layer thickness. (Measured by P. S. Klebanoff, Ref. 31.)

The intensity of turbulence is defined by the dimensionless factor

$$T = \frac{\sqrt{\frac{1}{3}\,(\overline{u'^2} + \overline{v'^2} + \overline{w'^2})}}{\overline{U}}$$

where $\overline{U}$ denotes the (temporal) mean flow speed. When the three components u', v', and w' are equal, the turbulence is called *isotropic*. For isotropic turbulence, which may be found in wind tunnels at a certain distance from the screens, the expression for the intensity of turbulence becomes $\sqrt{\overline{u'^2}}/\overline{U}$.

Mixing-Length Theories. Following the concept of the mean free path of a molecule, L. Prandtl in 1926 introduced to the analysis of a turbulent flow the concept of a "mixing length" which was considered to be a mean distance which a fluid particle traveled as a result of the turbulent velocity fluctuation before it lost its identity (characterized by its original velocity) and mixed with the surrounding fluid. Prandtl assumed that the momentum of the fluid particles was conserved over the mixing length. This theory was modified by G. I. Taylor (in 1932) who assumed that it was vorticity that was conserved over the mixing length, and by Theodor von Kármán (in 1930) who introduced a mixing length based on the assumption of similarity of the turbulence patterns everywhere within the turbulent boundary layer except for changes of linear scale and time.

Since by proper adjustments of the empirically determined constants all three theories agree reasonably well with experimental results, neither of them should be considered superior to the other two. However, it is difficult to defend some of the assumptions made in all these theories. [Observe that the concept of fluid particles which conserve such quantities as momentum or vorticity in their (turbulent) motion is in disagreement with the continuum approach to the study of fluid flow.] Nowadays the mixing-length theories lost their importance in analyses of turbulent flows that they once had, although they have served well in providing us with a number of semiempirical relations of practical usefulness.

In what follows we shall discuss briefly the mixing-length theory of Prandtl.

Consider a two-dimensional turbulent boundary layer as illustrated in Fig. 7-23 where $\bar{u}$ denotes the mean flow speed in the x-direction.

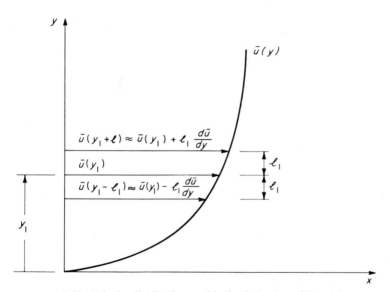

FIG. 7-23. Velocity distribution used in the derivation of the mixing length concept.

According to the mixing-length theory of Prandtl, fluid particles move from levels $y_1 + l_1$ and $y_1 - l_1$ and mix at level y_1 while retaining their initial velocities. Since the differences between the flow speeds of the incoming fluid particles and the prevailing flow speed at level y_1 are

$$\Delta u_1 = \bar{u}(y_1 - l_1) - \bar{u}(y_1) = -l_1 \frac{d\bar{u}}{dy}$$

$$\Delta u_2 = \bar{u}(y_1 + l_1) - \bar{u}(y_1) = l_1 \frac{d\bar{u}}{dy}$$

and these velocity differences can be looked upon as the fluctuating velocity components which characterize the turbulence at level y_1, the average of the absolute value of this fluctuation is

$$\overline{|u'|} = \frac{1}{2}(|\Delta u_1| + |\Delta u_2|) = l_1 \frac{d\bar{u}}{dy}$$

We assume now that the mean of the absolute value of the transverse component v' is related to the mean of the absolute value of the component u' by

$$\overline{|v'|} = \text{const.}\,\overline{|u'|} = \text{const.}\,l_1\frac{d\bar{u}}{dy}$$

and the expression for the magnitude of the Reynolds stress $\tau_{xy} = -\rho\overline{u'v'} = \tau$ is written as

$$\tau = -\rho\overline{u'v'} = \text{const.}\,\rho l_1^2 \left(\frac{d\bar{u}}{dy}\right)\left|\frac{d\bar{u}}{dy}\right|$$

The absolute value of the velocity gradient appears in the above equation because for $(d\bar{u}/dy) > 0$ we have $\tau > 0$, while for $(d\bar{u}/dy) < 0$ the shearing stress $\tau < 0$. The last expression can be rewritten as

$$\tau = \rho l^2 \left(\frac{d\bar{u}}{dy}\right)\left|\frac{d\bar{u}}{dy}\right| \qquad (7\text{-}75)$$

where l is proportional to the mixing length l_1. This is the principal result of the mixing-length theory of Prandtl.

Since, introducing the concept of eddy viscosity ϵ, we write for the sum of the viscous and turbulent stress

$$\tau = (\mu + \epsilon)\frac{d\bar{u}}{dy}$$

the term $\rho l^2 \left|\dfrac{d\bar{u}}{dy}\right|$ can be considered as representing the eddy viscosity.

Equation 7-75 can be utilized to derive the so-called *law of the wall* which is an expression for the velocity distribution in a turbulent incompressible boundary layer outside the thin viscous sublayer which exists at the (smooth) wall. (In our subsequent discussion, in Sec. 8-3, the law of the wall will be derived without reference to the mixing-length theories.) As Fig. 7-22 shows, near the wall the turbulent shearing stress is almost constant and is equal to the stress at the wall, τ_w. Therefore, neglecting μ we can write

$$\tau_w = \epsilon\frac{d\bar{u}}{dy} = \rho l^2 \left|\frac{d\bar{u}}{dy}\right|\frac{d\bar{u}}{dy}$$

If we now assume that the length l is proportional to the distance from the wall y

$$l = ky$$

where k denotes a constant, then, with $d\bar{u}/dy > 0$, we obtain

$$\tau_w = k^2 \rho y^2 \left(\frac{d\bar{u}}{dy}\right)^2$$

or

$$\frac{d\bar{u}}{dy} = \frac{\sqrt{\tau_w/\rho}}{ky} = \frac{u_\tau}{ky}$$

where $u_\tau = \sqrt{\tau_w/\rho}$ denotes the so-called *friction velocity*. Integration of the last equation gives

$$\bar{u} = \frac{u_\tau}{k} \ln y + \text{const.}$$

Introducing the thickness of the viscous sublayer y_l at the wall as the boundary conditions at which $\bar{u} = u(y_l)$, we obtain the expression for the mean flow speed in the turbulent boundary layer

$$\bar{u} = u(y_l) + \frac{u_\tau}{k} \ln\left(\frac{y}{y_l}\right) \tag{7-76}$$

The velocity in the viscous sublayer is assumed to be proportional to the distance from the wall. As a result,

$$u(y_l) = y_l \left(\frac{\partial u}{\partial y}\right)_{y=0} = \frac{y_l}{\mu} \tau_w = \frac{y_l}{\nu} u_\tau^2$$

In addition, the dimensional analysis indicates that $y_l = f(\nu / u_\tau)$. Writing $y_l = \text{const. } \nu/u_\tau$ we finally obtain relation

$$\frac{\bar{u}}{u_\tau} = \frac{1}{k} \ln\left(\frac{yu_\tau}{\text{const. } \nu}\right) + \text{const.}$$

or

$$\frac{\bar{u}}{u_\tau} = A \log\left(\frac{yu_\tau}{\nu}\right) + B \tag{7-77}$$

where A and B are constants. This expression is known as the law of the wall (for a turbulent incompressible boundary layer on a smooth wall). This law is sometimes written simply as

$$\frac{\bar{u}}{u_\tau} = \mathscr{F}\left(\frac{yu_\tau}{\nu}\right) \tag{7-78}$$

We shall return to the discussion of the law of the wall in Sec. 8-3.

REFERENCES

1. G. G. Stokes, *Mathematical and Physical Papers*. London: Cambridge U. P., 1880.

2. H. Lamb, *Hydrodynamics*. 6th ed. New York: Dover, 1932.

3. "A Discussion on the First and Second Viscosities of Fluids," *Proc. Roy. Soc. (London)*, Vol. 226 (October 1954), pp. 1–64.

4. C. E. Weatherburn, *Advanced Vector Analysis*. London: 1924.

5. L. Prandtl and O. G. Tietjens, *Fundamentals of Hydro- and Aero-Mechanics* (first published in 1934). New York: Dover, 1957.

6. J. A. Owczarek, *Fundamentals of Gas Dynamics*. Scranton, Pa.: International Textbook, 1964.

7. C. Truesdell, "On the Viscosity of Fluids According to the Kinetic Theory," *Physik*, Vol. 131 (1952), pp. 273–289.

8. V. G. Jenson, "Viscous Flow Round a Sphere at Low Reynolds Numbers (< 40)," *Proc. Roy. Soc. (London)*, Vol. 249A (1959), pp. 346–366.

9. W. Kaufmann, *Technische Hydro- und Aeromechanik*. 2nd ed. Berlin: Springer, 1958.

10. L. Prandtl and O. G. Tietjens, *Applied Hydro and Aeromechanics* (First published in 1934) New York: Dover, 1957.

11. H. L. Langhaar, "Steady Flow in the Transition Length of a Straight Tube," *J. Appl. Mech., Trans. ASME*, Vol. 9, No. 2 (1942), pp. A55–A58.

12. W. D. Campbell and J. C. Slattery, "Flow in the Entrance of a Tube," *Trans. ASME*, Vol. 85D (*J. Basic Eng.*) (1963), pp. 41–46.

13. L. N. Tao and W. F. Donovan, "Through-flow in Concentric and Excentric Annuli of Fine Clearance Width and Without Relative Motion of the Boundaries," *Trans. ASME*, Vol. 77 (1955), pp. 1291–1301.

14. L. Rosenhead (ed.), *Laminar Boundary Layers*. Oxford: Clarendon, 1963.

15. D. Coles, "Transition in Circular Couette Flow," *J. Fluid Mech.*, Vol. 21, part 3 (1965), pp. 385–425.

16. Görtler, H. "Über den Einfluss der Wandkrümmung auf die Entstehung der Turbulenz," *ZAMM*, Vol. 20 (1940), pp. 138–147.

17. W. R. Dean, "Fluid Motion in a Curved Channel," *Proc. Roy. Soc. (London)* Vol. A121 (1928), pp. 402–420.

18. H. Schlichting, *Boundary Layer Theory*, (trans. by J. Kestin), 4th ed., New York: McGraw-Hill, 1960.

19. J. O. Hinze, *Turbulence*. New York: McGraw-Hill, 1959.

20. W. R. Hawthorne, "Secondary Circulation in Fluid Flow," *Proc. Roy. Soc. (London)* Vol. A206 (1951), pp. 374–386.

21. J. H. Preston, "A Simple Approach to the Theory of Secondary Flows," *Aeron. Quarterly*, Vol. 5 (1954), pp. 218–234.

22. H. Z. Herzig, A. G. Hansen, and G. R. Costello, "A Visualization Study of Secondary Flows in Cascades," *N.A.C.A., T.N. 2947* (1953).

23. L. H. Smith, Jr., "Secondary Flow in Axial-Flow Turbomachinery," *Trans. A.S.M.E.*, Vol. 77, No. 7 (1955), pp. 1065–1077.

24. S. N. Barua, "Secondary Flow in a Rotating Straight Pipe," *Proc. Roy. Soc.*, Vol. A227 (1954), pp. 133–139.

25. C. C. Lin, *The Theory of Hydrodynamic Stability*, London: Cambridge P., 1955.

26. J. T. Stuart, "Hydrodynamic Stability," *Appl. Mech. Rev.*, Vol. 18, No. 7 (1965), pp. 523–531.

27. B. Thwaites, (ed.) *Incompressible Aerodynamics*, Oxford: Clarendon, 1960.

28. C. C. Lin, "Aspects of the Problem of Turbulent Motion," *Jour. Aeron. Sci.*, Vol. 23, No. 5 (1956), pp. 453–461.

29. G. B. Schubauer and P. S. Klebanoff, "Contributions on the Mechanics of Boundary-Layer Transition," *N.A.C.A. Report 1289* (1955).

30. G. B. Schubauer and C. M. Tchen, *Turbulent Flow*, Princeton, N. J.: Princeton U. P., (1961).

31. P. S. Klebanoff, "Characteristics of Turbulence in a Boundary Layer with Zero Pressure Gradient," *N.A.C.A. Report 1247* (1955).

32. W. J. Duncan, A. S. Thom, and A. D. Young, *Mechanics of Fluids*. London: Arnold, 1960.

33. N. Gregory and W. S. Walker, "The Effect on Transition of Isolated Surface Excrescences in the Boundary Layer," *Rep. Memor. Aero. Res. Counc.*, London, No. 2779 (1950).

34. N. Gregory, J. T. Stuart, and W. S. Walker, "On the Stability of Three-dimensional Boundary Layers, with Application to the Flow Due to a Rotating Disk," *Phil. Trans. Roy. Soc.*, London, Vol. A248 (1955), pp. 155–199.

PROBLEMS

7-1. By introducing Eqs. 7-9 and 7-3 into Eq. 7-7 obtain Eqs. 7-10, 7-11, and 7-12. (Sec. 7-2.)

7-2. By introducing Eqs. 7-36 into Eqs. 7-10, 7-11, and 7-12 obtain Eqs. 7-33, 7-34, and 7-35. (Assume constant gravitational force field). (Sec. 7-2.)

7-3. Show that the momentum-correction factor β, which was introduced in Sec. 4-2, for a fully developed laminar flow in a pipe having circular cross section is 4/3. (Sec. 7-4.)

7-4. Find the expression for the velocity distribution in a laminar steady incompressible flow of a Newtonian fluid between long vertical concentric cylinders which is caused by rotation of the outer cylinder with a constant angular velocity ω_0. Sketch this velocity distribution. Find also the expression for the magnitude of the resultant torque per unit length of the cylinders acting on the outer and inner cylinders. (Sec. 7-4.)

7-5. Find the expression for the velocity distribution in a laminar steady incompressible flow of a Newtonian fluid between long vertical concentric cylinders which is caused by rotation of the inner cylinder with a constant angular velocity ω_i. Sketch this velocity distribution. Find also the expression for the magnitude of the resultant torque per unit length of the cylinders acting on the inner cylinder, and show that it is the same as that acting on the outer cylinder. (Sec. 7-4.)

7-6. Calculate the velocity and pressure distributions in a laminar steady incompressible flow of a Newtonian liquid caused by rotation, with a constant angular velocity ω, of a vertical cylinder of radius R in a large body of the liquid subjected to gravitational attraction. What is the expression for the shape of the free surface of the liquid? Sketch the shape of the free surface. (Sec. 7-4.)

7-7. Consider a fully developed laminar steady incompressible flow of a Newtonian fluid in the annulus between two long and stationary concentric cylinders

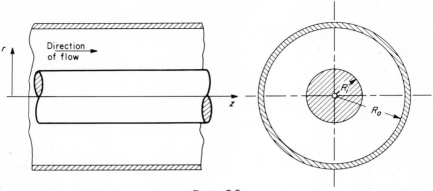

as shown in the sketch. The flow is in the direction of the axis of the cylinders. Show that the expression for the flow speed is

$$V = V_z = \frac{\Delta P}{4\mu L}\left[R_i^2 - r^2 + \frac{R_0^2 - R_i^2}{\ln\dfrac{R_0}{R_i}}\ln\frac{r}{R_i}\right]$$

where $\Delta P/L = -d(P + g\rho\zeta)/dz$ denotes the pressure drop per unit length (which, as you should show, is constant). Also show that the rate of mass flow through the annulus is given by

$$\dot{m} = A\rho\overline{V} = \frac{\pi\rho}{8\mu}\frac{\Delta P}{L}\left[R_0^4 - R_i^4 - \frac{(R_0^2 - R_i^2)^2}{\ln\dfrac{R_0}{R_i}}\right]$$

Sketch the velocity distribution. (Sec. 7-4.)

7-8. Solutions of Probs. 7-4, 7-5, and 7-6 show that a velocity field (or its component) of a steady incompressible Newtonian fluid may correspond to that of a two-dimensional free vortex. What are the expressions for the stress components in such free vortex flow, assumed to extend to infinity, in terms of the radius r and the pressure at infinity? (The expression for the variation of pressure with radius can be obtained from the Navier-Stokes equation. Neglect the gravitational force effects.) Show that the net viscous force acting on a fluid element in such flow is zero. (Consider the fluid element in a circular cylindrical coordinate system.) (Sec. 7-4.)

7-9. For a flow at very small Reynolds number (the so-called creeping flow) past a sphere the expressions for the pressure and the velocity components are:

$$P = P_\infty - \frac{3}{2}\mu\frac{U_\infty}{R}\left(\frac{R}{r}\right)^2\cos\theta$$

$$V_r = U_\infty\left[1 - \frac{3}{2}\left(\frac{R}{r}\right) + \frac{1}{2}\left(\frac{R}{r}\right)^3\right]\cos\theta$$

$$V_\theta = -U_\infty \left[1 - \frac{3}{4} \left(\frac{R}{r} \right) - \frac{1}{4} \left(\frac{R}{r} \right)^3 \right] \sin \theta$$

$$V_\phi = 0$$

where R denotes the radius of the sphere, U_∞ the speed of the uniform flow directed along the axis from which angle θ is measured as shown in the sketch, and P_∞ the pressure in the uniform flow.

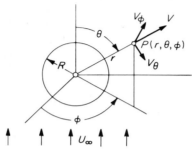

PROB. 7-9

The expressions for the stress components are

$$\sigma_{rr} = -P + 2\mu \frac{\partial V_r}{\partial r}$$

$$\tau_{r\theta} = \mu \left(\frac{1}{r} \frac{\partial V_r}{\partial \theta} + \frac{\partial V_\theta}{\partial r} - \frac{V_\theta}{r} \right)$$

Show that the drag of the sphere is given by $D = 6\pi\mu R U_\infty$. (Sec. 7-4.)

7-10. Consider a two-dimensional source flow of an incompressible Newtonian fluid. Is this flow irrotational? What are the expressions for the stress components in this flow in terms of the radius from the source and the pressure at infinity? By considering forces acting on a fluid element, derive the momentum equation valid for this flow. (Consider the fluid element in a circular cylindrical coordinate system.) In the derivation consider the action of the viscous forces and demonstrate that the net viscous force acting on the fluid element is zero. (That is, demonstrate that for this flow the Navier-Stokes equation is the same as the Euler equation.) Neglect the gravitational force effects. (Sec. 7-4.)

CHAPTER 8

Two-Dimensional Boundary Layer in Incompressible Flows; Separation of Flow; Wakes; Drag

8-1. LAMINAR BOUNDARY LAYERS

Introduction: Boundary Layers in General. When a body, such as a wing, immersed in a fluid possessing small viscosity is suddenly brought into translatory motion relative to the fluid, as a result of viscosity (tangential) vorticity starts to be created at the surface of the body in a very thin layer which we call a *vortex sheet* (see our discussion of vorticity in Sec. 3-4). The vorticity generated at the surface diffuses quickly into the irrotational flow outside this layer, which is known as the *free stream* or *main stream*. As a result, this very thin layer does not persist for long; the vorticity becomes quickly distributed and the so-called *boundary layer* formed. Across the boundary layer the tangential component of the flow velocity changes from that of the free stream to zero relative to the body.

And so the boundary layer is a region adjacent to the surface of a body in motion relative to the surrounding fluid, in which the action of viscosity takes place. This action manifests itself in creation of vorticity. As a result of the decrease of the flow speed across the boundary layer from that of the free stream to zero relative to the surface, the total pressure in the boundary layer is smaller than in the free stream. The large vorticity and small total pressure occur also in the *wake* which is the region downstream of the body, formed by the fluid from the boundary layer.

The boundary-layer flow can be laminar or turbulent. At the up-

328

stream part of the surface over which fluid flows, the boundary layer is laminar. The initially laminar boundary layer is unstable to small disturbances and transforms into the thicker turbulent boundary layer.

The experiments run at large values of the Reynolds number based on the typical length of the body (say 10^5 or 10^7) show that the thickness δ of the boundary layer is small. (Actually the thickness of a boundary layer cannot be defined precisely since the region of diffusion of vorticity extends into the main stream.) Our analysis in this section will show that the thickness of the laminar boundary layer is of the order $x/\sqrt{(Ux/\nu)}$, where x denotes the distance from the location on the body at which the boundary layer begins to form and U denotes the speed of the free stream (external flow). In Sec. 8-3 we will show that the thickness of the turbulent boundary layer is of the order of $x/(Ux/\nu)^{1/5}$. As a result, if the Reynolds number $Re_x = Ux/\nu$ is large, the boundary layer is thin.

As long as the boundary layer is thin and in contact with the body (that is, in the absence of separation of flow) the flow pattern of the free stream does not differ greatly from that calculated assuming that the fluid is perfect (irrotational flow theory). For that reason such fluid flows are usually analyzed first assuming irrotational flow. Subsequently, utilizing the knowledge of this flow we analyze the boundary-layer flow using various analytical methods. (Some such methods will be discussed in this chapter.) Finally, especially for flows in short ducts such as nozzles, etc., we introduce modifications to the previously determined irrotational flow which account for the decrease in the rate of flow of the fluid in the boundary layer when compared with the free stream. The analysis of the boundary layer provides us, in addition, with the information on the skin-friction drag of the body.

Figure 8-1 shows a sketch of the flow past an airfoil. The develop-

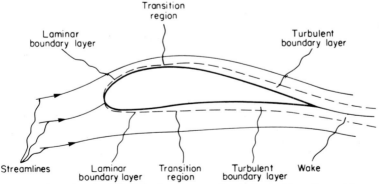

FIG. 8-1. Sketch of the boundary layer and wake formed in a flow without separation past an airfoil. (In the turbulent wake the streamline represents the direction of mean motion. The boundary-layer thickness is not shown to scale.)

ment of the boundary layer, first laminar and then turbulent, and of the wake is illustrated. (The thickness of the boundary layer is exaggerated for the purpose of illustration.) The streamline in the turbulent wake represents the direction of the mean fluid motion. Figure 8-2 is a shadow photograph showing the initially laminar and then turbulent boundary layer on the rear half of an airfoil and the turbulent wake.

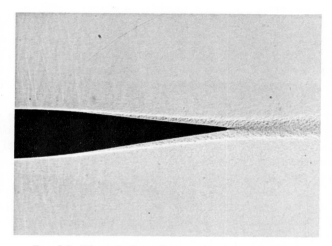

FIG. 8-2. Direct-shadow photograph of the boundary layer (first laminar, then turbulent) on the rear half of an airfoil, and of the turbulent wake. (Courtesy of the National Physical Laboratory, Teddington, Middlesex, England.)

In a flowing fluid, an adverse pressure gradient can produce near the wall fluid motion in the direction opposite to that of the free stream if the fluid in the boundary layer has lost sufficient amount of momentum as a result of viscous friction. [By *adverse pressure gradient* we mean the positive pressure gradient, which exists when the pressure increases in the direction of the (external) flow.] If this happens, we say that separation of flow from the wall takes place. Figure 8-3 illustrates the phenomenon of separation of the boundary-layer flow caused by an adverse pressure gradient. At the point of separation S the velocity gradient $\partial u/\partial y$ at the wall ($y = 0$) is zero.

When separation of the (boundary-layer) flow from the surface of a body takes place, the irrotational flow calculations lose their value.

Adverse pressure gradient is always present in ducts, known as *diffusers*, in which flowing fluid is decelerated. If separation of flow in diffusers is to be avoided, the adverse pressure gradient must be small.

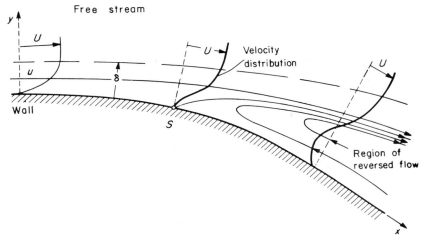

FIG. 8-3. Sketch illustrating the phenomenon of separation of a boundary-
layer flow. S denotes the point of separation; δ denotes the boundary-
layer thickness. The streamlines shown in the turbulent region of separated
flow represent direction of mean motion.

The turbulent boundary layer has less tendency to separate than the
laminar boundary layer because of the convective effects of turbulence.
These effects make the momentum of the fluid in the (turbulent) boundary
layer more readily available near the walls and thus oppose the action of
an adverse pressure gradient.

As a result of the convective effects of turbulence, the turbulent
boundary layer grows faster than the laminar boundary layer. From the
discussion in Secs. 1-4 and 7-6 it should be clear that the shearing stress,
or the resistance to flow due to shearing forces, offered by the turbulent
boundary layer is usually much larger than that of the laminar boundary
layer.

Figure 8-4 shows a sketch of a flow past an airfoil with separation
from the upper surface present (see also Fig. 1-11b). When separation is
present in a flow past an airfoil, we say that the flow is *stalled*, or that a
stall is present. The presence of separation in a flow past an object such
as an airfoil is an indication of large drag exerted by the object because
of the large amount of energy which is expended on the eddies which then
form in the wake.

We shall return in Sec. 8-4 to the discussion of flow separation.

As stated in Sec. 1-4, the concept of a boundary layer in flows of fluids
possessing small viscosity was first introduced by L. Prandtl in 1904 in
Germany. His paper, presented that year before an International Mathematical Congress, in which he postulated existence of a thin layer adjacent
to a solid surface where the velocity increased from zero at the surface

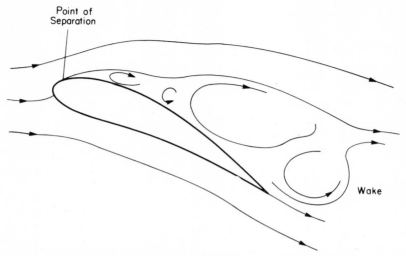

FIG. 8-4. Sketch of the wake formed in a flow past an airfoil with separation.

to that of the external stream, and in which the effects of viscosity were large, was a turning point in the study of flow of such fluids. The concept of the boundary layer allowed to reconcile the theoretical analyses of hydrodynamics with the empirical formulas of hydraulics, and paved the way for the progress in the understanding of fluid flows which followed. Although Prandtl initially was concerned only with the laminar boundary layers, when later experiments showed the transition of the boundary-layer flow from laminar to turbulent, it was he who discovered the important separation-delaying characteristic of the turbulent boundary-layer flow. In our study we shall concern ourselves with the two-dimensional laminar and turbulent boundary layers in steady incompressible flows. We shall also discuss the phenomenon of transition of the boundary layer from laminar to turbulent and the phenomena of flow separation and drag of objects around which fluid flows.

Laminar Boundary-Layer Equations. In this discussion we shall derive the equations of two-dimensional laminar boundary layers for incompressible steady flows. These equations will be derived from the Navier–Stokes equations using the so-called boundary-layer approximation of Prandtl. In the equations, the terms involving gravitational attraction will be omitted. (See discussion in Sec. 7-3.)

For a two-dimensional steady laminar incompressible flow, the Navier–Stokes equations and the continuity equation read

$$u\,\frac{\partial u}{\partial x} + v\,\frac{\partial u}{\partial y} = -\frac{1}{\rho}\,\frac{\partial P}{\partial x} + \nu\left(\frac{\partial^2 u}{\partial x^2} + \frac{\partial^2 u}{\partial y^2}\right) \tag{8-1}$$

$$u \frac{\partial v}{\partial x} + v \frac{\partial v}{\partial y} = -\frac{1}{\rho}\frac{\partial P}{\partial y} + v\left(\frac{\partial^2 v}{\partial x^2} + \frac{\partial^2 v}{\partial y^2}\right) \qquad (8\text{-}2)$$

$$\frac{\partial u}{\partial x} + \frac{\partial v}{\partial y} = 0 \qquad (8\text{-}3)$$

where v denotes the coefficient of kinematic viscosity, see Eqs. 7-33, 7-34, and 3-77. We shall orient the x-axis so that it points in the direction of flow, and make the y-axis normal to the plane surface along which the fluid flows, see Fig. 8-5.

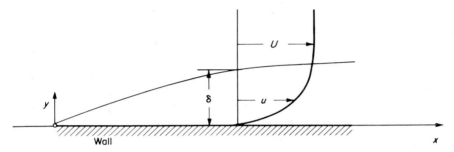

FIG. 8-5. Form of velocity distribution in a two-dimensional boundary layer.

The boundary-layer approximation of Prandtl is based on the assumption that in the laminar boundary layer the order of magnitude of the rate of change of momentum of the fluid due to viscous forces is the same as the order of magnitude of the rate of change of momentum due to the inertia force.

Consider a plate of length L and of unit width on which a boundary layer is formed having a thickness δ at some distance x from the leading edge. The inertia force per unit volume of the fluid in the boundary layer is equal to

$$\frac{\rho u^2 \delta 1}{x \delta 1} = \frac{\rho u^2}{x} = \mathcal{O}\left(\frac{\rho U^2}{L}\right)$$

where U denotes the flow speed outside the boundary layer, u the representative flow speed within the boundary layer, and symbol $\mathcal{O}$ means the order of magnitude of the term in the parentheses. The viscous force per unit volume is given by

$$\frac{\mu \dfrac{\partial u}{\partial y} x 1}{x \delta 1} = \mu \frac{\partial u}{\partial y}\frac{1}{\delta} = \mathcal{O}\left(\mu \frac{U}{\delta^2}\right)$$

Hence, after Prandtl, we assume

$$\mu \frac{U}{\delta} = \mathcal{O}\left(\rho U^2 \frac{\delta}{L}\right)$$

As a result

$$\frac{\delta}{L} = \mathcal{O}\left(\frac{\mu}{\rho U L}\right)^{1/2}$$

or

$$\frac{\delta}{L} = \mathcal{O}\,(\mathrm{Re}_L)^{-1/2} \tag{a}$$

where

$$\mathrm{Re}_L = \frac{\rho U L}{\mu} = \frac{U L}{\nu}$$

is the Reynolds number based on the length L and on the speed U of the free stream. Equation (a) indicates that for large Reynolds numbers Re_L, the thickness of the laminar boundary layer is small. The distance x is of the order of magnitude of L, the velocity component u is of the order of magnitude of U, while the distance y within the boundary layer is of the order of magnitude of δ. Therefore it follows from the continuity equation that the velocity component v is of the order of magnitude $U(\delta/L)$ where δ/L is small compared to unity [being of the order of magnitude of $(\mathrm{Re}_L)^{-1/2}$]. In the first momentum equation, Eq. 8-1, the terms $u(\partial u/\partial x)$ and $v(\partial u/\partial y)$ are of the order of magnitude U^2/L, while the terms $\nu(\partial^2 u/\partial x^2)$ and $\nu(\partial^2 u/\partial y^2)$ are of the order of magnitude $U^2/\mathrm{Re}_L L$ and U^2/L respectively.

The pressure P is of the order of magnitude of the dynamic pressure; hence $P = \mathcal{O}\,(\rho U^2)$ and the term $\dfrac{1}{\rho}\dfrac{\partial P}{\partial x}$ is of the order of magnitude of U^2/L. As a result, only the term $\nu(\partial^2 u/\partial x^2)$ is negligible when compared to other terms in Eq. 8-1. In the second momentum equation the terms $u(\partial v/\partial x)$ and $v(\partial v/\partial y)$ are of the order of magnitude of $U^2\delta/L^2$, the term $\dfrac{1}{\rho}\dfrac{\partial P}{\partial y}$ is of the order of magnitude U^2/δ, while the terms $\nu(\partial^2 v/\partial x^2)$ and $\nu(\partial^2 v/\partial y^2)$ are of the order of magnitude of $U^2\delta^3/L^4$ and $U^2\delta/L^2$ respectively. As a result, only the term involving the pressure remains, the other terms being of lower order of magnitude. These other terms are also smaller, by a factor δ/L, than the corresponding terms in Eq. 8-1. Thus we obtain the boundary-layer equations

$$u\frac{\partial u}{\partial x} + v\frac{\partial u}{\partial y} = -\frac{1}{\rho}\frac{\partial P}{\partial x} + \nu\frac{\partial^2 u}{\partial y^2} \tag{8-4}$$

$$\frac{1}{\rho}\frac{\partial P}{\partial y} = 0 \tag{8-5}$$

$$\frac{\partial u}{\partial x} + \frac{\partial v}{\partial y} = 0 \tag{8-3}$$

Equation 8-5 indicates that the pressure is constant across a two-dimensional boundary layer. For that reason it corresponds to the pressure in the external flow which is approximately irrotational, and can be determined from the Euler's momentum equation (valid for perfect fluids) which in this case reads

$$\frac{\partial P}{\partial x} = \frac{dP}{dx} = -\rho U \frac{dU}{dx} \tag{8-6}$$

For that reason, Eq. 8-4 can be rewritten in the form

$$u\frac{\partial u}{\partial x} + v\frac{\partial u}{\partial y} - \nu\frac{\partial^2 u}{\partial y^2} = U\frac{dU}{dx} \tag{8-7}$$

Observe that the boundary-layer equations, which represent a limiting form of the Navier–Stokes equations as the Reynolds number tends to very large values, or as the viscosity of the fluid tends to very small values, include a term involving viscosity.

In the case of a two-dimensional flow along a curved surface, as shown in Fig. 8-6, the boundary-layer equations must, in general, be

FIG. 8-6. Coordinates used in analysis of two-dimensional boundary layer flow on a curved wall.

modified to take into account the curvature of the wall. However, when the terms $\kappa\delta$ and $\delta L\, d\kappa/dx$ where κ denotes the curvature (that is, the reciprocal of the radius of curvature) are small then the first momentum equation and the continuity equation reduce to Eqs. 8-4 and 8-3 respectively. The second momentum equation then approximates to

$$\frac{\partial P}{\partial y} = \kappa\rho u^2$$

which is the pressure gradient balancing the centrifugal force resulting from the wall curvature. In many practical cases this pressure gradient is negligible.

The boundary conditions corresponding to the boundary-layer equations for a steady flow along a fixed solid surface are $u = v = 0$ at $y = 0$. For the external boundary condition we have $u = U$ at $y \to \infty$ (or at $y = \delta$ if the boundary-layer thickness is defined).

Dependence of the Laminar Boundary-Layer Characteristics on the Reynolds Number. Introduction of dimensionless flow variables u^*, v^*, x^*, y^* and $U^* = U/V_0$ into the boundary-layer equations (Eqs. 8-7 and 8-3), in the manner illustrated in Sec. 7-3 results in equations

$$u^* \frac{\partial u^*}{\partial x^*} + v^* \frac{\partial u^*}{\partial y^*} = U^* \frac{dU^*}{dx^*} + \frac{1}{Re_L} \frac{\partial^2 u^*}{\partial y^{*2}}$$

and

$$\frac{\partial u^*}{\partial x^*} + \frac{\partial v^*}{\partial y^*} = 0$$

The boundary conditions are $u^* = v^* = 0$ at $y^* = 0$, and $u^* = U^*(x^*)$ at $y^* = \infty$. The above equations indicate that, for a given free-stream velocity distribution, the two-dimensional boundary-layer solution depends on the Reynolds number Re_L.

This dependence can be eliminated by transformations

$$v^{**} = v^* \sqrt{Re_L} = \frac{v}{V_0} \sqrt{\frac{V_0 L}{\nu}}$$

and

$$y^{**} = y^* \sqrt{Re_L} = \frac{y}{L} \sqrt{\frac{V_0 L}{\nu}}$$

With the aid of these transformations we obtain the boundary-layer equations of the form

$$u^* \frac{\partial u^*}{\partial x^*} + v^{**} \frac{\partial u^*}{\partial y^{**}} = U^* \frac{dU^*}{dx^*} + \frac{\partial^2 u^*}{\partial y^{**2}}$$

$$\frac{\partial u^*}{\partial x^*} + \frac{\partial v^{**}}{\partial y^{**}} = 0$$

The corresponding boundary conditions are $u^* = v^{**} = 0$ at $y^{**} = 0$ and $u^* = U^*$ at $y^{**} = \infty$.

Since these equations do not contain the Reynolds number, the functions $u^*(x^*, y^{**})$ and $v^{**}(x^*, y^{**})$ do not depend on the Reynolds number. This fact can be expressed by saying that for a given body over which the fluid flows, the dimensionless velocity components u/V_0 and $(v/V_0)\sqrt{V_0 L/\nu}$ depend only on the dimensionless coordinates x/L and $(y/L)\sqrt{V_0 L/\nu}$ where V_0 and L are suitable reference flow speed and length, and not on the Reynolds number. This statement represents the so-called *principle of similarity of the laminar boundary layers with respect to the Reynolds number.*

In the case of a laminar boundary layer on a flat plate with no pressure gradient ($dU^*/dx^* = 0$ in such flow), there exists no characteristic length L and we can expect similar velocity profiles for various values of the coordinate x. Therefore, in such a case the coordinate x itself should be used as the reference length, and we can expect that the dimensionless velocity components u/U and $(v/U)\sqrt{Ux/v}$ will depend only on the dimensionless coordinate $\eta = (y/x)\sqrt{Ux/v}$ where $U = V_0$ represents the constant magnitude of the free-stream velocity which is then used as the reference flow speed.

Displacement Thickness and Momentum Thickness. While, as was mentioned earlier, the thickness δ of the boundary layer cannot be defined precisely, there exist other lengths describing the boundary layer whose exact definition is possible. One such length is the *displacement thickness* δ^* of the boundary layer. It is defined as the distance by which the external streamlines of the flowing fluid would be displaced inward if the fluid were nonviscous and flowing at the same free stream velocity; that is, if there were no deceleration of flow in the boundary layer. Figure 8-7

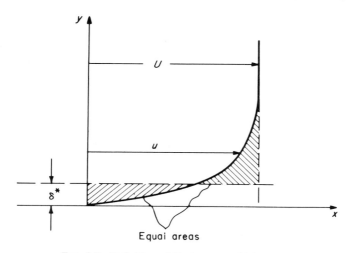

FIG. 8-7. Definition of displacement thickness.

illustrates the meaning of the displacement thickness δ^* for an incompressible plane flow. Mathematically, the definition of the displacement thickness of the boundary layer in an incompressible plane flow is given by

$$\delta^* = \int_0^\infty \left(1 - \frac{u}{U}\right) dy \qquad (8\text{-}8)$$

The expression $\delta^* \rho U$ represents the difference between the rate of mass flow of a nonviscous fluid and a viscous fluid flowing along the same surface.

Another length which is of importance in the study of the boundary layers is the *momentum thickness* θ which represents a measure of the momentum loss in the boundary layer. Since the loss of momentum as a result of the boundary-layer formation in an incompressible plane fluid flow, when compared with the nonviscous (potential) flow, is

$\rho \int_0^\infty u(U - u)dy$, we define the momentum thickness by writing

$$\theta \rho U^2 = \rho \int_0^\infty u(U - u)\, dy$$

For that reason the momentum thickness of the boundary layer in an incompressible plane flow is defined mathematically by

$$\theta = \int_0^\infty \frac{u}{U} \left(1 - \frac{u}{U}\right) dy \tag{8-9}$$

Observe that the definitions of the displacement thickness δ^* and momentum thickness θ are applicable to the turbulent as well as to the laminar boundary layers.

Exact Solution of the Laminar Boundary-Layer Equations for a Flat Plate with Zero Pressure Gradient (Blasius Solution). For a flow along a flat plate without a pressure gradient the boundary-layer equations reduce to

$$u \frac{\partial u}{\partial x} + v \frac{\partial u}{\partial y} = \nu \frac{\partial^2 u}{\partial y^2} \tag{8-10}$$

$$\frac{\partial u}{\partial x} + \frac{\partial v}{\partial y} = 0 \tag{8-3}$$

with the boundary conditions $u = v = 0$ at $y = 0$, and $u = U$ (= const.) at $y = \infty$.

As mentioned previously, in the flow under consideration there is no characteristic length and we can expect similar velocity profiles for various values of the distance coordinate x. This means that the velocity profiles $u = u(y)$ can be made the same for varying distances x if proper scale factors are selected for u and y. These scale factors are obviously the magnitude of the free stream velocity U and the boundary-layer thickness δ. Therefore we can express the similarity of the velocity profiles in the form of the equation

$$\frac{u}{U} = \mathscr{F}\left(\frac{y}{\delta}\right)$$

where $\mathscr{F}$ denotes a functional relationship.

Since, as we have already shown, for a laminar boundary layer

$$\frac{\delta}{L} = \mathcal{O}\left(\frac{1}{\mathrm{Re}_L}\right)^{1/2}$$

we have

$$\delta \sim \frac{x}{\sqrt{\mathrm{Re}_x}} = \sqrt{\frac{\nu x}{U}}$$

and we can use dimensionless vertical-distance coordinate

$$\eta = y \sqrt{\frac{U}{\nu x}} \qquad (8\text{-}11)$$

(The same conclusion concerning the vertical-distance coordinate we reached in our discussion of the dependence of the laminar boundary-layer characteristics on the Reynolds number.)

If we introduce the stream function $\psi(x, y)$ as a variable, then the continuity equation becomes satisfied, and we have only the momentum equation to consider. If the stream function is expressed in the form

$$\psi = \sqrt{\nu x U}\ f(\eta) \qquad (8\text{-}12)$$

then, since

$$u = \frac{\partial \psi}{\partial y} = \frac{\partial \psi}{\partial \eta}\frac{\partial \eta}{\partial y} = U f'(\eta)$$

where the prime represents differentiation with respect to η, and

$$v = -\frac{\partial \psi}{\partial x} = \frac{1}{2}\sqrt{\frac{\nu U}{x}}\,[\eta f'(\eta) - f(\eta)]$$

the momentum equation becomes

$$-\frac{U^2}{2x}\eta f' f'' + \frac{U^2}{2x}(\eta f' - f)f'' = \nu\frac{U^2}{x\nu}f'''$$

which reduces to

$$ff'' + 2f''' = 0 \qquad (8\text{-}13)$$

The boundary conditions are:

$$f = 0, \quad f' = 0 \quad \text{at} \quad \eta = 0$$
$$f' = 1 \quad \text{at} \quad \eta = \infty$$

And so, after H. Blasius (1908) [6] we transformed the system of partial differential equations (Eqs. 8-10 and 8-3) into an ordinary differential equation (Eq. 8-13). Equation 8-13 is nonlinear and can only be solved numerically. Blasius solved it by obtaining a series expansion about $\eta = 0$ and an asymptotic expansion about $\eta = \infty$ and joining these two solutions. More recently, in 1938, L. Howarth [7] developed another numerical solution procedure which produces a somewhat more accurate solution. The results, as given by Howarth, are summarized in Table 8-1. Figure 8-8 shows the velocity distribution (actually the distribution of the u component) in a laminar boundary layer on a flat plate with no pressure gradient (zero incidence). Figure 8-9 shows the distribution of the small

TABLE 8-1

VALUES OF THE FUNCTION $f(\eta)$ FOR THE BOUNDARY LAYER ON A FLAT PLATE WITHOUT PRESSURE GRADIENT (AFTER L. HOWARTH).

$\eta = y \sqrt{\dfrac{U}{\nu x}}$	f	$f' = \dfrac{u}{U}$	f''
0	0	0	0.33206
0.2	0.00664	0.06641	0.33199
0.4	0.02656	0.13277	0.33147
0.6	0.05974	0.19894	0.33008
0.8	0.10611	0.26471	0.32739
1.0	0.16557	0.32979	0.32301
1.2	0.23795	0.39378	0.31659
1.4	0.32298	0.45627	0.30787
1.6	0.42032	0.51676	0.29667
1.8	0.52952	0.57477	0.28293
2.0	0.65003	0.62977	0.26675
2.2	0.78120	0.68132	0.24835
2.4	0.92230	0.72899	0.22809
2.6	1.07252	0.77246	0.20646
2.8	1.23099	0.81152	0.18401
3.0	1.39682	0.84605	0.16136
4.0	2.30576	0.95552	0.06424
5.0	3.28329	0.99155	0.01591
6.0	4.27964	0.99898	0.00240
7.0	5.27926	0.99992	0.00022
8.0	6.27923	1.00000	0.00001

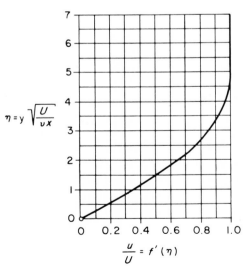

FIG. 8-8. Velocity distribution in laminar boundary layer on a flat plate. (Blasius solution.)

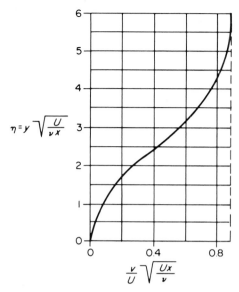

FIG. 8-9. Distribution of the transverse velocity component in laminar boundary layer on a flat plate.

transverse velocity component v. Observe that v increases across the boundary layer to an asymptotic value

$$v_\infty = 0.865\, U\, \sqrt{\frac{\nu}{Ux}} \tag{8-14}$$

Just as we have concluded in our discussion of the dependence of the laminar boundary-layer characteristics on the Reynolds number, we found that in this case the dimensionless velocity components u/U and $(v/U)\sqrt{Ux/\nu}$ depend only on the dimensionless coordinate

$$\eta = (y/x)\sqrt{Ux/\nu}$$

Figure 8-10 shows a comparison of the calculated and the experimentally determined velocity distribution in the laminar boundary layer on a flat plate with no pressure gradient at various values of the Reynolds number Re_x. The agreement between the two is very good. As a result of the principle of similarity with respect to the Reynolds number, the velocity distribution curve plotted in this manner is independent of the Reynolds number.

Skin Friction. The expression for the shearing stress at the wall is

$$\tau_w = \mu\left(\frac{\partial u}{\partial y}\right)_{y=0} = \mu U\, \sqrt{\frac{U}{\nu x}}\, f''(0)$$

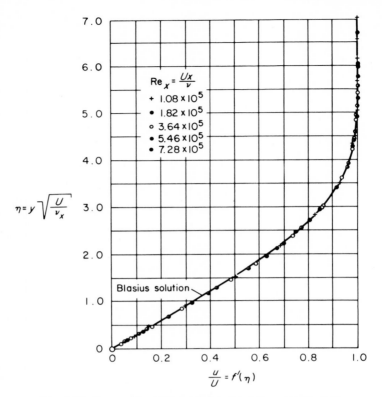

FIG. 8-10. Comparison of the calculated and the experimentally determined velocity distribution in the laminar boundary layer on a flat plate with no pressure gradient. (Experimental data by J. Nikuradse.)

because the term $(\partial v/\partial x)_{y=0} = 0$. The value of $f''(0)$, as given in Table 8-1, is 0.33206, and the expression for the (local) skin-friction coefficient becomes

$$c_f = \frac{\tau_w}{\frac{1}{2}\rho U^2} = 2f''(0)\sqrt{\frac{\nu}{Ux}}$$

$$= \frac{0.664}{\sqrt{\mathrm{Re}_x}} \tag{8-15}$$

The *mean skin-friction* coefficient is defined as

$$C_F = \frac{D}{\frac{1}{2}\rho U^2 A} \quad \left(= \frac{2D}{\frac{1}{2}\rho U^2(2A)}\right)$$

where D denotes the drag acting on one side of the plate and $A = bL$ the wetted area of one side of the plate of length L and width b. Since

$$D = b \int_0^L \tau_w \, dx$$

and $U = $ const. in this case, we have

$$C_F = \frac{b \int_0^L \tau_w \, dx}{\frac{1}{2} \rho U^2 bL} = \frac{\int_0^L \tau_w \, dx}{\frac{1}{2} \rho U^2 L} = \frac{\int_0^L c_f \, dx}{L}$$

$$= \frac{1}{L} \int_0^L \frac{0.664}{\sqrt{\frac{Ux}{\nu}}} \, dx = \frac{1.328}{\sqrt{Re_L}} \tag{8-16}$$

where Re_L denotes the Reynolds number based on the length of the plate L and the free-stream flow speed U. The correctness of Eq. 8-15 and 8-16 has been verified by many experiments.

Boundary-Layer Thickness δ. If we choose to define the boundary-layer thickness δ as that distance at which $u = 0.99\, U$ then, from Table 8-1, it follows that the thickness of the laminar boundary layer in an incompressible flow along a flat plate with no pressure gradient is

$$\delta \approx 5.0 \sqrt{\frac{\nu x}{U}} \tag{8-17}$$

or that

$$\frac{\delta}{x} \approx \frac{5.0}{\sqrt{Re_x}} \tag{8-17a}$$

where $Re_x = Ux/\nu$. This equation verifies equation (a) which is the basis of the boundary-layer approximation of Prandtl leading to the laminar boundary-layer equations (Eqs. 8-4, 8-5, and 8-6).

Boundary-Layer Displacement Thickness δ^*. For the laminar boundary-layer displacement thickness in the incompressible flow under consideration we obtain relation

$$\delta^* = \sqrt{\frac{\nu x}{U}} \int_0^\infty [1 - f'(\eta)] d\eta$$

$$= \sqrt{\frac{\nu x}{U}} [\eta_1 - f(\eta_1)]$$

where subscript 1 refers to a point outside the boundary layer ($\eta \to \infty$). The calculated values give

$$\frac{\delta^*}{x} = \frac{1.729}{\sqrt{Re_x}} \tag{8-18}$$

(Observe that in this case $\delta^* \approx \frac{1}{3}\delta$.)

Boundary-Layer Momentum Thickness θ. For the laminar boundary-layer momentum thickness in the incompressible flow under consideration we obtain relation

$$\theta = \sqrt{\frac{\nu x}{U}} \int_0^\infty f'(\eta)[1 - f'(\eta)]d\eta$$

which becomes

$$\frac{\theta}{x} = \frac{0.664}{\sqrt{\text{Re}_x}} = c_f \tag{8-19}$$

The Momentum Integral Equation for Two-Dimensional Steady Boundary-Layer Flow. The momentum integral equation represents a relation between the magnitude of the rate of change of momentum of the boundary-layer fluid in the direction of flow and the magnitudes of the viscous and pressure forces. It was first derived by Theodor von Kármán in 1912. Its main usefulness lies in the fact that it is the starting point of a number of approximate methods of solution of the boundary-layer flows. Its applicability is not restricted to the laminar boundary layers; it can also be used in the analyses of boundary layers which are turbulent provided that the analysis is not extended to the vicinity of the separation point, if any. There the pressure gradient across the (relatively thick) turbulent boundary layer, which is neglected in the momentum integral equation, may not be negligible. Also, near separation, the neglect of the turbulent (Reynolds) stresses may not be admissible.

Consider a small portion of a two-dimensional boundary-layer flow along a flat surface or a surface having small curvature as shown in Fig. 8-11, which is of unit thickness. The fixed volume 1–2–3–4 which extends into the free stream is of height h. The rate of mass flow through side 3–4 is

$$\int_0^h \rho u \, dy + \frac{d}{dx}\left[\int_0^h \rho u \, dy\right] \Delta x$$

while the rate of mass flow through side 1–2 is

$$\int_0^h \rho u \, dy$$

Hence the rate of mass flow out through side 2–3 of the fixed volume is

$$-\frac{d}{dx}\left[\int_0^h \rho u \, dy\right] \Delta x \tag{8-20}$$

(Since the transverse velocity component v is positive, see Fig. 8-9, the fluid flows out of side 2–3 and not in.)

The magnitude of the rate of transport of momentum in the x-direction into the fixed volume through side 1–2 is

$$\int_0^h \rho u^2 \, dy$$

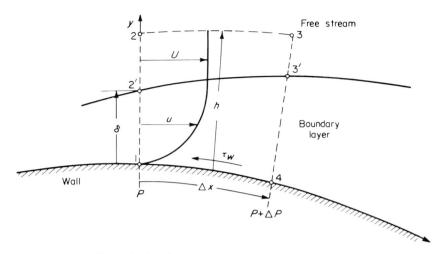

FIG. 8-11. Illustration for the derivation of the momentum integral equation.

while the magnitude of the rate of transport of momentum in the x-direction out through side 3–4 is

$$\int_0^h \rho u^2 \, dy + \frac{d}{dx} \left[\int_0^h \rho u^2 \, dy \right] \Delta x$$

The magnitude of the rate of transport of momentum in the x-direction out of the fixed volume through side 2–3 is

$$- U \frac{d}{dx} \left[\int_0^h \rho u \, dy \right] \Delta x$$

in view of Eq. 8-20. The magnitude of the forces in the x-direction due to pressure and viscous skin friction at the wall is

$$-h \frac{dP}{dx} \Delta x - \tau_w \Delta x$$

From the principle of conservation of linear momentum it follows that

$$\int_0^h \rho u^2 \, dy + \frac{d}{dx} \left[\int_0^h \rho u^2 \, dy \right] \Delta x - \int_0^h \rho u^2 \, dy$$

$$- U \frac{d}{dx} \left[\int_0^h \rho u \, dy \right] \Delta x = -h \frac{dP}{dx} \Delta x - \tau_w \Delta x$$

or that

$$\frac{d}{dx} \left[\int_0^h \rho u^2 \, dy \right] - U \frac{d}{dx} \left[\int_0^h \rho u \, dy \right] = -h \frac{dP}{dx} - \tau_w \quad (8\text{-}21)$$

The above equation is the *momentum integral equation*. In its newer form, due to H. Gruschwitz (1931), it is usually written in the form involving the displacement and momentum thicknesses of the boundary layer. Introducing Eq. 8-6 we can rewrite Eq. 8-21 in the form

$$\frac{d}{dx}\left[\int_0^h \rho u^2 \, dy\right] - U \frac{d}{dx}\left[\int_0^h \rho u \, dy\right] - h\rho U \frac{dU}{dx} = -\tau_w \qquad (8\text{-}22)$$

Since $U = U(x)$, we have

$$U \frac{d}{dx}\left[\int_0^h \rho u \, dy\right] = \frac{d}{dx}\left[\int_0^h \rho u U \, dy\right] - \frac{dU}{dx}\int_0^h \rho u \, dy$$

and Eq. 8-22 can be written as

$$\frac{dU}{dx}\left[\int_0^h \rho(U - u) \, dy\right] + \frac{d}{dx}\left[\int_0^h \rho u(U - u) \, dy\right] = \tau_w$$

or, for incompressible fluids,

$$\rho U \frac{dU}{dx}\left[\int_0^h \left(1 - \frac{u}{U}\right) dy\right] + \frac{d}{dx}\left[\rho U^2 \int_0^h \frac{u}{U}\left(1 - \frac{u}{U}\right) dy\right] = \tau_w$$

Introducing the expressions for the displacement thickness δ^* (Eq. 8-8) and the momentum thickness θ (Eq. 8-9) we obtain

$$\rho U \frac{dU}{dx} \delta^* + \frac{d}{dx}(\rho U^2 \theta) = \tau_w \qquad (8\text{-}23)$$

This equation is valid for both compressible and incompressible boundary-layer flows, although in our derivation we made use of the definitions of the displacement and momentum thicknesses which are valid only for incompressible flows. For incompressible flows we can write Eq. 8-23 in the form

$$U \frac{dU}{dx} \delta^* + \frac{d}{dx}(U^2 \theta) = \frac{\tau_w}{\rho} \qquad (8\text{-}24)$$

These are the newer forms of the momentum integral equation. They are often written in the form which involves the *shape factor* $H = \delta^*/\theta$. Eq. 8-24 then becomes

$$\frac{d\theta}{dx} + \frac{1}{U}\frac{dU}{dx} \, \theta(H + 2) = \frac{\tau_w}{\rho U^2} = \frac{c_f}{2} \qquad (8\text{-}24a)$$

Approximate Methods of Analysis of the Laminar Boundary Layer Using the Momentum Integral Equation. There exists a number of approximate methods of analysis of the laminar boundary layer based on the use of the momentum integral equation. We shall limit our attention to only two: one involving the simple case of the laminar boundary layer on a flat plate with no pressure gradient, and the Pohlhausen method for the laminar boundary-layer flow with pressure gradient.

For the boundary-layer flow with no pressure gradient the free-stream velocity gradient $dU/dx = 0$ (See Eq. 8-6) and the momentum integral equation (Eq. 8-24) reduces to

$$\frac{d\theta}{dx} = \frac{\tau_w}{\rho U^2} \qquad (8\text{-}25)$$

Since for the momentum thickness we can write

$$\theta = \int_0^\delta \frac{u}{U}\left(1 - \frac{u}{U}\right) dy$$

Eq. 8-25 can be solved by assuming various forms of velocity distribution in the boundary layer $(u/U) = f(y/\delta)$, where δ denotes the boundary-layer thickness. (See our discussion of the Blasius solution.)

Assuming a cubic form of the velocity distribution,

$$\frac{u}{U} = a + b\left(\frac{y}{\delta}\right) + c\left(\frac{y}{\delta}\right)^3$$

since the boundary conditions are $u = 0$ for $y = 0$ and $u = U$, $\dfrac{\partial u}{\partial y} = 0$ for $y = \delta$, we find that $a = 0$, $b = \frac{3}{2}$, and $c = -\frac{1}{2}$. That is, the velocity distribution is given by

$$\frac{u}{U} = \frac{3}{2}\left(\frac{y}{\delta}\right) - \frac{1}{2}\left(\frac{y}{\delta}\right)^3$$

Equation 8-25 transforms in this case into

$$\frac{d}{dx}\left\{\delta \int_0^1 \left[\frac{3}{2}\left(\frac{y}{\delta}\right) - \frac{1}{2}\left(\frac{y}{\delta}\right)^3\right]\left[1 - \frac{3}{2}\left(\frac{y}{\delta}\right) + \frac{1}{2}\left(\frac{y}{\delta}\right)^3\right] d\left(\frac{y}{\delta}\right)\right\}$$

$$= \frac{\tau_w}{\rho U^2} = \frac{1}{\rho U^2}\mu\left(\frac{\partial u}{\partial y}\right)_{y=0} = \frac{1}{\rho U^2}\frac{3}{2}\mu\frac{U}{\delta}$$

from which it follows that

$$\delta \frac{d\delta}{dx} = \frac{140}{13}\frac{\nu}{U}$$

or that

$$\frac{\delta}{x} = \frac{4.64}{\sqrt{\dfrac{Ux}{\nu}}}$$

In addition, we have

$$c_f = \frac{\tau_w}{\dfrac{1}{2}\rho U^2} = \frac{3\mu}{\rho U \delta} = \frac{0.646}{\sqrt{\dfrac{Ux}{\nu}}}$$

$$\frac{\theta}{x} = \frac{0.646}{\sqrt{\dfrac{Ux}{\nu}}} \quad \text{and} \quad \frac{\delta^*}{x} = \frac{1.740}{\sqrt{\dfrac{Ux}{\nu}}}$$

These results compare quite favorably with those corresponding to the exact solution of Blasius. Table 8-2 gives the results obtained assuming various velocity distributions $u/U = f(y/\delta)$ and those of Blasius. From it we can conclude that even crude approximations to the velocity distribution in the laminar boundary layer on a flat plate with no pressure gradient can yield fairly accurate results.

TABLE 8-2

RESULTS OF APPROXIMATE ANALYSES OF LAMINAR BOUNDARY LAYER ON A FLAT PLATE WITH NO PRESSURE GRADIENT

Assumed Velocity Distribution $\dfrac{u}{U} = f\left(\dfrac{y}{\delta}\right)$	$\dfrac{\delta^*}{x}\sqrt{\dfrac{Ux}{\nu}}$	$\dfrac{\theta}{x}\sqrt{\dfrac{Ux}{\nu}}$	$H = \dfrac{\delta^*}{\theta}$	$c_f\sqrt{Re_x}$	$C_F\sqrt{Re_L}$
$f\left(\dfrac{y}{\delta}\right) = \dfrac{y}{\delta}$	1.732	0.577	3.00	0.577	1.154
$f\left(\dfrac{y}{\delta}\right) = \dfrac{3}{2}\left(\dfrac{y}{\delta}\right) - \dfrac{1}{2}\left(\dfrac{y}{\delta}\right)^3$	1.740	0.646	2.70	0.646	1.292
$f\left(\dfrac{y}{\delta}\right) = 2\left(\dfrac{y}{\delta}\right) - 2\left(\dfrac{y}{\delta}\right)^3 + \left(\dfrac{y}{\delta}\right)^4$	1.752	0.686	2.55	0.686	1.372
$f\left(\dfrac{y}{\delta}\right) = \sin\left(\dfrac{\pi}{2}\dfrac{y}{\delta}\right)$	1.741	0.654	2.66	0.654	1.308
Exact solution	1.729	0.664	2.61	0.664	1.328

For the laminar boundary-layer flows with pressure gradient, the best-known approximate method of analysis which utilizes the momentum integral equation is that of Pohlhausen (1921). In this method the velocity distribution is assumed to be of the form

$$\frac{u}{U} = a\left(\frac{y}{\delta}\right) + b\left(\frac{y}{\delta}\right)^2 + c\left(\frac{y}{\delta}\right)^3 + d\left(\frac{y}{\delta}\right)^4$$

for $0 \leq \dfrac{y}{\delta} \leq 1$ $\left(\text{and } u = U \text{ for } \dfrac{y}{\delta} \geq 1\right)$. The boundary conditions are taken as follows:

$$y = 0: \quad u = 0, \quad \nu\frac{\partial^2 u}{\partial y^2} = \frac{1}{\rho}\frac{dP}{dx} = -U\frac{dU}{dx}$$

$$y = \delta: \quad u = U, \quad \frac{\partial u}{\partial y} = 0, \quad \frac{\partial^2 u}{\partial y^2} = 0$$

With these boundary conditions, the constants in the equation for the velocity distribution become

$$a = 2 + \frac{\Lambda}{6}, \quad b = -\frac{\Lambda}{2}, \quad c = -2 + \frac{\Lambda}{2}, \quad d = 1 - \frac{\Lambda}{6}$$

where the parameter

$$\Lambda = \frac{\delta^2}{\nu} \frac{dU}{dx}$$

The velocity distribution is therefore represented as a one-parameter family of curves with the form parameter Λ:

$$\frac{u}{U} = F\left(\frac{y}{\delta}\right) + \Lambda G\left(\frac{y}{\delta}\right)$$

where

$$F\left(\frac{y}{\delta}\right) = 1 - \left(1 - \frac{y}{\delta}\right)^3 \left(1 + \frac{y}{\delta}\right)$$

$$G\left(\frac{y}{\delta}\right) = \frac{1}{6} \frac{y}{\delta} \left(1 - \frac{y}{\delta}\right)^3$$

Since

$$\frac{\delta^*}{\delta} = \int_0^1 \left[1 - F\left(\frac{y}{\delta}\right) - \Lambda G\left(\frac{y}{\delta}\right)\right] d\left(\frac{y}{\delta}\right)$$

$$= \frac{3}{10} - \frac{1}{120} \Lambda$$

$$\frac{\theta}{\delta} = \int_0^1 \left[F\left(\frac{y}{\delta}\right) + \Lambda G\left(\frac{y}{\delta}\right)\right] \left[1 - F\left(\frac{y}{\delta}\right) - \Lambda G\left(\frac{y}{\delta}\right)\right] d\left(\frac{y}{\delta}\right)$$

$$= \frac{37}{315} - \frac{\Lambda}{945} - \frac{\Lambda^2}{9072}$$

$$\frac{\tau_w}{\rho U^2} = \frac{1}{\rho U^2} \mu \left(\frac{\partial u}{\partial y}\right)_{y=0}$$

$$= \frac{\nu}{U\delta} \left[F'(0) + \Lambda G'(0)\right] = \frac{\nu}{U\delta} \left(2 + \frac{\Lambda}{6}\right)$$

making use of the momentum integral equation we obtain a differential equation for δ (since Λ is related to δ and the velocity gradient dU/dx which is known if the pressure variation along the wall is known) which can be solved numerically.

This method has been modified by H. Holstein and T. Bohlen (in 1940) who introduced second form parameter

$$K = \frac{\theta^2}{\nu} \frac{dU}{dx}$$

If we use notation

$$Z = \frac{\theta^2}{\nu}$$

then the resultant set of equations which follows from the momentum integral equation is

$$\frac{dZ}{dx} = \frac{F(K)}{U}; \qquad K = Z\frac{dU}{dx}$$

where $F(K)$ is a universal function of Λ. The discussion of this method of analysis of laminar boundary layers can be found in Ref. 2. In general this method gives quite accurate results for flows with negative pressure gradient, and is less reliable only for flows with positive pressure gradient. The predicted separation point of the laminar boundary layer corresponds to $\Lambda = -12$ (and $K = -0.1567$), while more accurate analyses indicate that at separation of the value of Λ is somewhere between -7 and -8.

8-2. TRANSITION OF BOUNDARY-LAYER FLOW FROM LAMINAR TO TURBULENT

As was already indicated in the Introduction in Sec. 8-1, the boundary layer which builds upon the surface of an object exposed to a flowing fluid is laminar for some distance from the upstream stagnation point or from the leading edge of the object and, subsequently, transforms into a turbulent boundary layer. The problem of transition of the boundary-layer flow from laminar to turbulent is of great importance in the study of fluid flow because the characteristics of these two flows are quite different. While the laminar boundary layer characterizes itself by low skin-friction drag and thus may be desirable in many instances, the turbulent boundary-layer skin-friction drag is in general much higher. On the other hand, the turbulent boundary layer is much less susceptible to separation in an adverse pressure gradient than the laminar boundary layer. As a result, we are often interested in the ways in which the boundary-layer transition can be controlled so that it is delayed as far as possible so as to decrease the skin-friction drag, ensuring at the same time that the transition occurs soon enough so that early separation of flow is avoided.

Since the laminar boundary layer produces a different skin-friction drag than the turbulent boundary layer, the knowledge of the extent to which the surface of the object is covered by the laminar and turbulent boundary layers is necessary in the calculation of the skin-friction drag. As a result of different separation-of-flow characteristics, the state of the boundary layer affects also such aerodynamic characteristics as the pressure drag and performance of turbine and compressor blades and diffusers. The state of the boundary layer affects also the effectiveness of control surfaces of an airplane which are partially exposed to the wakes of the wings and of the fuselage of the airplane.

The role of transition of boundary layers (from laminar to turbulent) is also important in the interpretation of the results of experiments made on models. The state of the boundary layer affects also such processes as mass and heat transfer to flowing fluids.

While at low values of the Reynolds number (based on the distance along the surface in the direction of flow), say less than 10^6, the distance along which transition from laminar to turbulent boundary layer takes place is considerable, this distance decreases with increasing values of the Reynolds number, and for $Re_x = 2 \cdot \times 10^6$ it is already small enough to be called *transition point*.

During the early period of study of the phenomenon of transition before World War II there existed two schools of thought. One, that of G. I. Taylor in England (1936) believed that transition was set off by a small region of reverse flow in the laminar boundary layer, imposed by the turbulence of the main stream [13]. This line of thought was the result of hot-wire test data of H. Dryden who, at the Fourth International Congress for Applied Mechanics in Cambridge, England, in 1934, reported irregular motion of large amplitude in laminar boundary layers. These fluctuations were recognized as disturbances which were impressed on the boundary layer from the turbulence of the free stream. They were random, breaking into turbulence with no apparent amplification. The other school, that of W. Tollmien (1929) and H. Schlichting (1933) in Germany believed that when the Reynolds number based on the boundary-layer displacement thickness is larger than a certain critical value, the laminar boundary layer is unstable to small disturbances of wavelengths within a certain range which grow in amplitude until they cause transition to turbulence in the boundary layer. [Tollmien initiated development of the method for calculation of the curve of neutral stability (such curve is similar to that shown in Fig. 7-19), and has shown that the critical value of the Reynolds number based on displacement thickness was 420.]

Later work has shown that the turbulence of the main stream is not the determining factor affecting transition when the turbulence intensity of the main stream is low. In 1940 the experiments of G. B. Schubauer and H. K. Skramstad in the United States made in a wind tunnel in which the turbulence intensity was very low (less than 0.1 percent) proved the existence of the so-called Tollmien–Schlichting waves (whose existence was predicted by Tollmien and Schlichting) in the laminar boundary layer [14]. It appears now that these waves were not observed previously because they were masked by the disturbances caused by the high level of turbulence of the main stream. Figure 8-12 shows hot-wire oscillogram records of the fluctuations of the u component of the flow velocity in a laminar boundary layer on a flat plate. (The last record indicates a turbulent boundary layer.)

Schubauer and Skramstad also made tests in which they introduced into the boundary-layer flow small disturbances of known frequency by

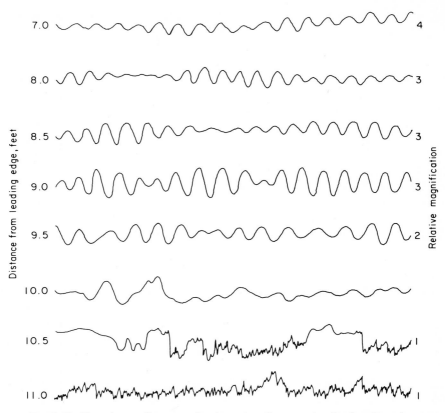

FIG. 8-12. Hot-wire oscillograms showing naturally occurring laminar-boundary layer fluctuations of the u-component of the flow velocity on a flat plate. Distance from surface = 0.023 in.; U = 53 ft/sec. (By G. B. Schubauer and H. K. Skramstad [14].)

vibrating electromagnetically a metal ribbon 0.002 in. thick about a mean position about 0.006 in. from the plate. The resulting velocity fluctuations they measured by hot-wire anemometer. The purpose of these tests was to determine the neutral stability curve. Figure 8-13 shows a comparison of the calculated neutral stability curves with the experimental results of Schubauer and Skramstad. (β_r denotes the frequency of the disturbance.)

The results of Schubauer and Skramstad were of great significance because they settled the dispute about the direction in which the problem of stability of laminar boundary layers should be approached. (Also, since in a flight of an airplane through the atmosphere the intensity of the small-scale turbulence is very low, their results could be applied directly in aeronautics.) The formidable difficulties which prevent us from reaching a complete understanding of the phenomenon of transition and from

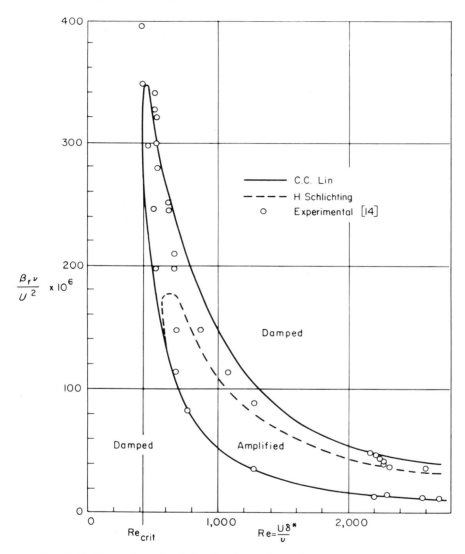

FIG. 8-13. Comparison of calculated and experimentally determined neutral stability curve for laminar boundary layer on a flat plate with no pressure gradient (Blasius flow). Experimental points by G. B. Schubauer and H. K. Skramstad. (Adapted from Ref. 18.)

being able to predict where it begins were not completely eliminated, however. These difficulties are connected mainly with the fact that the mainstream turbulence, even small, obscures the Tollmien-Schlichting waves and, no doubt, affects the transition, and the fact that the surface roughness in its various forms provides additional excitation of these waves.

(Observe that the transition Reynolds number is larger than the critical Reynolds number because, for the irregular velocity fluctuations which characterize turbulence to develop, the regular oscillations must become amplified to a sufficiently large magnitude.)

In 1951 H. W. Emmons [9,10] performed experiments on a water table and showed that the transition region begins with local spots of turbulence occurring in otherwise laminar flow. These spots grow, spread, and finally coalesce, thus forming a region of turbulent flow. Emmons assumed a turbulent-spot production and distribution function and developed a quantitative formulation of the transition process. However, his analysis does not tell us how the transition process starts.

In 1955 G. B. Schubauer and P. S. Klebanoff [16] were able to verify the findings of Emmons that a transition region is a region of growth of turbulent spots. They produced such spots artifically in a laminar boundary layer in air by an electric spark, and recorded their passage and growth using a hot-wire probe. Figure 8-14 shows an oscillogram record of the passage of a turbulent spot produced by an electric spark. For comparison, an oscillogram record of a natural transition is also shown.

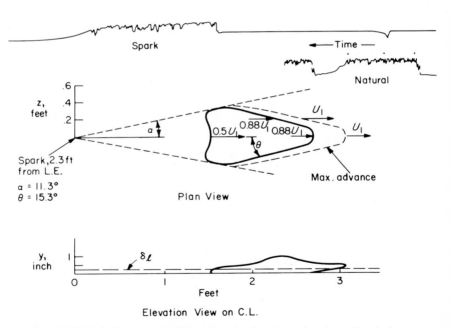

FIG. 8-14. Turbulent spot produced in a laminar boundary layer in air by an electric spark between a needle electrode and surface. At the top are hot-wire oscillograms; time interval between dots is 1/60 sec; time progression is from right to left; upper record shows spark discharge on right and spot passage on left; lower record shows natural transition. δ_l denotes the thickness of the laminar boundary layer. (By G. B. Schubauer and P. S. Klebanoff [16].)

In addition, Fig. 8-14 shows a drawing illustrating the shape and growth of a turbulent spot. The oscillogram shows that, like in the natural transition process, the start of the turbulent flow produced by an electric spark is characterized by an abrupt rise in flow velocity, while the ending is characterized by a slow decrease. These test results are considered as the evidence that the previous hot-wire records in the transition region recorded in fact the passage of turbulent patches as they moved downstream. The speed of propagation of a turbulent spot at the surface was about 0.5 U at the trailing end and 0.88 U at the leading end, where U denotes the flow speed in the free stream. At the leading end the speed of propagation varied from 0.88 U at the surface to the free-stream flow speed U at the end of the overhanging tip. The observed lag in the transportation of turbulence near the surface below the speed of the free stream can be explained by the delaying action of the laminar boundary layer on the penetration of the turbulent state. The angle α defining the spread of the turbulent spot was found to be about 11 deg for U = 30 ft/sec, and 8.6 deg for U = 10 ft/sec. M. Mitchner who in 1954 studied the growth of turbulent spots on a water table and in a low-turbulence wind tunnel observed α = 6.6 deg in water and 8.6 deg in air [21]. Hence it appears that angle α is affected by the Reynolds number.

We should realize that we cannot expect the patches of turbulence, which characterize the transition region, to have always the shapes shown in Fig. 8-14 because, although this may be the case in the early stages of their history, as soon as merging of patches occurs almost any shape may result.

Figure 8-15 shows the turbulence wedge produced in a laminar boundary layer in air by a three-dimensional roughness element. (Figure 7-20 represents parts of this figure.) The observations of the turbulent spot produced by an electric spark suggest that the turbulence wedge may represent "a succession of turbulent spots telescoped one into the other just far enough to form the fully turbulent core" [16].

The question which remained unanswered after the experiments of Schubauer and Skramstad in 1940 (in which the free-stream turbulence intensity was very low) was whether the stability of the Tollmien–Schlichting waves had any bearing on the transition process in flows in which the free-stream turbulence was low and medium. In 1953 H. W. Bennett, who used high-quality hot-wire and frequency-spectrum instrumentation, detected the growth of the Tollmien–Schlichting waves in the boundary-layer flow on a flat plate when the intensity of the free-stream turbulence was 0.42 percent [15]. He also showed that the wave frequency which was experiencing greatest amplification corresponded substantially to that predicted by the stability theory. Nevertheless, the stability theory, which deals only with two-dimensional waves cannot still be considered as being fully developed because the experiments indicate

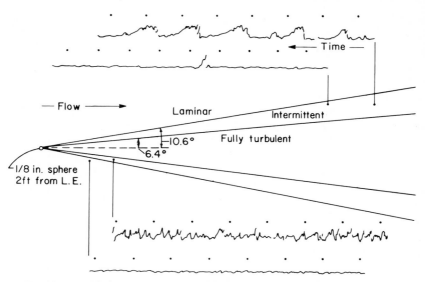

FIG. 8-15. Turbulence wedge produced by an 1/8-in. sphere on a surface. Time interval between dots in 1/60 sec. $U = 80$ ft/sec. (By G. B. Schubauer and P. S. Klebanoff [16].)

that the waves produced in a laminar flow are always three-dimensional, that is, there exists the w-component of the flow oscillations.

The present view on the subject of transition of the boundary-layer flow is that when the turbulence intensity of the free stream is very low or low (below a few percent), any small disturbances which are either initially present in the flow or come from internal or external sources (such as surface roughness or free-stream turbulence) agitate the laminar boundary layer which is initially stable to the Tollmien–Schlichting waves, render this layer unstable at some point and these waves begin to grow. The stability of the Tollmien–Schlichting waves is basically that predicted by the stability theory. When these waves grow to be large enough they roll up into eddies and initiate turbulence (the transition process following the description of Emmons). When the turbulence intensity of the free stream is high, the resulting fluctuations are large enough to result in local adverse pressure gradients which cause local separation and subsequent transition to turbulence. Thus it appears that both theories, that of Tollmien and Schlichting and that of Taylor, can be reconciled.

As far as the factors which affect the transition are concerned, these are as follows: (a) Reynolds number based on distance, Re_x, (b) surface roughness, (c) free-stream turbulence, (d) pressure gradient, (e) surface curvature, (f) noise and vibration, (g) heat transfer, (h) Mach number, (i) secondary flow effects, and (j) suction.

One of the few presently available methods of prediction of the location of the transition region in incompressible flows of very low turbulence on convex or flat surfaces is the empirical method of R. Michel. Its description, together with an analysis (based on stability calculations) of the reasons why it is successful, can be found in Ref. 15. Basically, this method assumes existence of a unique relation between the Reynolds number based on the momentum thickness, $Re_\theta = U\theta/\nu$, and that based on distance, $Re_x = Ux/\nu$, at transition. A. M. O. Smith and N. Gamberoni [15] give this relation as

$$(Re_\theta)_{tr} = 1.174\,(Re_x)^{0.46};\quad 0.3 \times 10^6 < Re_x < 20 \times 10^6 \quad (8\text{-}26)$$

The claimed error in the prediction of the transition point (or transition region, as the case may be) using this equation is less than 20 percent in most cases. For a flow along a smooth flat plate with no pressure gradient, this formula predicts transition at $Re_x = 1.58 \times 10^6$. (The expression for the momentum thickness θ of the laminar boundary layer in such flow is given by Eq. 8-19.) This is in the correct range of values observed in experiments for such flow (see Ref. 2, p. 538).

In what follows, we shall give a brief description of some of the factors affecting transition of the boundary-layer flow.

(a) *Reynolds Number* (based on the distance along the surface in the direction of flow), Re_x. This is the most important factor. While for $Re_x < 10^5$ the laminar boundary layer is stable, and it may be difficult to cause its transition by other factors, for $Re_x > 2 \times 10^6$ the turbulent boundary layer is stable and even such factors as cooling and favorable (negative) pressure gradients, which increase stability of laminar boundary-layer flows, may not be able to keep it laminar.

(b) *Surface Roughness.* The surface roughness (as well as waviness of the surface) has an effect on the transition of boundary layers because of the disturbances which it produces in the flow. The test results on single two-dimensional roughness elements indicate that to produce transition, the height of the roughness element must be comparable to that of the displacement thickness of the boundary layer. It appears that the transition Reynolds number $(Re_x)_{tr}$ for single roughness elements in form of cylindrical wires and flat ridges can be correlated with the aid of the intensity of turbulence of the free stream and the parameter k/δ_k^*, where k denotes the height of the roughness element and δ_k^* is the displacement thickness of the boundary layer at the location of the roughness element [22]. For a flow along a flat plate with no pressure gradient, for the values of $k/\delta_k^* < 0.3$ the effect of turbulence is large. In that range, $(Re_x)_{tr} \approx 2.6 \times 10^6$ for the free-stream turbulence intensity T of 0.14 percent, and about 0.8×10^6 for T = 0.9 percent. For the values of $k/\delta_k^* > 0.7$ the effect of the intensity of turbulence of the free stream becomes very small, and the value of $(Re_x)_{tr} \leq 0.4 \times 10^6$ [22]. The data on three-dimensional single roughness elements appears to correlate satisfactorily if we use the Reynolds number based on the height of the roughness element Uk/ν as a criterion for transition. The experimental data on single rows of spherical roughness elements indicates that the critical value of the Reynolds number Uk/ν below which the surface may be considered aerodynamically smooth, that is, below which the effect of the roughness elements on transition is negligible, is about 800. There is a dependence of the transition Reynolds number $(Re_x)_{tr}$ on the shape of the roughness element; however, not much is known on this subject. The rate of decrease of the value of $(Re_x)_{tr}$ with increase in the value of Uk/ν above the critical value is high. As far as the distributed three-dimensional roughness is concerned, a number of experimental results in which sandpaper was used to produce surface roughness indicate that the critical value of the Reynolds number Uk/ν is about 100. A more detailed discussion of this topic can be found in Ref. 22.

(c) *Free-Stream Turbulence.* The effect of the free-stream turbulence on the boundary-layer transition is usually represented in the form of a diagram showing the change in the transition Reynolds number $(Re_x)_{tr}$ versus turbulence intensity $T = \sqrt{\frac{1}{3}(\overline{u'^2} + \overline{v'^2} + \overline{w'^2})}/\overline{U}$. For flows along flat plates with no pressure gradient, the values of $(Re_x)_{tr}$ are approximately 2.8×10^6 for $T \approx 0$, 1.1×10^6 for $T \approx 0.5$ percent, and 0.5×10^6 for $T \approx 1.2$ percent. In general, the scale of turbulence is also known to have an effect on the value of $(Re_x)_{tr}$. [Observe that, as our previous discussion indicates, it is somewhat inaccurate to speak of the transition Reynolds number (or transition point), for Reynolds numbers Re_x of 10^6 or less.]

(d) *Pressure Gradient.* The pressure gradient of the main stream has a large effect on the location of the transition region. The negative pressure gradient has a stabilizing effect on laminar boundary layers, while the effect of the positive pressure gradient is opposite. This experimentally observed behavior is consistent with the calculations (by J. Pretsch in 1941 in Germany) of the neutral stability curves to the Tollmien–Schlichting waves in flows with pressure gradients. It is also in agreement with the observed behavior of the boundary-layer oscillations as reported by Schubauer and Skramstad [14]. Figure 8-16 shows the effect of falling and raising pressure on the laminar boundary-layer oscillations as reported by them. Observe the damping of the oscillations produced by the pressure drop (negative, or favorable, pressure gradient), and the large amplification of the oscillations in the region of pressure rise (positive, or adverse, pressure gradient).

(e) *Surface Curvature* [22]. An extensive study of uniform curvature on transition of two-dimensional boundary layers was made by H. W.

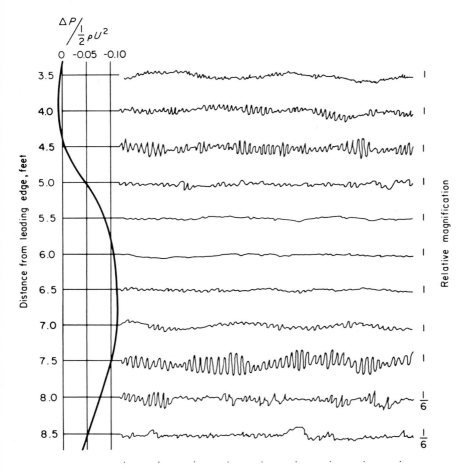

FIG. 8-16. Effect of pressure drop and of pressure rise on oscillations in laminar boundary layer. Scale at upper left gives the ratio of pressure change to the dynamic pressure of the free stream. The hot-wire measurements were made at a distance of 0.021 in. from the surface. U = 95 ft/sec. Time interval between dots, 1/30 sec. (By G. B. Schubauer and H. K. Skramstad [14].)

Liepmann during World War II [23]. On convex surfaces the effect of curvature is negligible. For the values of the ratio of the displacement thickness to the radius of curvature δ^*/R up to 0.0026 the boundary layer is unstable to the Tollmien–Schlichting waves, just as in the case of the flow along a flat plate. For a flow on a concave wall, as a result of centrifugal forces, the boundary-layer flow becomes unstable to the vortices predicted by H. Görtler (see our discussion in Sec. 7-5) for the ratio $\delta^*/R > 0.0013$. Görtler's analysis indicated that the stability parameter

for this type of flow was $\mathrm{Re}_\theta \sqrt{\dfrac{\theta}{R}}$. The experiments of Liepmann indicated that for the lowest intensity of turbulence of about 0.2 percent the
value of this parameter at transition was 9.0, while at higher turbulence
intensities it was about 6. It appears that for the values $0.00013 < \delta^*/R < 0.0013$ there is a continuous change between the Tollmien–
Schlichting and the Görtler types of instability.

As far as the other effects on the boundary-layer transition are concerned, the analysis of the neutral stability curves to two-dimensional disturbances indicates that cooling of the fluid increases stability of the
laminar flow (it causes the critical Reynolds number to increase), while
heating has a destabilizing effect (it causes the critical Reynolds number
to decrease). The experimental evidence supports this view. The experiments also indicate that the factors which affect boundary-layer transition
at subsonic speeds also affect it at supersonic speeds. As far as suction is
concerned, it has a stabilizing effect because it makes the boundary-layer
flow thinner and because it alters the boundary-layer velocity profile so
that it is more stable.

8-3. TURBULENT FLOW ALONG WALLS

In this section we consider the turbulent flow in pipes and channels,
and the turbulent flow bounded on one side by a wall (turbulent boundary
layers). (By a channel we mean here a duct of constant rectangular cross
section.) In our discussion we assume that the flow is incompressible.

Just as a laminar flow in a pipe or a channel requires a certain length
of transition, sometimes referred to as the *inlet length*, before a fully developed velocity profile is formed (see Sec. 7-4), so does a turbulent flow.
However, for a turbulent flow in a pipe or a channel the length of transition is appreciably shorter than for the laminar flow, and can vary between 25 and 100 pipe diameters ([2], p. 502; [28], p. 49). In our discussion
of turbulent flows in pipes and channels a fully developed flow will be
assumed.

The (fully developed) velocity profile of a turbulent flow in pipes differs appreciably from that corresponding to a laminar flow, the turbulent
velocity profile being much steeper near the walls and flatter near the center of the pipe. This fact is illustrated in Fig. 8-17.

In a flow along a wall, as already discussed in Sec. 8-1, a laminar
boundary layer, which forms initially, changes into a turbulent boundary
layer across the transition region. In the transition region the velocity
distribution undergoes a change from that characteristic of a laminar
boundary-layer flow to that characteristic of a turbulent boundary-layer
flow. This change in the (temporal) mean velocity distributions through
the transition region, for a flow along a flat plate with zero pressure gra-

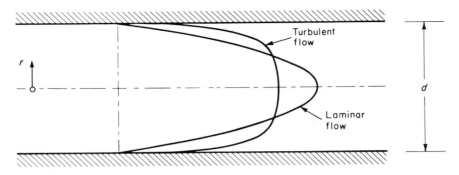

FIG. 8-17. Comparison between the laminar and turbulent flow velocity distribution in a pipe.

dient, is shown in Fig. 8-18. The parameter γ in Fig. 8-18 represents the intermittency factor which was defined in Sec. 7-5 ($\gamma = 0$ corresponds to a laminar flow, while $\gamma = 1$ corresponds to a fully turbulent flow.) U denotes the flow speed outside the boundary layer—that is, the speed of the free stream.

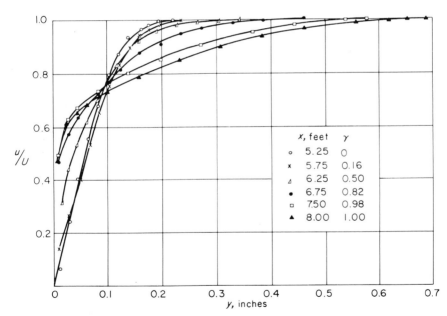

x, feet	γ
∘ 5.25	0
× 5.75	0.16
△ 6.25	0.50
• 6.75	0.82
□ 7.50	0.98
▲ 8.00	1.00

FIG. 8-18. Distribution of mean velocity through the transition region on a flat plate with no pressure gradient. Free-stream speed $U = 80$ ft/sec; free-stream turbulence intensity 0.03 percent. x denotes the distance from the leading edge, and y the vertical distance above the plate. (Measurements by G. B. Schubauer and P. S. Klebanoff [16].)

Power Law [24]. In the early analyses of turbulent flows along smooth walls, the turbulent velocity distribution in flows in which the pressure gradient was either very small (like in incompressible flows in pipes or channels) or entirely absent was approximated by the so-called *power law*. This empirical law, first derived for a flow in pipes, describes the turbulent velocity distribution in the overall character, but not in every detail. It was very useful in providing laws of resistance which are valid in certain limited range of the Reynolds number for flows in pipes and channels and along flat plates. The power law was first introduced by L. Prandtl who, in his derivation, was guided by the empirical equation of Blasius for the turbulent incompressible flow in smooth pipes:

$$f = 0.3164 \left(\frac{\overline{V}d}{\nu}\right)^{-1/4}$$

$$= \frac{0.3164}{\mathrm{Re}_d^{-1/4}} \tag{8-27}$$

where d denotes the diameter of the pipe, $\overline{V} = Q/A = 4Q/\pi d^2$ represents the average flow speed through the pipe, and the resistance coefficient f is defined by equation

$$\frac{P_1 - P_2}{L} = \frac{f}{d}\frac{\rho \overline{V}^2}{2} \tag{8-28}$$

where L denotes the length of the pipe between sections 1 and 2. The pressures P_1 and P_2 correspond to these sections. Observe that for an incompressible flow in a pipe, the momentum equation for a fixed volume shown in Fig. 8-19 can be written as

$$\frac{\pi d^2}{4}(P_2 - P_1) + \tau_w \pi dL = 0$$

where τ_w denotes the shearing stress at the wall. As a result,

$$\tau_w = \frac{d}{4}\frac{P_1 - P_2}{L} = \frac{f}{4}\frac{\rho \overline{V}^2}{2} \tag{8-29}$$

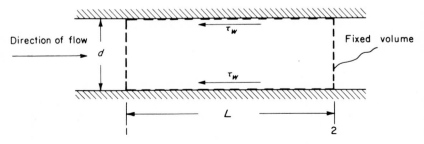

FIG. 8-19. Illustration for derivation of Eq. 8-29.

which indicates that, for an incompressible flow, the resistance coefficient f (defined by Eq. 8-28) is related to the resistance coefficient c_f' defined by equation

$$\tau_w = c_f' \frac{\rho \overline{V}^2}{2} \tag{8-30}$$

by formula

$$4 c_f' = f \tag{7-60}$$

This we already concluded in Sec. 7-4. Figure 8-20 shows the range of applicability of the Blasius formula (Eq. 8-27) for turbulent incompressible flows, which is below $\mathrm{Re}_d = 10^5$.

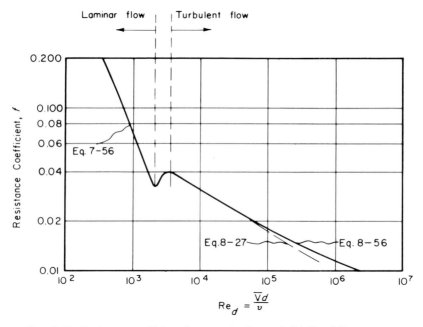

FIG. 8-20. Resistance coefficient for smooth pipes. Solid line follows experimental data.

Prandtl has found that the resistance formula for turbulent flows in pipes can be extended to flows in channels and along flat plates if we consider the radius of the pipe to be equivalent to one-half of the width of the channel or to the thickness of the boundary layer, respectively, and if the reference flow speed is not the average flow speed $\overline{V}$ but the maximum (temporal mean) flow speed $\overline{U}_m$ which exists at the center of a pipe or a channel, or in the free stream (that is, outside of the boundary layer).

Let us denote the distance y from the wall at which the mean flow speed reaches its maximum value $\overline{U}_m$ by δ, as shown in Fig. 8-21. We

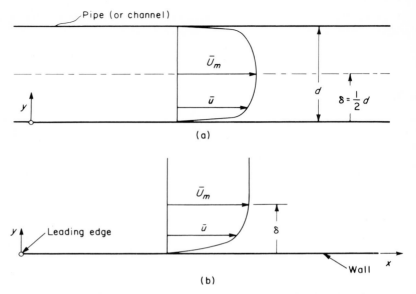

Fig. 8-21. Nomenclature used in deriving resistance formulas with the aid of the power law. (a) Flow in a pipe or a channel; (b) external flow along a wall.

define the resistance, or skin-friction, coefficient by

$$c_f = \frac{\tau_w}{\frac{1}{2}\,\rho\,\bar{U}_m^2} \tag{8-31}$$

and write

$$c_f = \frac{\text{const.}}{\left(\dfrac{\bar{U}_m\,\delta}{\nu}\right)^n} \tag{8-32}$$

where n is a constant. [While for the flows in pipes and channels the term resistance coefficient is appropriate, for the (external) boundary-layer flows along walls the term *skin-friction coefficient* should be used because in such flows skin friction represents in general only a part of the resistance, or drag, of the object.] Observe that while in the Blasius formula (Eq. 8-27) the Reynolds number is based on the pipe diameter and the average flow speed $\bar{V}$, in Eq. 8-32 the resistance, or skin-friction coefficient, is a function of the Reynolds number based on $\delta \left(= \frac{1}{2}\,d \text{ for a pipe}\right)$ and on the maximum mean speed $\bar{U}_m$.

Introducing the friction velocity

$$u_\tau = \sqrt{\frac{\tau_w}{\rho}} \tag{8-33}$$

(see Sec. 7-6), we can write

$$\frac{\bar{U}_m}{u_\tau} = \text{const.} \left(\frac{u_\tau \delta}{\nu}\right)^{\frac{n}{2-n}} \tag{8-34}$$

in view of Eqs. 8-31 and 8-32. We assume now that the mean velocity distribution throughout the region of turbulent flow is given by equation

$$\frac{\bar{u}}{u_\tau} = \text{const.} \left(\frac{u_\tau y}{\nu}\right)^{\frac{n}{2-n}} \tag{8-35}$$

which is obtained from Eq. 8-34 by putting $\bar{u}$ in place of $\bar{U}_m$ and y in place of δ. This is equivalent to the assumption that all mean velocity distributions are similar, since division of Eq. 8-35 by Eq. 8-34 gives relationship

$$\frac{\bar{u}}{\bar{U}_m} = \left(\frac{y}{\delta}\right)^{\frac{n}{2-n}} \tag{8-36}$$

Such type of similarity, which can be represented in form of equation $u/U = \mathcal{F}(y/\delta)$, can be strictly valid for laminar flow. (This we concluded in Sec. 8-1.) For a turbulent flow it can only be considered as an approximation.

If we take $n = \frac{1}{4}$, then Eq. 8-36 becomes

$$\frac{\bar{u}}{\bar{U}_m} = \left(\frac{y}{\delta}\right)^{1/7} \tag{8-37}$$

which agrees reasonably well with the measured velocity profile. For smooth pipes, the experimentally determined constant in Eq. 8-32 is 0.0466 giving the following expression for the resistance coefficient:

$$c_f = \frac{\tau_w}{\frac{1}{2}\rho \bar{U}_m^2} = 0.0466 \left(\frac{\bar{U}_m \delta}{\nu}\right)^{-1/4} \tag{8-38}$$

This equation is valid in the range $3{,}000 < \bar{U}_m \delta/\nu < 70{,}000$. It is left as a problem assignment to show that, for flows in pipes, this equation is equivalent to the Blasius formula, Eq. 8-27.

Equations 8-37 and 8-38 can be applied also to flows in smooth channels and along smooth flat plates. As in the case of pipe flows, the range of the Reynolds numbers in which these equations are applicable is limited.

From our discussion of the momentum integral equation in Sec. 8-1 it follows that for a flow *along a flat plate with no pressure gradient* we can write

$$\frac{d\theta}{dx} = \frac{\tau_w}{\rho \bar{U}_m^2} = \frac{1}{2} c_f \tag{8-39}$$

where θ denotes the momentum thickness (and $U = \bar{U}_m$ in this case). Since

$$\theta = \int_0^\delta \frac{\bar{u}}{\bar{U}_m} \left(1 - \frac{\bar{u}}{\bar{U}_m}\right) dy$$

substituting Eq. 8-37 we obtain

$$\theta = \frac{7}{72} \delta \tag{8-40}$$

If we assume that the turbulent boundary layer starts at the leading edge of the plate, (that is, $\delta = 0$ at $x = 0$), then, substituting Eq. 8-40 and Eq. 8-38 into Eq. 8-39 and integrating we obtain

$$\delta = 0.381x \left(\frac{\bar{U}_m x}{\nu}\right)^{-1/5} \tag{8-41}$$

where x denotes the distance from the leading edge of the plate, and $\bar{U}_m$ denotes the mean flow speed in the free stream outside the (turbulent) boundary layer. Introducing Eq. 8-41 into Eq. 8-38 gives the relation for the skin-friction coefficient

$$c_f = 0.0592 \left(\frac{\bar{U}_m x}{\nu}\right)^{-1/5} \tag{8-42}$$

For the mean skin-friction coefficients we obtain, in this case ($\bar{U}_m =$ const.),

$$C_F = \frac{\int_0^x \tau_w \, dx}{\frac{1}{2} \rho \bar{U}_m^2 x} = \frac{\int_0^x c_f \, dx}{x} = 0.074 \left(\frac{\bar{U}_m x}{\nu}\right)^{-1/5} \tag{8-43}$$

where x denotes the distance from the leading edge of the plate. This equation is valid for the Reynolds numbers $\bar{U}_m x/\nu$ up to about 3×10^6 [30]. Reference 2 gives the range of the Reynolds numbers $\bar{U}_m x/\nu$ in which this equation can be used as 5×10^5 to 10^7.

While the value of $n = \frac{1}{4}$ in Eq. 8-36 was used by von Kármán and Prandtl (in 1921), other values were used by some other investigators [3]. V. M. Falkner in 1943 used the value of $n = \frac{1}{5}$, for which

$$C_F = 0.0306 \left(\frac{\bar{U}_m x}{\nu}\right)^{-1/7} \tag{8-44}$$

while A. D. Young, in 1953, used the value of $n = \frac{1}{6}$ for which

$$C_F = 0.0450 \left(\frac{\bar{U}_m x}{\nu}\right)^{-1/6} \tag{8-45}$$

Law of the Wall and Velocity Defect Law. In a turbulent boundary layer most of the vorticity is concentrated in a region close to the wall.

It is also spread farther from the wall than in a laminar boundary layer. At the surface of a smooth wall, as a result of viscous diffusion, the vorticity reaches a uniform value in a very thin layer known as the *viscous sublayer*. At one time this layer has been called the "laminar sublayer." The name has been changed recently when it was discovered that this layer is not laminar in the ordinary sense because the root-mean-square fluctuations of vorticity in it are of the order of 30 percent of the mean [4, p. 100]. In this layer, the stress is predominantly the viscous stress and only very little Reynolds stress is present; nevertheless, the intensity of the turbulent velocity fluctuation parallel to the wall is high [29].

The experiments indicate that the viscous sublayer extends approximately to a distance corresponding to the value of dimensionless distance parameter $y\,u_\tau/\nu = 5$. The viscous diffusion loses its importance at a distance corresponding to $y\,u_\tau/\nu > 30$, at which turbulent diffusion is predominant. The range $5 < y\,u_\tau/\nu < 30$ corresponds to the so-called "overlapping region."

The shear of the mean flow is much greater near the surface than in the turbulent-flow region. Into this region near the surface the turbulent eddies transport the turbulent energy. There this energy is dissipated into heat.

And so the turbulent boundary-layer theory is based on the so-called *two-layer concept*, in which we differentiate between the viscous sublayer and the turbulent-flow region.

For incompressible turbulent boundary-layer flows, with which we will concern ourselves in this study, and for developed incompressible turbulent flows in pipes and channels, there exist two laws which pertain to the velocity distribution. One is the *law of the wall* (see Sec. 7-6) which is attributed to L. Prandtl, and the other is the *velocity defect law* of Theodor von Kármán. We shall concern ourselves now with these laws.

While the laminar velocity profiles in flows at constant pressure coincide when the ratio u/U is plotted versus y/δ, where U denotes the flow speed outside the boundary layer and δ the thickness of the boundary layer, this is not strictly the case for the turbulent-flow velocity profiles. In addition, the turbulent profiles show influence of the wall roughness. One would expect, therefore, that two parameters, the Reynolds number and some roughness parameter influence the turbulent-flow velocity distribution. Both these parameters affect the shearing stress at the wall, and it turns out that this (constant pressure) family of profiles can be made to coincide if the flow speeds are measured relative to the maximum, or free-stream, flow speed $\bar{U}_m$, and if this relative flow speed is divided by $\sqrt{\dfrac{1}{2}\,c_f}$. That is, we should use $\dfrac{\bar{u} - \bar{U}_m}{\bar{U}_m\sqrt{\dfrac{1}{2}\,c_f}}$ as a variable. Since

$$\sqrt{\frac{1}{2}\, c_f} = \frac{1}{\overline{U}_m}\sqrt{\frac{c_f \rho\, \overline{U}_m^{\,2}}{2\rho}} = \frac{1}{\overline{U}_m}\sqrt{\frac{\tau_w}{\rho}} = \frac{u_\tau}{\overline{U}_m}$$

the constant-pressure turbulent-flow velocity profiles can be made to coincide if we plot $(\bar{u} - \overline{U}_m)/u_\tau$ versus y/δ. Figure 8-22 shows such a plot. Such reduction of the turbulent-flow velocity profiles to one curve is

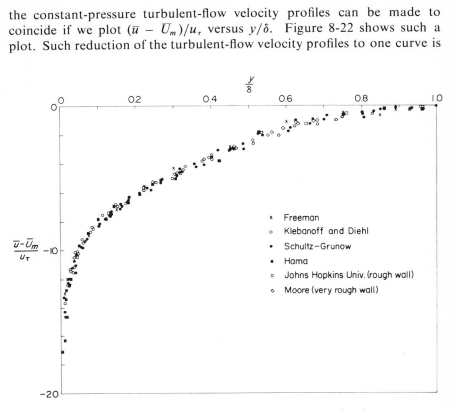

FIG. 8-22. Universal plot of constant-pressure turbulent boundary-layer profiles. (By permission of Dr. F. H. Clauser from Ref. 27.)

valid throughout the turbulent-flow region but not in the vicinity of the viscous sublayer. The formulation

$$\frac{\bar{u} - \overline{U}_m}{u_\tau} = f\left(\frac{y}{\delta}\right) \tag{8-46}$$

is known as the *velocity-defect law*. Note that it is valid for rough as well as for smooth walls. The function f is in general dependent on pressure gradient and on the free-stream turbulence. For that reason it is different for pipes and channels than for the boundary-layer flows.

While the velocity-defect law shows great sensitivity of the velocity distribution in the turbulent-flow region to the conditions outside the boundary layer, the law of the wall is based on the premise that the flow near the wall is ruled only by the local parameters such as the wall shearing stress, distance from the wall, and the viscosity and density of the fluid. Writing

$$\bar{u} = \mathscr{F}\left(\tau_w, y, \mu, \rho\right)$$

the dimensional analysis provides us with the expression

$$\frac{\bar{u}}{\sqrt{\tau_w/\rho}} = \frac{\bar{u}}{u_\tau} = \mathscr{F}\left(\frac{yu_\tau}{\nu}\right) \tag{8-47}$$

(see Eq. 7-78), which is known as the *law of the wall*. This law is valid only when the viscous sublayer exists, and therefore only for hydrodynamically smooth walls. As Fig. 8-23 shows, the law of the wall is valid not only for the viscous sublayer, but its validity extends well into the turbulent-flow region.

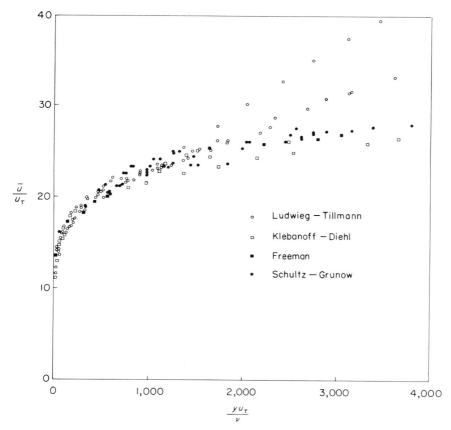

FIG. 8-23. Universal velocity distribution for turbulent-velocity profiles near smooth walls. (By permission of Dr. F. H. Clauser from Ref. 27.)

In the viscous sublayer, since the stress there is predominantly the viscous stress, and the variation of flow velocity with distance perpendicular to the wall is approximately linear, we have $\tau_w = \mu(u/y)$, and therefore the law of the wall in that layer becomes

$$\frac{u}{u_\tau} = \frac{u}{\sqrt{\tau_w/\rho}} = \frac{y\tau_w/\rho}{(\mu/\rho)\sqrt{\tau_w/\rho}} = \frac{y\sqrt{\tau_w/\rho}}{\nu} = \frac{yu_\tau}{\nu} \qquad (8\text{-}48)$$

The very important fact about the law of the wall and the velocity defect law is that there exists a region in which both of them are valid. C. B. Milikan in 1938 showed that, as a result, the functions f in Eq. 8-46 and $\mathscr{F}$ in Eq. 8-47 must be logarithms. That this must be the case becomes evident if we rewrite Eqs. 8-46 and 8-47 in the form

$$\frac{\bar{u}}{u_\tau} = \frac{\bar{U}_m}{u_\tau} + f\left(\frac{y}{\delta}\right) \qquad (8\text{-}46a)$$

and

$$\frac{\bar{u}}{u_\tau} = \mathscr{F}\left[\left(\frac{y}{\delta}\right)\left(\frac{\delta u_\tau}{\nu}\right)\right] \qquad (8\text{-}47a)$$

because the multiplying factor y/δ in Eq. 8-47a must become an additive factor in Eq. 8-46a. As a result, since

$$A\log\left(\frac{y}{\delta}\right) + A\log\left(\frac{\delta u_\tau}{\nu}\right) + B = \frac{\bar{U}_m}{u_\tau} + A'\log\left(\frac{y}{\delta}\right) + C$$

we have $A = A'$ and obtain expressions

$$\frac{\bar{u} - \bar{U}_m}{u_\tau} = A\log\left(\frac{y}{\delta}\right) + C \qquad (8\text{-}49)$$

and the so-called *universal logarithmic velocity distribution*:

$$\frac{\bar{u}}{u_\tau} = A\log\left(\frac{yu_\tau}{\nu}\right) + B \qquad (8\text{-}50)$$

In addition, we can write

$$\frac{\bar{U}_m}{u_\tau} = A\log\left(\frac{\delta u_\tau}{\nu}\right) + B - C \qquad (8\text{-}51)$$

The constants A, B, and C are determined from experiments. The constant C is the same for the fully-developed flow in pipes and channels but differs for turbulent boundary layers on flat plates. While the experimental data indicates that for pipes and channels

$$\frac{\bar{u} - \bar{U}_m}{u_\tau} = 5.75\log\left(\frac{y}{\delta}\right) - 0.65 \qquad (8\text{-}52)$$

for the boundary layers on flat plates

$$\frac{\bar{u} - \bar{U}_m}{u_\tau} = 5.75\log\left(\frac{y}{\delta}\right) - 2.35 \qquad (8\text{-}53)$$

The reason for the difference between the turbulent-flow velocity profiles along walls (that is, in boundary layers), and those in pipes and channels is because while in the boundary layers there exists a definite, though irregular, outer boundary between the free stream (in which the turbulence is very small) and the turbulent boundary layer, no such boundary exists in (fully developed) flows in pipes and channels. K. Wieghardt in 1944 showed that when the turbulence of the free stream is increased, the turbulent-flow velocity profile characteristic of a flow along a flat plate changes to that observed in pipe and channel flows.

According to various writers, the values of the constants A and B in the universal logarithmic velocity distribution are as follows [8]:

Author	A	B
Ludwieg and Tillman (1949)	5.75	5.7
Laufer (1950)	6.72	6.0
Coles (1953).	5.75	5.1
Clauser (1954).	5.6	4.9
Eskinazi and Yeh (1956)	5.02	6.5

Figure 8-24 shows a comparison of experimental data with the logarithmic velocity-distribution equation with Clauser's constants A and B. Observe the lack of agreement at large values of the distance paramater yu_τ/ν.

Recently certain doubts have been expressed as to whether the universal constants A, B, and C are in fact constants or exhibit a certain amount of dependence on the Reynolds number [25]. If there is such dependence, however, it appears to be relatively small at the high values of the Reynolds number usually encountered in practice.

Making use of Eq. 8-51 we can derive a formula for the resistance or skin-friction coefficient $c_f = \tau_w \frac{1}{2} \rho \bar{U}_m^2$.   Since,   as   we   have   shown,

$$\sqrt{\frac{1}{2} c_f} = u_\tau/\bar{U}_m,$$ we obtain the expression

$$\sqrt{\frac{2}{c_f}} = A \log (\mathrm{Re}_\delta \sqrt{c_f}) + \text{const.} \tag{8-54}$$

where $\mathrm{Re}_\delta = \bar{U}_m \delta/\nu$.

For fully developed turbulent flows in smooth pipes, according to von Kármán [30], the last equation becomes

$$\frac{1}{\sqrt{c_f}} = 4.15 \log (\mathrm{Re}_\delta \sqrt{c_f}) + 3.60 \tag{8-55}$$

Observe that for flows in pipes $\bar{U}_m$ represents the flow speed at the center of the pipe, while $\delta = \frac{1}{2} d$ where d denotes the diameter of the pipe. As noted by Prandtl (see Ref. 30), if the mean flow speed $\bar{V}$ based on the rate of flow through the pipe is used in the expression for Re_δ that is, if we write $\mathrm{Re}_\delta = \dfrac{\bar{V}d/2}{\nu}$, the form of Eq. 8-55 remains unchanged except for the

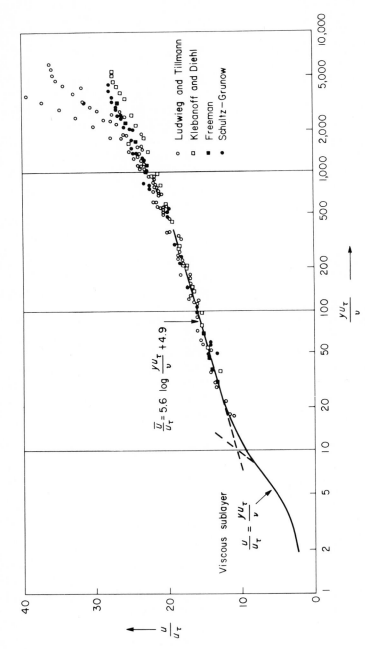

Fig. 8-24. Universal velocity distribution for turbulent-velocity profiles near smooth walls. (By permission of Dr. F. H. Clauser from Ref. 27.)

value of the constant. Using the law of the wall, the experimental data of Nikuradse, and employing the mean flow speed $\overline{V} = \dfrac{Q}{\pi d^2/4}$, Prandtl obtained the following expression for the resistance coefficient f (for definition of f see Eqs. 7-55 or 8-28) for fully developed turbulent incompressible flows in smooth pipes:

$$\frac{1}{\sqrt{f}} = 2.0 \log\left(\frac{\overline{V}d}{\nu}\sqrt{f}\right) - 0.8 \tag{8-56}$$

where, as noted earlier, $f = 4\,c_f$. This relation is indicated in Fig. 8-20.

For the turbulent boundary layers on a flat plate we have to introduce into the formula for the skin-friction coefficient the distance x from the leading edge where the turbulent boundary layer is assumed to start. The calculations, which utilize the law of the wall and the velocity-defect law, are rather complicated because, in the process, the formula for the turbulent boundary-layer thickness must also be derived. The resulting formula, which is obtained using somewhat modified values of the constants A and B (see Eq. 8-50) is [24]:

$$\frac{1}{\sqrt{c_f}} = 4.15 \log(\mathrm{Re}_x c_f) + 1.7 \tag{8-57}$$

where $\mathrm{Re}_x = \overline{U}_m x/\nu$ and c_f is the (local) skin-friction coefficient. The above equation is known as the *von Kármán–Schlichting formula for the skin-friction coefficient in a turbulent boundary layer on a smooth flat plate* (with no pressure gradient).

Since the calculation of the values of the coefficient c_f from the last equation is cumbersome, H. Schlichting fitted this relationship into an empirical equation for the mean skin-friction coefficient:

$$C_F = \frac{0.455}{(\log \mathrm{Re}_L)^{2.58}} \tag{8-58}$$

where $\mathrm{Re}_L = \overline{U}_m L/\nu$, the symbol L denoting the length of the plate [2]. The corresponding formula for the (local) skin-friction coefficient, as given by Schlichting, is

$$c_f = (2 \log \mathrm{Re}_x - 0.65)^{-2.3} \tag{8-59}$$

The drawback of the formulas for the skin-friction coefficient of flows along flat plates given above lies in the fact that the boundary layer is laminar for a certain distance downstream from the leading edge before it becomes turbulent. The existence of the laminar boundary layer results in a decreased value of the skin-friction drag. In order to account properly for this, we assume, after Prandtl, that downstream of the transition point (or region) the turbulent boundary layer on a flat plate behaves as though it were turbulent all the way from the leading edge. As a result of this assumption, we subtract from the calculated skin-friction drag of the wholly turbulent boundary layer the turbulent boundary-layer drag up to the transition point and add the laminar boundary-layer drag up to that point.

The presence of the laminar boundary layer up to the transition point can also be accounted for by modifying the formula for the mean skin-friction coefficient. This approach leads to the so-called *Prandtl–Schlichting mean skin-friction formula for smooth flat plates* (with no pressure gradient):

$$C_F = \frac{0.455}{(\log \mathrm{Re}_L)^{2.58}} - \frac{A'}{\mathrm{Re}_L} \tag{8-60}$$

The value of the coefficient A' in the above formula depends on the location of the point of transition of the boundary layer. The table below gives the values of the coefficient A' as a function of the Reynolds number at which transition of the boundary layer occurs, $(\mathrm{Re}_x)_{tr}$[2].

TABLE 8-3

VALUES OF COEFFICIENT A' FOR VARIOUS VALUES OF $(\mathrm{Re}_x)_{tr}$

$(\mathrm{Re}_x)_{tr}$	3×10^5	5×10^5	10^6	3×10^6
A'	1,050	1,700	3,300	8,700

Figures 8-25 and 8-26 show the variation of the values of the local and mean skin-friction coefficients for flows along smooth flat plates with no pressure gradient. In Fig. 8-25 the typical transition curves for $\mathrm{Re}_x = 4.3 \times 10^5$ and $\mathrm{Re}_x = 2.3 \times 10^6$ are shown [4].

Effect of Roughness[27]. Our inability to account properly for the effect of surface roughness on turbulent flow along a wall is mainly due to the fact that we do not know how to treat the nonuniform roughness and the different types of roughness. We know, for example, that if the wall

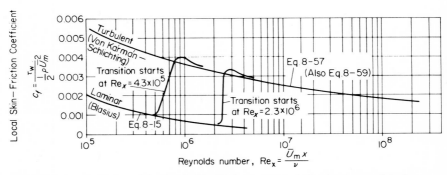

FIG. 8-25. Variation of the local skin-friction coefficient for laminar and turbulent boundary layers on a smooth flat plate with no pressure gradient.

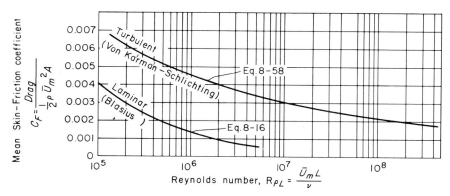

FIG. 8-26. Variation of the mean skin-friction coefficient for laminar and turbulent boundary layers on a smooth flat plate with no pressure gradient.

roughness has a wavy nature with an amplitude which is small relative to the average wavelength, the Reynolds number has an important effect on the values of the skin-friction, or resistance, coefficient, just as in the case of a flow over a smooth wall. Such is not the case, however, when the roughness of the wall is produced by glued sand. (We refer to such roughness as the "sand roughness." The technique of producing surface roughness by gluing sand to the wall is often used in experimental investigations.) In addition, the shape and size distribution of the roughness elements has effect on the flow. In the study of resistance of rough walls to flow the sand roughness has been accepted as a standard, the significant linear dimension being the mean height k of the roughness (sand) elements.

The universal plot shown in Fig. 8-22 indicates that the correlation of $(\bar{u} - \bar{U}_m)/u_\tau$ versus y/δ is valid for rough as well as for smooth walls. Since we found that the inner part of this velocity distribution is logarithmic for smooth walls, it follows that it is also logarithmic for rough walls. In the overlap region $(\bar{u} - \bar{U}_m)/u_\tau = A \log (y/\delta) + C$ (see Eq. 8-49), or

$$\frac{\bar{u}}{u_\tau} = A \log\left(\frac{y\,u_\tau}{\nu}\right) + C + \frac{U_m}{u_\tau} - A \log\left(\frac{\delta\,u_\tau}{\nu}\right)$$

This relation, which is valid for all values of the roughness Reynolds number $k\,u_\tau/\nu$, reduces to the relation

$$\frac{\bar{u}}{u_\tau} = A \log\left(\frac{y\,u_\tau}{\nu}\right) + B \qquad [8\text{-}50]$$

when $\dfrac{k\,u_\tau}{\nu} = 0$, that is, for smooth walls. We can conclude that for rough walls there must exist a skin-friction law which involves quantities $\bar{U}_m/u_\tau$, $\delta\,u_\tau/\nu$, and ku_τ/ν, namely a relation of the form

$$C + \frac{\bar{U}_m}{u_\tau} - A \log\left(\frac{\delta\,u_\tau}{\nu}\right) = -f\left(\frac{ku_\tau}{\nu}\right) + B \qquad (8\text{-}61)$$

with $f(0) = 0$, and that the general relation valid in the overlap region is

$$\frac{\bar{u}}{u_\tau} = A \log\left(\frac{yu_\tau}{\nu}\right) + B - f\left(\frac{ku_\tau}{\nu}\right) \qquad (8\text{-}62)$$

which indicates that on a semilogarithmic graph the effect of the wall roughness will result in a displacement of the velocity distribution in the turbulent flow region, the amount of displacement depending on the Reynolds number of the roughness elements, ku_τ/ν.

For the roughness elements which are appreciably higher than the thickness of the viscous sublayer, that is, for the values of $ku_\tau/\nu \gg 30$ (see Fig. 8-24), we would expect that the skin friction should show no dependence on viscosity. As a result, the expression for the function $f(ku_\tau/\nu)$ should tend toward the expression $A \log (ku_\tau/\nu) +$ const. in that region (see Eq. 8-61). Figure 8-27 confirms this conclusion.

The effect of the wall (sand) roughness on the velocity distribution in turbulent flow in pipes is shown in Fig. 8-28.

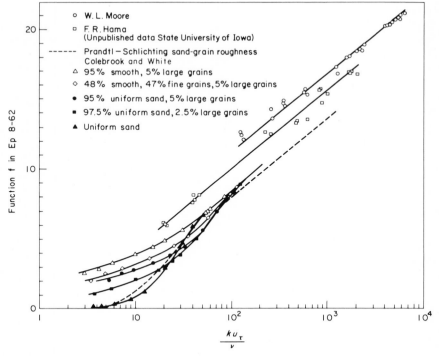

FIG. 8-27. Effect of roughness on universal turbulent velocity profiles. (By permission from Dr. F. H. Clauser from Ref. 27.)

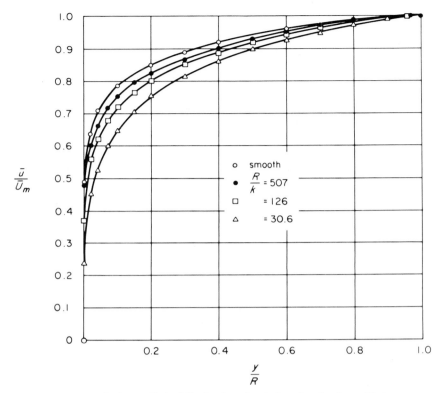

FIG. 8-28. Velocity profile in fully developed turbulent flow in pipes. Tests run at $Re_d = \overline{V}d/\nu = 10^6$. (After J. Nikuradse.)

There exists a number of formulas for the skin-friction coefficient in a flow along a flat plate with no pressure gradient, which account for the effect of roughness. The interested reader is referred to the article by F. H. Clauser [31] and to the book by H. Schlichting [2].

For the turbulent incompressible flow in pipes, a graph (prepared by L. F. Moody [32]) showing the variation of the resistance coefficient f with the Reynolds number based on the average flow velocity $\overline{V} = 4Q/\pi d^2$, $Re_d = \dfrac{\overline{V}d}{\nu}$, and the sand-roughness coefficient k/d is available. It is shown in Fig. 8-29. Figure 8-30 is an auxiliary diagram which allows estimation of the equivalent sand-roughness coefficient k/d for commercial pipes.

Effect of Pressure Gradient. In most cases of practical interest, the pressure varies in the neighborhood of an object around which a fluid flows. Since the boundary layers are usually quite thin in relation to the distances over which appreciable pressure changes take place, the pressure

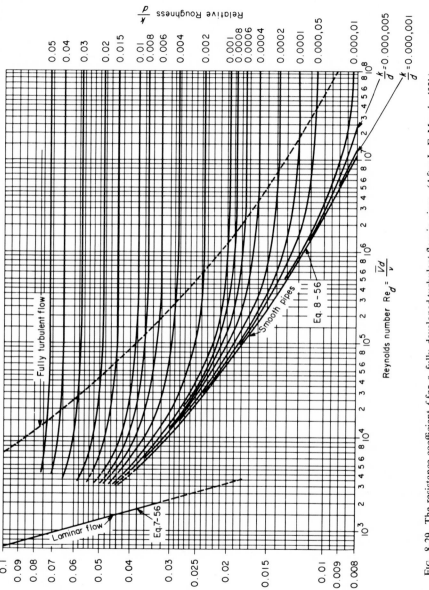

FIG. 8-29. The resistance coefficient f for a fully developed turbulent flow in pipes. (After L. F. Moody, [32].)

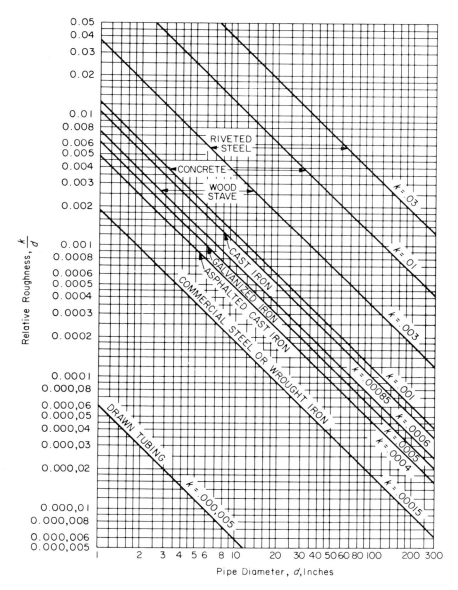

FIG. 8-30. Pertinent roughness heights k (in feet,) for various commercial pipes.

can be considered as constant across the boundary layers (see our discussion in Sec. 8-1).

When pressure variation occurs along a solid surface over which a fluid flows, the velocity profile at the surface undergoes change in its characteristics. As shown by F. Clauser [27], in the study of turbulent boundary layers subjected to pressure gradients we can introduce the concept of an *equilibrium* (turbulent) *boundary layer* which is a layer which shows no tendency to change its characteristics if allowed to proceed in the same environment. The developed turbulent flows in pipes and channels are typical examples of equilibrium flows, while in external flows along walls the equilibrium turbulent boundary layers can be attained only if the pressure gradient is suitably adjusted.

While the general behavior of the nonequilibrium turbulent boundary layers subjected to pressure gradients needs a thorough investigation, it appears that the equilibrium boundary layers are much better understood. For a discussion of the equilibrium boundary layers the reader is referred to Ref. [36].

An important conclusion reached concerning turbulent boundary layers with pressure gradient is that in the thin inner portion of the boundary layer the shearing forces exert larger influence than the pressure forces and, as a result, the law of the wall is still valid. The test data of Ludwieg and Tillmann for turbulent boundary layers in adverse pressure gradients, shown in Figs. 8-23 and 8-24 support this conclusion. The expression for the (local) skin-friction coefficient as obtained by Ludwieg and Tillmann is

$$c_f = \frac{0.246}{10^{0.678H} \, \text{Re}_\theta^{0.268}} \tag{8-63}$$

where $H = \delta^*/\theta$ is the form parameter, or *shape factor*, and $\text{Re}_\theta = \bar{U}_m \theta/\nu$. This formula is expected to give reasonable values of the skin-friction coefficient for the nonequilibrium velocity profiles which can be correlated with the aid of the form parameter H[24]. Recent information indicates that both the pressure gradient and the skin-friction coefficient affect the value of the shape parameter H[36].

A review of various new proposed methods for the calculation of the turbulent boundary layers with pressure gradients can be found in Refs. 35, 51, and 52.

8-4. SEPARATION OF FLOW

The phenomenon of separation of flow was briefly discussed in Secs. 1-4 and 8-1 and illustrated with the aid of Figs. 1-11, 1-12, and 8-3. In a given decelerating flow, the adverse pressure gradient can produce flow reversal if the loss of momentum of the fluid, resulting from the viscous friction at the wall, is large enough. The separation characteristics of a flow can be related to both the shearing stresses and the pressure gradient. As was mentioned earlier, laminar boundary layers are more susceptible to separation than the turbulent boundary layers.

Suppose that in a given decelerating flow along a wall the boundary layer is laminar, and separation of flow from the wall takes place. If the Reynolds number of the flow (based on the typical physical quantity having dimension of length, such as the chord in the case of a flow past an airfoil) is increased, we may find that the laminar boundary layer separates locally from the wall, changes into turbulent boundary layer, and reattaches itself to the wall. Or we may find that the laminar boundary layer changes into turbulent boundary layer ahead of the region where it became separated in the flow at a lower Reynolds number, and no separation of flow, or a considerable delay in the separation of flow, is observed. This boundary-layer transition and the accompanying change in the separation characteristics of a flow can be produced not only by an increase of the Reynolds number of the flow, but also by an increase in the wall roughness or in the free-stream turbulence. (Nevertheless, the Reynolds number is the most important similarity parameter affecting incompressible fluid flows, and we shall concentrate our attention on it in the discussion which follows.)

Flow Around Bluff Bodies. To obtain a better understanding of the phenomenon of separation in flows over objects, we shall discuss the flow patterns observed in incompressible flows, at various values of the Reynolds number, past a long bluff body in the form of a circular cylinder whose axis is perpendicular to the direction of flow. Figure 8-31 shows photographs of such flows in which the fluid was oil. The flow patterns were made visible by spraying the free surface of the oil with aluminium powder.

At very low Reynolds numbers, say for Re_d of the order of 1 or less, the viscous forces are much larger than the inertia forces, and the flow resembles somewhat the potential flow of a perfect fluid. However, in such flow the streamlines corresponding to the same rate of flow are spaced further away from the cylinder, and the flow speed at the surface of the cylinder is zero. The viscous effects extend far away from the cylinder. As was shown in Chapter 2 (Fig. 2-4) [and, for spheres in Chapter 7 (Fig. 7-3)], the drag coefficient in such flow decreases substantially with increasing Reynolds number. The drag force varies then as the first rather than the second power of the flow speed of the undisturbed flow.

In the range of the Reynolds number between (roughly) 1 and 10 there exists a separated-flow region on the downstream side of the cylinder in the form of two vortices which are fixed relative to the cylinder. A *separation surface*, which represents a vortex layer, forms a boundary between the main flow and the fixed vortex pair of the separated-flow region. It moves forward on the curved surface of the cylinder as the value of the Reynolds number increases above the value at which separa-

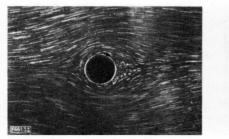

(a) $Re_d = 3.9$

(b) $Re_d = 18.6$

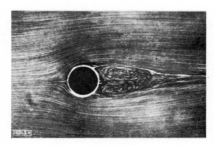

(c) $Re_d = 33.5$

(d) $Re_d = 31.6$

(e) $Re_d = 54.8$

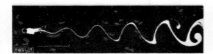

(f) $Re_d = 65.2$

(g) $Re_d = 73$

(h) $Re_d = 101.5$

(i) $Re_d = 161$

FIG. 8-31. Flow about a circular cylinder at various values of the Reynolds number, $Re_d = U_\infty d/\nu$. (Experimental results of F. Homann [37].)

tion of flow begins. The vortex layers of the separation surface join downstream of the vortex pair and form a laminar wake.

As the Reynolds number Re_d is further increased, above 30 or so, the wake develops a periodic pattern known as the *Kármán vortex street*. This flow pattern, representing eddies which break away alternately on either side of the cylinder, was shown in Fig. 1-17 and is shown again in Fig. 8-32. At these higher values of the Reynolds number, the effects of viscosity in the flow region along the surface of the cylinder become confined to a narrow region.

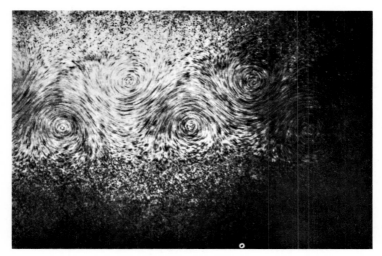

FIG. 8-32. Kármán vortex street downstream of a cylinder. (After G. J. Richards [39].)

Photographs denoted by letters *e*, *f*, *g*, *h*, and *i* in Fig. 8-31 show the development of the vortex street as the value of the Reynolds number Re_d increases to 161.

The experiments of A. Roshko [40], made in a wind tunnel indicate that the Reynolds number range in which periodic vortex shedding from circular cylinders takes place can be divided into two distinct subranges. Between $Re_d = 40$ and 150 regular vortex streets are formed and the flow is laminar. This range is referred to as the stable range. The range $Re_d =$ 150 to 300 is a transition range in which turbulent velocity fluctuations accompany the periodic formation of vortices. The initiation of turbulent motion occurs in the separation surfaces, known also as *free layers*. The range of Reynolds numbers $Re_d > 300$ is called the *irregular range*. In this range the wake becomes fully turbulent in 40 to 50 diameters downstream of the cylinder.

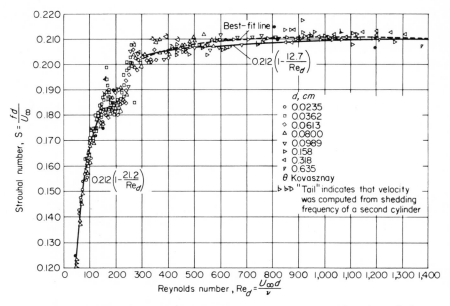

FIG. 8-33. Measured variation of the Strouhal number as a function of the Reynolds number for a circular cylinder. (After A. Roshko [40].)

Figure 8-33 shows the dependence of the vortex-shedding frequency from a circular cylinder expressed in the form of the Strouhal number (see Sec. 2-2), on the flow Reynolds number, Re_d.

(Formation of periodic vortex streets is not limited to flows over cylinders, but is a generally observed phenomenon in flows over blunt bodies. In the case of a flow past a ring, an annular vortex street is observed [40]. There is less information available on the effect of the Reynolds number on the flow past three-dimensional bluff bodies. It appears that the values of the Reynolds numbers at which the wake becomes unstable and develops a periodic pattern are higher than for two-dimensional bluff bodies such as cylinders. For spheres this value of the Reynolds number is about 500 [4]. One of the very important effects of the periodic vortex shedding is the fluctuating lift and drag which acts on the body from which the vortices are shed. Since the vortex-shedding frequency depends on the flow speed, resonant excitation of structures such as stacks or even bridges which are exposed to winds can sometimes occur. The periodic vortex streets are observed also in supersonic flows.)

The location in the free layer of the transition point between the laminar and turbulent flow depends on the Reynolds number. This transition was observed in experiments (by L. Schiller and W. Linke, 1933) in which the Reynolds numbers Re_d varied between 3,500 and 8,500.

In these tests the distance to the transition point, when measured from the separation point on the cylinder, was observed to decrease from 1.4 to 0.7 diameter as the Reynolds number was increased. A decrease in these distances was also observed as the free-stream turbulence was increased.

The experiments of H. Dryden [12] showed that the transition point in the free layer reaches the separation point on the cylinder at some value of the Reynolds number between 5,000 and 20,000, the exact value being dependent on the free-stream turbulence. From that point on, for a considerable range of the Reynolds number the transition begins at the separation point. At $\mathrm{Re}_d \cong 100,000$ and higher, the transition occurs in the boundary layer ahead of the separation point. The separation of the turbulent boundary-layer flow is delayed when compared with the laminar boundary-layer flow separation and the wake narrows appreciably. At these Reynolds numbers the periodicity in the wake disappears and the whole wake becomes turbulent. The drag coefficient of a cylinder decreases then to a value which is much lower than that at which laminar boundary-layer flow separation was taking place (see Fig. 2-4). This decrease in the value of the drag coefficient of a cylinder usually occupies the range $100,000 \leq \mathrm{Re}_d \leq 600,000$. This range of the Reynolds number, for flows past circular cylinders, is sometimes referred to as the "transition range," and the ranges of the Reynolds number below and above this range are referred to as "subcritical" and "supercritical" ranges.

Figure 8-34a shows the pattern of flow past a sphere when the laminar boundary-layer flow separation takes place. Figure 8-34b shows the corresponding flow pattern in which, as a result of attaching a "trip wire" to the sphere ahead of the laminar boundary-layer separation point, transition to turbulent boundary-layer flow takes place on the sphere and

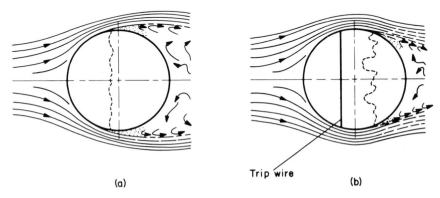

(a)   Trip wire   (b)

FIG. 8-34. Flow past a sphere. (a) Laminar boundary-layer flow separation. (b) Turbulent boundary-layer flow separation produced by attaching a "trip wire" ahead of the laminar boundary layer separation point. (After L. Prandtl.)

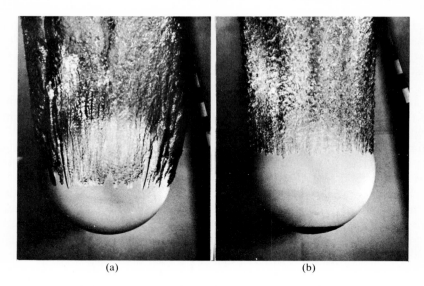

(a)   (b)

FIG. 8-35. Flow past a sphere. (a) Separation of laminar boundary-layer flow.
(b) Separation of turbulent boundary-layer flow. The boundary-layer flow is
turbulent upstream of the separation region in the flow shown in photograph (b) as
a result of surface roughness (black region on the sphere). (Courtesy of the U.S.
Naval Ordnance Test Station, Pasadena, California.)

the separation of flow is delayed. Figure 8-35a and 8-35b show photographs of flow of water over spheres which correspond to Figs. 8-34a and
8-34b. The only difference is that the transition to turbulence in the
photographed flow shown in Fig. 8-35b was achieved by roughening the
surface of the sphere in the vicinity of the forward stagnation point
rather than by the use of a wire. Observe that, as a result of the delay in
the separation, the wake occurring when the boundary layer is turbulent
is smaller than when it is laminar.

The above discussion illustrates well what was already pointed out in
Sec. 7-3, namely that at high values of the Reynolds number (of the order
of 10^5) the effect of small dimensionless parameters based on the height
of the roughness element or of the free-stream turbulence on the flow may
be large.

Figure 8-36 shows the variation of the pressure coefficient $C_P =$
$(P - P_\infty)/\left(\frac{1}{2}\rho U_\infty^2\right)$ with the angle θ for a sphere (angle $\theta = 0$ corresponding to the forward stagnation point) in flows at subcritical and
supercritical Reynolds numbers. In addition, the variation of the pressure
coefficient calculated using the irrotational-flow theory is also given. Observe that the supercritical pressure distribution differs little from that
corresponding to the irrotational flow all the way up to the separation

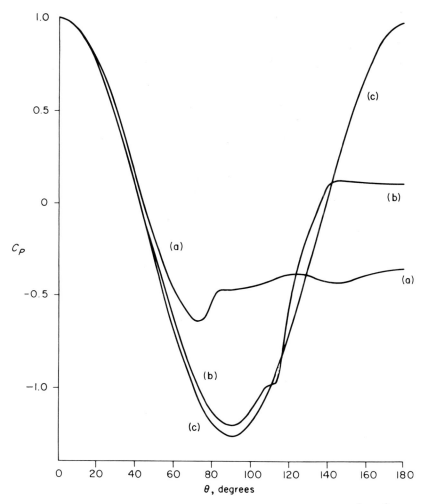

FIG. 8-36. Variation of the pressure coefficient $C_P = (P - P_\infty)/(\tfrac{1}{2}\rho U^2)$ with the angle θ from the stagnation point on a sphere in a uniform stream. (a) Subcritical flow ($\mathrm{Re}_d = 1.57 \times 10^5$). (b) Supercritical flow ($\mathrm{Re}_d = 4.24 \times 10^5$). (c) Calculated for irrotational flow. (After A. Fage, 1936. By permission from Ref. 4.)

point. The separation point corresponds in this case to $\theta = 140$ deg. There is a slight inflection of the pressure distribution curve at the transition point (or region) as a result of the decrease in the boundary-layer displacement thickness on transition. In the subcritical flow the separation occurs much earlier ($\theta = 70$ deg) than in the supercritical flow, and it produces an increase in the pressure upstream of the separation point.

If the Reynolds number were increased above 4.24×10^5 in this flow, the extent of the turbulent boundary layer on the sphere would increase and so would the drag coefficient.

In the case of flows about bodies having protruding edges, such as flat plates at large angles of incidence, the separation of flow occurs usually at the edges. This is so because the flow around such edges would require very large deceleration, and therefore adverse pressure gradients, which no boundary-layer flow could tolerate. Figure 8-37 shows a sketch of the flow pattern corresponding to such type of flow.

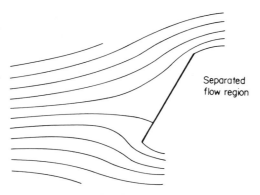

Separated
flow region

FIG. 8-37. Separation in a flow about a
flat plate. (After L. Prandtl.)

In the case of a flow along a wall which possesses a corner which is concave to the surface, the separation of flow occurs upstream of the corner. This is true for external flows over objects as well as for internal flow in ducts (see Fig. 1-12). In such flow the corner corresponds to a stagnation point in a fluid flow assumed to be irrotational.

Flow Around Streamlined Bodies. By a streamlined object we mean, in general, an object possessing a smooth convex nose and a sharp trailing edge. The surface of a streamlined object has continuously varying radius of curvature everywhere except at the trailing edge. The reason for "streamlining" an object is to reduce its drag coefficient (usually to a value much less than 1) by decreasing the size of the wake flow. When the Reynolds number is low enough so that the entire boundary-layer flow is laminar, separation of flow can be avoided only if the object is very slender. As the Reynolds number is progressively increased, the transition point (or region) moves upstream from the vicinity of the trailing edge until, for large enough Reynolds numbers, almost all boundary-layer flow is turbulent. As was mentioned earlier, the turbulent boundary-layer flow is much less prone to separation than the laminar flow. The separation of flow past a streamlined body can be prevented by such "boundary-layer control" devices as the suction slots (through which the boundary-layer flow is removed) or the "vortex generators" in form of small vanes protruding into the main stream which promote mixing and thus increase the momentum of the fluid near the wall. In streamlined objects such as wings, as the angle of attack is increased, before the flow separation from the upper surface occurs and a large wake is formed, there can occur a local separation of the laminar boundary-layer flow in the vicinity of the leading edge, which is followed by transition of the boundary-layer flow and reattachment of the flow to the wing surface. Such separated flow region is known as the "separation bubble."

In flows over wings in which supersonic flow is present and shock waves occur, separation of flow can be produced as a result of the interaction between the shock waves and the boundary-layer flow. Figure 8-38

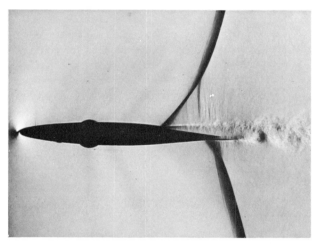

FIG. 8-38. Flow past a wing at the free-stream Mach number $M_\infty = 0.87$. (Crown Copyright. Courtesy of National Physical Laboratory, Teddington, Middlesex, England.)

shows a schlieren photograph of a flow past a wing at the free stream Mach number of 0.87. Observe separation of flow on the upper and lower wing surfaces caused by the presence of the shock waves. (The round object located at about $\frac{1}{3}$ of the chord from the leading edge is the fixture holding, from outside, the wing in the wind tunnel in which this photograph was taken.)

8-5. DRAG IN FLOWS OVER OBJECTS

The (total) drag, or resistance to flow of an object immersed in a flowing fluid in the direction parallel to the direction of flow of the undisturbed stream, can be considered to be made up of the *skin-friction drag* (or the surface-friction drag), and the *pressure drag*.

The *skin-friction drag* of an object is the drag arising from the resolved components of the tangential stresses acting on the surface of the object. For flows over streamlined objects, with no separation present, the skin-friction drag is usually much larger than the pressure drag.

The *pressure drag* of an object arises from the resolved components of the pressure forces acting on the object. (The pressure forces are normal to the surface of the object.) As explained in Sec. 6-4, (three-dimensional) lifting bodies experience the *induced drag* which is sometimes also called the *trailing vortex drag* [45].[1] [The product of the induced drag of an object and its velocity represents the (time) rate at which work is done in extending the trailing vortices. We can also say that the work done by the induced drag, or drag due to lift, supplies the energy required for the generation of trailing vortices.] The induced drag, when it occurs, represents a part of the pressure drag. The difference between the pressure drag and the induced drag is usually called the *form drag*, the *wake drag* [49], or the *boundary-layer pressure drag* [8]. (In general, there may exist another, third component of the pressure drag which we shall identify presently. The term *boundary-layer pressure drag* seems to be more appropriate for flows over streamlined objects, in which there is no separation of flow present, than for flows in which separation occurs.) In the case of a flow over a streamlined object with no separation present, the form drag exists because the boundary layer produces, in effect, displacement of the fluid away from the surface of the object (see our discussion of the boundary-layer displacement thickness in Sec. 8-1), and also produces a wake. This effect on the main stream is equivalent to an outward displacement of the surface of the object and to an extension of the object to infinity (as a result of the wake).

Both the form drag and the skin-friction drag are the result of viscosity. The sum of the two is usually called the *profile drag*, or the *boundary-layer drag* [8]. (Observe that the profile drag of a wing represents the drag of an airfoil in a two-dimensional flow, that is, when the span of the wing is infinite. There are no end effects in such flow, which result in formation of the trailing vortices and thus in the induced drag.)

In the case of a supersonic flow past an object, as well as in the case of a flow past an object which involves a free surface, there is another component of the pressure drag, the so-called *wave drag*. This is the third component of the pressure drag which was mentioned above.

The drag of an object can thus be classified into drag which is produced by the pressures (pressure drag) and drag which is produced by the

---

[1]Our study of potential (that is, irrotational) fluid flow has indicated that in a two-dimensional low-speed (subsonic) flow of a perfect fluid past an object there is no drag. In three-dimensional flows of a perfect fluid past lifting bodies there exists the induced drag.

shearing forces (skin-friction drag). It can also be classified into drag which depends on the lift (induced drag) and drag which depends on the profile (profile drag). (This second classification loses its value in supersonic flows because then part of the drag due to lift corresponds to the wave drag.)

The drag concepts discussed above are not independent of one another. For example, in a supersonic flow past an object, the boundary layer affects the pattern of the shock waves and a part of the boundary-layer pressure drag may appear as a contribution to the wave drag [45]. In addition, a change in one drag component resulting from some change in the flow will, in general, affect the other drag components. As an example, consider the effect of the change in the location of the boundary-layer transition region on the drag components.

From the principle of conservation of linear momentum it follows that the *total drag* is equal to the force corresponding to the rate of de-

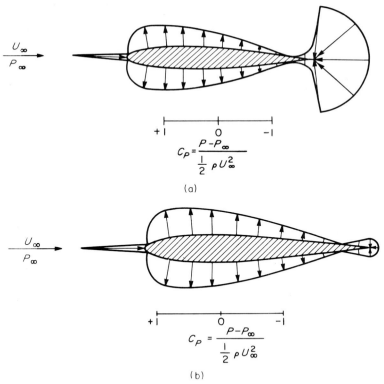

FIG. 8-39. Pressure distribution in an incompressible two-dimensional flow past a streamlined object. (a) For a fluid assumed to be perfect (irrotational flow theory). (b) For a real fluid. (After J. H. Dwinnell [47]. Reproduced by permission of the McGraw-Hill Book Co.)

crease of momentum, in a direction parallel to the undisturbed stream, of the external flow around the body, this decrease being calculated between stations at infinite distances upstream and downstream of the body.

Figures 8-39a and 8-39b show the pressure distributions in a low-speed flow past a streamlined two-dimensional object in form of a symmetrical wing at zero angle of attack, with no separation. Figure 8-39a corresponds to the flow of a perfect fluid, while Fig. 8-39b corresponds to the flow of a real fluid at some high Reynolds number. In the flow of a real fluid, as a result of the boundary-layer formation and the wake, the pressure near the trailing edge is appreciably lower than that corresponding to the irrotational flow and the form drag (or the boundary-layer pressure drag) is produced.

In the case of a flow over a blunt body, the main contribution to the pressure drag is provided by the separation of flow (see Fig. 8-36). (As a result of separation the force due to pressure acting on the downstream part of the body is lower than the corresponding force acting on the upstream part of the body.) The significant effect of the Reynolds number on the pressure drag, for blunt objects, can be inferred from Figs. 8-36 and 8-40.

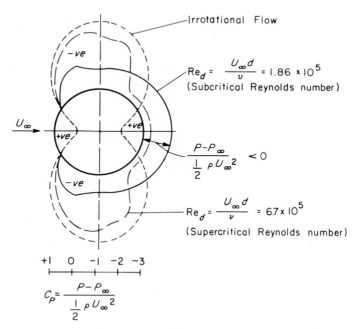

FIG. 8-40. Pressure distribution in a two-dimensional incompressible flow past a circular cylinder. (After O. Flachsbart.)

Figure 8-40 shows the measured pressure distributions in a two-dimensional incompressible flow over a circular cylinder at certain sub-critical and supercritical Reynolds numbers. For comparison, the pressure distribution corresponding to an irrotational incompressible flow is also shown (see Fig. 5-6).

The important effect of the Reynolds number and cross-sectional shape on low-speed (low-Mach-number) two-dimensional flows past non-circular cylinders is illustrated in Figs. 8-41 and 8-42. In these figures, the coefficient c_y' represents the section side-force coefficient defined by

$$c_y' = \frac{\text{side force (to the right) per unit length}}{b \, \dfrac{\rho U_\infty^2}{2}}$$

where b, which is indicated in the figures, denotes the widths of the cylinders. Figures 8-41 and 8-42 show the variation of the side-force coefficient c_y' in the subcritical, transition, and supercritical Reynolds number ranges for modified square and triangular cylinders at a flow incidence of 10 deg. (The cylinders were modified by rounding off their sharp edges.) In addition, they show the calculated pressures in the form of pressure coefficient distributions for the modified square and triangular cylinders under the assumption of an irrotational flow without circulation, and the measured pressures also in the form of the pressure-coefficient distributions (at subcritical and supercritical Reynolds numbers) on cylinders of similar cross sections. The measured pressure distributions shown correspond to the black dots on the side-force coefficient–Reynolds number plots.

Observe that the effect of the Reynolds number on the forces acting on the triangular cylinder (with rounded edges) is quite different from that on the square cylinder (also with rounded edges).

For the modified square cylinder shown in Fig. 8-41, there is a change in the direction of the side force (from that to the right to that to the left) occurring at approximately $\text{Re}_\ell = 0.55 \times 10^6$. At the subcritical Reynolds numbers attained in the tests the negative-pressure coefficient loops near the corners, which are calculated for the irrotational flow with no circulation, are almost completely eliminated as a result of separation of flow. One exception is the negative pressure coefficient loop at the right leading corner. At the supercritical Reynolds number the large negative-pressure coefficient loop on the left leading edge is produced and, as a result, a negative overall side force is developed. It is possible that at Reynolds numbers higher than those attained in the tests, flow attachment around the trailing corners might be maintained for a distance sufficient to develop the negative-pressure coefficient loops corresponding to the irrotational flow field. In such case the magnitude of the negative

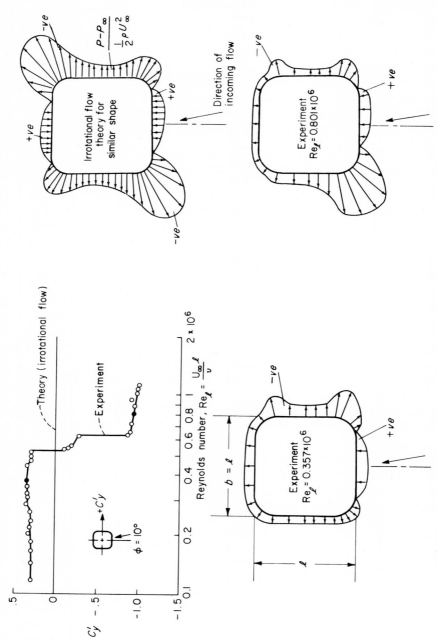

FIG. 8-41. Effect of Reynolds number on the side force and pressure distribution in a two-dimensional low-speed flow of air past a modified square cylinder at a flow incidence of 10 deg. (Adapted from Ref. 46.)

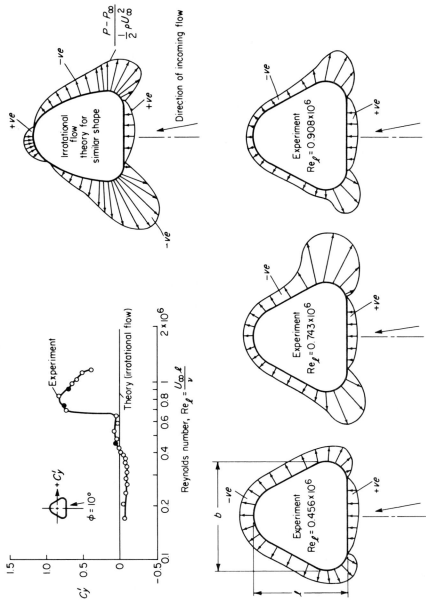

Fig. 8-42. Effect of Reynolds number on the side force and pressure distribution in a two-dimensional low-speed flow of air past a modified triangular cylinder at a flow incidence of 10 deg. (Adapted from Ref. 46.)

side force may be considerably decreased. Observe that the magnitude of the negative-pressure coefficient loop at the leading right corner is smaller at supercritical than at subcritical Reynolds number. A possible explanation can be found in the movement of the stagnation point which accompanies the change in the pressure distribution.

For the modified triangular cylinder shown in Fig. 8-42, very little side force is developed at the subcritical Reynolds number attained in the tests. At the supercritical Reynolds numbers attained, the side force is positive, and it is found to decrease in magnitude as the Reynolds number is increased. The experiments indicate that at subcritical Reynolds numbers the flow separates at both leading corners. (Observe large adverse pressure gradients at these corners in the irrotational flow field.) As a result, very small side force is produced. At supercritical Reynolds numbers the flow separates downstream of the leading corners and large negative-pressure coefficient loops are produced there. The pressure loop near the right leading edge is larger than near the left leading edge and thus a positive side force is developed. The size of the negative-pressure coefficient loop at the right leading edge is found to decrease with increasing Reynolds number and, as a result, the magnitude of the side force is found to decrease.

In addition to the Reynolds number and the shape of the body, the flow incidence also has a very important effect on the flow field (and therefore on the pressure distribution) in flows past noncircular cylinders.

From our discussion it follows that, in subsonic flows, the drag of a bluff body is usually quite large (large amount of energy is wasted on the eddies produced in the wake) and the form drag accounts for practically all the drag present. In subsonic flows past streamlined bodies, in which little or no separation occurs, the drag is relatively small, and is produced mainly by the shearing forces at the surface of the body (the skin-friction drag).

The tests show that while the drag coefficient of a circular disk placed normal to the stream at high Reynolds numbers is about 1.1, the drag coefficient of an ellipsoid (placed so that its major axis is in the direction of flow) at supercritical Reynolds numbers is less than 0.1 for elliptical sections having the length-to-diameter ratios of 2 or more. (Both of these drag coefficients are based on the projected area.) A thorough discussion of the experimental and theoretical results concerning the form and skin-friction drags of streamline bodies can be found in Ref. 5, pp. 505–526.

Although the importance of the Reynolds number has been stressed in our discussion, we should not overlook the effects that the free-stream turbulence and the wall roughness can have on the drag of objects.

In the case of flows involving liquids, the drag is affected by the presence of cavitation, or of the air-filled cavities, if any.

REFERENCES

1. H. L. Dryden, "Fifty Years of Boundary-Layer Theory and Experiment," *Science*, Vol. 121 (1955), pp. 375–380.

2. H. Schlichting, *Boundary Layer Theory*. 4th ed. (trans. by J. Kestin). New York: McGraw-Hill, 1960.

3. B. Thwaites (ed.), *Incompressible Aerodynamics*. Oxford: Clarendon, 1960.

4. M. J. Lightill, "Introduction to Boundary Layer Theory," in L. Rosenhead (ed.), *Laminar Boundary Layers*. Oxford: Clarendon, 1963, pp. 46–113.

5. S. Goldstein, *Modern Developments in Fluid Dynamics*. (First published in 1938.) New York: Dover, 1965.

6. H. Blasius, "Grenzschichten in Flüssigkeiten mit kleiner Reibung," *Z. Math. und Physik*, Vol. 56(1908). Also available as *N.A.C.A. TM* 1256.

7. L. Howarth, "On the Solution of the Laminar Boundary Layer Equations," *Proc. Roy. Soc.* (*London*) Vol. A164 (1938), p. 547.

8. W. J. Duncan, A. S. Thom, and A. D. Young, *Mechanics of Fluids*. London: Arnold, 1960.

9. H. W. Emmons, "The Laminar-Turbulent Transition in a Boundary Layer – Part I," *J. Aero. Sci.*, Vol. 18 (1951), pp. 490–498.

10. H. W. Emmons and A. E. Bryson, "The Laminar-Turbulent Transition in a Boundary Layer," *Proc. First U. S. National Congress of Applied Mechanics*, (1951), pp. 859–868.

11. C. Gazley, Jr., "Boundary-Layer Stability and Transition in Subsonic and Supersonic Flow," *J. Aero. Sci.*, Vol. 20, No. 1 (1953), pp. 19–28.

12. H. L. Dryden, "The Role of Transition from Laminar to Turbulent Flow in Fluid Mechanics," *Fluid Mechanics and Statistical Methods in Engineering*, Univ. of Pennsylvania Bicentennial Conference. Philadelphia: U. of Pennsylvania Press, 1941.

13. G. I. Taylor, "Statistical Theory of Turbulence: V—Effect of Turbulence on Boundary Layer, Theoretical Discussion of Relationship Between Scale of Turbulence and Critical Resistance of Spheres," *Proc. Roy. Soc.* (*London*) Vol. A-156 (1936), pp. 307–317.

14. G. B. Schubauer and H. K. Skramstad, "Laminar Boundary Layer Oscillations and Stability of Laminar Flow," *J. Aero. Sci.*, Vol. 14, No. 2 (1947), pp. 69–78.

15. A. M. O. Smith and N. Gamberoni, "Transition, Pressure Gradient and Stability Theory," *Douglas Aircraft Company Report* No. ES 26388 (1956).

16. G. B. Schubauer and P. S. Klebanoff, "Contributions on the Mechanics of Boundary-Layer Transition," *N.A.C.A. Report* 1289 (1955).

17. A. M. Kuethe, "Some Features of Boundary Layers and Transition to Turbulent Flow," *J. Aero. Sci.*, Vol. 23, No. 5 (1956), pp. 444–452, 506.

18. S. F. Shen, "Calculated Amplified Oscillations in Plane Poiseuille and Blasius Flows," *J. Aero. Sci.*, (Readers' Forum), Vol. 21 (1954), pp. 62–64.

19. C. C. Lin, "On the Stability of Two-Dimensional Parallel Flows," *Quart. Appl. Math.*, Vol. 3 (1945), pp. 117–142, 218–234, 277–301.

20. C. C. Lin, *The Theory of Hydrodynamic Stability*, London: Cambridge U. P., 1955.

21. M. Mitchner, "Propagation of Turbulence from an Instantaneous Point Disturbance," *J. Aero. Sci.*, (Readers' Forum), Vol. 21, No. 5 (1954), pp. 350–351.

22. H. L. Dryden, "Transition from Laminar to Turbulent Flow," in: *Turbulent Flows and Heat Transfer*, (C. C. Lin ed.), Vol. V of High Speed Aerodynamics and Jet Propulsion, Princeton: Princeton U. P., 1959, pp. 3–74.

23. H. W. Liepmann, "Investigation of Boundary Layer Transition on Concave Walls," *N.A.C.A. Wartime Report* W-87, 1945.

24. G. B. Schubauer and C. M. Tchen, "Turbulent Flow," in C. C. Lin, (ed.), *Turbulent Flows and Heat Transfer*, Vol. V of *High-Speed Aerodynamics and Jet Propulsion*. Princeton: Princeton U. P., 1959, pp. 75–195.

25. J. O. Hinze, "Turbulent Pipe Flow," in *The Mechanics of Turbulence*, International Symposium of the National Scientific Research Center, Marseille, 1961. New York: Gordon and Breach, 1964, pp. 129–165.

26. J. C. Rotta, "Incompressible Turbulent Boundary Layers," in *The Mechanics of Turbulence*, International Symposium of the National Scientific Research Center, Marseille, 1961. New York: Gordon and Breach, 1964, pp. 255–285.

27. F. H. Clauser, "The Behavior of Turbulent Boundary Layers," *Aerodynamics IV*. Baltimore, Md.: Johns Hopkins U. P.

28. L. Prandtl and O. G. Tietjens, *Applied Hydro- and Aeromechanics* (First published in 1934). New York: Dover, 1957.

29. A. A. Townsend, "Turbulence," Sec. 10 in: *Handbook of Fluid Dynamics*, (V. L. Streeter, ed.), New York: McGraw-Hill, 1961, pp. 10-1–10-33.

30. Theodor von Kármán, "Turbulence and Skin Friction," *Jour. Aero. Sci.*, Vol. 1, No. 1 (1934), pp. 1–20.

31. F. H. Clauser, "Turbulent Boundary Layers in Adverse Pressure Gradients," *Jour. Aero. Sci.*, Vol. 21 (1954), pp. 91–108.

32. L. F. Moody, "Friction Factors for Pipe Flow," *Trans. ASME*, Vol. 66 (1944), pp. 671–684.

33. E. M. Uram, "A Method of Calculating Velocity Distribution for Turbulent Boundary Layers in Adverse Pressure Distribution," *Jour. Aero/Space Sci.*, Vol. 27, No. 9 (1960), pp. 659–666.

34. H. Ludwieg and W. Tillmann, "Investigations of the Wall Shearing Stress in Turbulent Boundary Layers," N.A.C.A. TM 1285 (1950).

35. J. C. Rotta, "Recent Developments in Calculation Methods for Turbulent Boundary Layers with Pressure Gradients and Heat Transfer," ASME Paper No. 66–APM-F (1966).

36. F. H. Clauser, "The Turbulent Boundary Layer," in H. L. Dryden and Theodor von Kármán (eds.), *Advances in Applied Mechanics*. Vol. IV. New York: Academic, 1956.

37. F. Homann, "Einfluss grosser Zähigkeit bei Strömung um Zylinder," *Forschung auf dem Gebiete des Ingenieurwesens*, Vol. 7, No. 1 (1936), pp. 1–10.

38. A. Timme, "Über die Geschwindigkeitsverteilung in Wirbeln," *Ingenieur Archiv*, Vol. 25 (1957), pp. 205–225.

39. G. J. Richards, "An Experimental Investigation of the Wake Behind an Elliptic Cylinder," *Aero Res. Counc., London, Rep. and Memo.* 1590, (1933), Vol. 1 of Technical Report of ARC, (1934–35).

40. A. Roshko, "On the Development of Turbulent Wakes from Vortex Streets," *N.A.C.A. Report 1191* (1954).

41. R. Wille, "Karman Vortex Streets," in H. L. Dryden and Theodor von Kármán (eds.), *Advances in Applied Mechanics*. Vol. VI. New York: Academic, 1960, pp. 273–287.

42. A. W. Marris, "A Review on Vortex Streets, Periodic Wakes, and Induced Vibration Phenomena," *Trans. ASME*, Vol. 86D (*J. Basic Eng.*), 2 (June 1964), pp. 185–196.

43. Y. C. Fung, "Fluctuating Lift and Drag Acting on a Cylinder in a Flow at Supercritical Reynolds Number," *J. Aero Space Sciences*, Vol. 27, No. 11 (Nov. 1960), pp. 801–814.

44. L. V. Schmidt, "Measurements of Fluctuating Air Loads on a Circular Cylinder," *J. Aircraft* (AIAA), Vol. 2, No. 1 (January–February 1965), pp. 49–55.

45. "Definitions to be Used in the Description and Analysis of Drag" *J. Roy. Aeronaut. Soc.*, Vol. 62, No. 575 (1958), pp. 796–801.

46. E. C. Polhamus, E. W. Geller, and K. J. Grunwald, "Pressure and Force Characteristics of Noncircular Cylinders as Affected by Reynolds Number With a Method Included for Determining the Potential Flow About Arbitrary Shapes," *NASA Technical Report R-46* (1959).

47. J. H. Dwinnell, *Principles of Aerodynamics*. New York: McGraw-Hill, 1949.

48. S. F. Hoerner, *Fluid Dynamic Drag*, Midland Park, N.J.: published by the author (1958).

49. Theodor von Kármán, *Aerodynamics*, Ithaca, N.Y.: Cornell U. P., 1954.

50. A. E. von Doenhoff and N. Tetervin, "Determination of General Relations for the Behavior of Turbulent Boundary Layers," *N.A.C.A. Report 772* (1943).

51. G. L. Mellor and D. M. Gibson, "Equilibrium Turbulent Boundary Layers," *J. Fluid Mech.*, Vol. 24, part 2 (1966), pp. 225–253.

52. G. L. Mellor, "The Effects of Pressure Gradients on Turbulent Flow Near a Smooth Wall," *J. Fluid Mech.*, Vol. 24, part 2 (1966), pp. 255–274.

53. B. E. Launder, "An Improved Pohlhausen-Type Method of Calculating the Two-Dimensional Laminar Boundary Layer in a Pressure Gradient," *J. Heat Transfer, Trans. ASME*, Vol. 86, Series C, No. 3 (August 1964), pp. 360–364.

PROBLEMS

8-1. Calculate the values of $\dfrac{\delta^*}{x}\sqrt{\dfrac{Ux}{\nu}}, \dfrac{\theta}{x}\sqrt{\dfrac{Ux}{\nu}}, H, c_f\sqrt{\mathrm{Re}_x}$, and $C_F\sqrt{\mathrm{Re}_L}$ for the laminar incompressible boundary layer on a flat plate at zero incidence (that is, with no pressure gradient), corresponding to the following assumed velocity distributions:

(a) $\dfrac{u}{U} = A + B\left(\dfrac{y}{\delta}\right)$

(b) $\dfrac{u}{U} = A + B\left(\dfrac{y}{\delta}\right) + C\left(\dfrac{y}{\delta}\right)^2 + D\left(\dfrac{y}{\delta}\right)^3$

(c) $\dfrac{u}{U} = A + B\left(\dfrac{y}{\delta}\right) + C\left(\dfrac{y}{\delta}\right)^2 + D\left(\dfrac{y}{\delta}\right)^3 + E\left(\dfrac{y}{\delta}\right)^4$

(d) $\dfrac{u}{U} = A \sin\left(B\dfrac{y}{\delta}\right) + C \cos\left(D\dfrac{y}{\delta}\right)$

Investigate the necessary boundary conditions. Compare the calculated values with those given in Table 8-2. (Sec. 8-1.)

8-2. Plot Pohlhausen's velocity distribution u/U versus y/δ in the laminar incompressible boundary layer corresponding to $\Lambda > 12$, $\Lambda = 12$, $\Lambda = 0$, $\Lambda = -12$, and $\Lambda < -12$. What is the range to which the parameter Λ is restricted? Why? Compare the velocity distribution corresponding to $\Lambda = 0$ with the fourth-degree polynomial appearing in Table 8-2. (Sec. 8-1.)

8-3. Show that for an incompressible flow Eq. 8-38 for the resistance coefficient c_f is equivalent to the Blasius formula for the resistance coefficient f in a flow in smooth pipes, Eq. 8-27. (Sec. 8-3.)

8-4. Determine the momentum correction factor

$$\beta = \frac{\displaystyle\int_A V^2\, dA}{\bar{V}^2 A}$$

for a fully developed turbulent flow in a pipe of circular cross section. Assume the turbulent-velocity distribution given by Eq. 8-37. (Sec. 8-3.)

8-5. Solve Prob. 8-4 for a fully developed turbulent flow between parallel plates. (Sec. 8-3.)

8-6. Determine the kinetic-energy correction factor

$$\alpha = \frac{\displaystyle\int_A V^3\, dA}{\bar{V}^3 A}$$

for a fully developed turbulent flow in a pipe of circular cross section. Assume the turbulent-velocity distribution given by Eq. 8-37. (Sec. 8-3.)

8-7. Solve Prob. 8-6 for a fully developed turbulent flow between parallel plates. (Sec. 8-3.)

8-8. Calculate the drag offered by a thin smooth flat plate placed at zero incidence in a uniform stream flowing with a speed of $U = 4$ ft/sec if the density of the fluid $\rho = 62.4$ lbm/ft^3, the kinematic viscosity $\nu = 0.000012$ ft^2/sec, and the width and length of the plate are 4 and 6 ft respectively. Assume that the Reynolds number at which transition of the boundary layer occurs is $(\mathrm{Re}_x)_{\mathrm{trans}} = 10^6$. (Sec. 8-3.)

CHAPTER 9

Miscellaneous Topics

9-1. EFFECTS OF COMPRESSIBILITY ON FLUID FLOW

In this section we will consider briefly the expression for the speed of sound and, from purely phenomenological viewpoint, the continuous compression and expansion waves, and the shock waves which occur in supersonic compressible fluid flows. The simple analysis of the effect of change of the cross-sectional area on the subsonic and supersonic flows in ducts is left as a problem assignment (Prob. 9-2). So is the introductory analysis of an oblique shock wave (Prob. 9-3).

A flowing fluid is said to be "compressible" when the changes in the density of the fluid, brought about by the motion, are appreciable when compared with the density at rest. As was mentioned in Sec. 1-4, the parameter used in an analysis of the effects of compressibility on a fluid flow is the Mach number $M = V/a$, where V denotes the flow speed at a given location in the flow field and a the local speed of sound.

Expression for the Speed of Sound. Let us consider a plane sound wave propagating in a uniform fluid. The continuity equation, applied to the sound wave in the coordinate system moving with the wave, reads

$$\rho(-a) = (\rho + d\rho)(-a + du)$$

(We apply the continuity equation to the volume $\mathscr{V}$ fixed in space, see Fig. 9-1). We assume that the amplitude of sound wave is infinitesimal, so that it changes the flow speed of the fluid by $\dfrac{\partial u}{\partial x} dx = du$, the density by $\dfrac{\partial \rho}{\partial x} dx = d\rho$, and the pressure by $\dfrac{\partial P}{\partial x} dx = dP$. Neglecting the second-order quantity, the last equation results in the relation

$$\frac{d\rho}{\rho} = \frac{du}{a} \tag{9-1}$$

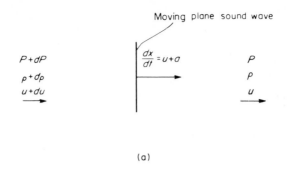

(a)

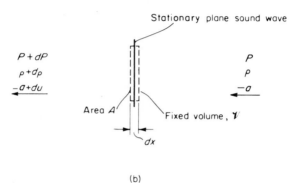

(b)

FIG. 9-1. Transformation from a "stationary" reference frame to the reference frame moving with the sound wave. (a) Flow in the "stationary" reference frame. (b) Flow in the reference frame of the sound wave.

The momentum equation applied to the fixed volume $\mathcal{V}$ reads

$$\rho(-a)\frac{\partial u}{\partial x} A \, dx = -[(P + dP) - P]A$$

which simplifies to

$$\rho a \, du = dP \qquad\qquad (9\text{-}2)$$

Combining Eqs. 9-1 and 9-2 gives the relation

$$a^2 = \frac{dP}{d\rho} = \frac{E}{\rho}$$

where E denotes the bulk modulus (see Sec. 1-5).

Newton, when applying the above equation, assumed that the process associated with the propagation of small disturbances (that is, sound waves) is isothermal. For such process, in an ideal gas

$$a^2 = \left(\frac{\partial P}{\partial \rho}\right)_T = \frac{P}{\rho} = RT$$

Experiments have shown that the value of the speed of sound calculated from this equation is too low. Laplace found the explanation for this discrepancy: Since the process associated with the propagation of sound waves is very fast, there is no time for heat transfer, and an adiabatic process should be assumed. For a small disturbance propagating in an ideal gas in a (reversible) adiabatic manner

$$a^2 = \left(\frac{\partial P}{\partial \rho}\right)_s = \gamma \frac{P}{\rho} = \gamma R T \tag{9-3}$$

and therefore the expression for the speed of sound in such gas is

$$a = \sqrt{\gamma \frac{P}{\rho}} = \sqrt{\gamma R T} \tag{9-3a}$$

Here $\gamma = c_P / c_V$ represents the ratio of the specific heats at constant pressure and at constant volume.

Table 9-1 gives the values of the speed of sound in the so-called "standard atmosphere" of the earth. Observe that these values are relatively large, being of the order of magnitude of 1,000 ft/sec.

TABLE 9-1
SPEED OF SOUND IN STANDARD ATMOSPHERE OF THE EARTH AT VARIOUS ELEVATIONS*

Elevation	Standard Temperature, °F	Speed of Sound, ft/sec
0	59.000	1,116.89
10,000	23.338	1,077.81
20,000	−12.323	1,037.26
30,000	−47.985	995.062
40,000	−69.700	968.465
50,000	−69.700	968.465

*Excerpts taken from "Standard Atmosphere—Tables and Data for Altitudes to 65,800 Feet," NACA Report 1235 (1955).

Spreading of Disturbances in Subsonic and Supersonic Flows; Mach Waves; Continuous Compression and Expansion Waves.[1] The importance of the flow Mach number on the manner in which a disturbing system can affect a fluid can best be illustrated by the way in which very weak compressive or expansive disturbances propagate in subsonic, sonic, and supersonic spatial flows.

The spreading of very weak compressive disturbances in a two-dimensional flow can be studied by considering the flows produced in a fluid, having a uniform thermodynamic state, by a relative motion at a constant speed of a semi-infinite wedge of infinitesimal angle at zero angle of attack. We stipulate that the wedge angle is infinitesimal, so that the changes in the thermodynamic properties of the fluid (brought about by the change in the direction of motion of the fluid particles flowing by)

[1] This part corresponds essentially to Sec. 1-3 of Ref. 1 by the author.

are infinitesimal, and, as a result, the disturbances produced propagate in the fluid with the speed of sound.

From our earlier discussion we are aware that the flow about this wedge of infinitesimal angle can be studied either in the reference frame of the fluid or in the reference frame of the wedge. In the reference frame of this elementary wedge, the flows appear as steady; in the reference frame of the fluid, unsteady.

If the flow speed relative to the elementary wedge is subsonic, then the infinitesimal disturbances produced by the wedge surfaces in the fluid surround the wedge and spread over the space. If the flow speed relative to the wedge is exactly equal to the speed of sound in the fluid, then the infinitesimal disturbances produced in the fluid by the leading edge of the wedge tend to form a plane front containing the leading edge of the wedge, which separates the undisturbed fluid ahead from the disturbed fluid behind it. If the flow relative to the wedge is supersonic, then the infinitesimal disturbances produced in the fluid by the leading edge of the wedge, as they move with a smaller speed than the speed of the wedge relative to the fluid, are overtaken by the wedge. The fronts of these disturbances form two inclined-plane surfaces, one above and one below the elementary wedge, known as the *Mach wedge*, which represents the boundary outside of which the fluid is not disturbed. The apex of this Mach wedge is formed by the leading edge of the wedge disturbing the fluid.

The different manners in which these infinitesimal disturbances spread are illustrated in Fig. 9-2. We consider that the wedge suddenly begins to move relative to the fluid with a constant velocity V, and we follow the motion of the compressive disturbances created in the fluid as time goes on. As the wedge begins to move relative to the fluid, an infinity of very weak compressive disturbances is produced all over the surface of the wedge. These disturbances move with the speed of sound a in the undisturbed fluid. For clarity, the positions of the disturbances and the wedge are indicated at only four equal time intervals Δt.

At the beginning of the motion, the wedge is at location 0. After a time interval Δt it is at location 1. By that time the disturbances have moved to a distance a/V times the distance $\Delta x = V\Delta t$ traveled by the wedge, away from the wedge surfaces at location 0. These disturbances are marked in Fig. 9-2 by the number 1. After the second time interval Δt, the wedge is at location 2. The compressive disturbances generated at location 0 have by now spread to a distance $2a/V$ times the distance Δx traveled by the wedge in a time interval Δt. The disturbances generated at location 1 have by now spread to a distance a/V times Δx from location 1. The positions of the disturbances after time interval $2\Delta t$ from the beginning of the motion are marked by the number 2. After the third time interval Δt, the wedge is at location 3. The corresponding positions

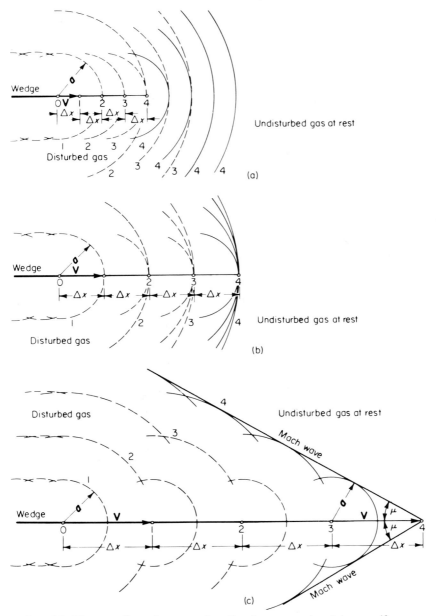

FIG. 9-2. The spreading of compressive disturbances produced in a uniform fluid by the motion at a constant speed of a wedge at zero angle of attack having an infinitesimal angle, studies in the reference frame of the undisturbed fluid. The initial position of the wedge, at the beginning of the motion, is denoted by the number 0. (a) Subsonic flow relative to the wedge. Flow Mach number $M = V/a = \frac{1}{2}$. (b) Sonic flow relative to the wedge. Flow Mach number $M = V/a = 1$. (c) Supersonic flow relative to the wedge. Flow Mach number $M = V/a = 2$.

of the disturbances are marked by the number 3. After the fourth time interval Δt, the wedge is at location 4, and the corresponding positions of the disturbances are marked by the number 4.

The angle μ, which the Mach wedge, representing the fronts of the advancing infinitesimal disturbances produced by the leading edge of the wedge in the supersonic flow (relative to the wedge), makes with the path of the wedge is related to the flow Mach number through the equation

$$\sin \mu = \frac{1}{M} \qquad (9\text{-}4)$$

This follows from inspection of Fig. 9-2. The angle μ is known as the *Mach angle*. The plane front which forms in the sonic flow represents the limiting form of the Mach wedge.

A flow pattern like the one illustrated in Fig. 9-2, but three-dimensional, would be produced in the fluid if it were disturbed not by a wedge but by a cone having infinitesimal angle. In such three-dimensional flow the shape of the spreading disturbances is spherical—not cylindrical, as in the two-dimensional case. In a supersonic flow in this case, the fronts of the infinitesimal disturbances produced by the apex of this elementary cone, which separate the disturbed flow from the undisturbed flow, form a *Mach cone* instead of a Mach wedge.

Figure 9-3 shows a Mach wedge and a Mach cone formed in a supersonic flow. A few streamlines are also indicated. The Mach wedge and the Mach cone represent the surfaces across which infinitesimal variation in the cross-sectional area of stream tubes, caused by the presence of the elementary wedge or cone, takes place in a supersonic flow.

The construction of the Mach wedge or the Mach cone produced by the leading edge of an elementary wedge or by the apex of an elementary cone in a constant-velocity supersonic flow relative to the wedge or the cone, studied in the reference frame of the wedge or the cone (in which it appears as a steady flow), is shown in Fig. 9-4. The numbers 1, 2, and 3 refer to the positions of the compressive disturbances after time intervals Δt, $2 \Delta t$, and $3 \Delta t$ from the beginning of the flow.

Instead of a supersonic flow about an elementary wedge we can consider such flow along a plane wall which turns by an infinitesimal angle, say angle $d\theta$, toward the flow deflecting the streamlines adjacent to the wall in the same direction, thus producing infinitesimal compressive disturbances whose (plane) front is shown in Fig. 9-5a. This front represents one-half of the Mach wedge shown in Fig. 9-3a. When the wall turns away from the flow by an infinitesimal angle $d\theta$, thus deflecting the streamlines adjacent to the wall away from the flow (as shown in Fig. 9-5b), the infinitesimal disturbances produced in a supersonic stream are expansive and their (plane) front again represents one-half of a Mach wedge.

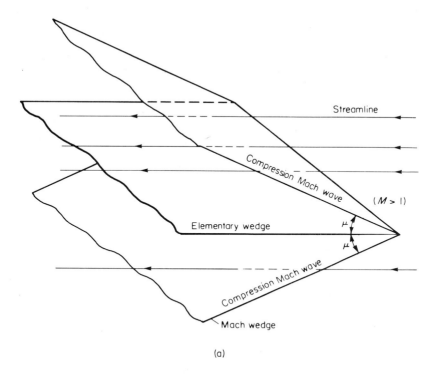

(a)

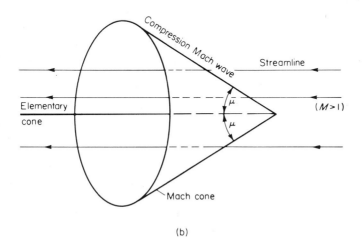

(b)

Fig. 9-3. (a) The Mach wedge and (b) the Mach cone.

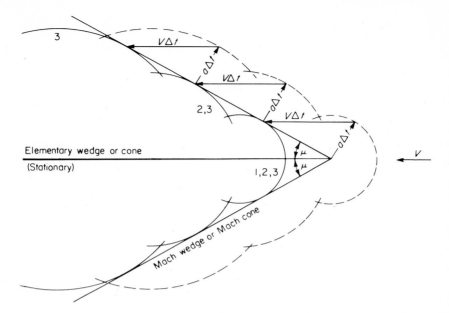

FIG. 9-4. Construction of the Mach wedge or the Mach cone in a constant-velocity supersonic flow relative to an elementary wedge or cone, studied in the reference frame of the wedge or cone disturbing the fluid.

In general, in a supersonic flow along a wall of an arbitrary shape, fronts of compressive or expansive infinitesimal disturbances form whenever the direction of the wall changes by an infinitesimal amount toward or away from the flow. The fronts of the advancing very weak compressive or expansive disturbances, across which the flow velocity and the thermodynamic properties of the fluid change by infinitesimal amounts (such as the Mach wedges and the Mach cones), are known as *Mach waves*.

A continuous wave, made up of an infinity of Mach waves, can be produced in a supersonic flow by a wall which curves in a continuous manner toward or away from the fluid flowing along it, as shown in Fig. 9-6. In this case each straight-line element of the wall surface perpendicular to the direction of the flow can be looked upon as a leading edge of an elementary wedge, and the curved section of the wall can be considered as being made up of an infinite number of such wedges stacked one on top of the other. From each leading edge of the elementary wedges emanates a Mach wave. Thus, as a result of the wall curvature, a *continuous compression wave* or a *continuous expansion wave*, made up of an infinity of Mach waves, is formed in the fluid across which the direction of the flow and the thermodynamic properties of the fluid are changed.

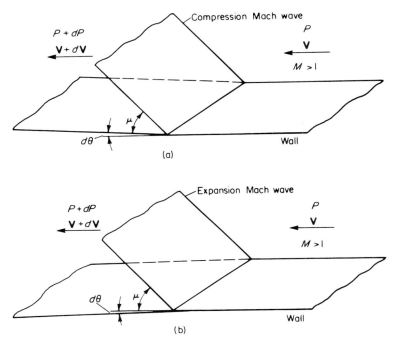

FIG. 9-5. Supersonic flow along a wall turning by an infinitesimal angle $d\theta$ (a) toward the flow, $dP > 0$, and (b) away from the flow, $dP < 0$.

The initial state of the gas, state 1, is changed to some state 2 by the compression wave and to some different state 3 by the expansion wave. The first Mach wave of a continuous wave is called the *head* and the last Mach wave is called the *tail*. The various states of the gas in Fig. 9-6 are denoted by numbers in circles to indicate that the states in question are uniform in the corresponding regions of flow. In the case of the compression wave, owing to the coalescence of the converging Mach waves, a thin region is formed across which the flow variables, such as the density and velocity of the gas, change by finite amounts. Such a region of flow is called a *shock wave*.

Figure 9-7 shows a photograph of a compression wave formed in a steady supersonic flow of air past a curved wall. It is similar to that illustrated in Fig. 9-6a except for reversed direction of flow. Note the shock wave formed by the coalescence of the Mach waves.

These phenomena occur also when the state of the fluid is initially nonuniform. The nonuniformity of the initial state will, in general, result in distortion of the shapes of the Mach waves.

Across the Mach waves we must expect discontinuities in the derivatives of some order of the flow speed and of the thermodynamic properties

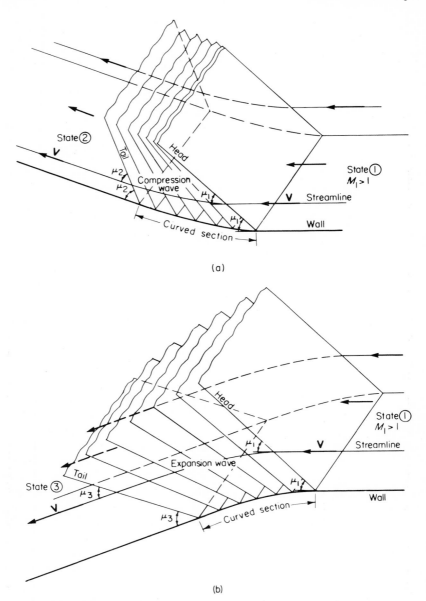

FIG. 9-6. Generation of continuous waves in a supersonic flow along a curved wall. (Only a few Mach waves are shown.) (a) Compression wave made up of an infinite number of compression Mach waves. (b) Expansion wave made up of an infinite number of expansion Mach waves.

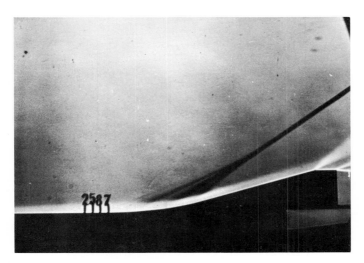

Fig. 9-7. A compression wave formed in a supersonic flow of
air past a curved wall. Upstream Mach number $M_1 = 2.75$.
(Courtesy of Flygtekniska Försökanstalten, Sweden.)

of the fluid. This possibility of the existence of discontinuous derivatives
along some surfaces in a region or regions of a flow field is characteristic
of the two- and three-dimensional flows which can be made steady by the
proper choice of the reference frame and are then supersonic, and of all,
one-dimensional, or spatial, and subsonic, or supersonic, unsteady flows
which cannot be made steady by a proper choice of the reference frame in
which they are studied. No such discontinuities in the derivatives of the
flow speed and of the thermodynamic properties are to be expected in any
region or regions of a steady subsonic flow field, because the whole field
(within the last Mach wave produced in the fluid which marks the establishment of a steady flow) has been affected by identical disturbances,
reaching, in general, different locations in the flow field from different
directions.

An unsteady flow can be created by a solid surface in motion relative
to the fluid. Unsteady flows which cannot be made steady by the proper
choice of a reference frame are also characterized by the existence of
continuous compression and expansion waves, formed by an infinite number of Mach waves which are created at the disturbing surface every time
the speed of this surface changes by an infinitesimal amount. These Mach
waves propagate with the (local) speed of sound relative to the fluid.

Figure 9-8 illustrates, on the distance-time planes, continuous one-
dimensional compression and expansion waves generated in a gas by a
piston accelerating in a duct. In the case of unsteady flows, time is one of
the independent variables of the flow.

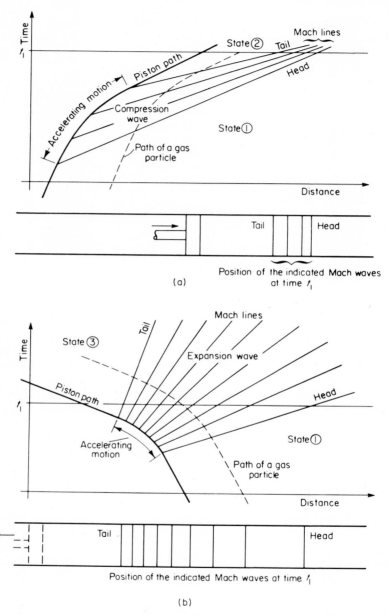

FIG. 9-8. (a) One-dimensional unsteady compression wave formed by a piston moving in a duct. (b) One-dimensional unsteady expansion wave formed by a piston moving in a duct.

The paths of the Mach waves in the so-called "physical planes," such as the (x, y) plane in the case of two-dimensional supersonic flow and the time-distance plane shown in Fig. 9-8, are known as *Mach lines*.

Shock Waves. As was mentioned earlier, the Mach waves of continuous compression waves coalesce and form shock waves. The thickness of a shock wave is very small. In monatomic gases it is of the order of a few mean free paths of a molecule. Across the shock wave the pressure, density, and temperature rise, while the flow speed relative to the shock wave decreases.

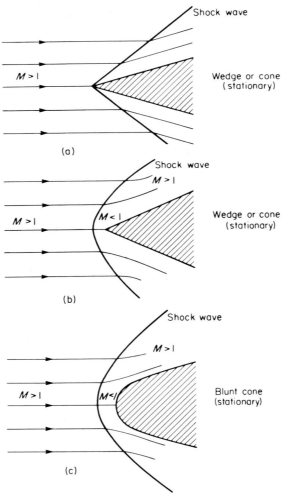

FIG. 9-9. Shock waves. (a) Attached shock wave. (b) Detached (bow) shock wave. (c) Detached (bow) shock wave in front of a blunt-nosed object.

In the case of a supersonic flow past a wedge (or a cone), the shock waves which form can be either attached to or detached from the wedge (or the cone), as shown in Fig. 9-9. The Mach number of the flow ahead of a stationary shock wave is always larger than unity (that is, the flow is supersonic relative to the shock wave). Downstream of the shock wave, the flow can be either supersonic or subsonic relative to the shock wave, depending on the inclination of the upstream flow velocity to the line normal to the shock wave. Downstream of a normal shock wave the flow is always subsonic relative to the shock wave. Whether the shock wave is attached to or detached from a wedge (or a sharp cone) depends on the wedge (or cone) angle and the Mach number of the undisturbed flow ahead. When the object past which the fluid flows is blunt-nosed (see Fig. 9-9c), the shock wave is always detached. The detached shock waves are usually called the *bow shock waves*.

Figure 9-10 shows a photograph of an attached shock wave in a supersonic (M_∞ = 2.0) flow of air past a 27-deg (sharp) cone.

Figure 9-11a shows the typical supersonic flow pattern past a sharp-nosed airfoil at zero angle of attack. The boundary layers and the wake are not shown. (In an actual flow, the flow pattern may deviate from the one shown as a result of interaction between the shock waves and the boundary layers near the trailing edge of the airfoil.) Figure 9-11b shows

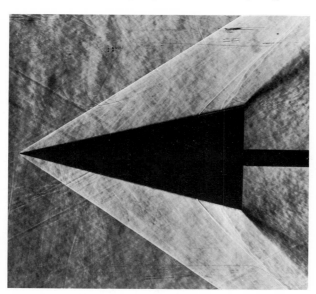

Fig. 9-10. Schlieren photograph of an attached shock wave in a supersonic (M_∞ = 2.0) flow of air past a 27-deg cone. (Courtesy of the U.S. Army Ballistic Research Laboratories, Aberdeen, Md.)

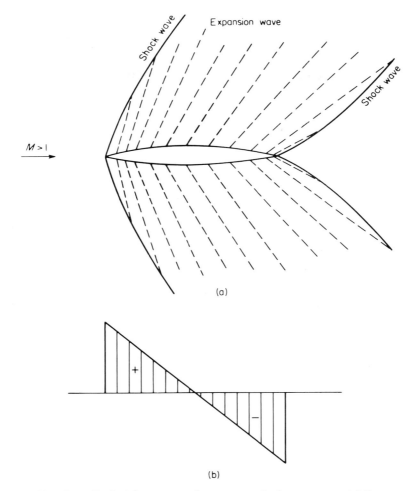

Fig. 9-11. Typical flow pattern in a supersonic flow past an airfoil having a sharp nose. (a) Shock waves and expansion waves. (b) Pressure distribution on the surface of the airfoil.

the pressure distribution on the upper and lower surfaces of the airfoil corresponding to the flow pattern shown in Fig. 9-11a. It should explain the existence of the wave drag in a supersonic flow.

9-2. HYDRAULIC TREATMENT OF LOSSES IN FLOWS IN DUCTS

By hydraulics we mean the experimental science dealing with incompressible fluid flows. In a narrow sense, we often mean by it the empirical science concerned mainly with the one-dimensional representation of incompressible flows of real fluids in ducts and in open channels. As such, hydraulics is concerned with the experimentally determined loss co- efficients.

In this section we will concern ourselves briefly with these loss co- efficients for a number of incompressible flows in ducts.

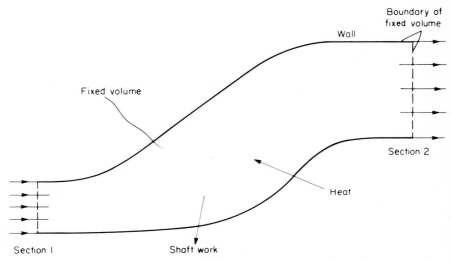

FIG. 9-12. Fixed volume whose boundary either follows fixed walls or intersects straight streamlines at right angle.

In the case when the boundary of a volume fixed in space (relative to an inertial system), when not following fixed walls, is perpendicular (at some sections 1 and 2) to straight and parallel streamlines of a steady flow (see Fig. 9-12), the energy equation (Eq. 4-14) becomes

$$\left(\frac{dQ}{dt}\right)_{1-2} = \left[\left(e + \alpha\,\frac{\overline{V}^2}{2} + \frac{P}{\rho} + g\zeta\right)_2 - \left(e + \alpha\,\frac{\overline{V}^2}{2} + \frac{P}{\rho} + g\zeta\right)_1\right]\rho_1\,\overline{V}_1 A_1$$
$$+ \left(\frac{dW_{\text{shaft}}}{dt}\right)_{1-2} \qquad (9-5)$$

where e denotes the average specific internal energy of the fluid, $\overline{V}$ denotes the average flow speed based on the rate of flow of the fluid, and α denotes the kinetic energy correction factor (see Eq. 5-22), because the continuity equation applied to sections 1 and 2 reads

$$\rho_1\,\overline{V}_1 A_1 = \rho_2\,\overline{V}_2 A_2$$

The term $(P/\rho + g\zeta)$ can be evaluated at any one location at sections 1 and 2, (see Eq. 5-20). As far as the kinetic energy correction factor α is concerned, for fully developed turbulent-velocity profiles its value is quite close to unity (see Probs. 8-6 and 8-7). For that reason this correction can be neglected in most engineering calculations; that is, $\alpha = 1$ can be assumed. (This is equivalent to the assumption that the flow is one-dimensional at the cross sections considered.) While for the laminar flow the value of α is relatively large, as a result of the fact that the flow speeds are usually very small in such flows, the effect of this correction is usually negligible.

Equation 9-5 can be rewritten in the form

$$q_{1\text{-}2} = \left(e + \alpha \frac{\overline{V}^2}{2} + \frac{P}{\rho} + g\zeta \right)_2 - \left(e + \alpha \frac{\overline{V}^2}{2} + \frac{P}{\rho} + g\zeta \right)_1 + (w_{\text{shaft}})_{1\text{-}2}$$

(9-6)

where the symbols $q_{1\text{-}2}$ and $(w_{\text{shaft}})_{1\text{-}2}$ represent the heat transferred to the fluid and the shaft work done by the fluid on the surroundings between sections 1 and 2 per unit mass of the fluid, respectively.

For incompressible fluid flows, the term $(e_2 - e_1 - q_{1\text{-}2})$ (which is different from zero in an incompressible flow of a real, i.e., viscous, fluid) is usually denoted by (gh_L), the factor h_L being known as the *head loss*, or *friction loss*. The term gh_L represents the work of viscous stresses inside the fixed volume which, in incompressible flows, results in an increase of the internal energy of the fluid (with accompanying rise in temperature) and, in general, in rejection of heat to the surroundings. (In compressible fluid flows, in addition, expansion of the fluid takes place as a result of viscous friction.) Since this internal energy rise is, in practical conditions, unrecoverable, the term gh_L represents a loss in the readily available mechanical energy of the fluid.

In hydraulics, the terms in Eq. 9-6 are usually expressed in units of height. For that reason, *for incompressible fluid flows*, this equation is usually written as

$$\left(\alpha \frac{\overline{V}^2}{2g} + \frac{P}{g\rho} + \zeta \right)_2 = \left(\alpha \frac{\overline{V}^2}{2g} + \frac{P}{g\rho} + \zeta \right)_1 - \left(\frac{w_{\text{shaft}}}{g} \right)_{1\text{-}2} - h_L \qquad (9\text{-}7)$$

For a one-dimensional flow $\alpha = 1$, $\overline{V} = V$, and the above equation becomes

$$\frac{V_2^2}{2g} + \frac{P_2}{g\rho} + \zeta_2 = \frac{V_1^2}{2g} + \frac{P_1}{g\rho} + \zeta_1 - \left(\frac{w_{\text{shaft}}}{g} \right)_{1\text{-}2} - h_L \qquad (9\text{-}8)$$

When no shaft work is involved, Eq. 9-8 reduces to

$$\frac{V_2^2}{2g} + \frac{P_2}{g\rho} + \zeta_2 = \frac{V_1^2}{2g} + \frac{P_1}{g\rho} + \zeta_1 - h_L \qquad (9\text{-}9)$$

Figure 9-13 illustrates the meaning of the terms appearing in Eq. 9-9 for an incompressible flow through a duct in which no shaft work is involved.

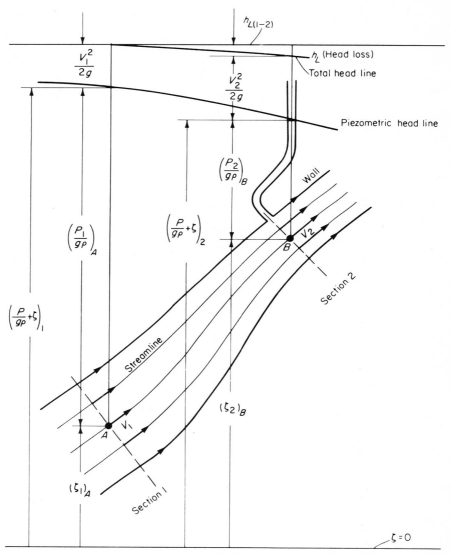

FIG. 9-13. One-dimensional approximation of an incompressible flow through a duct of varying cross section.

Head Loss. The head loss h_L can be considered to be made up of two losses: that resulting from the viscous friction along the walls over which the fluid flows, and that which occurs as a result of eddies produced by separation of flow or by secondary flow (such as exists in a flow through bent pipes, see Sec. 7-5). Separation of flow in a duct can occur whenever the cross section of the duct changes abruptly. The head loss that occurs as a result of eddies is known as the *form head loss*, $(h_L)_{form}$.

Denoting the head loss resulting from viscous friction by $(h_L)_{friction}$, we have

$$h_L = (h_L)_{friction} + (h_L)_{form} \tag{9-10}$$

The effect of viscous friction in an incompressible flow in a pipe was discussed in Sec. 7-4 for a (fully developed) laminar flow, and in Sec. 8-3 for a (fully developed) turbulent flow. For incompressible flows in ducts of constant cross-sectional area, the momentum equation for a volume fixed in space shown in Fig. 9-14 reads

$$A[(P_2 + g\rho\zeta_2) - (P_1 + g\rho\zeta_1)] + \tau_w CL = 0 \tag{9-11}$$

assuming constant shearing stress at the wall τ_w, because there is no change in the momentum of the flowing fluid between sections 1 and 2. In the above equation A denotes the cross-sectional area of the duct, and C

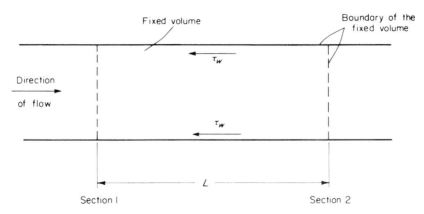

FIG. 9-14. Flow through a duct of constant cross section.

denotes the *wetted perimeter* [which is the outline of the duct, in the plane of the (normal) cross section, in contact with the fluid]. Introducing the so-called *hydraulic diameter* D_h defined by

$$D_h = \frac{4A}{C} \tag{9-12}$$

(observe that D_h is equal to the diameter d for a duct of circular cross section), we obtain the relation

$$\left(\frac{P_1}{g\rho} + \zeta_1\right) - \left(\frac{P_2}{g\rho} + \zeta_2\right) = \tau_w \frac{4L}{g\rho D_h}$$

As a result, the head loss resulting from viscous friction and the (mean) wall shearing stress, for flows in ducts of constant cross-sectional area, are related by

$$(h_L)_{\text{friction}} = \tau_w \frac{4L}{g\rho D_h}$$

$$= 4c_f' \frac{L}{D_h} \frac{\overline{V}^2}{2g}$$

$$= f \frac{L}{D_h} \frac{\overline{V}^2}{2g} \qquad (9\text{-}13)$$

The variation of the resistance coefficient f for a fully developed flow in smooth and rough pipes is given in Fig. 8-29. This diagram is approximately valid also for fully developed turbulent flows in ducts with annular cross sections. (For ducts with annular cross sections the ratio of the inner to outer diameter should not exceed 0.3 [16].)

As far as the form head loss is concerned, it is determined experimentally for each flow and duct configuration and is usually expressed in the form

$$(h_L)_{\text{form}} = K \frac{\overline{V}^2}{2g} \qquad (9\text{-}14)$$

where K denotes the *form-loss coefficient*. The form loss is often expressed as an excess loss over that which would exist if no separation of flow or no secondary flows were present in the duct.

The form-loss coefficient depends, in general, not only on the geometry of the duct, but also on the Reynolds number and the surface roughness. In most engineering estimates, for a turbulent flow, only the effect of the geometry of the duct need be considered.

For a flow in a duct possessing a sudden enlargement of its cross section, such as shown in Fig. 9-15, the expression for the form head loss can be easily calculated. Considering the flow to be one-dimensional (and incompressible), the momentum equation applied to the fixed volume

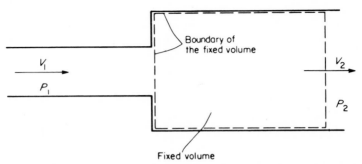

FIG. 9-15. Flow in a duct with a sudden enlargement of its cross section.

indicated in Fig. 9-15 reads

$$Q\rho(V_2 - V_1) = P_1 A_2 - P_2 A_2$$

Combining this equation with the equation

$$\frac{P_1}{g\rho} - \frac{P_2}{g\rho} = \frac{V_2^2}{2g} - \frac{V_1^2}{2g} + (h_L)_{form}$$

which corresponds to Eq. 9-9 with the terms representing the potential energy of gravitational attraction omitted, we obtain the relation

$$(h_L)_{SE} = \frac{(V_1 - V_2)^2}{2g} = \frac{V_1^2}{2g}\left(1 - \frac{A_1}{A_2}\right)^2 \qquad (9\text{-}15)$$

in view of the continuity equation

$$Q = V_1 A_1 = V_2 A_2$$

The symbol $(h_L)_{SE}$ denotes the form head loss corresponding to the sudden enlargement of cross section of a duct. Writing

$$(h_L)_{SE} = K_{SE}\frac{V_1^2}{2g} \qquad (9\text{-}16)$$

we find that the form-loss coefficient is in this case given by

$$K_{SE} = \left(1 - \frac{A_1}{A_2}\right)^2 \qquad (9\text{-}17)$$

where subscript SE refers to the sudden enlargement of cross section.

In the limiting case of $A_2 \rightarrow \infty$ (and $V_2 \rightarrow 0$) we obtain

$$(h_L)_{SE} \atop A_2 \rightarrow \infty = \frac{V_1^2}{2g} \qquad (9\text{-}18)$$

which indicates that, in a discharge of a stream into a large container, practically the whole kinetic energy of the stream becomes dissipated.

In low-speed (subsonic) *flows in ducts possessing a gradual enlargement of cross-sectional area* the flow speed decreases and the pressure increases along the duct. The ducts in which the pressure of the flowing fluid increases are known as *diffusers*. Diffusers are used to decrease the losses in ducts by decreasing the flow speed, and to produce efficient pressure recovery in flow systems. As long as the rate of increase of the cross-sectional area of a diffuser with distance is small enough (the adverse pressure gradient is then small) no separation of flow takes place, and the head loss h_L is small. Otherwise separation of flow occurs in the diffuser and large head loss results. Figure 9-16 shows the flow pattern in two-dimensional diffusers with small and large angles of inclination of the walls. The fluid is water, and the direction of streamlines was made visible by spraying aluminium powder on the water surface. For the (total) wedge angle of the diffuser of 13 deg no separation of flow was observed, while for the (total) wedge angle of 28 deg the flow was separated from

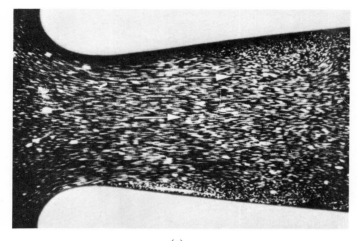

(a)

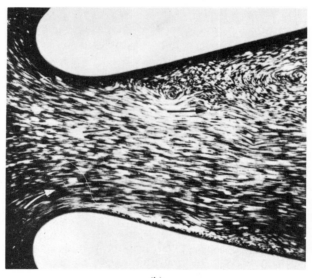

(b)

FIG. 9-16. Flow of water in two-dimensional diffusers.
(a) Diffuser wedge angle: 13 deg. Attached flow. (d)
Diffuser wedge angle: 28 deg. Separated flow. (The
first black arrow from the left should be inclined downward and not upward as shown.) (From Ref. 18 by
permission of Springer Verlag.)

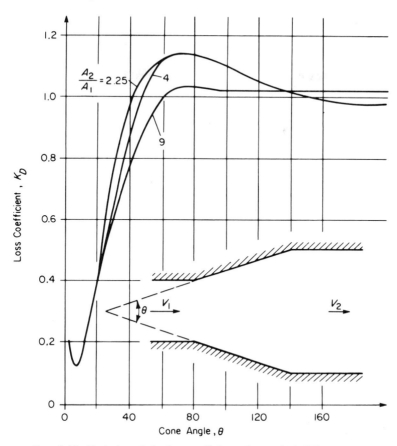

FIG. 9-17. Variation of the loss coefficient of a conical diffuser, with cone angle. (After A. H. Gibson, Ref. 21).

one wall of the diffuser. Figure 9-17 shows the variation of the (total) head-loss coefficient K_D of conical diffusers defined by

$$h_L = K_D \frac{(V_1 - V_2)^2}{2g} \tag{9-19}$$

with the cone angle θ as measured by Gibson [21]. The large values of the loss coefficient correspond to separated flow in the diffuser. The most efficient operation of a conical diffuser corresponds to $\theta \cong 7$ deg. Results of recent work on diffusers can be found in Refs. 56, 57, 58, 59, and 60.

In the case of a flow with a sudden contraction of its cross-sectional area, we can make an analysis similar to the one we made for a flow with a sudden expansion. However, as a result of formation of the so-called *vena contracta*, that is, contraction of the stream so that its cross-

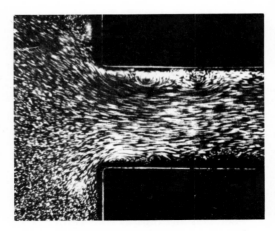

Fig. 9-18. Formation of vena contracta and
of separated flow region in case of a flow with
sudden contraction. (From Ref. 18 by permission of Springer Verlag.)

sectional area is smaller than that of the contracted duct, an unknown
contraction coefficient appears in the expression for the head loss. The
formation of the vena contracta can clearly be seen in Fig. 9-18. Applying
Eq. 9-15 between sections c and 2 shown in Fig. 9-19, we can write

$$h_L = \frac{V_c^2}{2g} \left(1 - \frac{A_c}{A_2}\right)^2$$

where A_c denotes the narrowest cross-sectional area of the stream. (The
area A_c does not include the cross-sectional area of the separated

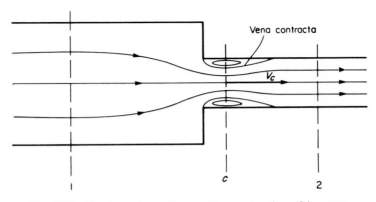

Fig. 9-19. Flow in a duct with a sudden contraction of its cross
section.

flow.) With the contraction coefficient C_c defined by

$$C_c = \frac{A_c}{A_2} \qquad (9\text{-}20)$$

we obtain

$$(h_L)_{SC} = \frac{V_2^2}{2g}\left(\frac{1}{C_c} - 1\right)^2 \qquad (9\text{-}21)$$

where the subscript SC refers to the sudden contraction, because $A_c V_c = A_2 V_2$. Writing

$$(h_L)_{SC} = K_{SC}\frac{V_2^2}{2g} \qquad (9\text{-}22)$$

we have

$$K_{SC} = \left(\frac{1}{C_c} - 1\right)^2 \qquad (9\text{-}23)$$

Table 9-2 gives the experimentally determined values of the contraction coefficient C_c and the loss coefficient K_{SC} for ducts with sharp sudden contractions as measured by Weisbach [19].

TABLE 9-2
VALUES OF THE CONTRACTION COEFFICIENT C_c AND THE LOSS COEFFICIENT K_{SC}

$\dfrac{A_2}{A_1}$	0	0.1	0.2	0.3	0.4	0.5	0.6	0.7	0.8	0.9	1.0
C_c	0.617	0.624	0.632	0.643	0.659	0.681	0.712	0.755	0.813	0.892	1.00
$K_{SC} = \left(\dfrac{1}{C_c} - 1\right)^2$	0.38	0.36	0.34	0.31	0.27	0.22	0.16	0.10	0.05	0.02	0

In our derivation of Eq. 9-21 we neglected the head loss in the acceleration zone (between sections 1 and c). This loss, however, is small compared to that in the deceleration zone (between sections c and 2). Also observe that, since a one-dimensional flow is assumed, the results should be more accurate for a turbulent than for a laminar flow.

For flows in 90-deg pipe bends, the (total) head loss (it represents the friction and form head losses) is a function of the ratio of the pipe diameter d to the mean radius of the bend R, the Reynolds number $\mathrm{Re}_d = \bar{V}d/\nu$, and the roughness of the wall. Table 9-3 gives approximate values for the loss coefficient K defined by

$$h_L = K\frac{\bar{V}^2}{2g} \qquad (9\text{-}24)$$

for smooth and rough pipes at $Re_d = 2.25 \times 10^5$ as given by Kaufmann [22]:

TABLE 9-3
HEAD-LOSS COEFFICIENT FOR 90° PIPE BENDS AT $Re_d = 2.25 \times 10^5$

R/d	1	2	4	6	10
Smooth pipe walls. . .	0.21	0.14	0.11	0.09	0.11
Rough pipe walls . . .	0.51	0.30	0.23	0.18	0.20

The results of a thorough investigation of head losses in turbulent flows in smooth pipe bends are described in Ref. 3. The results of experiments for laminar flow in pipe bends can be found in Ref. 23.

A collection of the experimentally determined values of the head loss coefficient, for pipes fitted with various types of valves and elbows can be found in Ref. 24.

In order to decrease the losses in elbows and to provide uniform flow downstream, turning vanes are often placed in them. Figure 9-20 shows a sketch of an elbow with turning vanes. Information concerning the shape of turning vanes for 90-deg elbows can be found in Ref. 25.

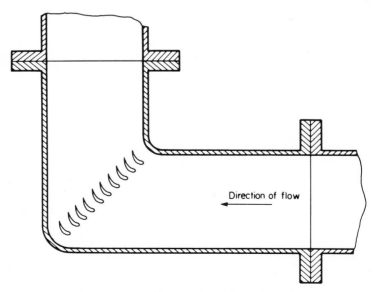

Direction of flow

FIG. 9-20. Turning vanes in a right-angle bend.

9-3. INTRODUCTION TO A STUDY OF FLOWS WITH FREE SURFACE

Surface Waves. In this discussion we will concern ourselves mainly with the speed of propagation of gravity waves of small amplitude.

The wave motion in a fluid is a time-dependent (unsteady) motion. We distinguish between two basic types of wave motion. One motion which repeats itself periodically in one location (the nodes in such motion are fixed parallel straight lines separated by a distance equal to one-half the wavelength), represents what is known as the *standing waves*. The other motion corresponds to the *progressive*, or *moving*, *waves*.

In our discussion we will concern ourselves only with the moving waves. The standing waves can be obtained by a superposition of two identical plane waves moving (with equal speed) in opposite directions.

The waves in liquids result from disturbances such as may be produced by moving objects, removal or addition of the fluid, wind action, etc. The forces at play in the wave motion are mainly the inertia and the gravity forces. (For waves of very small wavelengths, the surface tension forces must also be considered.)

By the *phase velocity*, or the *propagation velocity*, of the waves we mean the velocity with which the surface profile of the waves moves. This velocity has nothing to do with the velocity of the fluid elements. (When the amplitude of the waves is very small, the fluid elements move in closed elliptical paths whose size decreases rapidly with distance below the free surface.) In general, the phase velocity of waves depends on the wavelength λ. Such propagation of waves is known as *dispersive*. When the wavelength of small gravity waves is much larger than the (constant) depth of the fluid, the propagation of waves is not dispersive.

The assumptions which we shall make in our analysis of moving waves are as follows:

(a) The liquid, when not disturbed, is at rest and has a constant depth h.

(b) The field of gravitational attraction is constant.

(c) The wave motion is plane—i.e., all wave crests are parallel to each other and are perpendicular to the direction of propagation. (We shall take the x-axis to lie at the undisturbed surface of the liquid and to point in the direction of propagation of the waves. The y-axis shall point vertically downward, as shown in Fig. 9-21.)

(d) The fluid is perfect and the motion irrotational.

(e) The amplitude of the waves is small compared to the depth of the liquid.

The phase speed will be denoted by the letter c.

Since the motion is assumed to be irrotational, the velocity potential ϕ satisfies Laplace's equation

$$\frac{\partial^2 \phi}{\partial x^2} + \frac{\partial^2 \phi}{\partial y^2} = 0 \qquad (9\text{-}25)$$

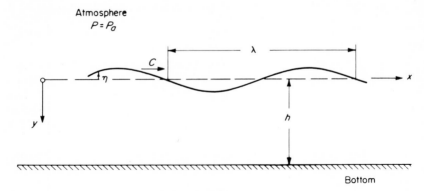

FIG. 9-21. Wave of a small amplitude.

The waves are assumed to propagate with the (phase) speed c in the direction of the positive x-axis. As a result, the flow variables are constant on lines $x = ct + $ const., and we can expect the velocity potential to be given by the equation

$$\phi(x, y, t) = Y(y) \sin \frac{2\pi(x - ct)}{\lambda} \qquad (9\text{-}26)$$

where Y is a function of the distance y only and λ denotes the wave length. Introducing Eq. 9-26 into Eq. 9-25 gives the relation

$$\frac{d^2 Y}{dy^2} - \left(\frac{2\pi}{\lambda}\right)^2 Y = 0 \qquad (9\text{-}27)$$

whose general solution is

$$Y = A e^{2\pi y/\lambda} + B e^{-2\pi y/\lambda}$$

where A and B are constants. Therefore

$$\phi(x, y, t) = (A e^{2\pi y/\lambda} + B e^{-2\pi y/\lambda}) \sin \frac{2\pi(x - ct)}{\lambda} \qquad (9\text{-}28)$$

The boundary condition that must be satisfied is that the flow velocity component in the y-direction is zero at the bottom. That is,

$$v = \frac{\partial \phi}{\partial y} = 0 \quad \text{at} \quad y = h$$

This condition results in the equation

$$\left[\frac{2\pi}{\lambda} (A e^{2\pi y/\lambda} - B e^{-2\pi y/\lambda}) \sin \frac{2\pi(x - ct)}{\lambda} \right]_{y=h} = 0$$

and therefore the constants A and B are related by

$$A e^{2\pi h/\lambda} = B e^{-2\pi h/\lambda} \qquad (9\text{-}29)$$

and Eq. 9-28 becomes

$$\phi(x, y, t) = A e^{2\pi h/\lambda} [e^{2\pi(y - h)/\lambda} + e^{-2\pi(y - h)/\lambda}] \sin \frac{2\pi(x - ct)}{\lambda}$$

Denoting $2Ae^{2\pi h/\lambda} = D$ we obtain,

$$\phi(x, y, t) = D \cosh\left[\frac{2\pi}{\lambda}(y - h)\right] \sin\frac{2\pi(x - ct)}{\lambda} \qquad (9\text{-}30)$$

To obtain the expression for the magnitude of the phase velocity we now make use of the Bernoulli-Euler equation written in the form

$$\frac{\partial\phi}{\partial t} + \frac{P}{\rho} + \frac{V^2}{2} - gy = C(t) \qquad (9\text{-}31)$$

(We have now $\zeta = -y$ and therefore the potential energy $\Omega = -gy +$ const.) The boundary condition that must be satisfied is

$$P = P_a = \text{const. at } y = -\eta$$

where η denotes the amplitude of the wave. For waves of small amplitude the flow speed is everywhere a small quantity, and the term $V^2/2$ can be considered negligible when compared with other terms. Hence Eq. 9-31 becomes

$$\frac{\partial\phi}{\partial t} + \frac{P}{\rho} - gy = 0$$

if we include the term $C(t)$ in the term $\partial\phi/\partial t$. Making use of the boundary condition we have, for $y = -\eta$,

$$\eta = -\left(\frac{1}{g}\frac{\partial\phi}{\partial t} + \frac{P_a}{g\rho}\right)_{y=-\eta} \qquad (9\text{-}32)$$

Since the values of the amplitude η are assumed to be small, we can write, as an approximation,

$$\eta = -\left(\frac{1}{g}\frac{\partial\phi}{\partial t} + \frac{P_a}{g\rho}\right)_{y=0} \qquad (9\text{-}33)$$

The vertical component of the flow speed at the surface is

$$v = \frac{\partial\phi}{\partial y} = -\frac{D\eta}{Dt} = -\left(\frac{\partial\eta}{\partial t} + u\frac{\partial\eta}{\partial x}\right) \approx -\frac{\partial\eta}{\partial t}$$

since both u and the slope $\partial\eta/\partial x$ are very small. Hence, as an approximation,

$$\frac{\partial\eta}{\partial t} = -\left(\frac{\partial\phi}{\partial y}\right)_{y=0} \qquad (9\text{-}34)$$

and, from Eq. 9-33, it follows that

$$\frac{1}{g}\left(\frac{\partial^2\phi}{\partial t^2}\right)_{y=0} = \left(\frac{\partial\phi}{\partial y}\right)_{y=0} \qquad (9\text{-}35)$$

because $P_a = \text{const.}$

Substituting Eq. 9-30 into Eq. 9-35 yields the following equation for the magnitude of the phase velocity:

$$c = \sqrt{\frac{g\lambda}{2\pi}\tanh\frac{2\pi h}{\lambda}} \qquad (9\text{-}36)$$

For waves of small amplitude whose wavelength λ is much larger than the depth, that is, for long waves of small amplitude in a shallow liquid, $h/\lambda \ll 1$ and $\tanh 2\pi h/\lambda \approx \dfrac{2\pi h}{\lambda}$. In such case

$$c = \sqrt{gh} \qquad (9\text{-}37)$$

For waves of small amplitude in a deep liquid, since $h/\lambda \gg 1$ for them, we have $\tanh 2\pi h/\lambda \approx 1$, and

$$c = \sqrt{\frac{1}{2\pi}} \sqrt{g\lambda} \qquad (9\text{-}38)$$

(see Prob. 2-5a). Observe that these waves are dispersive.

In conclusion, it should be added that the phase speed of waves of small wave lengths is markedly affected by the surface tension. The theory indicates that the magnitude of the phase velocity of such waves, in deep liquids, is given by

$$c = \sqrt{\frac{g\lambda}{2\pi} + 2\pi \frac{\sigma}{\lambda\rho}} \qquad (9\text{-}39)$$

where σ denotes the surface tension (see Prob. 2-5c). For waves of very small wavelengths,

$$c = \sqrt{2\pi \frac{\sigma}{\lambda\rho}} \qquad (9\text{-}40)$$

(see Prob. 2-5b). Such waves are called the *capillary waves*.

In the case in which the phase velocity of waves is dispersive, isolated groups of waves move with the so-called *group velocity*, which is different than the phase velocity. This is so because the individual waves either advance through or recede through the group. (Their amplitude decreases to zero at either end of the group.)

Steady Flow in Open Channels.   A liquid flowing in an open channel possesses a free surface. This fact distinguishes such flow from a flow in a pipe. At the free surface the prevailing pressure is that of the atmosphere with which the liquid is in contact. This atmospheric pressure is usually assumed to be constant.

Consider the propagation, in an open channel, of small gravity waves whose wavelength is much larger than the depth of the liquid. As we have shown, the speed of propagation (relative to the fluid) of such waves is $c = \sqrt{gh}$, where h denotes the depth of the liquid. When the flow speed $V < \sqrt{gh}$, that is, when the Froude number Fr $= V/\sqrt{gh} < 1$, then such waves can propagate both upstream and downstream in the channel. The speed of propagation of these waves, relative to the open channel, in the upstream direction is then $V - \sqrt{gh}$. It is equal to $V + \sqrt{gh}$ for such waves propagating in the downstream direction.

When the flow speed $V > \sqrt{gh}$, that is, when the Froude number $\text{Fr} = V/\sqrt{gh} > 1$, then the waves of the type under consideration can propagate only downstream. As we shall see, in such case the phenomenon known as the *hydraulic jump* may occur in the flow.

Observe that there is an analogy between the flow of a liquid in an open channel and the flow of a compressible fluid. The flow in an open channel with flow speeds $V < \sqrt{gh}$, that is, when $\text{Fr} = V/\sqrt{gh} < 1$, corresponds to the subsonic flow of a compressible fluid, while the open-channel flow with flow speeds $V > \sqrt{gh}$, that is, when $\text{Fr} = V/\sqrt{gh} > 1$, corresponds to the supersonic flow of a compressible fluid. The hydraulic jump corresponds to the shock wave.

Flow in Short Open-Channel Transitions. In this discussion we will analyze various types of flow which can occur in open channels in which change in the cross section of the channel takes place. This cross section will be assumed to be rectangular. Since our interest lies only in the analysis of the types of flow, we will neglect the viscous effects. In addition, we will assume that the flow is one-dimensional and horizontal, and that the curvatures of the streamlines, if different from zero, are small.

Consider a flow in an open channel having a contraction in both vertical and horizontal directions, as shown in Fig. 9-22. If the viscous effects are neglected—that is, if the flowing liquid is assumed to behave like a perfect fluid—the total head is constant and, if the atmospheric pressure is taken as zero, is equal to

$$H = \frac{V^2}{2g} + \frac{P}{g\rho} + \zeta$$

$$= \frac{V_1^2}{2g} + h_1 = \frac{V_2^2}{2g} + h_2 + \Delta\zeta_2 \qquad (9\text{-}41)$$

as shown in Fig. 9-22. This follows from Bernoulli's equation. Observe that the term $(h + P/g\rho)$ is constant along a normal to the direction of flow because the curvatures of the streamlines are assumed to be small. Making use of the continuity equation

$$Q = V_1 A_1 = V_2 A_2 \qquad (9\text{-}42)$$

where A_1 and A_2 denote the cross-sectional areas of the flowing fluid at sections 1 and 2, we can rewrite Eq. 9-41 in the form

$$\frac{Q^2}{2gA_1^2} + h_1 = \frac{Q^2}{2gA_2^2} + h_2 + \Delta\zeta_2 \qquad (9\text{-}43)$$

(Observe that, as a result of our assumption that the flow is one-dimensional, $V = \overline{V}$ where $\overline{V}$ denotes the mean flow speed.) Since A_1 and A_2 can be expressed in terms of the depth of the flowing liquid, h, (and of the width of the channel, W,) this equation allows us to solve a number of open-channel flow problems (under the assumptions made). For example,

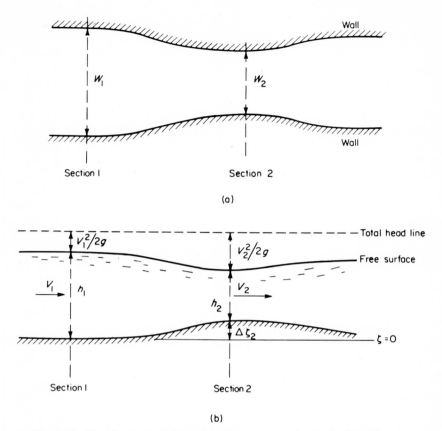

FIG. 9-22. Flow in an open channel having a contraction in horizontal and vertical directions. (a) Top view. (b) Side view.

if the volumetric rate of flow Q, the depth h_1, the widths of the channel W_1 and W_2, and the change in elevation $\Delta\zeta_2$ are known, the depth h_2 can be calculated.

To simplify the analysis of the possible flow types in an open channel, we shall limit our discussion to flows in open channels of constant width whose bottom boundary changes only in the vertical direction. We should keep in mind, however, that since in our analysis we assume the flow to be one-dimensional, the general flow characteristics that we shall determine are independent of the way in which the change is achieved in the flow depth (or the flow speed) in an open channel.

The term

$$H_0 = \frac{Q^2}{2gA^2} + h \qquad (9\text{-}44)$$

which first appeared in Eq. 9-43 is known as the *specific head*. For an open channel of rectangular cross section Eq. 9-44 can be written as

$$H_0 = \frac{Q^2}{2gW^2h^2} + h$$

$$= \frac{q^2}{2gh^2} + h \tag{9-45}$$

where $q = Q/W$. The specific head represents the difference between the total head H and the change in elevation of the bottom surface of the channel $\Delta \zeta$ relative to the reference plane $\zeta = 0$. It reaches a minimum when $dH_0/dh = 0$, or when

$$-\frac{Q^2}{gW^2h^3} + 1 = 0$$

Then

$$(h)_{H_0 \min} = h_c = \sqrt[3]{\frac{Q^2}{gW^2}} = \sqrt[3]{\frac{W^2h_c^2V^2}{gW^2}}$$

where h_c represents the so-called *critical depth*, from which it follows that

$$h_c = \frac{V^2}{g} \tag{9-46}$$

The flow speed

$$V = \sqrt{gh} = \sqrt{gh_c} = V_c \tag{9-47}$$

is known as the *critical flow speed*. It corresponds to the speed of propagation of a gravity wave of small amplitude whose wavelength is much larger than the depth of the fluid, in a fluid having critical depth. When the flow speed $V = V_c$, the Froude number $\mathrm{Fr} = V/\sqrt{gh} = 1$. The flow in an open channel in which the Froude number $\mathrm{Fr} < 1$ is known as the *subcritical, tranquil, or streaming flow*, while the flow in which $\mathrm{Fr} > 1$ is known as the *supercritical, rapid, or shooting flow*. The flow in an open channel may be wholly subcritical, wholly supercritical, or may include both the subcritical and the supercritical flow regions.

Figure 9-23 shows the specific-head-depth diagram which allows us to make an analysis of the flow pattern in a rectangular open channel of constant width. Observe that if the initial flow is subcritical (say it corresponds to point 1 in Fig. 9-23), an increase in the elevation of the bottom surface of the channel, since it results in a decrease of the specific head H_0, results in a decrease in depth and increase of the flow speed. For a given rate of flow and channel width, the depth of the liquid can be decreased in this way only to the minimum value h_c . When $h = h_c$, the flow becomes critical. If the elevation of the bottom surface of the channel were further increased, the rate of flow would be decreased because the specific head corresponding to the critical depth is the minimum

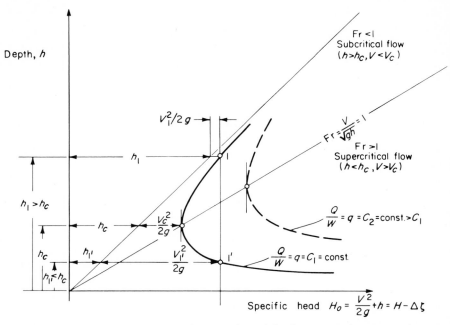

FIG. 9-23. Specific head diagram for open channels having rectangular cross section.

for the given rate of flow. Once the critical depth is reached and the elevation of the bottom surface of the channel decreases downstream of the section in which the flow is critical, the flow can become either subcritical or supercritical, depending on the downstream conditions. When the flow becomes supercritical—that is, when $h < h_c$ (and $V > V_c$)—the flow may experience a sudden increase in depth known as the *hydraulic jump* (downstream of which the flow is subcritical). If the initial flow is supercritical, an increase in the elevation of the bottom surface of the channel results in an increase in the depth of the liquid. If the depth at the highest elevation of the bottom surface of the channel is less than the critical depth, the flow is everywhere supercritical. When the critical depth is attained at the highest elevation, both supercritical and subcritical flows downstream of the region of maximum elevation are possible, the particular flow depending on the downstream conditions.

Figure 9-24 shows some of the observed types of flow in a rectangular open channel produced by a local rise in the elevation of the bottom surface. It is based on photographs in Ref. 26.

Hydraulic Jump. Observations indicate that in a fast-flowing liquid in an open channel, when the depth of the liquid is not very large, a sudden increase in the depth of the liquid may take place. The zone across which the depth of the liquid increases is known as the *hydraulic jump.*

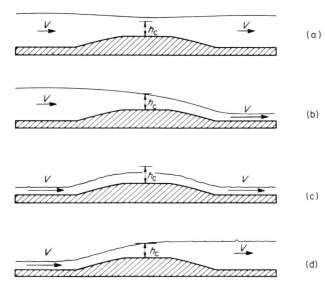

Fig. 9-24. Flow types in a rectangular open channel
produced by a local rise in the elevation of the bottom
surface. (a) Subcritical flow. (b) Subcritical flow upstream and supercritical flow downstream of the rise in
the elevation. (c) Supercritical flow. (d) Supercritical
flow upstream and subcritical flow downstream of the
rise in the elevation. (Based on photographs in
Ref. 26.)

Within the hydraulic jump the upper layer of the fluid tends to move upstream, but it is kept in position by the forces arising due to viscosity and
due to transport of momentum by turbulent mixing with the lower layer.

In this discussion we will consider the hydraulic jump in a channel
having a rectangular cross section. We will neglect the effect of viscous
friction at the walls of the channel. We will also assume that the flow is
one-dimensional and steady at section 1 upstream and section 2 downstream of the hydraulic jump, as shown in Fig. 9-25.

The momentum equation (Eq. 4-3) in the direction of flow, applied to
the volume fixed in space shown in Fig. 9-25, reads

$$\rho V_2^2 A_2 - \rho V_1^2 A_1 = \int_0^{h_1} g\rho h\, W dh - \int_0^{h_2} g\rho h\, W dh$$

$$= \int_{h_1}^0 g\rho(-\zeta + h_1) W(-d\zeta)$$

$$- \int_{h_2}^0 g\rho(-\zeta + h_2) W(-d\zeta)$$

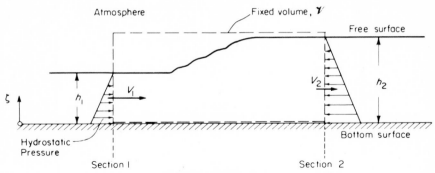

FIG. 9-25. Hydraulic jump.

or

$$\rho V_1 A_1 (V_2 - V_1) = g\rho W\left(\frac{h_1^2 - h_2^2}{2}\right) \tag{9-48}$$

where W denotes the width of the channel, since

$$V_1 A_1 = V_2 A_2 = Q$$

The areas A_1 and A_2 are related to the depths h_1 and h_2 by equations

$$A_1 = h_1 W \quad \text{and} \quad A_2 = h_2 W$$

Equation 9-48 can be rewritten in the form

$$\rho V_1^2 A_1\left(\frac{A_1}{A_2} - 1\right) = \frac{1}{2} g\rho W(h_1^2 - h_2^2)$$

or

$$V_1^2 h_1 (h_1 - h_2) = \frac{1}{2} gh_2(h_1^2 - h_2^2) \tag{9-49}$$

The possible solutions of Eq. 9-49 are:

$$h_1 = h_2 \tag{9-50}$$

in which case there is no hydraulic jump, and

$$h_2 = -\frac{1}{2} h_1 + \frac{1}{2} h_1 \sqrt{1 + 8 \, \text{Fr}_1^2} \tag{9-51}$$

where $\text{Fr}_1 = V_1/\sqrt{gh_1}$ denotes the Froude number corresponding to the upstream section 1.

The energy equation (Eq. 9-9) applied to the sections upstream and downstream of the hydraulic jump reads

$$\frac{V_1^2}{2} + \left(\frac{P_1}{\rho} + g\zeta_1\right) = \frac{V_2^2}{2} + \left(\frac{P_2}{\rho} + g\zeta_2\right) + gh_L$$

which can be rewritten in this case as

$$\frac{V_1^2}{2} + gh_1 = \frac{V_2^2}{2} + gh_2 + gh_L \tag{9-52}$$

because

$$\left(\frac{P_1}{\rho} + g\zeta_1\right) - \left(\frac{P_2}{\rho} + g\zeta_2\right) = g(h_1 - h_2)$$

the term $(P/\rho + g\zeta)$ being constant across sections 1 and 2. (See discussion in Sec. 5-3.)

Combining the continuity equation

$$V_2 = V_1 \frac{h_1}{h_2} \tag{9-53}$$

with Eq. 9-49 written in the form

$$V_1^2 = \frac{1}{2} g(h_1 + h_2) \frac{h_2}{h_1} \tag{9-54}$$

(because we consider the case when $h_1 \neq h_2$), gives the relation

$$\frac{V_1^2 - V_2^2}{g} = \frac{1}{2} (h_1 + h_2) \frac{(h_2^2 - h_1^2)}{h_1 h_2}$$

Equation 9-52 can be rewritten as

$$\frac{V_1^2 - V_2^2}{g} + 2 (h_1 - h_2) = 2h_L$$

Eliminating the term $(V_1^2 - V_2^2)/g$ from the last two equations gives the equation for the head loss:

$$h_L = \frac{(h_2 - h_1)^3}{4 h_1 h_2} \tag{9-55}$$

Since the energy dissipated h_L must be positive, $h_2 > h_1$. Therefore, in a hydraulic jump the depth downstream of the jump must always be larger than the depth ahead of it.

If we consider a very weak hydraulic jump, so that $h_2 = h_1 + \epsilon$ where ϵ is a very small number, then Eq. 9-51 simplifies to

$$h_1 \sqrt{1 + 8 \frac{V_1^2}{gh_1}} \approx 3h_1 + 2\epsilon$$

Squaring, we obtain

$$V_1^2 \approx gh_1 + \frac{3}{2} g\epsilon$$

or

$$V_1 \approx \sqrt{gh_1 + \frac{3}{2} g\epsilon}$$

For $\epsilon \to 0$ (note that $\epsilon > 0$), $V_2 \to V_1 = V$, and

$$V = \sqrt{gh} = V_c$$

This is the minimum flow speed required for the occurrence of a hydraulic jump (see Eq. 9-54). It is equal to the critical flow speed (which corresponds to the speed of propagation of gravity waves of small amplitude whose wavelengths are much larger than the depth of the fluid).

This result allows us to conclude that a hydraulic jump can occur in an open channel having rectangular cross section only if the flow speed is larger than critical—that is, when $V > V_c = \sqrt{gh}$.

Combining Eqs. 9-53 and 9-54 gives

$$V_2^2 = V_1^2 \left(\frac{h_1}{h_2}\right)^2 = \frac{1}{2} g(h_1 + h_2) \left(\frac{h_1}{h_2}\right)$$

and therefore also

$$V_1 V_2 = g \frac{h_1 + h_2}{2} \tag{9-56}$$

which indicates that the product of the flow speeds upstream and downstream of a hydraulic jump in an open channel having rectangular cross section is equal to the square of the critical speed corresponding to the mean depth $(h_1 + h_2)/2$.

Since the critical flow speed downstream of a hydraulic jump is $V_{c2} = \sqrt{gh_2}$, we have

$$\left(\frac{V_2}{V_{c2}}\right)^2 = \frac{1}{2} \left(\frac{h_1}{h_2} + 1\right) \left(\frac{h_1}{h_2}\right) \tag{9-57}$$

(from Eqs. 9-53 and 9-54), which is less than unity for $h_2 > h_1$. As a result, the flow speed downstream of a hydraulic jump in an open channel of rectangular cross section is smaller than the corresponding critical speed.

Empirical Formula for a Flow in an Open Channel. In an open channel both laminar and turbulent flow can occur, just as in the case of a flow in a pipe. However, laminar flow in open channels is very rare. It can sometimes be observed as water runs off in a thin film on a highway. It is then referred to as the "sheet flow." In most practical applications the flow in an open channel is turbulent and the surfaces over which the liquid (usually water) flows are quite rough. In addition, a flow in an open channel is seldom steady and uniform. (Such conditions are quite common in flows in pipes.) By a uniform flow we mean here a flow in which the flow velocity is constant along streamlines. [A turbulent flow is considered to be steady when the flow velocity averaged over an appreciable period of time is constant. (See discussion in Secs. 1-4 and 7-6.)]

Nevertheless, a steady-flow analysis allows us to solve a number of problems involving flows in open channels. The assumption that the flow is uniform is valid only in channels whose cross section is constant. In addition, it requires that there be no acceleration of the flowing fluid; the gravitational and frictional forces must be in equilibrium. In general, a uniform flow can be attained only in a long open channel having constant cross section.

In addition to assuming that the flow is steady and uniform, we will assume that the effect of surface tension, which is usually very small, can be neglected.

Referring to Fig. 9-26, since the atmospheric pressure is assumed to be constant and the pressure forces at the corresponding points in any two normal cross sections balance each other (the flow is assumed to be

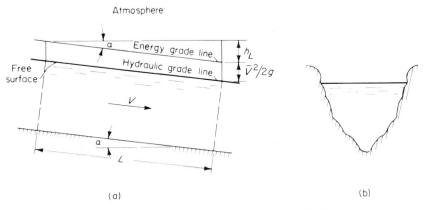

(a)   (b)

FIG. 9-26. Uniform flow in an open channel. (a) Longitudinal cross section. (b) Normal cross section.

uniform), the component of the gravitational force in the direction of flow and the frictional force must balance and we can write the equation

$$AL\rho g \sin \alpha = \tau_w \, CL$$

where C denotes the wetted wall perimeter and τ_w the mean wall shearing stress. Denoting $\sin \alpha$ by the letter S we obtain relation

$$\tau_w = \frac{A}{C} \, g\rho S$$

The ratio

$$\frac{A}{C} = m$$

is known as the *hydraulic mean depth*. (Sometimes it is called hydraulic radius and denoted by symbol R_h. However, such definition of hydraulic radius would be inconsistent with the definition of hydraulic diameter given by Eq. 9-12 for flows in closed ducts.) Thus we have

$$\tau_w = mg\rho S \tag{9-58}$$

In general,

$$\frac{\tau_w}{\frac{1}{2}\rho \bar{V}^2} = \mathscr{F}\left(\mathrm{Re}_m, \frac{k}{m}\right) \tag{9-59}$$

where k denotes the mean height of the roughness elements, $\overline{V} = Q/A$ denotes the mean flow speed, and $\text{Re}_m = \overline{V}m/\nu$ denotes the Reynolds number based on the hydraulic mean depth. As a result,

$$\frac{mgS}{\frac{1}{2}\,\overline{V}^2} = \mathscr{F}\left(\text{Re}_m, \frac{k}{m}\right)$$

or

$$\overline{V} = \sqrt{2mgS\;\mathscr{F}_1\!\left(\text{Re}_m, \frac{k}{m}\right)} \qquad (9\text{-}60)$$

where the functional relationship $\mathscr{F}_1 = 1/\mathscr{F}$. This last relation is usually written as

$$\overline{V} = C'\sqrt{Sm} \qquad (9\text{-}61)$$

which is known as the *Chézy formula* (so named after the French engineer A. de Chézy who derived it empirically in 1775), where

$$C' = \sqrt{2g\,\mathscr{F}_1\!\left(\text{Re}_m, \frac{k}{m}\right)} \qquad (9\text{-}62)$$

denotes the so-called *flow-resistance factor*, or the *Chézy coefficient*.

One of the most generally accepted expressions for the flow resistance factor C' is that formulated by the Irish engineer R. Manning in 1890. It reads

$$C' = \frac{1.49}{n}\,(m)^{1/6} \qquad (9\text{-}63)$$

where n denotes an empirically determined measure of roughness. With this coefficient the expression for the mean flow speed (in feet per second) becomes

$$\overline{V} = \frac{1.49}{n}\,(m)^{2/3}\,(S)^{1/2} \qquad (9\text{-}64)$$

Typical values of the coefficient n are given in Table 9-4.

TABLE 9-4
TYPICAL VALUES OF COEFFICIENT n

Channel Surface	Condition	n
Wood	Planed	0.010–0.012
	Unplaned	0.012–0.014
Concrete	Finished	0.011–0.013
	Unfinished	0.013–0.016
Brick	Good	0.013
	Rough	0.020
Riveted steel		0.015–0.020
Corrugated steel		0.022–0.026
Earth		0.020–0.035

9-4. BASIC MEASUREMENT TECHNIQUES

Wind Tunnels, Water Tunnels, and Water Towing Tanks. A wind
tunnel is an apparatus so designed that it can produce a uniform flow of
air in the so-called test section, thus allowing observation and measurement of the aerodynamic characteristics of various objects. Wind tunnels
can be designed for subsonic, transonic, and supersonic flow in the test
section. We shall limit our attention to subsonic wind tunnels designed
for continuous operation. These wind tunnels can be of the enclosed or
open type, depending on whether the test section is enclosed or open to
the atmosphere. In addition, wind tunnels can be of the closed-circuit or
recirculating type (in which case the tunnel has a continuous path for the
air), or of the open-circuit type (in which case the tunnel has no guided
return of air).

Figure 9-27 shows a sketch of an enclosed open-circuit subsonic wind
tunnel, while Fig. 9-28 shows a sketch of an enclosed recirculating sub-

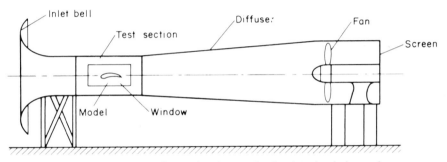

FIG. 9-27. Sketch of an enclosed open-circuit subsonic wind tunnel.

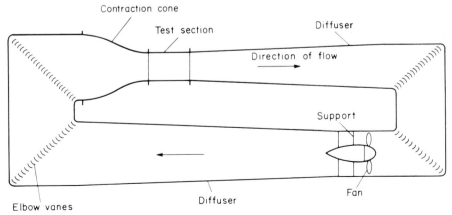

FIG. 9-28. Sketch of a closed recirculating single-return subsonic wind tunnel.

sonic wind tunnel. The motion of the air in the tunnel is produced by a
fan whose speed is controlled. Often a honeycomb or one or more screens
are provided ahead of the contraction cone (in case of a recirculating wind
tunnel) or at the entrance to the inlet bell (in case of an open-circuit wind
tunnel). Their object is to smooth the flow. In the inlet bell or in the
contraction cone the air is accelerated to the desired speed. In the test
section the flow speed is larger than anywhere else in the tunnel. The test
section is usually provided with a door through which models can be in-
serted, and one or more windows through which observation of flow can
be made using various optical systems. After passing through the test
section, the flow is decelerated in a diffuser. Turning vanes are provided
in the elbows to ensure minimal disturbance of the flow as a result of the
change in the direction of flow.

A water tunnel is similar in design to the enclosed recirculating wind
tunnel. The main difference between the two is that in a water tunnel
water instead of air is the flowing fluid. Figure 9-29 shows a sketch of a

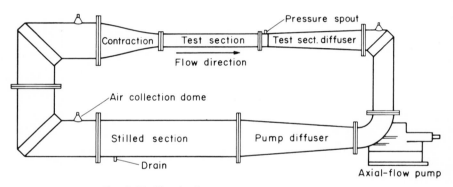

FIG. 9-29. Sketch of a water tunnel. (From Ref. 35.)

water tunnel. The pressure spout shown is used whenever the water in the
tunnel is pressurized to avoid cavitation in flow past objects. As a result
of the fact that the kinematic viscosity of water is very low (much lower
than for air—see Fig. 1-25), relatively low speed of the water in the test
section results in high values of the Reynolds number.

A towing tank is an open horizontal tank filled with water in which
models (usually of ships) are brought into motion relative to the water.
The models are suspended from a propelled carriage mounted on rails,
and are partially immersed in the water. The force necessary to tow the
model is registered by a dynamometer mounted on the carriage. The
towing tanks are often referred to as the "model basins."

Measurement of Flow Velocity. The basic instrument for the
measurement of the velocity of a flowing fluid is the *Pitot-static tube.*

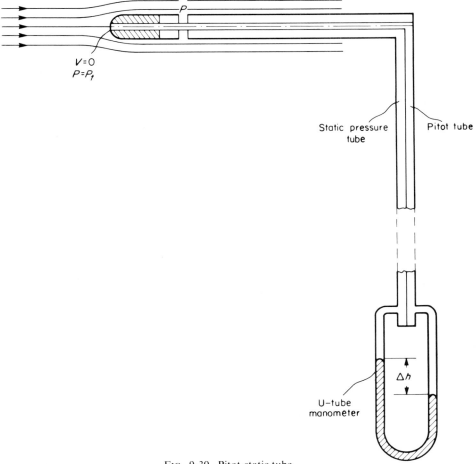

$$P$$

$$V=0$$
$$P=P_t$$

Static pressure tube

Pitot tube

$$\Delta h$$

U–tube manometer

FIG. 9-30. Pitot-static tube.

Such a tube is shown in Fig. 9-30. The Pitot-static tube is a combination of a *Pitot tube* (known also as the *impact tube*) which measures the local stagnation, or total pressure P_t (gage), and of a *static pressure tube* which measures the local static pressure P (gage). The Pitot-static tube measures the dynamic pressure P_d which, for an incompressible fluid flow, is given by

$$P_d = P_t - P = \frac{\rho V^2}{2}$$

Knowing the density of the flowing fluid, we can calculate the flow speed.

At low Reynolds numbers the reading of the Pitot tube (impact tube) must be corrected for the viscous effects. These effects depend on the Reynolds number and the geometry of the tube. A discussion of these effects can be found in Refs. 42 and 43.

At high Reynolds numbers the error that can occur in a Pitot-static tube arises from the fact that the rounded nose of the tube tends to produce, at the static pressure tube openings, flow speeds in excess of those prevailing in the stream. (See discussion in Sec. 5-3.) This effect is at least partially counterbalanced by the effect of the stem of the tube. For that reason, care should be exercised in the design of this instrument.

In addition, the Pitot-static tube gives a correct reading only if it is aligned with the direction of the incoming stream. The direction of a stream can be determined with the aid of a yawmeter. Figure 9-31 shows a few yawmeter designs. In the claw and the cylindrical types the direction of flow is found by rotating the yawmeter until the pressures registered by the two holes equalize. If the flow is three-dimensional, a sphere with four small holes is used in place of the cylinder (shown in Fig. 9-31c). The direction of flow can also be found with the aid of the hot-wire anemometer. In addition, the velocity of a fluid can sometimes be determined by injecting a dye (in case of liquids) or smoke (in case of gases) into the fluid.

The speed of the atmospheric air (or the wind speed) is usually

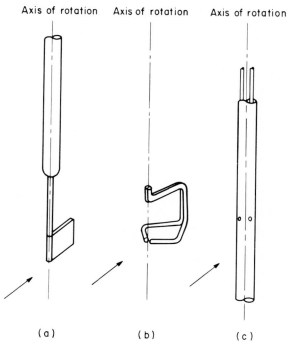

Axis of rotation   Axis of rotation   Axis of rotation

(a)   (b)   (c)

FIG. 9-31. Some types of a yawmeter. (a) Vane type, (b) claw type, (c) cylindrical type.

measured with the aid of a cup anemometer whose angular speed is correlated with the wind speed.

The turbulent flow velocity fluctuations are usually measured with the aid of the *hot-wire anemometer*. (The flow velocity can also be measured with the hot-wire anemometer.) The principle behind the operation of the hot-wire anemometer is that of heat transfer between a small object, in this case a very thin wire, and the surrounding flowing fluid. For the given physical configuration of the object, the rate of heat transfer depends on the physical properties of the flowing fluid and on the flow conditions. Any deviation from equilibrium conditions caused by a change in the flow conditions results in a change in the rate of heat transfer. The thin wire of the anemometer is heated electrically.

There are two basic types of hot-wire anemometer. In one, the current heating the wire is kept constant. As a result, a fluctuation in the flow speed results in a fluctuation of the temperature of the wire. In the other type the heating current is so controlled that even if fluctuations in the flow speed occur the temperature of the wire is always constant. The response of the wire may be its resistance, the heating current required to keep the temperature constant, or the voltage drop across the wire.

Measurement of Pressure. The static pressure in a flowing fluid can be measured with the aid of a U-tube manometer utilizing a static pressure probe or a wall tap. These methods are illustrated in Fig. 9-32. The effect of size and shape of a static pressure tap (or hole) on the error in static pressure measurement in an incompressible turbulent flow is discussed in Ref. 45. Sometimes when the pressure is large, we use a Bourdon gage in place of the U-tube. In addition, especially when the flow is unsteady, we often employ pressure-sensitive devices which are used to indicate pressures electronically. The most widely used such

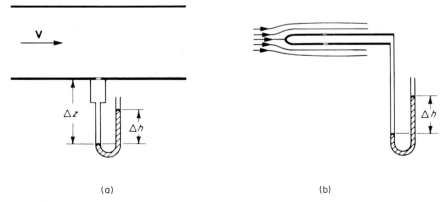

(a)   (b)

FIG. 9-32. Measurement of static pressure. (a) Wall tap, (b) static pressure tube.

device is one which utilizes the piezoelectric properties of certain crys- ᵧ
talline substances.

As mentioned earlier, the total pressure $\left[P_t = P + \dfrac{1}{2}(\rho V^2) \right.$ in an incompressible flow$\left.\right]$ can be measured with the aid of the Pitot tube (which is also known as the impact tube). At low Reynolds numbers the pressure coefficient $C_P = (P - P_\infty)\left/ \dfrac{1}{2}\rho U_\infty^2\right.$ of a Pitot tube differs from unity [42, 43].

Measurement of Temperature.   When the Mach number of a flow is very low (such flow can usually be considered as incompressible), there is little change in the temperature of the fluid as a result of flow.   In such a case the temperature of the fluid can be measured with ease using a thermometer of a thermocouple.   In high-speed (that is, high-Mach-number) flows, however, only the *stagnation* (or *total*) *temperature* can be measured directly, utilizing special thermocouple probes which decelerate the fluid to low flow speeds and which are shielded to ensure small radiation losses to the duct in which the fluid flows.

Measurement of the Rate of Flow.   The principal instruments used in measurement of the rate of fluid flow are the *Venturi meters, orifices, nozzles,* and *weirs.*

Figure 9-33 shows a sketch of a Venturi meter.   The equation for the volumetric rate of flow through a Venturi meter, for an incompressible flow, is

$$ Q = c_d \frac{A_2}{\sqrt{1 - \left(\dfrac{A_2}{A_1}\right)^2}} \sqrt{2\left[\left(\frac{P_1}{\rho} + g\zeta_1\right) - \left(\frac{P_2}{\rho} + g\zeta_2\right)\right]} \qquad (9\text{-}65) $$

where subscripts 1 and 2 refer to the cross sections 1 and 2 shown in Fig. 9-33, respectively.   The symbol c_d denotes the *discharge coefficient,* defined by

$$ c_d = \frac{Q_{\text{actual}}}{Q_{\text{theoretical}}} $$

The flow through a Venturi meter (or Venturi tube) has already been discussed in Chapter 5 (see Eq. 5-25 for the volumetric rate of flow through a horizontal Venturi meter).

For the Venturi meter employing a U-tube manometer, as shown in Fig. 9-33, the equation for the volumetric rate of flow (of an incompressible fluid) can be written in the form

$$ Q = c_d \frac{A_2}{\sqrt{1 - \left(\dfrac{A_2}{A_1}\right)^2}} \sqrt{2g\Delta h\left(\frac{S_{\text{man}}}{S_{\text{fluid}}} - 1\right)} \qquad (9\text{-}66) $$

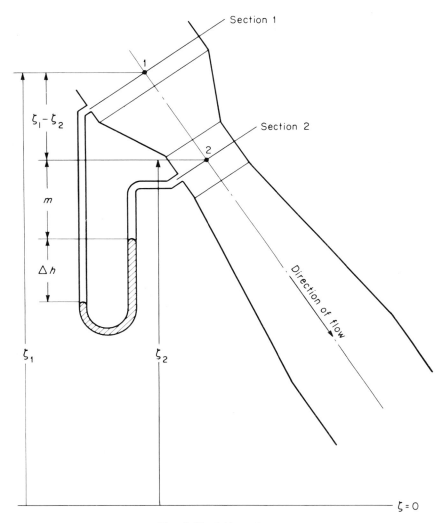

FIG. 9-33. A Venturi meter.

where Δh denotes the manometer reading, and s_{man} and s_{fluid} represent the specific gravities of the manometer fluid and of the flowing fluid, respectively. Derivation of this equation is left as a problem assignment. Observe that the rate of flow depends only on the manometer reading Δh and not on the angle of inclination of the Venturi meter.

Figure 9-34 shows the variation of the discharge coefficient, for the type of the Venturi meter shown, with the Reynolds number based on the pipe diameter.

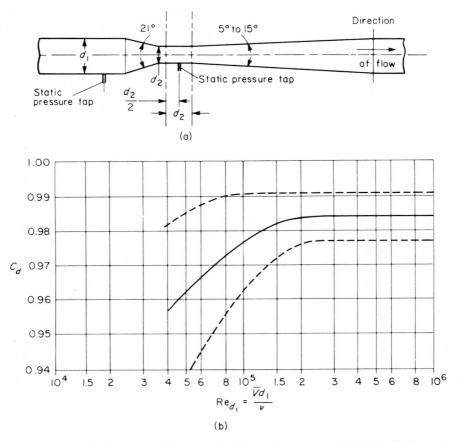

FIG. 9-34. Discharge coefficient c_d of a Venturi meter as a function of the Reynolds number. (a) General proportions of a standard Venturi meter. (b) Corresponding discharge coefficient for ratio $d_2/d_1 = 0.25$ to 0.75 in pipes of 2-in. inside diameter and larger. (Adapted from Ref. 48.)

An arrangement in which an orifice is used to measure the rate of flow of an incompressible fluid is shown in Fig. 9-35. The smallest cross-sectional area of the jet of the fluid occurs downstream of the orifice, as shown. The expression for the volumetric rate of flow in this case is

$$Q = c_d A_0 \sqrt{\frac{\dfrac{2(P_1 - P_2)}{\rho}}{1 - C_c^2 \left(\dfrac{A_0}{A_1}\right)^2}} \qquad (9\text{-}67)$$

where A_0 denotes the cross-sectional area of the orifice and $C_c = A_c/A_0$ denotes the contraction coefficient. (A_c denotes the smallest cross-

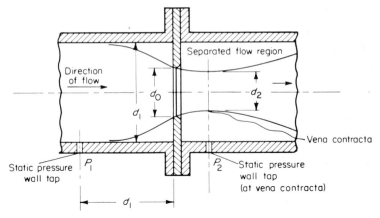

FIG. 9-35. Flow through a sharp-edged orifice in a pipe.

sectional area of the jet.)   The discharge coefficient $c_d = C_v C_c$ where $C_v = V_{2,\,actual} / V_{2,\,ideal}$ denotes the velocity coefficient.   Derivation of Eq. 9-67 is left as a problem assignment.

In the case of an incompressible flow through well-rounded nozzles, Eq. 9-67 is also applicable except that the contraction coefficient $C_c = 1$. Figure 9-36 shows a sketch of a nozzle in a pipe.

In case of a compressible flow through the Venturi meters, orifices, or nozzles, the formulas derived have to be multiplied by the so-called *expansion factor Y* which depends on the pressure ratio P_2/P_1.

The values of the discharge coefficients and of the expansion factors for standard ASME Venturi meters, orifices, and nozzles can be found in Ref. 48.

An accurate flow measurement can be attained only if the fluid enters the flow metering instrument with a fully developed turbulent velocity profile, free from large eddies. To ensure this, adequate lengths of straight pipe should precede and follow the flow metering instrument. The minimum lengths of such piping, for various arrangements of piping, can be

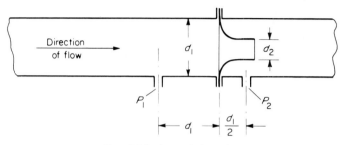

FIG. 9-36. A nozzle in a pipe.

found in Ref. 48. In a case when it is not possible to arrange the pipe to obtain the specified lengths of straight pipe, flow straighteners should be used.

A flow through a sharp-crested weir is illustrated in Fig. 9-37. The form of the relation between the rate of flow of the liquid over the weir

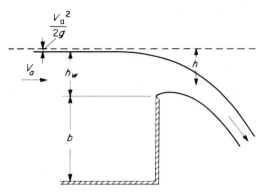

FIG. 9-37. Cross-sectional view of a flow over a sharp-crested weir.

and the surface elevation h_w can be derived as follows. Since in the free-falling jet the velocity component in the horizontal direction is proportional to $\sqrt{2gh}$, if the width of the weir crest is denoted by L (we assume the weir to be rectangular), then

$$Q \sim L \int \sqrt{2gh}\, dh = \frac{2}{3}\sqrt{2g}\, Lh^{3/2}$$

and we write

$$Q = c_d \frac{2}{3}\sqrt{2g}\, Lh_w^{3/2} \tag{9-68}$$

where, in general, the discharge coefficient depends on the ratio b/h_w as well as on the ratio L/h_w. For rectangular weirs often the Francis formula (applicable to a flow of water)

$$Q = 3.33 Lh_w^{3/2}\left[1 + 0.26\left(\frac{Lh_w}{A}\right)^2\right] \tag{9-69}$$

is used, where A denotes the cross-sectional area of the channel of approach [50]. The quantities in the above formula are in foot-second units. Observe that when the channel of approach is very large, in which case the term $\left(\dfrac{Lh_w}{A}\right)^2 \to 0$, the above equation reduces to

$$Q = 3.33 Lh_w^{3/2}$$

$$= 3.33 h_w^{5/2}\,\frac{L}{h_w}$$

which is in agreement with the general formula derived with the aid of dimensional analysis (Eq. 2-42a) which can be written in the form

$$Q = \frac{W}{g\rho} = g^{1/2} h_w^{5/2} \mathscr{F}\left(\frac{h_w}{L}\right)$$

Flow Visualization. The most important flow visualization techniques used in the study of flows of liquids are those utilizing dyes and hydrogen bubbles. In the study of flow of gases, the most important flow-visualization techniques are those utilizing smoke, those utilizing china clay or oil premixed with a fine powder (usually lampblack) applied to the surfaces along which fluid flows, and the optical (direct-shadow, schlieren, and interferometer) techniques.

An important requirement for a success of the dye- or smoke-injection techniques is a low speed and very small turbulence of the flowing fluid. Otherwise the dye or smoke streams quickly cease to be clearly defined. This requirement limits severely the Reynolds number of the flow studied.

The hydrogen-bubble technique is described in Ref. 55. It is restricted to water flowing at relatively low speeds.

In the surface oil-flow technique, the oil premixed with a fine powder is applied to the surface on which fluid flows. The pattern made by streaky deposits of the powder can provide information on the flow separation, boundary-layer transition, and on the direction of flow at the surface. A study of the flow of a thin film of oil on a solid surface by L. C. Squire is reported in Ref. 52. The conclusions drawn are that the oil does in fact follow the boundary-layer surface streamlines except near separation, and that the test results at low Reynolds number should be treated with caution because boundary-layer transition may be erroneously interpreted as separation.

The china-clay technique is used to locate the boundary-layer transition. In this technique the model is coated with a deposit of china clay (kaolin) which appears white when dry. This coating is subsequently sprayed with a volatile liquid of about the same refractive index; after spraying, the coating appears transparent. Usually methyl salicylate is used for this purpose. When the model is exposed to a flowing fluid, the liquid exposed to the turbulent boundary-layer flow evaporates quickly (sooner than that exposed to the laminar boundary-layer flow), and the coating in that flow region becomes white.

Very important techniques used in the study of high-speed flows of gases and in the study of heat transfer are the optical techniques. These techniques can be used whenever the phenomenon studied involves changes of the refractive index of the fluid. The refractive index may change across a flow field of a homogeneous fluid whenever the density of the fluid changes. The changes in the density of a fluid can be caused by nonuniformity of pressure, temperature, or both. For gases, the refractive index n can be related to the density ρ by the expression

$$n - 1 = k\rho$$

where k is a constant depending on the gas and on the wavelength of light. As a result, we can write

$$\frac{n - 1}{n_0 - 1} = \frac{\rho}{\rho_0}$$

where subscript 0 refers to a reference temperature and pressure.

   In a high-speed wind tunnel changes in the density of the air flowing past a two-dimensional model produce changes in the refractive index in planes parallel to the observation windows. If two beams of collimated light, initially in phase, are taken over separate paths of equal lengths such that one of them passes through the test section of the wind tunnel in which changes in the refractive index of the air occur, and subsequently are projected on a screen, patterns of varying intensity of illumination in the form of dark and light bands, known as *interference fringes*, are observed. This is so because, as a result of nonuniformity of density in the test section of the wind tunnel, the time at which a particular point of a light wave arrives on the screen changes in accordance with equation

$$c = \left(\frac{1}{n}\right) c_{\text{vacuum}}$$

where c is the speed of light. This interferometer technique, which allows us to measure the variation of the refracting index of the fluid in the test section, is due to L. Mach (1889). The interferometer can be so adjusted that the fringes represent approximately lines of constant density of the flowing gas. Figure 9-38 shows a sketch of an interferometer.

   The last equation indicates that the light rays passing through the test section of the wind tunnel will become deflected whenever there is a

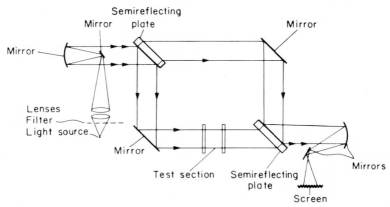

FIG. 9-38. Sketch of an interferometer.

gradient of the refracting index in the direction perpendicular to the direction of the rays. This deflection of light rays, which is a measure of the gradient of the density of the flowing fluid, is observed using the so-called schlieren technique (of A. Toepler, 1866). Figure 9-39 shows a sketch of the Toepler schlieren optical system.

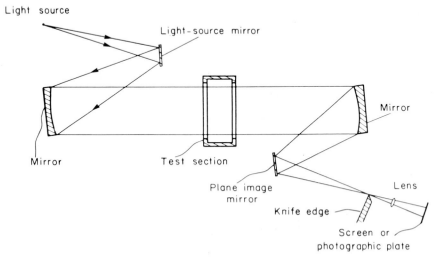

FIG. 9-39. Sketch of a Toepler schlieren optical system using two mirrors.

The variation of the gradient of the refractive index in the direction perpendicular to the direction of the light rays is observed, in the form of regions of high or low illumination, by the direct-shadow (or shadow-graph) method. Figure 9-40 shows a sketch of a direct-shadow optical system.

Figure 9-41 shows interferometer, schlieren, and direct-shadow photographs of a high-speed flow (at free-stream Mach number $M_\infty = 0.95$) of air past an airfoil. The interferometer fringes correspond closely

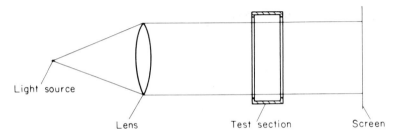

FIG. 9-40. Sketch of a direct-shadow optical system.

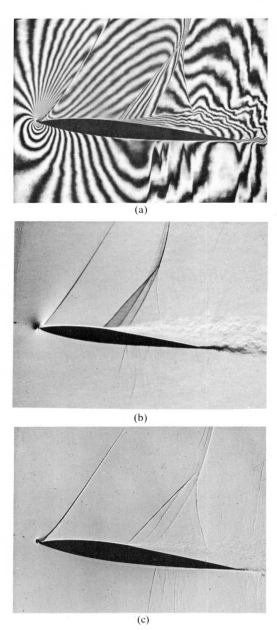

(a)

(b)

(c)

FIG. 9-41. High-speed flow past an airfoil. (a) Interferometer photograph. (b) Schlieren photograph. (c) Direct-shadow photograph. (Crown Copyright. Courtesy of the National Physical Laboratory, Teddington, Middlesex, England.)

to the lines of constant density of air. Observe the shock waves on the upper side of the airfoil and the shock-induced separation of flow. Observe also the weak shock waves on the bottom side of the airfoil.

REFERENCES

1. J. A. Owczarek, *Fundamentals of Gas Dynamics*. Scranton, Pa.: International Textbook, 1964.

2. J. K. Vennard, "One-Dimensional Flow," in V. L. Streeter (ed.), *Handbook of Fluid Dynamics*. New York: McGraw-Hill, 1961.

3. H. Ito, "Pressure Losses in Smooth Pipe Bends," *J. Basic Eng. (Trans. ASME)* Vol. 92, Ser. D, No. 1 (1959), pp. 131–143.

4. D. Haase, "Untersuchungen über Strömungen in 90°—Knien," *Z. VDI*, Vol. 97, No. 33 (1955), pp. 1209–1210.

5. W. Muller and H. Stratmann, "Friction Losses in Penstocks," *Sulzer Tech. Rev.*, Vol. 46, No. 3 (1964), pp. 111–120.

6. A. J. W. Smith, "The Flow and Pressure Losses in Smooth Pipe Bends of Constant Cross Section," *J. Roy. Aeron. Soc.*, Vol. 67, No. 631 (July, 1963), pp. 437–447.

7. A. E. Perry, "The Concept of Hydraulic Diameter," *ASME Paper* 64-WA/FE-31 (1964).

8. W. B. Hall, "Flow of a Compressible Fluid Through a Sudden Enlargement in a Pipe," *Proc. Inst. Mech. Engrs.* (Gt. Britain), Vol. 169, No. 49 (1955).

9. B. Mills and B. N. Cole, "Compressible Gas-Flow in Commercial Pipes," *Proc. Inst. Mech. Engrs.* (Gt. Britain), Vol. 171, No. 19 (1957).

10. W. G. Cornell, "Losses in Flow Normal to Plane Screens," *ASME Paper* 57-F-19 (1957).

11. W. J. D. Annand, "The Resistance to Air Flow of Wire Gauzes," *J. Roy. Aeron. Soc.*, Vol. 57 (March 1953), pp. 141–146.

12. P. Grootenhuis, "A Correlation of the Resistance to Air Flow of Wire Gauzes," *Proc. Inst. Mech. Engrs.* (Gt. Britain), Vol. 168, No. 34 (1954).

13. P. G. Morgan, "Fluid Flow Through Screens of Low Solidity," *J. Roy. Aeron. Soc.*, Vol. 66, No. 613 (January 1962), pp. 54–56.

14. F. O. Smetana, "On the Prediction of Gas Flow Rates Through Round Wire Screens," *J. Basic Eng. (Trans. ASME)*, Vol. 85, Ser. D., No. 4 (December 1963), pp. 620–624.

15. J. C. Hunsaker and B. G. Rightmire, *Engineering Applications of Fluid Mechanics*. New York: McGraw-Hill, 1947.

16. H. O. Croft, *Thermodynamics, Fluid Flow and Heat Transmission*. New York: McGraw-Hill, 1938.

17. R. J. S. Pigott, "Losses in Pipes and Fittings," *Trans. ASME*, vol. 79 (1957), pp. 1767–1783.

18. B. Eck, *Technische Strömungslehre*. 6th ed. Berlin: Springer, 1961.

19. J. Weisbach, *Die Experimentalhydraulik*, Freiburg: Engelhardt, 1855.

20. H. Frost, "The Compressible Discharge Coefficient of a Borda Pipe and Other Nozzles," *J. Roy. Aeron. Soc.*, Vol. 68, No. 641 (May 1964), pp. 346–349.

21. A. H. Gibson, *Hydraulics and Its Applications*. 5th ed. London: Constable, 1952.

22. W. Kaufmann, *Fluid Mechanics* (trans. by E. G. Chilton). New York: McGraw-Hill, 1963.

23. M. Adler, "Strömung in gekrümmten Rohren," *ZAMM*, Vol. 14 (1934), p. 257.

24. Crane Company, "Flow of Fluids," Tech. Paper 409 (May 1942).

25. A. R. Collar, "Some Experiments with Cascades of Aerofoils," *Aeron. Res. Counc., London, Rep. and Memo. No. 1768* (December 1936).

26. H. Rouse, *Elementary Mechanics of Fluids*, New York: Wiley, 1960.

27. W. J. Duncan, A. S. Thom, and A. D. Young, *Mechanics of Fluids*. London: Arnold, 1960.

28. H. M. Morris, *Applied Hydraulics in Engineering*, New York: Ronald, 1963.

29. T. Sarpkaya, "Oscillatory Gravity Waves in Flowing Water," *Trans. Am. Soc. Civil Eng.*, Vol. 122 (1957), pp. 564–586.

30. F. M. Henderson, *Open Channel Flow*. New York: Macmillan, 1966.

31. C. A. Coulson, *Waves*. 7th ed. New York: Interscience, 1961.

32. G. I. Taylor, "An Experimental Study of Standing Waves," *Proc. Roy. Soc.*, Ser. A, Vol. 218 (1953), pp. 44–59.

33. C. C. L. Sells, "Surface Tension Effect on Waves in a Liquid Layer," *Proc. Camb. Phil. Soc.*, Vol. 60, No. 3 (July 1964), pp. 657–666.

34. S. Goldstein, *Modern Developments in Fluid Dynamics*. Vol. 1. (First published in 1938.) New York: Dover, 1965.

35. J. E. Wolfe, Jr., "Design and Component Fabrication of a Closed Jet Water Tunnel and Performance of Plane-Walled, Two-Dimensional Diffusers and Conical Diffusers," M. Sc. Thesis, Lehigh University (1966).

36. R. C. Dean, Jr., *Aerodynamic Measurements*, M.I.T. Gas Turbine Laboratory (1953).

37. "Hot Wire Measurements of Air Velocity Direction, and Temperature," Tech. Memo. Bull. 94B, Cambridge, Mass.: Flow Corporation.

38. J. C. Laurence and L. G. Landes, "Applications of the Constant Temperature Hot-Wire Anemometer to the Study of Transient Flow," *Instruments*, Vol. 26, No. 12 (December 1953), pp. 1890–1894.

39. L. S. G. Kovásznay, "Turbulence Measurements," in R. W. Ladenburg et al. (eds.), *Physical Measurements in Gas Dynamics and Combustion*. Vol. IX of *High-Speed Aerodynamics and Jet Propulsion*. Princeton: Princeton U. P., 1954, pp. 213–285.

40. K. W. Todd, "Some Developments in Instrumentation for Air-Flow Analysis," *Proc. Inst. Mech. Eng. (Applied Mechanics)*, Vol. 161 (1949), pp. 213–226.

41. L. Rosenhead (ed.), *Laminar Boundary Layers*, Oxford: Clarendon, 1963.

42. C. W. Hurd, K. P. Chesky, and A. H. Shapiro, "Influence of Viscous Effects on Impact Tubes," *J. Appl. Mech.*, Vol. 20, No. 2 (June 1953), pp. 253–256.

43. F. A. Macmillan, "Viscous Effects on Pitot Tubes at Low Speeds," *J. Roy. Aero. Soc.*, Vol. 58, No. 524 (August 1954), pp. 570–572.

44. R. G. Folsom, "Review of the Pitot Tube," *Trans. ASME*, Vol. 78, No. 7 (October 1956), pp. 1447–1460.

45. R. Shaw, "Influence of Hole Dimensions on Static Pressure Measurements," *J. Fluid Mech.*, Vol. 7 (April 1960), pp. 550–564.

46. M. A. Rivas and A. H. Shapiro, "On the Theory of Discharge Coefficients for Rounded-Entrance Flowmeters and Venturis," *Trans. ASME*, Vol. 78, No. 3 (April 1956), pp. 489-497.

47. A. Lichtarowicz, R. K. Duggins, and E. Markland, "Discharge Coefficients for Incompressible Non-Cavitating Flow Through Long Orifices," *J. Mech. Eng. Sci.*, Vol. 7 (June 1965), pp. 210-219.

48. Flow Measurement, (Chapter 4), Supplement to ASME Power Test Codes, PTC 19.5; 4-1959. New York: American Society of Mechanical Engineers (1959).

49. F. V. A. Engel and W. Stainsby, "Discharge Coefficient Characteristics of Orifices," *Engineer*, Vol. 218, No. 5662 (July 1964), pp. 161-168.

50. R. A. Dodge and M. J. Thompson, *Fluid Mechanics*. New York: McGraw-Hill, 1937.

51. R. L. Maltby and R. F. Keating, "Flow Visualization in Low-Speed Wind Tunnels: Current British Practice," Royal Aircraft Establishment (Bedford, England), *Technical Note* No. AERO. 2715 (August 1960).

52. R. L. Maltby, "Flow Visualization in Wind Tunnels Using Indicators," NATO Advisory Group for Aeronautical Research and Development, *AGARDograph* 70 (April 1962).

53. D. W. Holder and R. J. North, "Schlieren Methods," National Physical Laboratory (England), *Notes on Applied Science*, No. 31 (1963).

54. D. Wilkie and S. A. Fisher, "Measurement of Temperature by Mach-Zender Interferometry," *Inst. of Mech. Engrs.* (Gt. Britain) *Proceedings 1963-1964*, Vol. 178, Part 1, No. 17.

55. F. A. Schraub, S. J. Kline, J. Henry, P. W. Runstadler, Jr., and A. Littell, "Use of Hydrogen Bubbles for Quantitative Determination of Time-Dependent Velocity Fields in Low-Speed Water Flows," ASME Paper No. 64-WA/FE-20 (1964).

56. G. N. Patterson, "Modern Diffuser Design," *Aircraft Eng.*, Vol. 10 (1938), pp. 267-273.

57. S. J. Kline, D. E. Abbott, and R. W. Fox, "Optimum Design of Straight-Walled Diffusers," *J. Basic Eng.*, Trans. *ASME*, Series D, Vol. 81 (1959), pp. 321-329.

58. B. A. Waitman, L. R. Reneau, and S. J. Kline, "Effects of Inlet Conditions on Performance of Two-Dimensional Diffusers," *J. Basic Eng.*, Trans. *ASME*, Series D, Vol 83 (1961), pp. 349-360.

59. L. R. Reneau, J. P. Johnston, and S. J. Kline, "Performance and Design of Straight, Two-Dimensional Diffusers," Report PD-8, Thermosciences Division, Dept. of Mechanical Engineering, Stanford University (1964).

60. D. O. Rockwell, "Flow in a Two-Dimensional Diffuser with Extraction of Fluid on the Diverging Walls," Ph.D. Thesis, Lehigh University (1967).

PROBLEMS

9-1. Calculate the values of the speed of sound (in feet per second) at a temperature of 70°F for the following gases: helium (γ = 5/3, mol. wt. 4.003), oxygen (γ = 7/5, mol. wt. 32.000), and ammonia (γ = 1.31, mol. wt. 17.032). (Sec. 9-1.)

9-2. Consider a steady one-dimensional flow of a perfect gas through a duct of variable cross-sectional area. Write the continuity and momentum equations (for a fixed volume) and, assuming that the flow is reversible adiabatic—that is, that the pressure and density changes are related by the equation $dP = a^2 d\rho$—derive relations

$$\frac{dA}{A} = (1 - M^2) \frac{dP}{\rho u^2}$$

and

$$\frac{dA}{A} = -(1 - M^2) \frac{du}{u}$$

where u is the flow speed, A the cross-sectional area of the duct, and $dA = \dfrac{\partial A}{\partial x} dx$,

$dP = \dfrac{\partial P}{\partial x} dx$, $du = \dfrac{\partial u}{\partial x} dx$. From these relations draw conclusions concerning the changes in pressure and in flow speed in convergent and in divergent ducts for a subsonic ($M < 1$) flow and for a supersonic ($M > 1$) flow. Neglect body forces such as the force of gravitational attraction. (Sec. 9-1.)

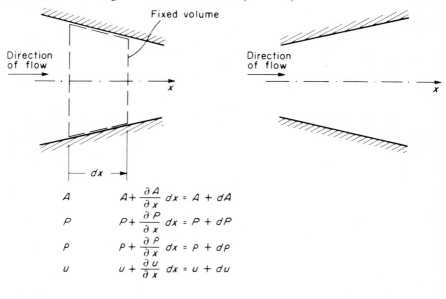

A	$A + \dfrac{\partial A}{\partial x} dx = A + dA$
P	$P + \dfrac{\partial P}{\partial x} dx = P + dP$
ρ	$\rho + \dfrac{\partial \rho}{\partial x} dx = \rho + d\rho$
u	$u + \dfrac{\partial u}{\partial x} dx = u + du$

Convergent Duct   PROB. 9-2   Divergent Duct

9-3. The continuity, momentum, and energy equations written for an infinitely thin fixed volume element whose bounding surface encloses an element of area of a stationary oblique shock wave in a perfect fluid relate the flow variables on the upstream and downstream sides of such shock wave. Write these equations and demonstrate that

$$\rho_1 V_{1n} = \rho_2 V_{2n}$$
$$V_{1t} = V_{2t}$$
$$h_{t1} = h_{t2}$$

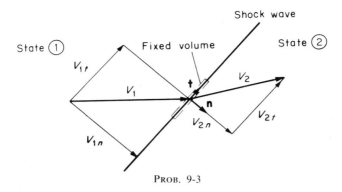

PROB. 9-3

where $h_t = h + \dfrac{V^2}{2}$ denotes the total enthalpy of the gas, subscript 1 refers to
the state of the gas upstream and subscript 2 to the state of the gas downstream of
the shock wave as shown in the sketch. The tangential unit vector **t** (shown in the
sketch) lies in the plane of the velocity vector $\mathbf{V}_1$ and the normal unit vector to
the shock wave **n**. (Sec. 9-1.)

9-4. Water flows at a rate of 1.5 ft³/sec in a horizontal smooth pipe 1,000 ft
long and having an inside diameter $d = 6$ in. What is the pressure loss (in lbf/in²)
in the pipe if the water temperature is 60°F and if $g = 32.174$ ft/sec²? What is the
corresponding temperature rise if the pipe is thermally insulated? The pressure in
the pipe is such that the density of water $\rho = 62.35$ lbm/ft³. (Sec. 9-2.)

9-5. Consider a steady flow of water in a pipe between two very large open
reservoirs. The pipe is 3,000 ft long and its inside diameter is 1 ft. If the difference
between the levels of the free surfaces in the two reservoirs is 100 ft, what is the
total head loss? (Sec. 9-2.)

9-6. Water at 60°F flows from a reservoir through a pipe having an inside

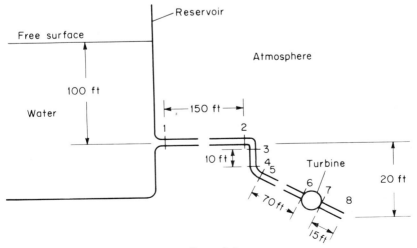

PROB. 9-6

diameter of 2 ft, and passes through a turbine as shown on the sketch. If the volumetric rate of flow is 60 ft³/sec, what is the power developed by the turbine (in horsepower)? Make a one-dimensional flow analysis. For the round entrance to the pipe from the reservoir take the loss coefficient $K_1 = 0.01$, for the 90 deg bend take $K_2 = 0.30$, and for the 45 deg bend take $K_3 = 0.10$. The pipe is made of concrete and the average height of the roughness elements is $k = 0.003$ ft. Assume turbine efficiency $\eta_T = 0.85$. (Sec. 9-2.)

9-7. Combustion gas at 815°F escapes from an oven through a stack 150 ft high and having an inside diameter of 18 in. The pressure in the oven, where the velocity of the air is very small, is approximately equal to the atmospheric pressure P_a at the inlet to the oven which is 14.7 lbf/in.². The temperature of the atmospheric air is 50°F. The entrance-loss coefficient (based on the average flow speed in the stack) is 0.25, while the resistance coefficient due to friction $f = 0.015$. What is the rate of mass flow of the gas through the stack in lbm/sec? Assume an incompressible flow. For the combustion gas take $R = 53.7$ lbf ft/lbm °R. For air $R = 53.5$ lbf ft/lbm °R. (Sec. 9-2.)

9-8. A pump transports water between two large reservoirs, as shown in the sketch, through a pipe having an inside diameter of 2.5 in. The rate of flow of water is 210 gallons per minute, the efficiency of the pump is 75 percent, and the loss coefficients are as follows:

$$K_{\text{inlet}} = 0.3, \quad K_{\text{elbow}} = 0.5, \quad K_{\text{valve}} = 0.7, \quad K_{\text{friction}} = f\,\frac{L}{d} = 0.018\,\frac{L}{d}$$

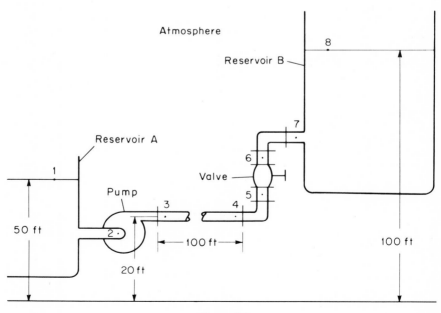

PROB. 9-8

The text should be consulted for the value of the loss coefficient at the sudden en-largement at the inlet to the reservoir *B*. Estimate the power required to drive the pump (in horsepower), and the pressure at the exit from the pump, P_3 in psig. (Sec. 9-3.)

9-9. Making use of Eq. 9-39 find the expression for the minimum wave-length and the minimum phase speed for waves in a deep liquid. (Observe that this limitation on the speed of propagation of waves should be kept in mind when making model experiments in which the effect of the waves is not negligible.) What are the values of the minimum wavelength and the minimum phase speed for water waves in contact with air if $t = 60°F$ and the pressure is atmospheric? (Sec. 9-3.)

9-10. Show that for standing deep water waves, whose wavelength is small compared to the depth, the period of oscillation $T = (2\pi\lambda/g)^{1/2}$. Assume that the standing waves are made by superposition of surface waves whose equations are

$$\eta_1 = A \sin \left[\frac{2\pi(x - ct)}{\lambda}\right]$$

and

$$\eta_2 = A \sin \left[\frac{2\pi(x + ct)}{\lambda}\right]$$

(Sec. 9-3.)

9-11. Starting with Eq. 9-30, derive the expression for the paths of the fluid particles in moving waves of small amplitude. In the derivation, approximate the values of x and y in the expressions for the velocity components $u = dx/dt$ and $v = dy/dt$ by their average values. (Sec. 9-3.)

9-12. Consider a flow of a liquid in an open channel of rectangular cross section. The channel, which is 4 ft wide at one section (section 1), contracts to a width of 3 ft at another section (section 2). The elevation of the bottom of the channel at section 2 is 0.25 ft higher than at section 1. Making a one-dimensional flow analysis and neglecting the viscous effects, determine the depth of the liquid at section 2 if the depth at section 1 is 3.5 ft and the rate of flow is 30 ft³/sec. Take $g = 32.17$ ft/sec². (Sec. 9-3.)

9-13. Water flows in an open channel having rectangular cross section whose width changes from W_1 at section 1 to W_2 at section 2 located downstream of section 1. If the head loss between sections 1 and 2 is h_L, show that the depth of the water at section 2, h_2, can be evaluated from equation

$$h^3 - \left(\frac{V_1^2}{2g} + h_1 - h_L\right)h_2^2 + \frac{V_1^2}{2g}\left(\frac{W_1 h_1}{W_2}\right)^2 = 0$$

(Sec. 9-3.)

9-14. By a *surge* we mean an unsteady motion of a liquid produced by a rapid increase in the rate of flow (and hence also in the depth of the liquid). Consider a flow of a liquid in an open channel having a rectangular cross section. The depth of the liquid is 3 ft and the flow speed is 5 ft/sec. What is the (absolute) speed of propagation of the surge produced by increasing abruptly the rate of inflow to the channel so that the depth of the liquid is increased to 7 ft? Also, what is the flow speed downstream of the surge? As shown in the accompanying sketch,

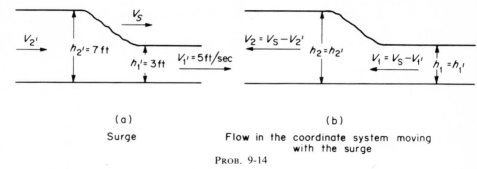

(a)

Surge

(b)

Flow in the coordinate system moving
with the surge

PROB. 9-14

make use of the Galilean transformation and solve the problem by considering
the flow in the coordinate system moving with the surge, so that the surge appears
as a stationary hydraulic jump. (Sec. 9-3.)

9-15. Consider a flow of a liquid in an open channel of rectangular cross
section whose slope changes abruptly from mild to steep, as shown in the sketch.

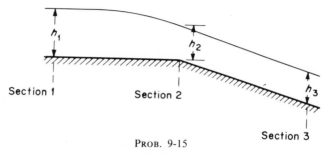

PROB. 9-15

If the flow is subcritical at section 1 and supercritical at section 3, then it is
critical at section 2 corresponding to the corner at which the slope of the channel
changes. If the volumetric rate of flow $Q = 150$ ft^3/sec and the (constant) width
of the channel $W = 5$ ft while the depth $h_1 = 4$ ft and depth $h_3 = 1.5$ ft, what is
the depth h_2? Take $g = 32.174$ ft/sec^2. (Sec. 9-3.)

9-16. Consider a flow of water in an open channel whose cross section is that
shown in the sketch. If the walls of the channel are made of brick (in good condi-

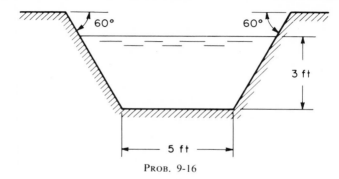

PROB. 9-16

tion) and the rate of flow is 100 ft^3/sec, what is the slope S ($= \sin \alpha$) of the channel. Take $g = 32.174$ ft/sec^2. (Sec. 9-3.)

9-17. A Pitot-static tube, such as shown in Fig. 9-30, is used to measure the flow speed in a liquid whose specific weight $\gamma_{fl} = 55$ lbf/ft^3. If the U-tube manometer reading $\Delta h = 4.3$ in. and the manometer fluid is mercury (take $\gamma_{Hg} = 846.3$ lbf/ft^3), what is the flow speed? $g = 32.17$ ft/sec^2. (Sec. 9-4.)

9-18. Static pressure is measured in a flowing fluid with the aid of a wall tap as shown in Fig. 9-32a. If $\Delta z = 14$ in., $\Delta h = 3.2$ in., the specific weight of the flowing fluid is $\gamma_{fl} = 62.4$ lbf/ft^3, while the specific weight of the manometer fluid is $\gamma_{man} = 848$ lbf/ft^3, what is the static pressure (gage) at the tap in lbf/in.^{2}? (Sec. 9-4.)

9-19. Derive Eq. 9-66 for the volumetric rate of flow of an incompressible fluid through a Venturi meter. (Sec. 9-4.)

9-20. A liquid having specific gravity $s_{fl} = 0.85$ flows through a Venturi meter as shown in Fig. 9-33. If the specific gravity of the manometer liquid is $s_{man} = 13.55$, the diameters of the meter are $d_1 = 8$ in., $d_2 = 4$ in., and if the manometer reading $\Delta h = 8$ in., what is the volumetric rate of flow of the liquid through the meter? Take the discharge coefficient $C_d = 0.985$. (Sec. 9-4.).

9-21. Derive Eq. 9-67 for the volumetric rate of flow of an incompressible fluid through an orifice in a pipe. (Sec. 9-4.)

Review of Vector Algebra and Calculus

A-1. VECTOR ALGEBRA

A vector represents a physical quantity that possesses magnitude, described by a positive real number, and direction. Two vectors are equal if they have the same direction and magnitude. Typical examples of vectors are displacement, velocity, and acceleration. Vectors are usually denoted by boldface symbols, by underlined symbols, or by arrows placed over the symbols. The magnitude of a vector $\mathbf{V}$ is denoted either by the corresponding lightface symbol V or as $|\mathbf{V}|$. Graphically, vectors are represented by arrows whose lengths are proportional to their magnitudes.

Like a scalar quantity, a vector is independent of the coordinate system in which it is studied. In this review of the basic formulas of vector algebra and calculus we will define various vector quantities in such a way as to clearly indicate their independence of the coordinate system used in the analysis. Subsequently, we will derive expressions that are valid in a rectangular cartesian coordinate system and in circular cylindrical and spherical coordinate systems. The notation of Gibbs [1] will be used throughout.

The *addition* of two vectors is accomplished by the parallelogram construction or by placing the origin of the second vector on the terminus of the first, and drawing the vector representing the sum from the origin of the first vector to the terminus of the second, because the vectors can be regarded as defining translations in space (velocity space in the case of acceleration). The addition of two vectors $\mathbf{V}$ and $\mathbf{U}$ is illustrated in Fig. A-1. Vectors obey the laws

$$\mathbf{V} + \mathbf{U} = \mathbf{U} + \mathbf{V} \quad \text{(commutative law)} \tag{A-1}$$

$$\mathbf{V} + (\mathbf{U} + \mathbf{W}) = (\mathbf{V} + \mathbf{U}) + \mathbf{W} \quad \text{(associative law)} \tag{A-2}$$

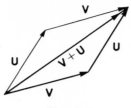

FIG. A-1

The *subtraction* of vectors is accomplished in the same manner as addition, because $-\mathbf{U}$ is a vector having the magnitude of vector $\mathbf{U}$ but an opposite direction (Fig. A-2).

FIG. A-2

Two vectors are said to be *collinear*, or *linearly dependent*, if they are parallel to the same line. Thus vectors $\mathbf{V}$ and $\mathbf{U}$ are collinear if there are two scalars c and d such that the sum

$$c\mathbf{V} + d\mathbf{U} = \mathbf{0} \tag{A-3}$$

Three vectors lying in one plane are said to be *coplanar*. A vector $\mathbf{V}$, coplanar with two noncollinear vectors $\mathbf{A}$ and $\mathbf{B}$, may be resolved into vectors parallel to these two vectors by constructing a parallelogram, as shown in Fig. A-3. Thus

$$\mathbf{V} = a\mathbf{A} + b\mathbf{B} = \mathbf{V}_A + \mathbf{V}_B \tag{A-4}$$

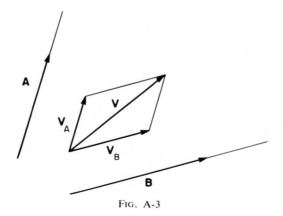

FIG. A-3

where a and b are the scalar ratios (they can be positive or negative) of the lengths of the vectors $\mathbf{V}_A$ and $\mathbf{V}_B$ to the lengths of the vectors $\mathbf{A}$ and $\mathbf{B}$, respectively.

Any vector in space may be resolved into three vectors parallel to any three noncoplanar vectors. Figure A-4 illustrates the resolution of a vector into vectors parallel to three orthogonal vectors.

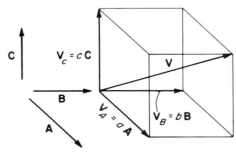

FIG. A-4

A study of vector quantities is usually made in an orthogonal co-ordinate system, say a system x_1, x_2, x_3. Any vector in space can be determined by three scalars representing the lengths of its orthogonal projections on the coordinate axes, taken with the proper sign. These positive or negative scalars are called the components of a vector. The components of a vector $\mathbf{V}$, in directions x_1, x_2, x_3, will be denoted as V_1, V_2, and V_3. A vector can be thought of, therefore, as a set of three numbers referring to certain coordinate axes. This way of looking at a vector is very useful in the development of tensor analysis.

The *magnitude* of a vector $\mathbf{V}$ can be determined from

$$V = |\mathbf{V}| = \sqrt{V_1^2 + V_2^2 + V_3^2} \qquad (A\text{-}5)$$

By a *unit vector* we mean a vector whose magnitude is unity. By a *null* or *zero vector*, $\mathbf{0}$, we mean a vector whose magnitude is zero.

The product of the components of a vector $\mathbf{V}$ and the corresponding unit vectors $\mathbf{u}_1, \mathbf{u}_2, \mathbf{u}_3$, along the three coordinate axes x_1, x_2, x_3, gives vectors $\mathbf{V}_1, \mathbf{V}_2, \mathbf{V}_3$, which are the *resolutes* of vector $\mathbf{V}$ whose sum is equal to $\mathbf{V}$. Thus,

$$V_1\mathbf{u}_1 + V_2\mathbf{u}_2 + V_3\mathbf{u}_3 = \mathbf{V}_1 + \mathbf{V}_2 + \mathbf{V}_3 = \mathbf{V} \qquad (A\text{-}6)$$

Base vectors are vectors (usually unit vectors) having the directions of the coordinate axes. Although the scalar and vector quantities are in-variant to the change of the coordinate system in which they are studied, the base vectors are not. Their directions change, in general, with the change of the coordinate system. When resolving a vector at a point in space in a certain coordinate system, we do so in the directions of the base vectors at that particular point.

Multiplication of a vector **V** *by a scalar b* results in a vector whose magnitude is equal to the product of the magnitude of vector **V** and scalar b, and whose direction is the same as or opposite to that of vector **V**, depending on whether $b < 0$. The following laws apply to the multiplication of vectors by scalars:

$$b\mathbf{V} = \mathbf{V}b \quad \text{(commutative law)} \tag{A-7}$$

$$c(b\mathbf{V}) = b(c\mathbf{V}) \quad \text{(associative law)} \tag{A-8}$$

$$(b + c)\mathbf{V} = b\mathbf{V} + c\mathbf{V} \quad \text{(distributive law)} \tag{A-9}$$

The *scalar product of two vectors* **V** and **U**, sometimes referred to as the *dot product*, or the inner product, is a scalar quantity defined by

$$\mathbf{V} \cdot \mathbf{U} = VU \cos \not{\triangleleft} (\mathbf{V}, \mathbf{U}) \tag{A-10}$$

When two vectors are perpendicular, their scalar product is equal to zero. From the definition of the scalar product, it follows that it is commutative; that is,

$$\mathbf{V} \cdot \mathbf{U} = \mathbf{U} \cdot \mathbf{V} \tag{A-11}$$

$U \cos \not{\triangleleft} (\mathbf{V}, \mathbf{U})$ represents the component of vector **U** in the direction of vector **V**, as shown in Fig. A-5. This component is positive for

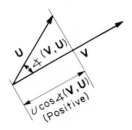

Fig. A-5

an acute angle and negative for an obtuse angle between vectors **V** and **U**. We can write

$$U \cos \not{\triangleleft} (\mathbf{V}, \mathbf{U}) = \text{comp}_\mathbf{V} \mathbf{U} \tag{A-12}$$

and

$$\text{comp}_\mathbf{V} \mathbf{U} = \frac{\mathbf{V} \cdot \mathbf{U}}{V} \tag{A-13}$$

Similarly,

$$\text{comp}_\mathbf{U} \mathbf{V} = \frac{\mathbf{V} \cdot \mathbf{U}}{U} \tag{A-14}$$

The scalar product of a vector by itself represents the square of the magnitude of the vector

$$\mathbf{V} \cdot \mathbf{V} = V^2 = |\mathbf{V}|^2 \tag{A-15}$$

It is readily seen, from the definition, that the scalar products are not associative:

$$(V \cdot U)W \neq V(U \cdot W) \qquad (A-16)$$

where $(V \cdot U)$ and $(U \cdot W)$ are scalars, but they are distributive

$$V \cdot (U + W) = V \cdot U + V \cdot W \qquad (A-17)$$

The *vector product of two vectors* V and U, sometimes referred to as the *cross product*, is a vector defined by

$$V \times U = [VU \sin \sphericalangle (V, U)] n_{VU} \qquad (A-18)$$

where n_{vu} is a unit vector normal to the plane in which the vectors lie, pointing in the direction of advancement of a right-handed screw rotated from vector V to vector U through the smaller angle (less than 180 deg) between the positive directions of the vectors, $\sphericalangle (V, U)$, as shown in Fig. A-6. The vectors V, U and n_{VU} form what is known as a *positive*

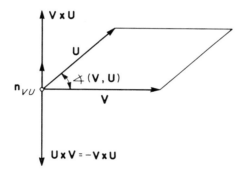

FIG. A-6

triple or a *right-handed system*. The vector product V × U represents the area of the parallelogram whose sides are vectors V and U.

From the definition of the vector product, it follows that it is not commutative. We have

$$V \times U = -U \times V \qquad (A-19)$$

The vector product of two parallel vectors vanishes. Hence

$$V \times V = 0$$

The vector product is not associative, because

$$W \times (V \times U) \neq (W \times V) \times U \qquad (A-20)$$

However, it is distributive, because

$$V \times (U + W) = V \times U + V \times W \qquad (A-21)$$

In vector analysis the following multiple products are of importance: $(V \times U) \cdot W$, known as the *scalar triple product*, and the *vector triple product* $(V \times U) \times W$.

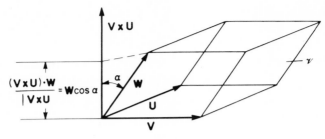

Fig. A-7

The scalar triple product $(V \times U) \cdot W$ is equal to the volume $\mathcal{V}$ of the parallelepiped formed from vectors V, U, and W, as shown in Fig. A-7. Since the volume of the parallelepiped is constant, regardless of whether the vectors V and U, U and W, or W and V, are considered as the base, the following relation holds:

$$(V \times U) \cdot W = (U \times W) \cdot V = (W \times V) \cdot U \qquad (A-22)$$

In view of the fact that the scalar product is commutative, the last relation is equivalent to

$$W \cdot (V \times U) = V \cdot (U \times W) = U \cdot (W \times V) \qquad (A-23)$$

The vector triple product $(V \times U) \times W$ can be written in the form

$$(V \times U) \times W = (W \cdot V)U - (W \cdot U)V \qquad (A-24)$$

In view of Eq. A-19, the vector triple product $W \times (V \times U)$ can be written as

$$W \times (V \times U) = (W \cdot U)V - (W \cdot V)U \qquad (A-25)$$

The proof of the above relations is as follows [2, 4]: Denote the vector triple product $W \times (V \times U)$ by F and the vector product $V \times U$ by A. Then

$$F = W \times (V \times U) = W \times A$$

as shown in Fig. A-8. Vector F lies in the plane containing vectors V and U, while vector A is perpendicular to this plane. In addition, vector F is

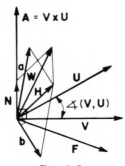

Fig. A-8

perpendicular to vectors **W** and **A**. If vector **W** were perpendicular to the plane containing vectors **V** and **U**, we would have **F = 0**. Resolving vector **W** into vectors **H** and **N** such that vector **N** is perpendicular to the plane containing vectors **V** and **U** while vector **H** lies in this plane, we have **N × (V × U) = 0**, while vector **H × (V × U) = F** is a vector perpendicular to vector **H**. Now, resolving vector **H** into vectors **a** and **b** such that vector **a** is perpendicular to vector **V** and vector **b** is perpendicular to vector **U**, we have

$$\mathbf{a} \times (\mathbf{V} \times \mathbf{U}) = \mathbf{u}_v aVU \sin \sphericalangle (\mathbf{V},\mathbf{U}) = VaU \cos \sphericalangle (\mathbf{a},\mathbf{U})$$
$$= \mathbf{V}(\mathbf{a} \cdot \mathbf{U}) = \mathbf{V}(\mathbf{H} \cdot \mathbf{U}) = \mathbf{V}(\mathbf{W} \cdot \mathbf{U})$$

where $\mathbf{u}_v$ is a unit vector in the direction of vector **V**. Similarly, it can be shown that

$$\mathbf{b} \times (\mathbf{V} \times \mathbf{U}) = -\mathbf{U}(\mathbf{W} \cdot \mathbf{V})$$

Therefore,

$$\mathbf{F} = \mathbf{W} \times (\mathbf{V} \times \mathbf{U}) = \mathbf{H} \times (\mathbf{V} \times \mathbf{U}) = \mathbf{a} \times (\mathbf{V} \times \mathbf{U}) + \mathbf{b} \times (\mathbf{V} \times \mathbf{U})$$
$$= (\mathbf{W} \cdot \mathbf{U})\mathbf{V} - (\mathbf{W} \cdot \mathbf{V})\mathbf{U}$$

A-2. DIFFERENTIATION OF VECTORS

The formulas for the differentiation of vectors which are functions of one scalar variable (such as time) can be derived from

$$\frac{d\mathbf{V}(t)}{dt} = \lim_{\Delta t \to 0} \frac{\Delta \mathbf{V}}{\Delta t} = \lim_{\Delta t \to 0} \frac{\mathbf{V}(t + \Delta t) - \mathbf{V}(t)}{\Delta t} \qquad \text{(A-26)}$$

where t is the scalar variable (Fig. A-9). If the vector **V** has resolutes **U** and **W**, then

$$\frac{d\mathbf{V}}{dt} = \frac{d(\mathbf{U} + \mathbf{W})}{dt} = \frac{d\mathbf{U}}{dt} + \frac{d\mathbf{W}}{dt} \qquad \text{(A-27)}$$

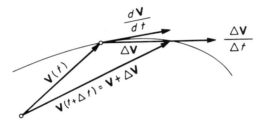

FIG. A-9

The derivative of a vector $\mathbf{V} = f\mathbf{U}$, where f is a scalar function of the variable t, can be written as

$$\frac{d(f\mathbf{U})}{dt} = \lim_{\Delta t \to 0} \frac{(f + \Delta f)(\mathbf{U} + \Delta \mathbf{U}) - f\mathbf{U}}{\Delta t}$$

$$= \lim_{\Delta t \to 0} \frac{\Delta f \mathbf{U} + f \Delta \mathbf{U} + \Delta f \Delta \mathbf{U}}{\Delta t}$$

$$= \frac{df}{dt} \mathbf{U} + f \frac{d\mathbf{U}}{dt} \qquad (A\text{-}28)$$

The derivative of the scalar product of two vectors $\mathbf{V}$ and $\mathbf{U}$ is given by

$$\frac{d(\mathbf{V} \cdot \mathbf{U})}{dt} = \lim_{\Delta t \to 0} \frac{(\mathbf{V} + \Delta \mathbf{V}) \cdot (\mathbf{U} + \Delta \mathbf{U}) - \mathbf{V} \cdot \mathbf{U}}{\Delta t}$$

$$= \lim_{\Delta t \to 0} \frac{\mathbf{U} \cdot \Delta \mathbf{V} + \mathbf{V} \cdot \Delta \mathbf{U} + \Delta \mathbf{V} \cdot \Delta \mathbf{U}}{\Delta t}$$

$$= \mathbf{U} \cdot \frac{d\mathbf{V}}{dt} + \mathbf{V} \cdot \frac{d\mathbf{U}}{dt} \qquad (A\text{-}29)$$

The derivative of the vector product of two vectors $\mathbf{V}$ and $\mathbf{U}$ is

$$\frac{d(\mathbf{V} \times \mathbf{U})}{dt} = \lim_{\Delta t \to 0} \frac{(\mathbf{V} + \Delta \mathbf{V}) \times (\mathbf{U} + \Delta \mathbf{U}) - \mathbf{V} \times \mathbf{U}}{\Delta t}$$

$$= \lim_{\Delta t \to 0} \frac{\mathbf{V} \times \Delta \mathbf{U} + \Delta \mathbf{V} \times \mathbf{U} + \Delta \mathbf{V} \times \Delta \mathbf{U}}{\Delta t}$$

$$= \mathbf{V} \times \frac{d\mathbf{U}}{dt} + \frac{d\mathbf{V}}{dt} \times \mathbf{U} \qquad (A\text{-}30)$$

A-3. SCALAR AND VECTOR FIELDS

By the field of a scalar point function, or the field of a vector point function, we mean the ensemble of points in a region in space together with the corresponding scalar or vector point function. In our considerations, except when stated to the contrary, we will assume that the scalar and vector point functions and their space derivatives are continuous, finite, and single-valued.

The field of a scalar point function f can be represented by a number of surfaces on which the function f is constant. As shown in Fig. A-10a, the surfaces corresponding to different values of a single-valued function do not intersect.

The field of a vector point function $\mathbf{F}$ can be represented by the *vector lines* (in this case the $\mathbf{F}$ lines) whose direction at every point in space is that of the vector function $\mathbf{F}$. The magnitude of the vector function $\mathbf{F}$ is represented by the number of $\mathbf{F}$ lines passing through a surface of unit area

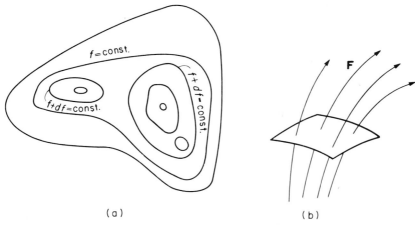

FIG. A-10

normal to the **F** lines, as shown in Fig. A-10b. Two different **F** lines do not intersect when the vector function **F** is single-valued. By a *vector sheet* of **F** we mean a surface tangent to the vector field **F**. A *vector tube* of **F** is a vector sheet passing through a closed curve in the field.

A-4. LINE AND SURFACE INTEGRALS OF VECTOR POINT FUNCTIONS

Consider vector field **F** in space, and curve C having a unique tangent at each point which changes in a continuous manner as we move along it.

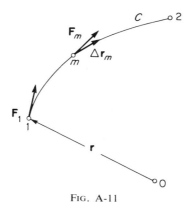

FIG. A-11

Such a curve, known as "smooth," is shown in Fig. A-11. If we take the sum

$$\lim_{\Delta r \to 0} \sum_C \mathbf{F}_m \cdot \Delta \mathbf{r}_m = \int_C \mathbf{F} \cdot d\mathbf{r} = \int_C \mathbf{F} \cdot \mathbf{u}_s \, ds = \int_C F_s \, ds \quad \text{(A-31)}$$

along the whole curve C, then this integral represents the *line integral of* **F** *along curve C.* In the above equation $d\mathbf{r} = \dfrac{d\mathbf{r}}{ds} ds = \mathbf{u}_s ds$, where ds denotes the differential arc length along C, $\mathbf{u}_s$ the unit vector along line C, F_s the component of **F** along line C in the direction tangent to line C, and $d\mathbf{r}$ is the differential of the position vector **r** from some fixed point 0 (which is a bound vector and which is indicated in Fig. A-11). The line integral from points 2 to 1 is the negative of the line integral from 1 to 2.

Consider a smooth surface S bounded by a simple closed curve C, as shown in Fig. A-12.[1] The surface integral of a vector field **F** over the

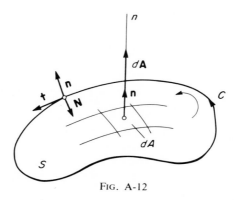

FIG. A-12

surface S can be formed, provided that the surface is "oriented" in space. This can be accomplished by choosing a field of unit normal vectors to the surface, **n**, which varies in a continuous manner on S. The *integral of the vector field* **F** *over surface S* is given by

$$\lim_{\Delta A \to 0} \sum_S \mathbf{F} \cdot \Delta \mathbf{A} = \int_S d\mathbf{A} \cdot \mathbf{F} = \int_S \mathbf{n} \cdot \mathbf{F} \, dA \qquad (A\text{-}32)$$

where $d\mathbf{A} = \mathbf{n}\, dA$ represents the differential area vector. In the case of a closed surface, the orientation of the unit vector **n** normal to the surface at any point is, in general, taken as outward.

Once the field of normal vectors which determines the positive side of the surface has been chosen, we can assign a *positive direction to the curve C bounding the surface S.* As the positive direction of a simple closed curve C, we take the direction of the tangent vector **t** so oriented that the vectors **t**, **N**, and **n**, where **N** is the inner normal vector, form a right-handed system (a positive triple) at each point along curve C.

A piecewise smooth surface, such as the surface of a cylinder, becomes oriented if the direction along each curve forming a common boundary is positive for one piece of the surface and negative for the other.

---

[1] A surface is said to be smooth if the normal to the surface varies continuously over it.

A-5. GRADIENT OF A SCALAR FIELD; DIVERGENCE AND CURL OF A VECTOR FIELD

Consider a scalar point function f which is continuous and has continuous derivatives. We define a vector which points in the direction in which function f increases at the highest rate (that is, in which the directional derivative $\partial f/\partial l = \lim_{\Delta l \to 0} \Delta f/\Delta l$ is maximum) and whose magnitude is equal to that maximum derivative, as the *gradient of the scalar point function f*, and we denote it by the symbol grad f.[2] Figure A-13 shows

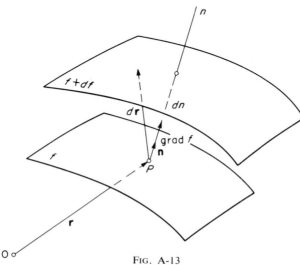

FIG. A-13

two surfaces on which the scalar point function f is constant in space. From our definition, the gradient of f at point P is

$$\text{grad } f = \mathbf{n}\, \frac{\partial f}{\partial n} \qquad (A\text{-}33)$$

where $\mathbf{n}$ is the unit vector along the normal n to the surface on which function f is constant, pointing in the direction of increasing f. (We usually employ partial derivatives in the definition of the gradient of a scalar point function f because, in general, f can depend on a scalar variable, such as time.) Let $\mathbf{r}$ denote the position vector drawn from some fixed point 0 to a point P on the surface f = const. The position vector of any nearby point on the surface $f + df$ = const. is $\mathbf{r} + d\mathbf{r}$. Taking the scalar product (grad f) $\cdot$ $d\mathbf{r}$, we find that

$$(\text{grad } f) \cdot d\mathbf{r} = \frac{\partial f}{\partial n}\, \mathbf{n} \cdot d\mathbf{r} = \frac{\partial f}{\partial n}\, dn = df \qquad (A\text{-}34)$$

[2] Note that the maximum directional derivative at some point P on the surface f = constant is the derivative taken along the normal to the surface at P. The gradient of a scalar point function can also be called the gradient of a scalar-field function, or the gradient of a scalar field.

which relation can also be used as a definition of the gradient of a scalar field f.

The component of grad f in the direction of some vector $\mathbf{l}$ is

$$\text{comp}_{\mathbf{l}}(\text{grad } f) = (\text{grad } f) \cdot \mathbf{u}_l = \frac{\partial f}{\partial l} \tag{A-35}$$

where $\mathbf{u}_l$ is the unit vector in the direction of $\mathbf{l}$.

The *divergence of a vector field* $\mathbf{F}$ at some point P is a scalar defined as the limiting value to which the ratio of the integral of $\mathbf{F}$ over a closed surface S to the volume inside the surface S tends as this volume approaches zero and the surface S shrinks down to point P. Thus by definition,

$$\text{div } \mathbf{F} = \lim_{\mathscr{V} \to 0} \frac{\oint_S d\mathbf{A} \cdot \mathbf{F}}{\mathscr{V}} \tag{A-36}$$

where $\mathscr{V}$ denotes the volume inside the closed surface S, and the vector $d\mathbf{A} = \mathbf{n}\, dA$ represents the differential area vector (having magnitude equal to the area of the surface element and direction of the outward normal unit vector $\mathbf{n}$ to the surface S).

The integral $\oint_S d\mathbf{A} \cdot \mathbf{F}$ denotes the number of $\mathbf{F}$ lines which pass through the surface S from within. Therefore div $\mathbf{F}$ represents the number of $\mathbf{F}$ lines created per unit volume.

In a vector field $\mathbf{F}$ in a region in space in which div $\mathbf{F} = 0$, the vector tubes of $\mathbf{F}$ must be closed or start at the boundary of the region, because they are not generated anywhere inside the region. Such a vector field is called *solenoidal*. The points in space in which the vector tubes of $\mathbf{F}$ are generated are called *sources*, and the points in which the vector tubes of $\mathbf{F}$ end are known as *sinks*.

Figure A-14 shows an arbitrary oriented surface S bounded by a closed curve C. The *component of the curl* (a curl is a vector) *of a vector field* $\mathbf{F}$ *at some point* P *in the direction of the positive normal* n is defined as the limiting value of the line integral of $\mathbf{F}$ along the closed curve C

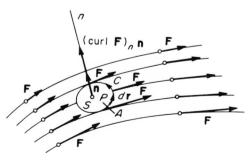

FIG. A-14

bounding the surface S oriented by n (taken in the positive direction along curve C) divided by the area A of the surface S as this area approaches zero. Thus

$$\text{comp}_n(\text{curl } \mathbf{F}) \equiv (\text{curl } \mathbf{F})_n = \mathbf{n} \cdot \text{curl } \mathbf{F} = \lim_{A \to 0} \frac{\oint_C \mathbf{F} \cdot d\mathbf{r}}{A} \qquad (\text{A-37})$$

where $d\mathbf{r}$ represents the differential of the position vector.

Observe that, in general, the value of the expression

$$\lim_{A \to 0} \frac{\oint_C \mathbf{F} \cdot d\mathbf{r}}{A}$$

at some point P in the vector field $\mathbf{F}$ (with the line integral along C taken in the positive direction), depends on the direction of the positive normal n. In general, there exists a direction of the normal n for which the value of this expression reaches a maximum. This direction and this value define the curl $\mathbf{F}$ at point P.

The definitions of the gradient of a scalar field and of the divergence and curl of a vector field indicate that they are valid in any coordinate system we may choose in our analysis. These definitions can be unified in the following way:

$$\text{grad } f = \lim_{\mathcal{V} \to 0} \frac{\oint_S d\mathbf{A}\, f}{\mathcal{V}} \qquad (\text{A-38})$$

$$\text{div } \mathbf{F} = \lim_{\mathcal{V} \to 0} \frac{\oint_S d\mathbf{A} \cdot \mathbf{F}}{\mathcal{V}} \qquad (\text{A-36})$$

$$\text{curl } \mathbf{F} = \lim_{\mathcal{V} \to 0} \frac{\oint_S d\mathbf{A} \times \mathbf{F}}{\mathcal{V}} \qquad (\text{A-39})$$

where $d\mathbf{A}$ denotes the vectorial element of area (pointing outward) of closed surface S enclosing volume $\mathcal{V}$.[3]

---

[3] These relations correspond to the transformations of Green (1828):

$$\int_\mathcal{V} \text{grad } \phi\, d\mathcal{V} = \oint_S d\mathbf{A}\,\phi$$

$$\int_\mathcal{V} \text{div } \phi\, d\mathcal{V} = \oint_S d\mathbf{A} \cdot \phi$$

$$\int_\mathcal{V} \text{curl } \phi\, d\mathcal{V} = \oint_S d\mathbf{A} \times \phi$$

which are valid for continuous and continuously differentiable components of an arbitrary integrable scalar, vector, or tensor field ϕ (provided that the formula has sense) and convergent integrals [7].

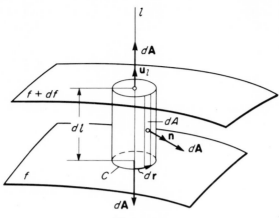

FIG. A-15

To prove Eq. A-38, consider an element of volume in the form of a cylinder whose axis has direction of some chosen unit vector $\mathbf{u}_l$ and whose base and top are perpendicular to $\mathbf{u}_l$, as shown in Fig. A-15. Forming the scalar product of both sides of identity (Eq. A-38) with the unit vector $\mathbf{u}_l$ (which is a constant vector), we obtain

$$(\text{grad } f) \cdot \mathbf{u}_l = \lim_{\mathcal{V} \to 0} \frac{\oint_S (d\mathbf{A} \cdot \mathbf{u}_l) f}{\mathcal{V}}$$

The contribution of the curved surface to the integral is zero, because $d\mathbf{A}$ and $\mathbf{u}_l$ are perpendicular there. The scalar-field function f can be assumed to be constant on the base and on the top of the cylinder, and changes from the base to the top by $\partial f / \partial l$. The contribution to the integral from the top and the base of the cylinder is thus

$$\int_S (d\mathbf{A} \cdot \mathbf{u}_l) f = dA\left(f + \frac{\partial f}{\partial l} dl\right) - dA f = \frac{\partial f}{\partial l} dl\, dA = \frac{\partial f}{\partial l} d\mathcal{V}$$

where $d\mathcal{V} = dl\, dA$ is the volume of the element. Thus we have shown that

$$(\text{grad } f) \cdot \mathbf{u}_l = \lim_{\mathcal{V} \to 0} \frac{\oint_S (d\mathbf{A} \cdot \mathbf{u}_l) f}{\mathcal{V}} = \frac{\frac{\partial f}{\partial l} d\mathcal{V}}{d\mathcal{V}} = \frac{\partial f}{\partial l}$$

which corresponds to Eq. A-35. Therefore, Eq. A-38 has been proved.

Equation A-36 is the definition of divergence and therefore does not require a proof.

To prove Eq. A-39, consider a cylindrical volume element whose height is very small compared with the dimensions of the end surfaces, so that the vector-field function $\mathbf{F}$ can be assumed to be constant along lines

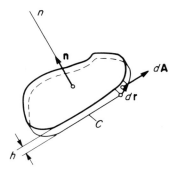

Fig. A-16

on the curved (cylindrical) surface which are parallel to the axis n of the cylinder. Such an element of volume is shown in Fig. A-16. Let us form a scalar product of the outward normal unit vector $\mathbf{n}$ of the top surface of the volume element and the identity of Eq. A-39. The result is

$$\mathbf{n} \cdot (\text{curl } \mathbf{F}) = \lim_{\mathcal{V} \to 0} \frac{\oint_S \mathbf{n} \cdot (d\mathbf{A} \times \mathbf{F})}{\mathcal{V}} = \lim_{\mathcal{V} \to 0} \frac{\oint_S \mathbf{F} \cdot (\mathbf{n} \times d\mathbf{A})}{\mathcal{V}} \qquad (\text{A-40})$$

in view of Eq. A-23. As the vector elements of area of the top and base of the cylinder are parallel to $\mathbf{n}$, they contribute nothing to the integral. The contribution of the cylindrical surface is

$$\oint_S \mathbf{F} \cdot (\mathbf{n} \times d\mathbf{A}) = \oint_C \mathbf{F} \cdot (h \, d\mathbf{r}) = h \oint_C \mathbf{F} \cdot d\mathbf{r}$$

where h is the height of the volume element, and $d\mathbf{r}$ represents the differential of the position vector having the direction of the circumferential boundary C; that is, of vector $\mathbf{n} \times d\mathbf{A}$. The vector $d\mathbf{r}$, the inner normal vector, and the vector $\mathbf{n}$ form a right-handed system. What we have shown, therefore, is that

$$\mathbf{n} \cdot (\text{curl } \mathbf{F}) = \lim_{\mathcal{V} \to 0} \frac{h \oint_C \mathbf{F} \cdot d\mathbf{r}}{\mathcal{V}} = \lim_{\substack{h \to 0 \\ A \to 0}} \frac{\oint_C \mathbf{F} \cdot d\mathbf{r}}{A}$$

where A is the area of the end surface of the volume element. In the process of going over the limit, we should think first about going over to the limit $h \to 0$ and subsequently to limit $A \to 0$, so that the base and the top of the volume element collapse together, and the positive normal unit vector to area enclosed by C is $\mathbf{n}$. The above equation corresponds to the definition of the component of curl $\mathbf{F}$ in the direction of the positive normal n [2]. Hence we have proved Eq. A-39.

A-6. THE VECTOR OPERATOR ∇; USEFUL VECTOR RELATIONS

To abbreviate the notation for the gradient, divergence, and curl (and for no other purpose), it is useful to introduce the *vector operator* ∇ (nabla), first used by Hamilton. This vector operator can be applied to scalars and vectors and can result in such products as, for example ∇f, $\nabla \cdot \mathbf{F}$, and $\nabla \times \mathbf{F}$.

The definition of ∇, which represents the rule for the formation of these products, follows directly from Eqs. A-38, A-36, and A-39: In the product, ∇ is replaced by a directed element of area $d\mathbf{A}$ of a closed surface S having direction of the outward normal ($d\mathbf{A} = n\,dA$), and integration is performed over the closed surface S, followed by division by the volume $\mathcal{V}$ enclosed by the surface in the limit as $\mathcal{V}$ approaches zero and the surface S shrinks to a point. The quantities which precede the vector operator ∇, if any, should be regarded as constant in the process of integration over the surface S [2,4,8].

With the vector operator ∇ thus defined, the expressions for grad f, div $\mathbf{F}$, and curl $\mathbf{F}$ become

$$\text{grad } f = \lim_{\mathcal{V} \to 0} \frac{\oint_S d\mathbf{A}\, f}{\mathcal{V}} \equiv \nabla f \qquad (\text{A-38a})$$

$$\text{div } \mathbf{F} = \lim_{\mathcal{V} \to 0} \frac{\oint_S d\mathbf{A} \cdot \mathbf{F}}{\mathcal{V}} \equiv \nabla \cdot \mathbf{F} \qquad (\text{A-36a})$$

$$\text{curl } \mathbf{F} = \lim_{\mathcal{V} \to 0} \frac{\oint_S d\mathbf{A} \times \mathbf{F}}{\mathcal{V}} \equiv \nabla \times \mathbf{F} \qquad (\text{A-39a})$$

Vector Relations. From the definition of the gradient of a scalar field, it follows that

$$\nabla (f + \rho) = \nabla f + \nabla \rho \qquad (\text{A-41})$$

where both f and ρ are scalar-field functions.

From the definition of the divergence of a vector field (Eq. A-36) and from Eq. A-17, we find that

$$\nabla \cdot (\mathbf{F} + \mathbf{U}) = \nabla \cdot \mathbf{F} + \nabla \cdot \mathbf{U} \qquad (\text{A-42})$$

where $\mathbf{F}$ and $\mathbf{U}$ are vector-field functions:

To explain the general method of driving various useful relations involving the gradient of scalar fields and the divergence and curl of vector fields, we will derive the expression for $\nabla \cdot (f\mathbf{F})$ [4]. Consider a small region occupying volume $\mathcal{V}$, containing a fixed point P, bounded by a closed surface S. Assume that the region considered is small enough so that, on the surface S, we have $f = f_P + df$ and $\mathbf{F} = \mathbf{F}_P + d\mathbf{F}$, where

f_P and $\mathbf{F}_P$ are some scalar- and vector-field functions at point P. We can write

$$\nabla \cdot (f\mathbf{F}) = \lim_{\mathcal{V} \to 0} \frac{\oint_S d\mathbf{A} \cdot (f\mathbf{F})}{\mathcal{V}} = f_P \lim_{\mathcal{V} \to 0} \frac{\oint_S d\mathbf{A} \cdot \mathbf{F}}{\mathcal{V}} + \lim_{\mathcal{V} \to 0} \frac{\oint_S df(d\mathbf{A} \cdot \mathbf{F})}{\mathcal{V}}$$

$$= f_P \lim_{\mathcal{V} \to 0} \frac{\oint_S d\mathbf{A} \cdot \mathbf{F}}{\mathcal{V}} + \mathbf{F}_P \cdot \lim_{\mathcal{V} \to 0} \frac{\oint_S d\mathbf{A}\, df}{\mathcal{V}} + \lim_{\mathcal{V} \to 0} \frac{\oint_S df(d\mathbf{A} \cdot d\mathbf{F})}{\mathcal{V}}$$

The higher-order term on the right-hand side can be neglected. To the second term on the right-hand side, we can add

$$f_P \mathbf{F}_P \cdot \lim_{\mathcal{V} \to 0} \frac{\oint_S d\mathbf{A}}{\mathcal{V}} = \mathbf{F}_P \cdot \lim_{\mathcal{V} \to 0} \frac{\oint_S f_P d\mathbf{A}}{\mathcal{V}}$$

because $\oint_S d\mathbf{A} = \mathbf{0}$. As a result, it becomes

$$\mathbf{F}_P \cdot \lim_{\mathcal{V} \to 0} \frac{\oint_S d\mathbf{A} f}{\mathcal{V}}$$

Therefore,

$$\nabla \cdot (f\mathbf{F}) = f_P \lim_{\mathcal{V} \to 0} \frac{\oint_S d\mathbf{A} \cdot \mathbf{F}}{\mathcal{V}} + \mathbf{F}_P \cdot \lim_{\mathcal{V} \to 0} \frac{\oint_S d\mathbf{A} f}{\mathcal{V}}$$

or

$$\nabla \cdot (f\mathbf{F}) = f(\nabla \cdot \mathbf{F}) + (\nabla f) \cdot \mathbf{F} \qquad (A\text{-}43)$$

because $f_P \to f$ and $\mathbf{F}_P \to \mathbf{F}$ as $\mathcal{V} \to 0$. In a similar manner we can derive

$$\nabla (f\rho) = f\nabla \rho + \rho \nabla f \qquad (A\text{-}44)$$

$$\nabla \times (f\mathbf{F}) = \nabla f \times \mathbf{F} + f\nabla \times \mathbf{F} \qquad (A\text{-}45)$$

and

$$\nabla \cdot (\mathbf{F} \times \mathbf{U}) = \mathbf{U} \cdot (\nabla \times \mathbf{F}) - \mathbf{F} \cdot (\nabla \times \mathbf{U}) \qquad (A\text{-}46)$$

where f and ρ are scalar-, and $\mathbf{F}$ and $\mathbf{U}$ vector-field functions.

In vector analysis we often make use of the scalar operator $\mathbf{U} \cdot \nabla$, with which we can operate on a scalar- or a vector-field function. If $\mathbf{F}$ denotes a vector-field function, then

$$(\mathbf{U} \cdot \nabla)\mathbf{F} = \lim_{\mathcal{V} \to 0} \frac{\oint_S (\mathbf{U} \cdot d\mathbf{A})\mathbf{F}}{\mathcal{V}} \qquad (A\text{-}47)$$

If we choose, as our volume element, a cylinder at height dl whose axis l is parallel to vector $\mathbf{U}$, then the curved surface of the volume element contributes nothing to the integral, because $\mathbf{U}$ is normal to $d\mathbf{A}$ there. We obtain

$$\oint_S (\mathbf{U} \cdot d\mathbf{A})\mathbf{F} = U\,dA\left(\mathbf{F} + \frac{\partial \mathbf{F}}{\partial l}\,dl\right) - U\,dA\,\mathbf{F}$$

where the first term on the right-hand side is the contribution from the top, and the second is the contribution from the base of the volume element. In the integration, $\mathbf{U}$ is regarded as constant because it is in front of the vector operator ∇. As $d\mathcal{V} = dl\,dA$, we have

$$(\mathbf{U} \cdot \nabla)\mathbf{F} = U\,\frac{\partial \mathbf{F}}{\partial l} \qquad (\text{A-48})$$

Thus, $(\mathbf{U} \cdot \nabla)\mathbf{F}$ represents the derivative of the vector function of position in space (i.e., vector field) $\mathbf{F}$ in direction of vector $\mathbf{U}$, times the magnitude of vector $\mathbf{U}$.

When vector $\mathbf{U}$ represents an elementary change in position $d\mathbf{r} = \dfrac{d\mathbf{r}}{ds}\,ds = \mathbf{u}_s\,ds$, then

$$(d\mathbf{r} \cdot \nabla)\mathbf{F} = \frac{\partial \mathbf{F}}{\partial s}\,ds = d\mathbf{F} \qquad (\text{A-49})$$

which can be written as

$$\frac{\partial \mathbf{F}}{\partial s} = (\mathbf{u}_s \cdot \nabla)\mathbf{F} \qquad (\text{A-50})$$

The term $\partial \mathbf{F}/\partial s$ represents the *directional derivative of the vector-field function* $\mathbf{F}$ in the direction of $d\mathbf{r} = \mathbf{u}_s\,ds$. The term $\nabla\mathbf{F}$, or the gradient of a vector-field function, is a dyadic.

When operating with the scalar operator $\mathbf{U} \cdot \nabla$ on a scalar-field function f, we obtain

$$(\mathbf{U} \cdot \nabla)f = U\,\frac{\partial f}{\partial l} \qquad (\text{A-51})$$

which represents the derivative of the function f in the direction of vector $\mathbf{U}$, times the magnitude of $\mathbf{U}$. From Eq. A-35 it follows that Eq. A-51 can be rewritten as

$$(\mathbf{U} \cdot \nabla)f = \mathbf{U} \cdot \operatorname{grad} f = \mathbf{U} \cdot \nabla f \qquad (\text{A-52})$$

In view of Eq. A-52 and of the fact that $\nabla\mathbf{F}$ can be treated as a separate entity, when operating with the scalar operator $\mathbf{U} \cdot \nabla$, the parentheses are usually omitted.

When, in Eq. A-48, $\mathbf{F} = f\mathbf{V}$, then

$$(\mathbf{U} \cdot \nabla)(f\mathbf{V}) = U\,\frac{\partial(f\mathbf{V})}{\partial l} = fU\,\frac{\partial \mathbf{V}}{\partial l} + \mathbf{V}U\,\frac{\partial f}{\partial l}$$

$$= f(\mathbf{U} \cdot \nabla)\mathbf{V} + \mathbf{V}(\mathbf{U} \cdot \nabla f) \qquad (\text{A-53})$$

While in deriving the expression for the scalar operator $\mathbf{U} \cdot \nabla$, we regard $\mathbf{U}$ as a constant vector, we may ask what would be the form of

$$\oint_S \mathbf{F}(\mathbf{U} \cdot d\mathbf{A})$$

if both $\mathbf{U}$ and $\mathbf{F}$ were considered as variable. Referring again to a cylindrical volume element of height dl whose axis l is parallel to vector $\mathbf{U}$, and making use of the expression for the divergence of $\mathbf{U}$, we obtain

$$\lim_{\mathscr{V} \to 0} \frac{\displaystyle\oint_S \mathbf{F}(\mathbf{U} \cdot d\mathbf{A})}{\mathscr{V}} = \mathbf{U} \cdot \nabla \mathbf{F} + \mathbf{F}(\nabla \cdot \mathbf{U}) \qquad \text{(A-54)}$$

or

$$\oint_S \mathbf{F}(\mathbf{U} \cdot d\mathbf{A}) = \int_{\mathscr{V}} [\mathbf{U} \cdot \nabla \mathbf{F} + \mathbf{F}(\nabla \cdot \mathbf{U})] d\mathscr{V} \qquad \text{(A-55)}$$

The derivation of the above equation is left as a problem assignment.

Using the technique employed in the derivation of Eq. A-43, the following additional relations can be derived:

$$\nabla \times (\mathbf{F} \times \mathbf{U}) = \mathbf{U} \cdot \nabla \mathbf{F} - \mathbf{F} \cdot \nabla \mathbf{U} + \mathbf{F}(\nabla \cdot \mathbf{U}) - \mathbf{U}(\nabla \cdot \mathbf{F}) \quad \text{(A-56)}$$

$$\nabla (\mathbf{U} \cdot \mathbf{F}) = \mathbf{U} \cdot \nabla \mathbf{F} + \mathbf{F} \cdot \nabla \mathbf{U} + \mathbf{U} \times (\nabla \times \mathbf{F}) + \mathbf{F} \times (\nabla \times \mathbf{U})$$
$$\text{(A-57)}$$

and

$$\nabla \times (\nabla \times \mathbf{U}) = \nabla (\nabla \cdot \mathbf{U}) - \nabla^2 \mathbf{U} \qquad \text{(A-58)}$$

where

$$\nabla^2 \mathbf{U} = \nabla \cdot (\nabla \mathbf{U})$$

A-7. GAUSS'S DIVERGENCE THEOREM

We will now consider transformations of a certain volume integral, taken over a region R in space having volume $\mathscr{V}$, into a surface integral over the smooth or piecewise smooth surface S bounding region R. The scalar-field function f and the vector-field function $\mathbf{F}$ in these integrals will, as usual, be assumed finite and single-valued, with finite and continuous derivatives.

We divide region R into volume elements $d\mathscr{V}$, as shown in Fig. A-17. We multiply Eq. A-36 by $d\mathscr{V} = \lim_{\mathscr{V} \to 0} \mathscr{V}$, perform integration for each volume element, and add up all contributions. The contributions from all surfaces of the volume elements which touch other volume elements cancel out. This is so because the outward normal unit vectors $\mathbf{n}$ of two touching surfaces have opposite directions. The only noncanceling contributions come from the surfaces of the volume elements which form the

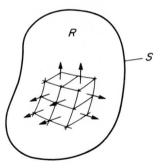

FIG. A-17

surface S, bounding region R occupying volume λ. As a result,

$$\int_{\gamma} \boldsymbol{\nabla} \cdot \mathbf{F}\, d\mathcal{V} = \oint_{S} \mathbf{n} \cdot \mathbf{F}\, dA \qquad \text{(A-59)}$$

which can also be written as

$$\int_{\gamma} \boldsymbol{\nabla} \cdot \mathbf{F}\, d\mathcal{V} = \oint_{S} d\mathbf{A} \cdot \mathbf{F}$$

Equation A-59 can be expressed in words by saying that the volume integral of the divergence of $\mathbf{F}$ is equal to the integral of $\mathbf{F}$ over the surface which bounds the volume considered. This is known as the *divergence theorem of Gauss* or *Gauss's integral theorem*.

Utilizing the divergence theorem of Gauss, we can derive two additional useful relations between surface and volume integrals. Forming the scalar product of the integral

$$\oint_{S} d\mathbf{A}\, f = \oint_{S} f\mathbf{n}\, dA$$

where $\mathbf{n}$ is the outward normal unit vector to the closed surface S, and an arbitrary constant vector field $\mathbf{B}$, and making use of Gauss's divergence theorem, we obtain

$$\oint_{S} f\mathbf{n} \cdot \mathbf{B}\, dA = \int_{\gamma} \boldsymbol{\nabla} \cdot (f\mathbf{B})\, d\mathcal{V}$$

In view of Eq. A-43 and the fact that $\boldsymbol{\nabla} \cdot \mathbf{B} = 0$, we have

$$\oint_{S} f\mathbf{n} \cdot \mathbf{B}\, dA = \int_{\gamma} (\mathbf{B} \cdot \boldsymbol{\nabla} f)\, d\mathcal{V}$$

Since $\mathbf{B}$ is an arbitrary constant vector field,

$$\int_{\gamma} \boldsymbol{\nabla} f\, d\mathcal{V} = \oint_{S} \mathbf{n} f\, dA \qquad \text{(A-60)}$$

Similarly, taking scalar product of an arbitrary constant vector field **B** and the integral $\oint_S \mathbf{V} \times \mathbf{n}\, dA$, where **n** is the outward normal unit vector to the closed surface S, and applying Gauss's divergence theorem, we obtain

$$\oint_S \mathbf{B} \cdot (\mathbf{V} \times \mathbf{n})\, dA = \oint_S \mathbf{n} \cdot (\mathbf{B} \times \mathbf{V})\, dA = \int_V \nabla \cdot (\mathbf{B} \times \mathbf{V})\, d\mathcal{V}$$

in view of Eq. A-23. Making use of Eq. A-46 and noting that $\nabla \times \mathbf{B} = \mathbf{0}$, we have

$$\oint_S \mathbf{B} \cdot (\mathbf{V} \times \mathbf{n})\, dA = -\int_V \mathbf{B} \cdot (\nabla \times \mathbf{V})\, d\mathcal{V}$$

Since **B** is a constant and arbitrary vector field,

$$\int_V \nabla \times \mathbf{V}\, d\mathcal{V} = \oint_S \mathbf{n} \times \mathbf{V}\, dA \qquad \text{(A-61)}$$

A-8. STOKES'S THEOREM

Consider now an arbitrary, oriented, smooth (or piecewise smooth) surface S having as its edge (boundary) a simple smooth (or piecewise smooth) closed curve C, as shown in Fig. A-18. By a simple curve we

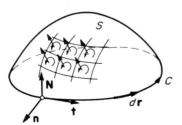

FIG. A-18

mean one which does not have any multiple points, and by a smooth curve we mean a curve which has a unique tangent at each point which changes in a continuous manner as we move along the curve. *Stokes's theorem*, known also as *Kelvin's transformation*,[4] says that the line integral of a vector field function **F** having continuous and differentiable components over a closed curve C, is equal to the integral of the normal component of curl **F** taken over the surface bounded by curve C. This statement can be represented by

$$\oint_C \mathbf{F} \cdot d\mathbf{r} = \int_S \mathbf{n} \cdot (\nabla \times \mathbf{F})\, dA \qquad \text{(A-62)}$$

[4] Actually due to Kelvin [7, pp. 12–13].

The proof of Stokes's theorem follows from Eq. A-37, multiplied by $dA = \lim_{A \to 0} A$, and summed up for each area element of surface S. Since the sides of each area element, except the sides which form curve C, are traversed, in the process of integration, twice in the opposite directions, their contributions to the sum of the line integrals are zero. The only contributions come from the sides of the elements forming curve C. This proves Eq. A-62.

If the surface S represents a closed surface made up by joining two surfaces bounded by the same closed curve C, then, if $\mathbf{n}$ denotes the outward normal unit vector to the surface S, we have, from Stokes's theorem,

$$\oint_S \mathbf{n} \cdot (\nabla \times \mathbf{F})\, dA = \oint_S dA \cdot (\nabla \times \mathbf{F}) = \oint_S (\operatorname{curl} \mathbf{F})_n\, dA = 0 \quad (A\text{-}63)$$

because the integration along curve C is made twice in opposite directions. As a result we can conclude that, if a vector $\mathbf{V}$ can be expressed as the curl of some other vector $\mathbf{F}$, then the $\mathbf{V}$ lines form lines closed in space.

If, in Gauss's divergence theorem, we put $\mathbf{F} = \nabla \times \mathbf{U}$, we obtain

$$\int_\gamma \nabla \cdot (\nabla \times \mathbf{U}) d\mathcal{V} = 0$$

in view of Eq. A-63. The integrand must vanish at any point in space, because the region occupying volume $\mathcal{V}$ is arbitrary. Therefore, the divergence of a curl of the vector-field function $\mathbf{U}$ is zero. This can be written as

$$\nabla \cdot (\nabla \times \mathbf{U}) = 0 \qquad\qquad (A\text{-}64)$$

A-9. POTENTIAL VECTOR FIELDS

The line integral of a vector-field function $\mathbf{F}$, $\displaystyle\int_1^2 \mathbf{F} \cdot d\mathbf{r}$, depends, in general, not only on the initial and final limits but also on the path of integration. The line integral of $\mathbf{F}$ is independent of the path of integration only when the product $\mathbf{F} \cdot d\mathbf{r}$ represents the total differential of some single-valued scalar-field function f,

$$\mathbf{F} \cdot d\mathbf{r} = df$$

Then, in view of Eq. A-34,

$$\mathbf{F} = \operatorname{grad} f = \nabla f$$

and

$$\int_1^2 \mathbf{F} \cdot d\mathbf{r} = \int_1^2 \nabla f \cdot d\mathbf{r} = \int_1^2 df = f_2 - f_1 \qquad (A\text{-}65)$$

A vector function of position $\mathbf{F}$ which can be expressed as the gradient of a scalar-field function f is known as a *potential vector function*. The scalar function of position f is known as the *potential* of the vector field $\mathbf{F}$.

From Eq. A-65 it follows that, for a single-valued function f, the integral of **F** along any closed curve C vanishes; that is,

$$\oint_C \mathbf{F} \cdot d\mathbf{r} = \oint_C \nabla f \cdot d\mathbf{r} = 0$$

If the vector-field function **F** in Eq. A-62 representing Stokes's theorem is the gradient of a single-valued scalar field function f, then, in view of the above equation,

$$\int_S \mathbf{n} \cdot (\nabla \times \nabla f)\, dA = \int_S (\text{curl grad } f)_n\, dA = 0$$

Since the integrand must vanish everywhere in space because the surface is arbitrary, we find that the curl of the gradient of a single-valued scalar-field function f vanishes. This can be written as

$$\nabla \times (\nabla f) = \mathbf{0} \tag{A-66}$$

An important question which we must be able to answer is this: If curl **F** = **0** in a certain region in space, can **F** always be represented as the gradient of a single-valued scalar-field function f? At first glance, from Stokes's theorem it would appear that this must always be the case. However, Stokes's theorem is valid, in general, only in a *simply connected*, or *acyclic*, *region*. In such a region the scalar-field function f is single-valued. By a *simply connected*, or *acyclic*, *region* we mean a region in which it is possible to describe a surface lying wholly within the region and whose edge is formed by any closed line in the region. Thus, a simply connected region cannot have any holes in it. If it does, it is called a *multiply connected*, or *cyclic*, *region*. A region is said to be n-ply connected if insertion of $(n - 1)$ barriers, across which no line can pass, makes it simply connected. Simply connected and doubly connected regions are shown in Fig. A-19.

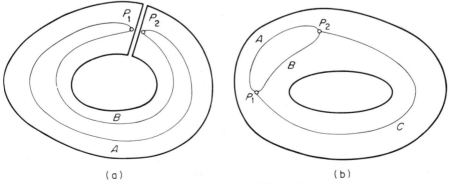

FIG. A-19. (a) Simply connected region, (b) doubly connected region.

The paths joining points P_1 and P_2 in a region are said to be *reconcilable* if it is possible to deform continuously one path into the other while remaining within the region. Otherwise, they are *irreconcilable*. The paths $P_1 A P_2$ and $P_1 B P_2$ in Figs. A-19a and A-19b are reconcilable, but the paths $P_1 C P_2$ and $P_1 B P_2$ in Fig. A-19b are irreconcilable.

A circuit (that is, a closed path) which lies completely within a region is called *reducible* if it can be contracted to a point while always remaining in the region. A reducible circuit is made of reconcilable paths.

If curl $\mathbf{F} = \mathbf{0}$ within a multiply connected region but not outside it, then the scalar-field function f will, in general, be multiple-valued when the circuit of integration is not reducible, because then, on a part of the surface over which integration is made, curl $\mathbf{F} \neq \mathbf{0}$, and as a result,

$$\oint_C \mathbf{F} \cdot d\mathbf{r} = \Gamma$$

where Γ represents the value of the surface integral. Only in the special case in which the curl $\mathbf{F}$ lines cross, in both directions, the surface over which integration is made and the surface integral vanishes is the scalar field function f single-valued when the circuit is not reducible.

If, within the doubly connected region created by removing the barrier between points P_1 and P_2 in Fig. A-19a we have curl $\mathbf{F} = \mathbf{0}$ (and outside it curl $\mathbf{F} \neq \mathbf{0}$), and we write $\mathbf{F} = \nabla f$ for that region, then ∇f must be continuous and single-valued, just like $\mathbf{F}$. However, for a circuit which is not reducible, the scalar-field function f is, in general, not single-valued. In order that ∇f be continuous and single-valued, the function f must differ between points P_1 and P_2 by a constant Γ (multiplied by the number of times the path has encircled the region in which curl $\mathbf{F} \neq \mathbf{0}$).

Thus in a simply connected region in which curl $\mathbf{F} = \mathbf{0}$, we have, for any circuit within the region,

$$\oint_C \mathbf{F} \cdot d\mathbf{r} = 0 \tag{A-67}$$

and therefore there exists a single-valued scalar-field function f such that

$$\mathbf{F} = \nabla f$$

In a multiply connected region in which curl $\mathbf{F} = \mathbf{0}$, and outside of which curl $\mathbf{F} \neq \mathbf{0}$, however, while the line integral about any reducible circuit is zero and therefore, for such circuits, the scalar-field function f is single-valued, for a circuit which is not reducible we have, in general,

$$\oint_C \mathbf{F} \cdot d\mathbf{r} = f^+ - f^- = \Gamma \tag{A-68}$$

where f^+ and f^- refer to the values of the scalar-field function on both sides of the surface across which it changes in a discontinuous manner, and thus the scalar-field function f is, in general, multiple-valued.

A-10.   DIVERGENCE AND CURL OF THE POSITION VECTOR

The divergence of the position vector $\mathbf{r}$ can be determined as follows. Consider a volume element having the shape of a frustrum of a cone of height $d\mathbf{r}$ and solid angle $d\phi$, as shown in Fig. A-20.   In view of Eq. A-36,

$$\text{div } \mathbf{r} = \boldsymbol{\nabla} \cdot \mathbf{r} = \lim_{\mathscr{V} \to 0} \frac{\oint_S d\mathbf{A} \cdot \mathbf{r}}{\mathscr{V}}$$

The contribution from the conical surface of the frustrum is zero, because

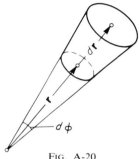

FIG. A-20

the position vector $\mathbf{r}$ is perpendicular to $d\mathbf{A}$ there.   The contributions from the top and the base are

$$\oint_S d\mathbf{A} \cdot \mathbf{r} = (r + dr)^2 \, d\phi \, (r + dr) - r^2 \, d\phi r \approx 3r^2 \, dr \, d\phi$$

Therefore

$$\boldsymbol{\nabla} \cdot \mathbf{r} = \lim_{\mathscr{V} \to 0} \frac{\oint_S d\mathbf{A} \cdot \mathbf{r}}{\mathscr{V}} = \frac{3r^2 \, dr \, d\phi}{r^2 \, d\phi \, dr} = 3 \qquad \text{(A-69)}$$

To show that the curl of the position vector $\mathbf{r}$ vanishes, that is, that

$$\boldsymbol{\nabla} \times \mathbf{r} = \mathbf{0} \qquad \text{(A-70)}$$

is left as a problem assignment.

A-11.   VECTOR RELATIONS IN A RECTANGULAR CARTESIAN COORDINATE SYSTEM x, y, z

Consider a right-handed rectangular cartesian coordinate system as shown in Fig. A-21.[5] The base unit vectors $\mathbf{i}, \mathbf{j}, \mathbf{k}$ are constant and parallel

---

[5] By a right-handed coordinate system x_1, x_2, x_3 we mean a system in which, if we rotate the x_1-axis toward the x_2-axis, the direction of advancement of a right-handed screw is in the direction of the positive x_3-axis.   We will concern ourselves only with right-handed coordinate systems.

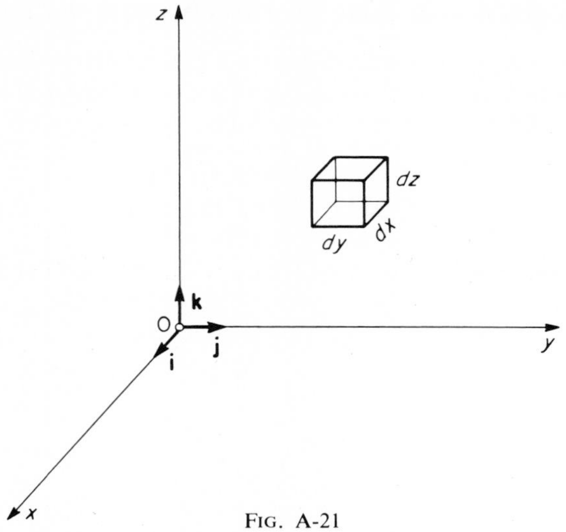

FIG. A-21

to the axes x, y, and z, respectively. Any vector $\mathbf{V}(x, y, z, t)$ in space can be represented in this system in the form

$$\mathbf{V} = V_x(x, y, z, t)\,\mathbf{i} + V_y(x, y, z, t)\,\mathbf{j} + V_z(x, y, z, t)\,\mathbf{k} \qquad \text{(A-71)}$$

where V_x, V_y, V_z are the components of vector $\mathbf{V}$ in directions x, y, z, and where t denotes time. The following relations between the unit vectors $\mathbf{i}, \mathbf{j}, \mathbf{k}$ hold:

$$\left.\begin{array}{lll} \mathbf{i}\cdot\mathbf{i} = 1, & \mathbf{j}\cdot\mathbf{j} = 1, & \mathbf{k}\cdot\mathbf{k} = 1 \\ \mathbf{i}\cdot\mathbf{j} = 0, & \mathbf{j}\cdot\mathbf{k} = 0, & \mathbf{k}\cdot\mathbf{i} = 0 \end{array}\right\} \qquad \text{(A-72)}$$

and

$$\left.\begin{array}{lll} \mathbf{i}\times\mathbf{i} = \mathbf{0}, & \mathbf{j}\times\mathbf{j} = \mathbf{0}, & \mathbf{k}\times\mathbf{k} = \mathbf{0} \\ \mathbf{i}\times\mathbf{j} = \mathbf{k}, & \mathbf{j}\times\mathbf{k} = \mathbf{i}, & \mathbf{k}\times\mathbf{i} = \mathbf{j} \end{array}\right\} \qquad \text{(A-73)}$$

The scalar product of two vectors $\mathbf{V}$ and $\mathbf{U}$ can be written in the form

$$\begin{aligned} \mathbf{V}\cdot\mathbf{U} &= (V_x\mathbf{i} + V_y\mathbf{j} + V_z\mathbf{k})\cdot(U_x\mathbf{i} + U_y\mathbf{j} + U_z\mathbf{k}) \\ &= V_xU_x + V_yU_y + V_zU_z \end{aligned} \qquad \text{(A-74)}$$

For the cross product of vectors $\mathbf{V}$ and $\mathbf{U}$, we obtain

$$\begin{aligned} \mathbf{V}\times\mathbf{U} &= (V_x\mathbf{i} + V_y\mathbf{j} + V_z\mathbf{k}) \times (U_x\mathbf{i} + U_y\mathbf{j} + U_z\mathbf{k}) \\ &= (V_yU_z - V_zU_y)\,\mathbf{i} + (V_zU_x - V_xU_z)\,\mathbf{j} + (V_xU_y - V_yU_x)\,\mathbf{k} \end{aligned} \qquad \text{(A-75)}$$

In a concise form the cross product of vectors $\mathbf{V}$ and $\mathbf{U}$ can be written in the form of the determinant

$$\mathbf{V}\times\mathbf{U} = \begin{vmatrix} \mathbf{i} & \mathbf{j} & \mathbf{k} \\ V_x & V_y & V_z \\ U_x & U_y & U_z \end{vmatrix} \qquad \text{(A-75a)}$$

The expression for the scalar triple product $\mathbf{W} \cdot (\mathbf{V} \times \mathbf{U})$ becomes

$$\mathbf{W} \cdot (\mathbf{V} \times \mathbf{U}) = \begin{vmatrix} W_x & W_y & W_z \\ V_x & V_y & V_z \\ U_x & U_y & U_z \end{vmatrix} = \begin{vmatrix} W_x & V_x & U_x \\ W_y & V_y & U_y \\ W_z & V_z & U_z \end{vmatrix} \qquad (A\text{-}76)$$

The expression for the gradient of a scalar-field function f can be obtained from Eq. A-35 or Eq. A-38. We will derive it, making use of Eq. A-38. With f denoting the value of the scalar-field function at the center of an infinitesimal volume element, as shown in Fig. A-21, we obtain

$$\text{grad } f = \lim_{\mathcal{V} \to 0} \frac{\oint_S d\mathbf{A}\, f}{\mathcal{V}}$$

$$= \left[\mathbf{i}\, dy\, dz \left(f + \frac{1}{2} \frac{\partial f}{\partial x} dx \right) - \mathbf{i}\, dy\, dz \left(f - \frac{1}{2} \frac{\partial f}{\partial x} dx \right) \right.$$

$$+ \mathbf{j}\, dx\, dz \left(f + \frac{1}{2} \frac{\partial f}{\partial y} dy \right) - \mathbf{j}\, dx\, dz \left(f - \frac{1}{2} \frac{\partial f}{\partial y} dy \right)$$

$$\left. + \mathbf{k}\, dx\, dy \left(f + \frac{1}{2} \frac{\partial f}{\partial z} dz \right) - \mathbf{k}\, dx\, dy \left(f - \frac{1}{2} \frac{\partial f}{\partial z} dz \right) \right] / dx\, dy\, dz$$

$$= \mathbf{i} \frac{\partial f}{\partial x} + \mathbf{j} \frac{\partial f}{\partial y} + \mathbf{k} \frac{\partial f}{\partial z} = \nabla f \qquad (A\text{-}77)$$

In this derivation we assumed that the value of the scalar-field function is constant on each side of the infinitesimal volume element. That the above expression satisfies Eq. A-35 can be shown by forming scalar products of this expression with the base unit vectors $\mathbf{i}$, $\mathbf{j}$, and $\mathbf{k}$.

From Eq. A-77 we can conclude that in a rectangular cartesian co-ordinate system the vector operator ∇ can be represented in the form

$$\nabla = \mathbf{i} \frac{\partial}{\partial x} + \mathbf{j} \frac{\partial}{\partial y} + \mathbf{k} \frac{\partial}{\partial z} \qquad (A\text{-}78)$$

Note that in the expression for ∇ the base unit vectors should precede the partial-differentiation symbols. Although this is of little importance in the case of a rectangular cartesian coordinate system, in which the base unit vectors of the vector on which ∇ operates are independent of x, y, and z, it is important in curvilinear coordinate systems in which the base unit vectors are functions of the coordinate parameters.

The expression for the divergence of a vector-field function $\mathbf{V} = V_x \mathbf{i} + V_y \mathbf{j} + V_z \mathbf{k}$ at some point in space can be obtained by forming the scalar product of ∇ with $\mathbf{V}$:

$$\text{div } \mathbf{V} = \boldsymbol{\nabla} \cdot \mathbf{V} = \left(\mathbf{i}\, \frac{\partial}{\partial x} + \mathbf{j}\, \frac{\partial}{\partial y} + \mathbf{k}\, \frac{\partial}{\partial z} \right) \cdot \mathbf{V}$$

$$= \mathbf{i} \cdot \frac{\partial \mathbf{V}}{\partial x} + \mathbf{j} \cdot \frac{\partial \mathbf{V}}{\partial y} + \mathbf{k} \cdot \frac{\partial \mathbf{V}}{\partial z}$$

$$= \mathbf{i} \cdot \frac{\partial (V_x \mathbf{i} + V_y \mathbf{j} + V_z \mathbf{k})}{\partial x} + \mathbf{j} \cdot \frac{\partial (V_x \mathbf{i} + V_y \mathbf{j} + V_z \mathbf{k})}{\partial y}$$

$$+ \mathbf{k} \cdot \frac{\partial (V_x \mathbf{i} + V_y \mathbf{j} + V_z \mathbf{k})}{\partial z} \qquad\qquad \text{(A-79)}$$

$$= \frac{\partial V_x}{\partial x} + \frac{\partial V_y}{\partial y} + \frac{\partial V_z}{\partial z}$$

because the base unit vectors **i**, **j**, **k** are independent of the coordinate parameters x, y, z. The expression for the divergence of a vector field can also be derived by making use of Eq. A-36, which defines it. With $\mathbf{V} = V_x \mathbf{i} + V_y \mathbf{j} + V_z \mathbf{k}$ denoting the vector-field function at the center of an infinitesimal volume element, we obtain

$$\text{div } \mathbf{V} = \lim_{\mathscr{V} \to 0} \frac{\oint_S d\mathbf{A} \cdot \mathbf{V}}{\mathscr{V}}$$

$$= \left[(\mathbf{i}\, dy\, dz) \cdot \left(\mathbf{V} + \frac{1}{2} \frac{\partial \mathbf{V}}{\partial x}\, dx \right) - (\mathbf{i}\, dy\, dz) \cdot \left(\mathbf{V} - \frac{1}{2} \frac{\partial \mathbf{V}}{\partial x}\, dx \right) \right.$$

$$+ (\mathbf{j}\, dx\, dz) \cdot \left(\mathbf{V} + \frac{1}{2} \frac{\partial \mathbf{V}}{\partial y}\, dy \right) - (\mathbf{j}\, dx\, dz) \cdot \left(\mathbf{V} - \frac{1}{2} \frac{\partial \mathbf{V}}{\partial y}\, dy \right)$$

$$+ (\mathbf{k}\, dx\, dy) \cdot \left(\mathbf{V} + \frac{1}{2} \frac{\partial \mathbf{V}}{\partial z}\, dz \right)$$

$$\left. - (\mathbf{k}\, dx\, dy) \cdot \left(\mathbf{V} - \frac{1}{2} \frac{\partial \mathbf{V}}{\partial z}\, dz \right) \right] / dx\, dy\, dz$$

$$= \frac{\partial V_x}{\partial x} + \frac{\partial V_y}{\partial y} + \frac{\partial V_z}{\partial z} = \boldsymbol{\nabla} \cdot \mathbf{V}$$

The Laplacian operator, defined as $\boldsymbol{\nabla}^2 = \boldsymbol{\nabla} \cdot \boldsymbol{\nabla}$, can be expressed as

$$\boldsymbol{\nabla}^2 = \left(\mathbf{i}\, \frac{\partial}{\partial x} + \mathbf{j}\, \frac{\partial}{\partial y} + \mathbf{k}\, \frac{\partial}{\partial z} \right) \cdot \left(\mathbf{i}\, \frac{\partial}{\partial x} + \mathbf{j}\, \frac{\partial}{\partial y} + \mathbf{k}\, \frac{\partial}{\partial z} \right)$$

$$= \mathbf{i} \cdot \frac{\partial \left(\mathbf{i}\, \frac{\partial}{\partial x} + \mathbf{j}\, \frac{\partial}{\partial y} + \mathbf{k}\, \frac{\partial}{\partial z} \right)}{\partial x} + \mathbf{j} \cdot \frac{\partial \left(\mathbf{i}\, \frac{\partial}{\partial x} + \mathbf{j}\, \frac{\partial}{\partial y} + \mathbf{k}\, \frac{\partial}{\partial z} \right)}{\partial y}$$

$$+ \mathbf{k} \cdot \frac{\partial \left(\mathbf{i}\, \frac{\partial}{\partial x} + \mathbf{j}\, \frac{\partial}{\partial y} + \mathbf{k}\, \frac{\partial}{\partial z} \right)}{\partial z} = \frac{\partial^2}{\partial x^2} + \frac{\partial^2}{\partial y^2} + \frac{\partial^2}{\partial z^2} \qquad \text{(A-80)}$$

With the Laplacian operator we can operate on scalar or vector-field functions. When operating on a vector-field function $\mathbf{V} = V_x\mathbf{i} + V_y\mathbf{j} + V_z\mathbf{k}$, we obtain

$$\nabla^2\mathbf{V} = \frac{\partial^2\mathbf{V}}{\partial x^2} + \frac{\partial^2\mathbf{V}}{\partial y^2} + \frac{\partial^2\mathbf{V}}{\partial z^2}$$

$$= \left(\frac{\partial^2 V_x}{\partial x^2} + \frac{\partial^2 V_x}{\partial y^2} + \frac{\partial^2 V_x}{\partial z^2}\right)\mathbf{i} + \left(\frac{\partial^2 V_y}{\partial x^2} + \frac{\partial^2 V_y}{\partial y^2} + \frac{\partial^2 V_y}{\partial z^2}\right)\mathbf{j}$$

$$+ \left(\frac{\partial^2 V_z}{\partial x^2} + \frac{\partial^2 V_z}{\partial y^2} + \frac{\partial^2 V_z}{\partial z^2}\right)\mathbf{k} \quad \text{(A-81)}$$

For the curl of a vector-field function $\mathbf{V}$ at some point in space, we obtain

$$\text{curl } \mathbf{V} = \nabla \times \mathbf{V} = \left(\mathbf{i}\frac{\partial}{\partial x} + \mathbf{j}\frac{\partial}{\partial y} + \mathbf{k}\frac{\partial}{\partial z}\right) \times \mathbf{V}$$

$$= \mathbf{i} \times \frac{\partial\mathbf{V}}{\partial x} + \mathbf{j} \times \frac{\partial\mathbf{V}}{\partial y} + \mathbf{k} \times \frac{\partial\mathbf{V}}{\partial z}$$

$$= \mathbf{i} \times \frac{\partial(V_x\mathbf{i} + V_y\mathbf{i} + V_z\mathbf{k})}{\partial x} + \mathbf{j} \times \frac{\partial(V_x\mathbf{i} + V_y\mathbf{j} + V_z\mathbf{k})}{\partial y}$$

$$+ \mathbf{k} \times \frac{\partial(V_x\mathbf{i} + V_y\mathbf{j} + V_z\mathbf{k})}{\partial z} = \left(\frac{\partial V_z}{\partial y} - \frac{\partial V_y}{\partial z}\right)\mathbf{i}$$

$$+ \left(\frac{\partial V_x}{\partial z} - \frac{\partial V_z}{\partial x}\right)\mathbf{j} + \left(\frac{\partial V_y}{\partial x} - \frac{\partial V_x}{\partial y}\right)\mathbf{k} \quad \text{(A-82)}$$

which can be represented in the form

$$\text{curl } \mathbf{V} = \nabla \times \mathbf{V} = \begin{vmatrix} \mathbf{i} & \mathbf{j} & \mathbf{k} \\ \dfrac{\partial}{\partial x} & \dfrac{\partial}{\partial y} & \dfrac{\partial}{\partial z} \\ V_x & V_y & V_z \end{vmatrix} \quad \text{(A-82a)}$$

The expression for curl $\mathbf{V}$ can also be obtained by making use of the Eq. A-37, which defines it. We will make such a derivation in the next section.

The expression for the scalar operator $\mathbf{V} \cdot \nabla$ becomes

$$\mathbf{V} \cdot \nabla = \mathbf{V} \cdot \left(\mathbf{i}\frac{\partial}{\partial x} + \mathbf{j}\frac{\partial}{\partial y} + \mathbf{k}\frac{\partial}{\partial z}\right)$$

$$= \mathbf{V} \cdot \mathbf{i}\frac{\partial}{\partial x} + \mathbf{V} \cdot \mathbf{j}\frac{\partial}{\partial y} + \mathbf{V} \cdot \mathbf{k}\frac{\partial}{\partial z}$$

$$= V_x\frac{\partial}{\partial x} + V_y\frac{\partial}{\partial y} + V_z\frac{\partial}{\partial z} \quad \text{(A-83)}$$

When operating with the scalar operator $\mathbf{V} \cdot \boldsymbol{\nabla}$ on a vector $\mathbf{U} = U_x\mathbf{i} + U_y\mathbf{j} + U_z\mathbf{k}$, we obtain

$$\mathbf{V} \cdot \boldsymbol{\nabla} \mathbf{U} = V_x \frac{\partial \mathbf{U}}{\partial x} + V_y \frac{\partial \mathbf{U}}{\partial y} + V_z \frac{\partial \mathbf{U}}{\partial z}$$

$$= \left(V_x \frac{\partial U_x}{\partial x} + V_y \frac{\partial U_x}{\partial y} + V_z \frac{\partial U_x}{\partial z} \right) \mathbf{i}$$

$$+ \left(V_x \frac{\partial U_y}{\partial x} + V_y \frac{\partial U_y}{\partial y} + V_z \frac{\partial U_y}{\partial z} \right) \mathbf{j}$$

$$+ \left(V_x \frac{\partial U_z}{\partial x} + V_y \frac{\partial U_z}{\partial y} + V_z \frac{\partial U_z}{\partial z} \right) \mathbf{k} \qquad \text{(A-84)}$$

which can also be written in the form

$$\mathbf{V} \cdot \boldsymbol{\nabla} \mathbf{U} = (\mathbf{V} \cdot \boldsymbol{\nabla} U_x)\mathbf{i} + (\mathbf{V} \cdot \boldsymbol{\nabla} U_y)\mathbf{j} + (\mathbf{V} \cdot \boldsymbol{\nabla} U_z)\mathbf{k} \qquad \text{(A-85)}$$

because the unit vectors $\mathbf{i}, \mathbf{j}, \mathbf{k}$ are constant and do not depend on the coordinates x, y, z. Operating with the scalar operator $\mathbf{V} \cdot \boldsymbol{\nabla}$ on a scalar-field function f yields

$$\mathbf{V} \cdot \boldsymbol{\nabla} f = V_x \frac{\partial f}{\partial x} + V_y \frac{\partial f}{\partial y} + V_z \frac{\partial f}{\partial z} \qquad \text{(A-86)}$$

A-12. VECTOR RELATIONS IN AN ORTHOGONAL CURVILINEAR COORDINATE SYSTEM

As will become apparent in our study, it is often very convenient to use other than rectangular cartesian coordinates when analyzing fluid flows. For example, in the case of three-dimensional flows with axial symmetry, the use of cylindrical coordinates reduces the number of independent variables to two, thus simplifying the boundary conditions. Similar simplification of the mathematical description arises in the case of conical flows when they are studied in spherical coordinates.

Consider a transformation from rectangular cartesian coordinates x, y, z to curvilinear coordinates given by

$$\left. \begin{array}{l} u_1 = F_1(x, y, z) \\ u_2 = F_2(x, y, z) \\ u_3 = F_3(x, y, z) \end{array} \right\} \qquad \text{(A-87)}$$

where u_1, u_2, and u_3 represent three independent, single-valued, and continuous scalar-field functions. We assume that there is a unique correspondence between the two coordinate systems so that to each point in space there corresponds a unique set of values for u_1, u_2, and u_3 and to each set of values for u_1, u_2, and u_3 there corresponds one point in space, and that the functions u_1, u_2, and u_3 can be solved for x, y, and z to give

$$\left.\begin{array}{l} x = f_1(u_1, u_2, u_3) \\ y = f_2(u_1, u_2, u_3) \\ z = f_3(u_1, u_2, u_3) \end{array}\right\} \qquad \text{(A-88)}$$

Equation A-87 defines three surfaces u_1 = const., u_2 = const., and u_3 = const. The line of intersection of two of these surfaces represents a coordinate curve along which the third coordinate varies. Thus, the line of intersection of surfaces u_2 = const. and u_3 = const. represents the u_1 curve on which coordinate u_1 is variable.

We will consider only orthogonal coordinate curves which form a right-handed system, such as that shown in Fig. A-22. The following

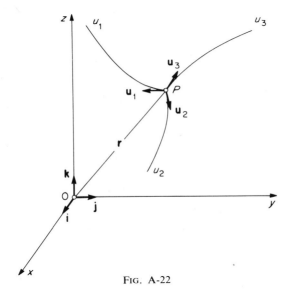

FIG. A-22

relations hold for the base unit vectors $\mathbf{u}_1$, $\mathbf{u}_2$, $\mathbf{u}_3$ along the coordinate curves u_1, u_2, and u_3.

$$\left.\begin{array}{lll} \mathbf{u}_1 \cdot \mathbf{u}_1 = 1, & \mathbf{u}_2 \cdot \mathbf{u}_2 = 1, & \mathbf{u}_3 \cdot \mathbf{u}_3 = 1 \\ \mathbf{u}_1 \cdot \mathbf{u}_2 = 0, & \mathbf{u}_2 \cdot \mathbf{u}_3 = 0, & \mathbf{u}_3 \cdot \mathbf{u}_1 = 0 \end{array}\right\} \qquad \text{(A-89)}$$

and

$$\left.\begin{array}{lll} \mathbf{u}_1 \times \mathbf{u}_1 = \mathbf{0}, & \mathbf{u}_2 \times \mathbf{u}_2 = \mathbf{0}, & \mathbf{u}_3 \times \mathbf{u}_3 = \mathbf{0} \\ \mathbf{u}_1 \times \mathbf{u}_2 = \mathbf{u}_3, & \mathbf{u}_2 \times \mathbf{u}_3 = \mathbf{u}_1, & \mathbf{u}_3 \times \mathbf{u}_1 = \mathbf{u}_2 \end{array}\right\} \qquad \text{(A-90)}$$

The vector ∇u_1 at some point $P(x, y, z)$ is perpendicular to the surface u_1 = constant and hence is parallel to the unit vector $\mathbf{u}_1$. Consider a vector $d\mathbf{r}_1$, tangent at some point P to the coordinate curve u_1, and having a magnitude of the differential arc length along this curve ds_1. We have

$$d\mathbf{r}_1 = \mathbf{u}_1\, ds_1 = h_1\, \nabla u_1\, ds_1$$

where h_1 is the proportionality factor between the unit vector $\mathbf{u}_1$ and the vector ∇u_1. Forming the scalar product of $d\mathbf{r}_1$ with $\mathbf{u}_1$, we obtain

$$d\mathbf{r}_1 \cdot \mathbf{u}_1 = ds_1 = h_1 ds_1 \mathbf{u}_1 \cdot \nabla u_1 = h_1 ds_1 \frac{\partial u_1}{\partial s_1} = h_1\, du_1 \qquad (A\text{-}91)$$

in view of Eq. A-35. Therefore,

$$ds_1 = h_1\, du_1$$

Similarly,

$$ds_2 = h_2\, du_2 \qquad\qquad (A\text{-}92)$$

and

$$ds_3 = h_3\, du_3$$

As a result,

$$d\mathbf{r} = \mathbf{u}_1 ds_1 + \mathbf{u}_2 ds_2 + \mathbf{u}_3 ds_3 = h_1 \mathbf{u}_1 du_1 + h_2 \mathbf{u}_2 du_2 + h_3 \mathbf{u}_3 du_3 \qquad (A\text{-}93)$$

Thus the factor h represents the ratio of the differential arc lengths, or distances, to the differentials of the coordinate parameters. They are, in general, functions of the coordinate parameters u_1, u_2, u_3.

Since we are considering only orthogonal coordinates, the square of the element of length of a curve in space is

$$(ds)^2 = (ds_1)^2 + (ds_2)^2 + (ds_3)^2 = h_1^2 (du_1)^2 + h_2^2 (du_2)^2 + h_3^2 (du_3)^2 \tag{A-94}$$

The infinitesimal element of volume can be expressed as

$$d\mathcal{V} = ds_1 ds_2 ds_3 = h_1 h_2 h_3 du_1 du_2 du_3 \qquad (A\text{-}95)$$

The scalar product of two vectors $\mathbf{V} = V_1\mathbf{u}_1 + V_2\mathbf{u}_2 + V_3\mathbf{u}_3$ and $\mathbf{U} = U_1\mathbf{u}_1 + U_2\mathbf{u}_2 + U_3\mathbf{u}_3$, where subscripts 1, 2, 3 refer to the coordinates u_1, u_2, u_3, can be written as

$$\begin{aligned}\mathbf{V} \cdot \mathbf{U} &= (V_1\mathbf{u}_1 + V_2\mathbf{u}_2 + V_3\mathbf{u}_3) \cdot (U_1\mathbf{u}_1 + U_2\mathbf{u}_2 + U_3\mathbf{u}_3) \\ &= V_1 U_1 + V_2 U_2 + V_3 U_3 \end{aligned} \qquad (A\text{-}96)$$

For the cross product $\mathbf{V} \times \mathbf{U}$, we obtain

$$\mathbf{V} \times \mathbf{U} = \begin{vmatrix} \mathbf{u}_1 & \mathbf{u}_2 & \mathbf{u}_3 \\ V_1 & V_2 & V_3 \\ U_1 & U_2 & U_3 \end{vmatrix} \qquad (A\text{-}97)$$

Since

$$d\mathbf{r} = h_1 du_1 \mathbf{u}_1 + h_2 du_2 \mathbf{u}_2 + h_3 du_3 \mathbf{u}_3$$

we have

$$\frac{\partial \mathbf{r}}{\partial u_1} = h_1 \mathbf{u}_1; \qquad \frac{\partial \mathbf{r}}{\partial u_2} = h_2 \mathbf{u}_2; \qquad \frac{\partial \mathbf{r}}{\partial u_3} = h_3 \mathbf{u}_3$$

As a result we can write

$$\frac{\partial (h_1 \mathbf{u}_1)}{\partial u_2} = \frac{\partial (h_2 \mathbf{u}_2)}{\partial u_1} \tag{a}$$

$$\frac{\partial (h_1 \mathbf{u}_1)}{\partial u_3} = \frac{\partial (h_3 \mathbf{u}_3)}{\partial u_1} \tag{b}$$

$$\frac{\partial (h_2 \mathbf{u}_2)}{\partial u_3} = \frac{\partial (h_3 \mathbf{u}_3)}{\partial u_2} \tag{c}$$

For relation (a) it follows that

$$h_1 \frac{\partial \mathbf{u}_1}{\partial u_2} - h_2 \frac{\partial \mathbf{u}_2}{\partial u_1} = \mathbf{u}_2 \frac{\partial h_2}{\partial u_1} - \mathbf{u}_1 \frac{\partial h_1}{\partial u_2}$$

and, since the vector $\partial \mathbf{u}_1 / \partial u_2$ is parallel to $\mathbf{u}_2$, while the vector $\partial \mathbf{u}_2 / \partial u_1$ is parallel to $\mathbf{u}_1$, we obtain relations

$$\frac{\partial \mathbf{u}_1}{\partial u_2} = \frac{\mathbf{u}_2}{h_1} \frac{\partial h_2}{\partial u_1}$$

$$\frac{\partial \mathbf{u}_2}{\partial u_1} = \frac{\mathbf{u}_1}{h_2} \frac{\partial h_1}{\partial u_2}$$

Similar expressions can be obtained from relations (b) and (c). Since $\mathbf{u}_1 = \mathbf{u}_2 \times \mathbf{u}_3$, we have

$$\frac{\partial \mathbf{u}_1}{\partial u_1} = \frac{\partial \mathbf{u}_2}{\partial u_1} \times \mathbf{u}_3 + \mathbf{u}_2 \times \frac{\partial \mathbf{u}_3}{\partial u_1}$$

$$= -\frac{\mathbf{u}_2}{h_2} \frac{\partial h_1}{\partial u_2} - \frac{\mathbf{u}_3}{h_3} \frac{\partial h_1}{\partial u_3} \tag{d}$$

In similar way we obtain expressions

$$\frac{\partial \mathbf{u}_2}{\partial u_2} = -\frac{\mathbf{u}_1}{h_1} \frac{\partial h_2}{\partial u_1} - \frac{\mathbf{u}_3}{h_3} \frac{\partial h_2}{\partial u_3} \tag{e}$$

$$\frac{\partial \mathbf{u}_3}{\partial u_3} = -\frac{\mathbf{u}_1}{h_1} \frac{\partial h_3}{\partial u_1} - \frac{\mathbf{u}_2}{h_2} \frac{\partial h_3}{\partial u_2} \tag{f}$$

The expression for the gradient of a scalar-field function becomes (see Fig. A-23)

$$\operatorname{grad} f = \lim_{\mathscr{V} \to 0} \frac{\oint_S d\mathbf{A} f}{\mathscr{V}}$$

$$= \left\{ \mathbf{u}_1 (h_2 \, du_2 h_3 \, du_3) f + \frac{\partial}{\partial u_1} \left[\mathbf{u}_1 (h_2 \, du_2 h_3 \, du_3) f \right] du_1 \right.$$

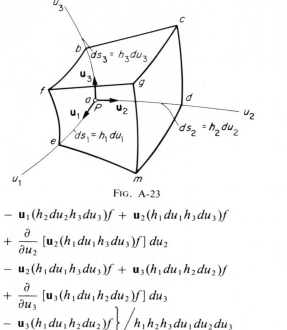

FIG. A-23

$$- \mathbf{u}_1 (h_2 du_2 h_3 du_3) f + \mathbf{u}_2 (h_1 du_1 h_3 du_3) f$$

$$+ \frac{\partial}{\partial u_2} [\mathbf{u}_2 (h_1 du_1 h_3 du_3) f] \, du_2$$

$$- \mathbf{u}_2 (h_1 du_1 h_3 du_3) f + \mathbf{u}_3 (h_1 du_1 h_2 du_2) f$$

$$+ \frac{\partial}{\partial u_3} [\mathbf{u}_3 (h_1 du_1 h_2 du_2) f] \, du_3$$

$$\left. - \mathbf{u}_3 (h_1 du_1 h_2 du_2) f \right\} \bigg/ h_1 h_2 h_3 \, du_1 \, du_2 \, du_3$$

$$= \frac{\mathbf{u}_1}{h_1} \frac{\partial f}{\partial u_1} + \frac{\mathbf{u}_2}{h_2} \frac{\partial f}{\partial u_2} + \frac{\mathbf{u}_3}{h_3} \frac{\partial f}{\partial u_3}$$

$$+ \frac{f}{h_1 h_2 h_3} \left[\frac{\partial (\mathbf{u}_1 h_2 h_3)}{\partial u_1} + \frac{\partial (\mathbf{u}_2 h_1 h_3)}{\partial u_2} + \frac{\partial (\mathbf{u}_3 h_1 h_2)}{\partial u_3} \right]$$

which reduces to

$$\operatorname{grad} f = \nabla f = \frac{\mathbf{u}_1}{h_1} \frac{\partial f}{\partial u_1} + \frac{\mathbf{u}_2}{h_2} \frac{\partial f}{\partial u_2} + \frac{\mathbf{u}_3}{h_3} \frac{\partial f}{\partial u_3} \qquad \text{(A-98)}$$

in view of the relations (d), (e), and (f) given above.

The vector operator ∇ has, thus, the following form in an orthogonal curvilinear coordinate system:

$$\nabla = \frac{\mathbf{u}_1}{h_1} \frac{\partial}{\partial u_1} + \frac{\mathbf{u}_2}{h_2} \frac{\partial}{\partial u_2} + \frac{\mathbf{u}_3}{h_3} \frac{\partial}{\partial u_3} \qquad \text{(A-99)}$$

As we have demonstrated, in a curvilinear coordinate system the base unit vectors $\mathbf{u}_1, \mathbf{u}_2, \mathbf{u}_3$ are, in general, functions of the coordinate parameters u_1, u_2, u_3. The expression for the divergence of a vector-field function $\mathbf{V} = V_1 \mathbf{u}_1 + V_2 \mathbf{u}_2 + V_3 \mathbf{u}_3$ can be obtained directly from the definition of div $\mathbf{V}$ (Eq. A-36). We have

$$\operatorname{div} \mathbf{V} = \lim_{\mathcal{V} \to 0} \frac{\oint_S \mathbf{n} \cdot \mathbf{V} \, dA}{\mathcal{V}} = \frac{\Sigma (V_n \, dA)}{d\mathcal{V}}$$

where V_n denotes the component of vector $\mathbf{V}$ in the direction of the outward normal to surface S bounding the infinitesimal volume element. Let us first consider the faces *abcd* and *efgm* of the volume element shown in Fig. A-23. Assuming the component V_1 in the direction u_1 to be constant on these faces, we obtain

$$\Sigma\, V_{n1}dA_1 \;=\; -V_1 h_2\, du_2\, h_3\, du_3 \;+\; V_1 h_2\, du_2\, h_3\, du_3 \;+\; \frac{\partial(V_1 h_2 du_2 h_3 du_3)}{h_1\, \partial u_1} h_1\, du_1$$

$$=\; \frac{\partial(V_1 h_2 h_3)}{\partial u_1} du_1\, du_2\, du_3$$

Similarly,

$$\Sigma\, V_{n2}dA_2 \;=\; \frac{\partial(V_2 h_1 h_3)}{\partial u_2} du_1\, du_2\, du_3$$

and

$$\Sigma\, V_{n3}dA_3 \;=\; \frac{\partial(V_3 h_1 h_2)}{\partial u_3} du_1\, du_2\, du_3$$

Therefore

$$\frac{\Sigma\, V_n dA}{d\mathcal{V}} \;=\; \frac{\left[\dfrac{\partial(V_1 h_2 h_3)}{\partial u_1} + \dfrac{\partial(V_2 h_1 h_3)}{\partial u_2} + \dfrac{\partial(V_3 h_1 h_2)}{\partial u_3}\right] du_1\, du_2\, du_3}{h_1 h_2 h_3 du_1 du_2 du_3}$$

and the expression for div $\mathbf{V} = \nabla \cdot \mathbf{V}$ becomes

$$\text{div } \mathbf{V} \;=\; \nabla \cdot \mathbf{V} \;=\; \frac{1}{h_1 h_2 h_3}\left[\frac{\partial(h_2 h_3 V_1)}{\partial u_1} + \frac{\partial(h_3 h_1 V_2)}{\partial u_2} + \frac{\partial(h_1 h_2 V_3)}{\partial u_3}\right] \quad \text{(A-100)}$$

Utilizing the above result and the expression for the vector operator ∇, we obtain the following expression for the Laplacian operator ∇^2:

$$\nabla^2 \;=\; \nabla \cdot \nabla \;=\; \frac{1}{h_1 h_2 h_3}\left[\frac{\partial}{\partial u_1}\left(\frac{h_2 h_3}{h_1}\frac{\partial}{\partial u_1}\right)\right.$$

$$\left. +\; \frac{\partial}{\partial u_2}\left(\frac{h_3 h_1}{h_2}\frac{\partial}{\partial u_2}\right) + \frac{\partial}{\partial u_3}\left(\frac{h_1 h_2}{h_3}\frac{\partial}{\partial u_3}\right)\right] \quad \text{(A-101)}$$

The expression in the u_1, u_2, u_3 coordinates for the curl of a vector field $\mathbf{V} = V_1\mathbf{u}_1 + V_2\mathbf{u}_2 + V_3\mathbf{u}_3$ can be derived by considering vector components normal to the surfaces $u_1 = $ const., $u_2 = $ const., $u_3 = $ const. and utilizing Eq. A-37, which defines the component of curl of a vector field, written in the form

$$\mathbf{n} \cdot \text{curl } \mathbf{V} \;=\; (\text{curl } \mathbf{V})_n \;=\; \frac{\Sigma\,(\mathbf{V} \cdot d\mathbf{r})}{dA_n}$$

The component of curl $\mathbf{V}$ in the direction of the u_1 coordinate is

$$\mathbf{u}_1 \cdot \text{curl } \mathbf{V} = (\text{curl } \mathbf{V})_{u_1}$$

$$= \left[V_2 h_2 du_2 + V_3 h_3 du_3 + \frac{\partial (V_3 h_3 du_3)}{h_2 \partial u_2} h_2 du_2 - V_2 h_2 du_2 \right.$$

$$\left. - \frac{\partial (V_2 h_2 du_2)}{h_3 \partial u_3} h_3 du_3 - V_3 h_3 du_3 \right] / h_2 du_3 h_3 du_3$$

$$= \frac{1}{h_2 h_3} \left[\frac{\partial (h_3 V_3)}{\partial u_2} - \frac{\partial (h_2 V_2)}{\partial u_3} \right]$$

Similarly, for the components of $\nabla \times \mathbf{V}$ in the directions of u_2 and u_3 coordinates, we obtain

$$\mathbf{u}_2 \cdot \text{curl } \mathbf{V} = (\text{curl } \mathbf{V})_{u_2} = \frac{1}{h_3 h_1} \left[\frac{\partial (h_1 V_1)}{\partial u_3} - \frac{\partial (h_3 V_3)}{\partial u_1} \right]$$

$$\mathbf{u}_3 \cdot \text{curl } \mathbf{V} = (\text{curl } \mathbf{V})_{u_3} = \frac{1}{h_1 h_2} \left[\frac{\partial (h_2 V_2)}{\partial u_1} - \frac{\partial (h_1 V_1)}{\partial u_2} \right]$$

Thus the curl of a vector-field function $\mathbf{V}$ can be expressed in the concise form as

$$\text{curl } \mathbf{V} = \nabla \times \mathbf{V} = \frac{1}{h_1 h_2 h_3} \begin{vmatrix} h_1 \mathbf{u}_1 & h_2 \mathbf{u}_2 & h_3 \mathbf{u}_3 \\ \dfrac{\partial}{\partial u_1} & \dfrac{\partial}{\partial u_2} & \dfrac{\partial}{\partial u_3} \\ h_1 V_1 & h_2 V_2 & h_3 V_3 \end{vmatrix} \qquad \text{(A-102)}$$

The expression for the scalar operator $\mathbf{V} \cdot \nabla$ can be written as

$$\mathbf{V} \cdot \nabla = \mathbf{V} \cdot \mathbf{u}_1 \frac{1}{h_1} \frac{\partial}{\partial u_1} + \mathbf{V} \cdot \mathbf{u}_2 \frac{1}{h_2} \frac{\partial}{\partial u_2} + \mathbf{V} \cdot \mathbf{u}_3 \frac{1}{h_3} \frac{\partial}{\partial u_3}$$

$$= \frac{V_1}{h_1} \frac{\partial}{\partial u_1} + \frac{V_2}{h_2} \frac{\partial}{\partial u_2} + \frac{V_3}{h_3} \frac{\partial}{\partial u_3} \qquad \text{(A-103)}$$

When operating with the scalar operator $\mathbf{V} \cdot \nabla$ on a vector, we must not forget that not only the components of this vector but also the base unit vectors $\mathbf{u}_1, \mathbf{u}_2, \mathbf{u}_3$ are, in general, functions of the coordinate parameters $u_1, u_2,$ and u_3.

A-13. VECTOR RELATIONS IN A CIRCULAR CYLINDRICAL COORDINATE SYSTEM r, θ, z

Consider a right-handed circular cylindrical coordinate system, as shown in Fig. A-24. With $u_1 = r, u_2 = \theta,$ and $u_3 = z$, the square of the

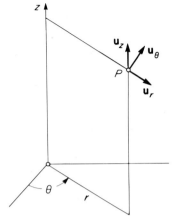

FIG. A-24

element of length of a curve in space is given by

$$(ds)^2 = (ds_1)^2 + (ds_2)^2 + (ds_3)^2 = (dr)^2 + r^2(d\theta)^2 + (dz)^2$$

From Eq. A-94 it follows that

$$h_r = 1, \qquad h_\theta = r, \qquad h_z = 1 \qquad (A\text{-}104)$$

As a result, we obtain

$$\text{grad } f = \nabla f = \mathbf{u}_r \frac{\partial f}{\partial r} + \frac{\mathbf{u}_\theta}{r} \frac{\partial f}{\partial \theta} + \mathbf{u}_z \frac{\partial f}{\partial z} \qquad (A\text{-}105)$$

$$\text{div } \mathbf{V} = \nabla \cdot \mathbf{V} = \frac{1}{r} \frac{\partial}{\partial r}(rV_r) + \frac{1}{r} \frac{\partial V_\theta}{\partial \theta} + \frac{\partial V_z}{\partial z} \qquad (A\text{-}106)$$

$$\nabla^2 f = \frac{1}{r} \frac{\partial}{\partial r}\left(r \frac{\partial f}{\partial r}\right) + \frac{1}{r^2} \frac{\partial^2 f}{\partial \theta^2} + \frac{\partial^2 f}{\partial z^2} \qquad (A\text{-}107)$$

$$\text{curl } \mathbf{V} = \nabla \times \mathbf{V} = \frac{1}{r} \begin{vmatrix} \mathbf{u}_r & r\mathbf{u}_\theta & \mathbf{u}_z \\ \dfrac{\partial}{\partial r} & \dfrac{\partial}{\partial \theta} & \dfrac{\partial}{\partial z} \\ V_r & rV_\theta & V_z \end{vmatrix} \qquad (A\text{-}108)$$

For the scalar operator $\mathbf{V} \cdot \nabla$, we obtain

$$\mathbf{V} \cdot \nabla = V_r \frac{\partial}{\partial r} + \frac{V_\theta}{r} \frac{\partial}{\partial \theta} + V_z \frac{\partial}{\partial z} \qquad (A\text{-}109)$$

A-14. VECTOR RELATIONS IN A SPHERICAL COORDINATE SYSTEM, r, θ, ϕ

With $u_1 = r$, $u_2 = \theta$, $u_3 = \phi$, the square of the element of length of a curve in space in a spherical coordinate system, shown in Fig. A-25, is

$$(ds)^2 = (ds_1)^2 + (ds_2)^2 + (ds_3)^2 = (dr)^2 + r^2(d\theta)^2 + r^2 \sin^2 \theta (d\phi)^2$$

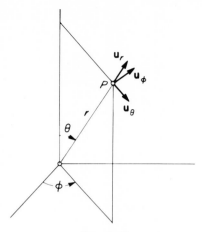

FIG. A-25

Hence

$$h_r = 1, \qquad h_\theta = r, \qquad h_\phi = r \sin \theta \qquad\qquad \text{(A-110)}$$

and we obtain the following expressions:

$$\text{grad } f = \nabla f = \mathbf{u}_r \frac{\partial f}{\partial r} + \frac{\mathbf{u}_\theta}{r} \frac{\partial f}{\partial \theta} + \frac{\mathbf{u}_\phi}{r \sin \theta} \frac{\partial f}{\partial \phi} \qquad\qquad \text{(A-111)}$$

$$\text{div } \mathbf{V} = \nabla \cdot \mathbf{V} = \frac{1}{r^2} \frac{\partial}{\partial r} (r^2 V_r) + \frac{1}{r \sin \theta} \frac{\partial}{\partial \theta} (V_\theta \sin \theta) + \frac{1}{r \sin \theta} \frac{\partial V_\phi}{\partial \phi}$$

$$\text{(A-112)}$$

$$\nabla^2 f = \frac{1}{r^2} \frac{\partial}{\partial r} \left(r^2 \frac{\partial f}{\partial r} \right) + \frac{1}{r^2 \sin \theta} \frac{\partial}{\partial \theta} \left(\sin \theta \frac{\partial f}{\partial \theta} \right) + \frac{1}{r^2 \sin^2 \theta} \frac{\partial^2 f}{\partial \phi^2} \qquad \text{(A-113)}$$

$$\text{curl } \mathbf{V} = \nabla \times \mathbf{V} = \frac{1}{r^2 \sin \theta} \begin{vmatrix} \mathbf{u}_r & r\mathbf{u}_\theta & r \sin \theta\, \mathbf{u}_\phi \\ \dfrac{\partial}{\partial r} & \dfrac{\partial}{\partial \theta} & \dfrac{\partial}{\partial \phi} \\ V_r & rV_\theta & r \sin \theta\, V_\phi \end{vmatrix} \qquad \text{(A-114)}$$

$$\mathbf{V} \cdot \nabla = V_r \frac{\partial}{\partial r} + \frac{V_\theta}{r} \frac{\partial}{\partial \theta} + \frac{V_\phi}{r \sin \theta} \frac{\partial}{\partial \phi} \qquad\qquad \text{(A-115)}$$

A-15. INTENSITY OF THE GRAVITATIONAL FIELD AND THE GRAVITATIONAL POTENTIAL

According to Newton's law, the gravitational force which the matter in an element of volume $d\mathcal{V}$ at some point O in space exerts on a unit mass at some point P (Fig. A-26), or the intensity of the gravitational

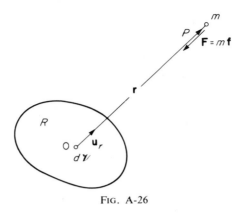

FIG. A-26

field **f**, is given by

$$d\mathbf{f} = -k \frac{\mathbf{u}_r}{r^2} \rho \, d\mathcal{V} \tag{A-116}$$

where ρ denotes the density of the matter at O, and k is a proportionality constant which depends on units. If the unit mass is chosen as the concentrated mass of each of two bodies which, when a unit distance apart, attract each other with a unit force, then $k = 1$, and we can write

$$d\mathbf{f} = -\frac{\mathbf{u}_r}{r^2} \rho \, d\mathcal{V} = \nabla \left(\frac{1}{r}\right) \rho \, d\mathcal{V} = \nabla \left(\frac{\rho}{r}\right) d\mathcal{V}$$

where the vector operator ∇ operates only on r.

The intensity of the gravitational field at P, which is due to the matter in the region R, is

$$\mathbf{f} = -\int \frac{\mathbf{u}_r}{r^2} \rho \, d\mathcal{V} = \int \nabla \left(\frac{\rho}{r}\right) d\mathcal{V} = \nabla \int \frac{\rho}{r} \, d\mathcal{V} = \nabla V \tag{A-117}$$

where V is the (scalar) potential of density ρ, known as the *gravitational potential*. Thus, the gravitational force intensity is a potential vector.

Equation A-117 indicates that

$$\nabla \times \mathbf{f} = 0$$

which means that the intensity of the gravitational field is lamellar.

The line integral of **f**, along any closed path, vanishes:

$$\oint_C \mathbf{f} \cdot d\mathbf{r} = 0$$

A force field for which the above equation is valid anywhere in the region considered is called a *conservative force field*.

The work done by such a force field on a unit mass (concentrated to a point) represents the difference between the gravitational potential at the initial and final positions of the unit mass:

$$w = \int_1^2 \mathbf{f} \cdot d\mathbf{r} = \int_1^2 \nabla V \cdot d\mathbf{r} = V_2 - V_1 \qquad \text{(A-118)}$$

The *potential energy Ω due to gravitational attraction per unit mass* is taken as being equal to $-V$, because the direction of force is always that in which the potential energy decreases most rapidly. Thus

$$\mathbf{f} = \nabla V = -\nabla\Omega \qquad \text{(A-119)}$$

and the work of the gravitational force intensity $\mathbf{f}$

$$w = \int_1^2 \mathbf{f} \cdot d\mathbf{r} = \Omega_1 - \Omega_2 \qquad \text{(A-120)}$$

is positive when the potential energy decreases.

Making use of Eqs. A-116 and A-119, it is easy to show that the potential energy of gravitational attraction on the earth can be represented in the form

$$\Omega = -\frac{kM}{r} = -g(r)r = -g_0\frac{r_0^2}{r} \qquad \text{(A-121)}$$

where $M = \int \rho\, d\mathcal{V}$ is the mass of the earth, r is the distance coordinate pointing radially outward from the center of gravity of the earth, $g(r) = |\mathbf{f}| = kM/r^2 = g_0(r_0/r)^2$ is the magnitude of the acceleration due to gravity at r, and g_0 is the value of g at $r = r_0$. The derivation of the above equation is left as a problem assignment.

Note that

$$d\Omega = g_0\frac{r_0^2}{r^2}\,dr = g(r)\,dr$$

and that

$$\Omega_2 - \Omega_1 = -g_0 r_0^2\left(\frac{1}{r_2} - \frac{1}{r_1}\right)$$
$$= -g_2 r_2 + g_1 r_1$$

Since

$$g_2 = g_1\frac{r_1^2}{r_2^2}$$

we obtain

$$-w = \Omega_2 - \Omega_1 = g_1\frac{r_1}{r_2}(r_2 - r_1) \qquad \text{(A-122)}$$

Therefore, only when $r_1/r_2 \simeq 1$ can we, as an approximation, consider the magnitude of the gravitational acceleration to be constant, when determining the change in the potential energy Ω.

Also note that the value of the potential energy at $r = \infty$ is 0 and at $r = 0$ is $-\infty$.

REFERENCES

1. J. W. Gibbs, (by E. B. Wilson). *Vector Analysis*. (First published in 1901.), New Haven: Yale U. P., 1922.

2. W. Ignatowsky, *Die Vektroanalysis*. 3rd ed. (First published in 1909.) Leipzig: Teubner, 1926.

3. A. P. Willis, *Vector Analysis with an Introduction to Tensor Analysis*. (First published in 1931.) New York: Dover, 1958.

4. R. Gans, *Vector Analysis* (trans. from 6th German ed., 1931.) Glasgow: Blackie, 1950.

5. C. E. Weatherburn, *Advanced Vector Analysis*. London: Bell, 1924.

6. H. B. Phillips, *Vector Analysis*. New York: Wiley, 1959.

7. C. Truesdell, *The Kinematics of Vorticity*. Bloomington: Indiana U. P., 1954.

8. L. M. Milne-Thompson, *Theoretical Hydrodynamics*. 4th ed. New York: Macmillan, 1960.

PROBLEMS

A-1. If $\mathbf{w}$, $\mathbf{v}$, and $\mathbf{u}$, which are arbitrary noncoplanar vectors, are expressed in terms of vectors $\mathbf{W}$, $\mathbf{V}$, and $\mathbf{U}$ as

$$\mathbf{w} = a_1 \mathbf{W} + a_2 \mathbf{V} + a_3 \mathbf{U}$$

$$\mathbf{v} = b_1 \mathbf{W} + b_2 \mathbf{V} + b_3 \mathbf{U}$$

$$\mathbf{u} = c_1 \mathbf{W} + c_2 \mathbf{V} + c_3 \mathbf{U}$$

where the a's, b's and c's are appropriate constants, show that the volume $\mathcal{V}$ of the parallelepiped formed from vectors $\mathbf{w}$, $\mathbf{v}$, and $\mathbf{u}$ and the volume $\mathcal{V}_0$ of the parallelepiped formed from vectors $\mathbf{W}$, $\mathbf{V}$, and $\mathbf{U}$ are related by

$$\mathcal{V} = \begin{vmatrix} a_1 & a_2 & a_3 \\ b_1 & b_2 & b_3 \\ c_1 & c_2 & c_3 \end{vmatrix} \mathcal{V}_0$$

A-2. Derive vector relation (Eq. A-44):

$$\boldsymbol{\nabla}(f\rho) = f\boldsymbol{\nabla}\rho + \rho\boldsymbol{\nabla}f$$

A-3. Derive vector relation (Eq. A-45):

$$\boldsymbol{\nabla} \times (f\mathbf{F}) = \boldsymbol{\nabla}f \times \mathbf{F} + f\boldsymbol{\nabla} \times \mathbf{F}$$

A-4. Derive vector relation (Eq. A-46):

$$\boldsymbol{\nabla} \cdot (\mathbf{F} \times \mathbf{U}) = \mathbf{U} \cdot (\boldsymbol{\nabla} \times \mathbf{F}) - \mathbf{F} \cdot (\boldsymbol{\nabla} \times \mathbf{U})$$

A-5. Derive relation (Eq. A-55):

$$\oint_S \mathbf{F}(\mathbf{U} \cdot d\mathbf{A}) = \int_V [(\mathbf{U} \cdot \boldsymbol{\nabla})\mathbf{F} + \mathbf{F}(\boldsymbol{\nabla} \cdot \mathbf{U})]d\mathcal{V}$$

Start with the derivation of Eq. A-54.

A-6. Derive vector relation (Eq. A-58):

$$\nabla \times (\nabla \times U) = \nabla(\nabla \cdot U) - \nabla^2 U$$

A-7. Show that the curl of the position vector **r** is zero.

A-8. Derive the expression for the divergence of a vector field **U**, in a rectangular cartesian coordinate system, by considering the flux of **U** out of a volume element. Subsequently, derive the expression for the divergence of **U**, in a circular cylindrical coordinate system, by considering the flux of **U** out of the volume element shown here.

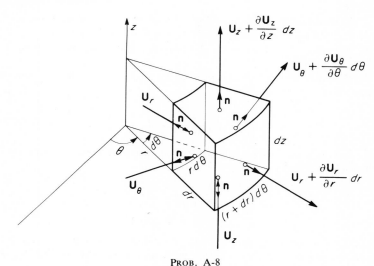

PROB. A-8

A-9. Show that the potential energy due to the gravitational attraction on earth is given by

$$\Omega = -\frac{kM}{r} = -g(r)r = -g_0 \frac{r_0^2}{r}$$

where r is the distance coordinate axis pointing radially outward the center of gravity of the earth, and $g(r) = |\mathbf{f}| = kM/r^2 = g_0(r_0/r)^2$ is the magnitude of the acceleration due to gravity at r. Sketch the variation of the potential energy Ω with r.

System of Units

In mechanics there are three systems of units in general use. In one of them, in the system known as the *absolute system*, the fundamental units are those of mass, length, and time. The second system is based on the units of force, length, and time. In the third system four fundamental units—those of mass, force, length, and time—are used.

The unit of force in the first (absolute) system, and the unit of mass in the second system are derived quantities. They are so defined that the Newton's second law of motion can be represented by

$$\mathbf{F} = m\mathbf{a}$$

with $\mathbf{F}$ denoting the force, m the mass, and $\mathbf{a}$ the acceleration.

The English units of mass, length, and time used in the first (absolute) system are pound mass (symbol: lbm), foot (ft), and second (sec). The derived unit of force, known as a *poundal*, is

$$1 \text{ poundal} = (1 \text{ lbm}) \left(1 \, \frac{\text{ft}}{\text{sec}^2} \right)$$

Thus, the force whose magnitude is one poundal is that force which results in an acceleration of 1 ft/sec^2 when acting on a mass of 1 lbm.

The English units of force, length, and time of the second system are pound force (lbf), foot (ft), and second (sec). The pound force, although used as a fundamental unit in the second system, is derived from the first (absolute) system. It is defined as the force that acts on the mass of 1 lbm at a point on the earth where the magnitude of the gravitational acceleration is 32.174 ft/sec^2. Such acceleration is known as the standard (gravitational) acceleration. The derived unit of mass in the second system, known as a *slug*, is

$$1 \text{ slug} = \frac{1 \text{ lbf}}{1 \, \dfrac{\text{ft}}{\text{sec}^2}}$$

The mass of 1 slug is the mass which accelerates at a rate of 1 ft/sec² when acted upon by a force of 1 lbf.

The English units of mass, force, length, and time in the third system are pound mass (lbm), pound force (lbf), foot (ft), and second (sec). When this system of units is used, the Newton's second law of motion has to be represented in the form of equation

$$\mathbf{F} = \frac{1}{g_0} m \mathbf{a}$$

where g_0 is the proportionality constant which makes the units on the left-hand side of the above equation the same as those on the right-hand side. From the definition of pound force it follows that

$$1 \text{ lbf} = \frac{1}{g_0} (1 \text{ lbm}) \left(32.174 \frac{\text{ft}}{\text{sec}^2} \right)$$

and, as a result,

$$g_0 = 32.174 \frac{\text{lbm ft}}{\text{lbf sec}^2}$$

In the first (absolute) and second systems of units, the numerical values of g_0 are unity, and we can write

$$g_0 = 1 \frac{\text{lbm ft}}{\text{poundal sec}^2} = 1$$

and

$$g_0 = 1 \frac{\text{slug ft}}{\text{lbf sec}^2} = 1$$

which relations are useful in obtaining consistent systems of units in equations.

In this book, when writing equations, we use the second system of units. That is, we consider $g_0 = 1$, and, when using English units, we make use of the unit of mass of 1 slug, and unit of force of 1 lbf. When we find that conversion from pound mass to slug is necessary, we make use of the relation

$$1 \text{ slug} = 32.174 \text{ lbm}$$

Sometimes metric units will be used. Tables in Appendix C give the conversion factors between various units.

PROBLEMS

B-1. Consider the relation

$$h_t = h + \frac{V^2}{2}$$

in which symbols h denote enthalpies of a fluid and V the flow speed. If $h = 1250$ Btu/lbm and $V = 1300$ ft/sec, what is the value of h_t in Btu/slug? What is the value of h_t in Btu/lbm?

B-2. The value of the dimensionless rate of mass-flow parameter $\dot{m}\sqrt{RT_t}/AP_t$ is 0.6. If the gas constant $R = 53.35$ lbf ft/lbm $°R$, $T_t = 600° R$, $A = 3$ in.^{2}, and $P_t = 100$ lbf/in.^{2}, what is the rate of mass flow $\dot{m}$ in lbm/sec?

Conversion Factors of Units*

TABLE C-1
Conversion Factors for Units of Length

Multiply by appropriate entry ↓ to obtain ⟶	cm	m	in.	ft	yd
1 cm	1	0.01	0.3937	0.032808333	0.010936111
1 m	100	1	39.37	3.2808333	1.0936111
1 in.	2.5400051	0.025400051	1	0.083333333	0.027777778
1 ft	30.480061	0.30480061	12	1	0.33333333
1 yd	91.440183	0.91440183	36	3	1

TABLE C-2
Conversion Factors for Units of Area

Multiply by appropriate entry ↓ to obtain ⟶	cm^2	m^2	in.^{2}	ft^2
1 cm^2	1	10^{-4}	0.15499969	1.0763867×10^{-3}
1 m^2	10^4	1	1,549.9969	10.763867
1 in.^{2}	6.4516258	6.4516258×10^{-4}	1	6.9444444×10^{-3}
1 ft^2	929.03412	0.092903412	144	1

*From L. Fano, J. H. Hubbell, and C. W. Beckett, "Compressibility Factor, Density, Specific Heat, Enthalpy, Entropy, Free-Energy Function, Viscosity, and Thermal Conductivity of Steam," *NACA TN* 3273 (1956).

TABLE C-3
CONVERSION FACTORS FOR UNITS OF VOLUME

Multiply by appropriate entry ↓ to obtain ⟶	cm³	in.³	ft³
1 cm³	1	0.061023378	3.5314455×10^{-5}
1 in.³	16.387162	1	5.7870370×10^{-4}
1 ft³	28,317.017	1,728	1
1 ml	1.000028	0.06102509	3.531544×10^{-5}
1 liter	1,000.028	61.02509	0.03531544
1 gal	3,785.4345	231	0.13368056

TABLE C-4
CONVERSION FACTORS FOR UNITS OF MASS

Multiply by appropriate entry ↓ to obtain ⟶	gm	kgm	lbm
1 gm	1	10^{-3}	2.2046223×10^{-3}
1 kgm	10^3	1	2.2046223
1 lbm	453.59243	0.45359243	1

TABLE C-5
CONVERSION FACTORS FOR UNITS OF ENERGY

Mult. by appropriate entry ↓ to obtain ⟶	cal	Btu	int. kw-hr	hp-hr	ft-lbf
1 cal	1	3.96573×10^{-3}	1.162030×10^{-6}	1.558562×10^{-6}	3.08595
1 Btu	252.161	1	2.93018×10^{-4}	3.93008×10^{-4}	778.156
1 int. kw-hr	860,563	3,412.76	1	1.341241	2,655,656
1 hp-hr	641,617	2,544.48	0.745578	1	1,980,000
1 ft-lbf	0.324049	1.285089×10^{-3}	3.76555×10^{-7}	5.05051×10^{-7}	1

TABLE C-6
Conversion Factors for Units of Pressure

Multiply by appropriate entry to obtain →	dyne/cm²	bar	atm	kgf/cm²	mm Hg	in. Hg	lbf/in.²
1 dyne/cm²	1	10^{-6}	0.9869233×10^{-6}	1.0197162×10^{-6}	7.500617×10^{-4}	2.952993×10^{-5}	1.4503830×10^{-5}
1 bar	10^{6}	1	0.9869233	1.0197162	750.0617	29.52993	14.503830
1 atm	1,013,250	1.013250	1	1.0332275	760	29.92120	14.696006
1 kgf/cm²	980,665	0.980665	0.9678411	1	735.5592	28.95897	14.223398
1 mm Hg	1,333.2237	1.3332237×10^{-3}	1.3157895×10^{-3}	1.3595098×10^{-3}	1	0.03937	0.019336850
1 in. Hg	33,863.95	0.03386395	0.03342112	0.03453162	25.40005	1	0.4911570
1 lbf/in.²	68,947.31	0.06894731	0.06804570	0.07030669	51.71473	2.036009	1

Index